The Biology of
Crop Productivity

The Biology of Crop Productivity

EDITED BY

Peter S. Carlson

Department of Crop and Soil Science
Michigan State University
East Lansing, Michigan

1980

ACADEMIC PRESS
A Subsidiary of Harcourt Brace Jovanovich, Publishers
New York   London   Toronto   Sydney   San Francisco

ACADEMIC PRESS, INC.
111 Fifth Avenue, New York, New York 10003

United Kingdom Edition published by
ACADEMIC PRESS, INC. (LONDON) LTD.
24/28 Oval Road, London NW1 7DX

Library of Congress Cataloging in Publication Data

Main entry under title:

The Biology of crop productivity.

 Includes bibliographies and index.
 1. Crop yields. I. Carlson, Peter S.
S494.5.P75B56 631   79–28261
ISBN 0–12–159850–0

PRINTED IN THE UNITED STATES OF AMERICA

80 81 82 83 9 8 7 6 5 4 3 2 1

Contents

SECTION IV   GENETIC MANIPULATIONS

Chapter 9   Molecular Biology of Higher Plants
VIRGINIA WALBOT

Chapter 10   Mutagenesis and Crop Improvement
R. D. BROCK

SECTION V   FUTURE PROSPECTS

Chapter 11   The Shape of Things to Come
SYLVAN H. WITTWER

List of Contributors

Numbers in parentheses indicate the pages on which the authors' contributions begin.

Duncan H. Bell (3), Department of Botany and Plant Pathology, Michigan State University, East Lansing, Michigan 48824

Winston J. Brill (53), Department of Bacteriology and Center for Studies of Nitrogen Fixation, University of Wisconsin, Madison, Wisconsin 53706

R. D. Brock* (383), Plant Breeding and Genetics Section, Joint FAO/IAEA Division of Atomic Energy in Food and Agriculture, Vienna, Austria

Albert H. Ellingboe (203), Genetics Program and Department of Botany and Plant Pathology, Michigan State University, East Lansing, Michigan 48824

Norman E. Good (3), Department of Botany and Plant Pathology, Michigan State University, East Lansing, Michigan 48824

Andrew D. Hanson (77), MSU-DOE Plant Research Laboratory, Michigan State University, East Lansing, Michigan 48824

V. Hari (155), Department of Biology, Wayne State University, Detroit, Michigan 48202

B. J. Miflin (255), Department of Biochemistry, Rothamsted Experimental Station, Harpenden, Herts. AL5 2JQ, United Kingdom

Charles E. Nelsen† (77), MSU-DOE Plant Research Laboratory, Michigan State University, East Lansing, Michigan 48824

*Present address: CSIRO Division of Plant Industry, Canberra City A.C.T. 2601, Australia

†Present address: Department of Botany and Plant Pathology, Michigan State University, East Lansing, Michigan 48824

Gene R. Safir (231), Department of Botany and Plant Pathology, Michigan State University, East Lansing, Michigan 48824

Albert Siegel (155), Department of Biology, Wayne State University, Detroit, Michigan 48202

Virginia Walbot (343), Department of Biology, Washington University, St. Louis, Missouri 63130

Ian F. Wardlaw (297), CSIRO Division of Plant Industry, Canberra City A.C.T. 2601, Australia

Sylvan H. Wittwer (413), Michigan Agricultural Experiment Station, Michigan State University, East Lansing, Michigan 48824

Preface

Crop productivity or crop yield is a quantity often expressed in bushels per acre, tons per acre, kilograms per hectare, or jin per mu. This notation is a physical description of a biological endpoint, for productivity is the sum of the biological components which result in a population of mature plants. Although this expression is often a satisfactory one for farmers, economists, or statisticians it hides the extent of our biological ignorance. Not enough is known about the underlying biology which directly or indirectly determines crop yield. Furthermore, what is known is inadequate for our needs. This volume describes some of the biology that is known, points to what needs to be known, and attempts to move toward a biological description of crop productivity. Such a description is an important exercise. Contemporary research efforts in other biological disciplines have revealed and will continue to revel new methods for genetic manipulation with higher plants. These new methods, which include manipulations such as defined genetic selection systems, rapid multiplication of superior genotypes, cellular genetic alterations, and recombinant DNA technologies, should be of direct utility to plant breeders and agronomists. To utilize these techniques adequately it is important to have a clear biochemical description of what needs to be altered. What are the biological limitations of plant growth and productivity, and how does this biology interact with the environment? Defined genetically encoded processes can be directly manipulated while kilograms per hectare cannot.

Since our knowledge of and insights into crop productivity are fragmentary and still forming, so too is this volume. It is not an all inclusive tome, but one of a number of volumes which begin a biological adventure. This volume is intended primarily for persons interested or actively engaged in research in the agricultural plant sciences. It is not an endpoint but only an early milepost on the journey.

Peter S. Carlson

xiii

Introduction

Susanne Langer, in her book, "Philosophy in a New Key," noted that certain ideas thrust themselves upon the intellectual landscape with tremendous force. The ideas resolve so many fundamental problems that they seem to promise a resolution to all fundamental problems and to clarify all obscure issues. The ideas become the focal point about which a comprehensive system of analysis is built. The scientific establishment is overtaken by the sudden vogue of such a *grand idee,* and the brilliance of its synthetic and predictive quality eclipses almost everything else for a time. Langer says this is due "to the fact that all sensitive and active minds turn at once to exploiting (the idea). We try it in every connection, for every purpose, experiment with possible stretches of its meaning, with generalizations and derivatives."

Once we have become familiar with the idea and it has become part of our general stock of theoretical concepts, our expectations come into balance with its actual usefulness, and its excessive application is ended. It no longer has the grandiose, all-promising scope, the infinite versatility of apparent application it once had. The second law of thermodynamics, or the principle of natural selection, or the idea of unconscious motivation, or the organization of the means of production do not explain everything—not even everything in their own sphere—but they do explain something and attention shifts to deciding just what that something is.

I doubt that this is the way that all important scientific ideas develop; however, it seems to me that this pattern fits the development of molecular biology over the past quarter century. Molecular biology was the result of the fusion of two components: a reductionistic world view inherited from the physical sciences and an experimental system which was amenable to biochemical, physiological, and genetic manipulation. The central success of the molecular biological approach was the correlation between *in vitro* experimental results and *in vivo* phenomenon observed with an intact cell. This correlation stimulated the elaboration of cause–effect models which could be tested experi-

mentally, and, in time, it gave rise to a universally applicable biological
dogma. This dogma provides a mechanistic interpretation of biological
phenomenon, and it offers the possibility of modifying biological processes. These possibilities of understanding and modification have had
a tremendous impact upon microbiology and upon the fields which
depend upon this discipline, such as industrial microbiology and
medicine.

From a gaggle of recent reports and recommendations both public
and private in origin has come the expectation (nay, anticipation) that
molecular biology will contribute to the goals and methods of agricultural research. Can the experimental approach and reductionistic world
view of molecular biology be utilized for the solution of problems in
agricultural plant biology? Will a correlation of *in vitro* events with the
responses of crop plants in the field allow a better understanding (and
perhaps more important, allow manipulation) of the biological processes underlying crop productivity? There are several possible responses to these questions, all of which have been expressed in one
form or another during the numerous recent debates concerning the
potential of increasing agricultural productivity. The first response
points out that our current levels of crop productivity were achieved in
the absence of a direct knowledge of molecular mechanisms and that
there is no reason to believe this knowledge would enhance productivity. A second response, the direct opposite of the first, asserts
that only by a complete molecular analysis of the processes underlying
crop productivity is there any hope of manipulating the components of
yield in a rational way. A third and more realistic response suggests
that a molecular analysis will be of importance in manipulating some
biological processes but will not be a panacea for all the problems of
agricultural biology. Whatever the eventual role of molecular biology,
it is essential to begin to approach the classical holistic descriptions of
plant productivity with reductionistic and analytical tools. In this process a number of traditionally disparate biological disciplines (e.g.,
agronomy, developmental biology, physiology, biochemistry, and
genetics) can be brought to bear on the unique and complex problems
of agricultural plant biology.

This volume is but one of a number of the current attempts to reassess
and restate what is known about the biology underlying crop productivity. Its genesis stems, in large measure, from a personal sense of
frustration I have experienced in attempting to decipher the literature
on crop production. Which biological processes are directly involved
in determining crop yield? Obviously, any biological process can affect
yield, however, the central dilemma is which of these many processes

actually do affect yield under field conditions? Which processes are rate limiting? The prime question which this volume attempts to address is, "What is known about the biology of crop productivity from a range of diverse biological disciplines, and what needs to be known?" Is it possible to formulate the important biological questions, can we begin to discern the biological mechanisms and limitations which underline crop production? This volume is certainly not an all-inclusive survey. It attempts to supplement and explicate material presented in other volumes. As a consequence, biological questions which have been reviewed to the current state of the art in other volumes are not restated here.

The varities of approach and depth of the chapters in this volume are a reflection of the differences in development of the various scientific disciplines which deal with topics relevant to crop productivity. In all developing scientific fields, the texture, tone, and rate of progress is a function of personalities as well as of experimental data. As such, I have found many of the contributions to this volume to be interesting and exciting reading and that their importance goes beyond their content of quantitative information. The volume is organized into five broad areas: the first deals with various interactions of plants and their environments, the second deals with the interactions of plants with other organisms, the third treats some aspects of the internal organization of plants, the fourth examines genetic manipulations utilizing plant materials, and the fifth outlines a perspective for future research efforts.

As the work toward a molecular understanding of crop productivity proceeds, it is important to remember that the responsibility for the utility of this information lies with the basic scientist. Applause will not be forthcoming from the real world and from applied scientists until all of this intellectual gingerbread results in real world consequences. Those amber, ochre, and opal waves of grain are still just a twinkle in the molecular biologist's eye, and that's no nonsense!

Peter S. Carlson

SECTION I

INTERACTION OF PLANTS AND THE ENVIRONMENT

Chapter 1

Photosynthesis, Plant Productivity, and Crop Yield

Norman E. Good and Duncan H. Bell

I. INTRODUCTION

Crop plants grow almost entirely by photosynthesis, that is to say, by the photochemical reduction of carbon dioxide with electrons from water. Thus plant productivity is simply a measure of the total photosynthesis of the plant less any respiration which has occurred during its growth. This truism leads inevitably to the further truism that the factors limiting plant productivity are factors limiting net photosynthesis. In the following chapter we have attempted to analyze these limitations.

In our discussion, we will have many occasions to use the terms efficiency, productivity, biomass, yield, and limiting factors. A great deal of confusion can be avoided if we give these terms explicit, agreed-upon meanings. As employed here, the terms have the following meanings:

Efficiency always refers to a ratio of output to input. However, the

3

The Biology of Crop Productivity

outputs and inputs vary depending on the topic under discussion. Herein lies a great opportunity for errors in logic. Thus the theoretical efficiency of storage of solar energy in the products of photosynthesis may or may not have anything to do with the efficiency of water utilization during carbon dioxide uptake (see below). The units used to determine the two efficiency ratios are different and one, both, or neither kind of efficiency may contribute to the magnitude of photosynthesis in a given situation. Moreover, the word "efficiency" is sometimes erroneously used in the sense of maximization of output. The reader cannot be warned too strongly against indulging in this kind of imprecision when he is attempting to analyze the individual factors contributing to plant productivity.

Plant productivity itself is used throughout the discussion in the sense of primary production of biomass, where *biomass* means the accumulation of combustible plant parts. For obvious reasons, many of the available data deal with the accumulation of above-ground parts, but some deal with the whole plant. However, this confusion will probably not lead us into serious error since we will usually be dealing with very rough estimates.

Crop yield refers to the production of economically desirable plant parts. The concept is very difficult to deal with in biological terms, since it is subjective and contains elements of technology, economics, and even aesthetics. For instance, the yield of the same maize crop may be different depending on whether it is used for grain or for silage. Considerations of quality also enter the picture. What is the yield of a maize crop that does not properly mature before frost and partly or entirely rots? Then, too, are we justified in thinking only in terms of the economically desirable part of the plant when residues left on the field are in the long run indispensable for continued productivity? Maximization of the production of biomass may also be inconsistent with the maturation of crops, especially when the crops are the ripened seeds of cereals or legumes. Yet optimization of crop yield must always take precedence over the maximization of production of biomass. These considerations are outside the scope of our discussion, but they must be kept in mind.

Finally, we come to the difficult concept of *limiting factors*. The concept can be approached from several points of view. If something, for instance light, is in very short supply and everything else necessary for photosynthesis is in abundant supply, the rate of photosynthesis may reflect only the light intensity. Light is then said to be *the* limiting factor. It should be pointed out that, although this condition can be approached, it is rarely attained in practice. Certainly in the field the rate of photosynthesis is controlled simultaneously and to varying extents by a number of "limiting factors." Some of these are external to the plant, but many are internal, associated with the plant's metabolic processes. Moreover, the limiting factors are ever-changing as night gives place to day, as temperatures rise and fall, as drought follows rain, and as the plant passes through different developmental stages.

Nevertheless, the concept of limiting factors is useful if we wish to determine boundaries, theoretical upper limits beyond which productivity can never rise even if one makes the unreasonable assumption that the one factor being considered provides the only limitation. Boundary values so obtained are of course unrealistic, but they are instructive and they can be determined with considerable accuracy from well-known principles of physics and biochemistry. This approach of establishing theoretical limits has been extensively used in the first section of our discussion.

II. CONSTRAINTS ON PHOTOSYNTHESIS

A. Light

It has often been pointed out that agriculture conserves in the products of photosynthesis less than 1% of the energy of sunlight falling on a field in the course of a year (see Table I). From such observations, it has been inferred that there are remarkable opportunities for the improvement of agriculture. However, as we shall see, the real efficiency of conservation of light energy in the field is not nearly as low as it seems, if by efficiency in this case we mean the ratio of that attained to that theoretically attainable.

Let us consider the proportion of the sun's energy which could in principle be conserved by plants if light were the sole limiting factor, given the nature of sunlight and the nature of the photosynthetic process. Photosynthesis starts with the act of light absorption. Light is delivered directly or indirectly to the photosynthetically active pigment chlorophyll, in minute packets called quanta. These quanta have definite energy contents that depend on the frequency of the light waves. Each quantum, if absorbed by appropriate pigments, is capable of exciting one chlorophyll molecule, which then can give up an electron to be used in the reduction of carbon dioxide. Next the electron-depleted chlorophyll molecule takes up another electron, which came originally from water, and the chlorophyll is restored to its original condition. When enough electrons have been thus transferred via ex-

TABLE I
Efficiency of Conservation of Light Energy in Various Crops[a]

Crop	Energy conserved annually in products of photosynthesis (kcal/m^2 × 10^{-3})	Efficiency of use of sunlight[2b] (%)
Wheat (Netherlands)	4.4	0.35
Wheat (World average)	1.3	0.10
Corn (United States)	4.5	0.35
Corn (World average)	2.4	0.17
Rice (Japan)	5.5	0.42
Rice (World average)	2.3	0.18
Potatoes (United States)	4.1	0.31
Potatoes (World average)	2.2	0.17
Soybeans (Canada)	2.4	0.18
Soybeans (World average)	1.4	0.10
Sugar cane (Hawaii)	12.3	0.95
Sugar cane (Cuba)	3.7	0.30
Sugar beets (Netherlands)	7.3	0.56

[a] From Odum, 1971. These data represent the year-round productivities obtained by widely used current agricultural practices.

[b] Energy conserved each year in the biomass of the entire planet divided by the energy content of the sunlight falling each year on the crop lands (assumed to be about $1.3 × 10^6$ kcal/m^2).

cited chlorophyll from water to carbon dioxide, the water is converted into oxygen and the carbon dioxide is converted into cell substances such as carbohydrates and fats. Four electrons from water are required to reduce one carbon dioxide molecule to the level of carbohydrate. Therefore, one might suppose that four quanta of light would suffice, since ordinarily one quantum moves one electron. But in this case four quanta are not enough. The electron transport pathway in photosynthesis is such that two sequential photochemical acts are required to transfer each electron (Hill and Bendall, 1960). These two photochemical acts are carried out at two somewhat different chlorophyll-containing reaction centers (Photosystem I and Photosystem II). Therefore, eight quanta are required to reduce one carbon dioxide molecule. (See Fig. 1 for an illustration of these considerations.)

Now we must inquire into what proportion of the energy of the eight quanta is conserved in the carbohydrate formed. One mole of carbon dioxide ($6.02 × 10^{23}$ molecules), when reduced to the level of carbohydrate, conserves about 114 kcal. That is to say, the combustion of this amount of carbohydrate back to water and carbon dioxide yields about

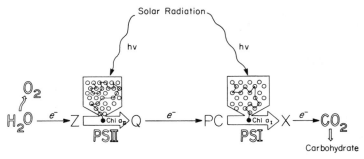

Fig. 1. A simplified version of the process of photosynthesis. There are two photochemical reactions carried on by two different photosystems (PSI and PSII), driving two different steps in the sequence of reactions transferring electrons from H_2O to CO_2. Each of these photosystems consists of an array of bulk pigment molecules associated with a special chlorophyll a molecule so situated that it can give up an electron when excited. These special molecules, indicated by solid circles, are referred to as reaction center chlorophylls and are designated Chl a_I and Chl a_{II}. A molecule of the bulk pigment in either of the photosystems absorbs a quantum of sunlight and becomes excited. The excitation energy is then transferred from pigment molecule to pigment molecule until it reaches the reaction center chlorophyll where it may be used up in doing chemical work. In the case of PSII, an electron is transferred from the excited Chl a_{II} to an electron carrier Q of unknown chemistry. The resulting oxidized Chl a_{II} is reduced back to chlorophyll by an unknown electron donor, Z, which then recovers its missing electron from water. In the case of PSI the process is the same, except that a different acceptor, X, and a different electron donor, plastocyanin (PC), are used. The net result is that an electron is transferred from water to carbon dioxide, using energy from two light quanta. If Q and X are already reduced because the electron transport or CO_2 reduction steps cannot keep up to the photochemistry, they cannot participate in the primary photochemical reaction and therefore the reaction center is "closed." In that case, the excitation energy already trapped in the bulk pigment array decays as heat and the energy from the absorbed light is lost to photosynthesis.

114 kcal. As already indicated, the energy content of a quantum depends on the frequency of the light and therefore varies inversely with the wavelength. If we assume that a reasonable average wavelength for photosynthetically useful light is 550 nm, we can calculate the energy content, E, of an average-sized quantum of useful light:

$$E = h\nu \tag{1}$$

where h = Planck's constant = 6.62×10^{-34} joule sec and ν = frequency = speed of light/wavelength.

$E = (6.62 \times 10^{-34} \text{joule sec}) (3 \times 10^8 \text{ m sec}^{-1}) (550 \times 10^{-9} \text{ m})^{-1}$

$= 3.61 \times 10^{-19}$ joules

$= 8.76 \times 10^{-20}$ cal

Thus at eight quanta per CO_2 molecule reduced, to conserve 114 kcal in the products of photosynthesis $8 \times 6.02 \times 10^{23} \times 8.76 \times 10^{-20}$ cal or 422 kcal of the energy of sunlight are required. This represents a maximum energy conservation efficiency of only 114/422 or 27% of the absorbed short wavelength light.

But how many of the quanta of sunlight are in the usable shorter wavelengths, and therefore how much of the sunlight can actually be used with 27% efficiency? Only the light that is absorbed by chlorophyll (or by "accessory" pigments able to transfer their excitation to chlorophyll) can function in photosynthesis. This is because the transfer of excitation from pigment to pigment must be energetically downhill and not uphill, which means that the longer wavelengths with their smaller quanta cannot excite chlorophyll. Thus wavelengths longer than about 700 nm cannot be employed to reduce carbon dioxide. The proportion of energy of sunlight in wavelengths longer than 700 nm depends on the time of day and on cloud cover. However it is generally accepted that, on the average, only about 45% of the energy of the sunlight falling on fields consists of photosynthetically useful wavelengths (Yocum et al., 1964). Finally, it is inevitable that some of these useful wavelengths must be reflected and transmitted—otherwise fields would be black not green and there would be total darkness in the shade of the crop. Reflectivity and transmission vary from crop to crop and with the stage of development of the crop. However, there is probably an irreducible minimum given the nature of leaf surfaces and leaf pigments and the fact that the lower leaves need some light. Observed reflections of photosynthetically active wavelengths from fields range between 5 and 10% (Yocum et al., 1964). If we take 5% as the minimum and allow for 5% transmission through the crop canopy (also probably a minimum), it follows that only about 40% of the total light falling on a field can be used for photosynthesis even when the field is fully covered with vegetation.

From the above it is clear that the theoretical maximum utilization of the energy of sunlight in photosynthesis is only about 11% (40% of 27%). It is important to realize that *nothing whatsoever can be done about this upper limit to efficiency until evolution develops an entirely new mechanism of photosynthesis*. It is also important to realize that the "low" efficiencies of the type discussed above disregard production costs in the form of respiration. Plants require energy to build and maintain the photosynthetic system. This energy probably all comes from respiration, which is subtracted from gross photosynthesis. Furthermore, for reasons that will become apparent, the 11% theoretical efficiency of gross photosynthesis is only attainable at low light intensities and low rates of photosynthesis, where the correction for respiration becomes large. It is not possible in the present state of our ignorance to estimate the maximum energy conservation efficiency of net photosynthesis (as opposed to gross photosynthesis) but it is clearly considerably less than 11%.

In terms of field photosynthesis, the above calculations are abstractions since the light intensity in the field is very high during much of the day and photosynthesis must be very rapid if as much light energy as possible is to be conserved. However, rapid rates of reactions are subject to two kinds of added inefficiencies. In the case of photosynthesis, the energy provided by the absorbed quanta cannot be stored as excited pigment. Therefore, the energy is transformed into heat unless a photochemical act is performed almost immediately. But no useful photochemical act is performed unless the enzyme system of the plant can keep up with the incoming flux of light, providing the pigments with substances directly involved in the photochemistry of photosynthesis at all times. This the enzyme systems can never fully accomplish unless light is the only factor limiting the rate of photosynthesis, a condition that only occurs at very low light intensities.

A second kind of inevitable energy loss has to do with the disequilibrium conditions necessary for any reaction to occur. These are known as irreversibility losses. The faster a reaction goes, the farther it must be from equilibrium and the smaller is the proportion of the theoretically available energy that is conserved by the reaction.

To illustrate the nature of irreversibility losses it is useful to consider a different but analogous system. The chemical reactions in a battery produce an excess of free electrons at one pole and a deficiency of electrons at the other pole. The energy theoretically available from the chemical reactions generating the electrons and "holes" is expressed in terms of the open-circuit voltage, which is simply a way of stating the work potential of each electron when the rate of reaction is virtually zero. Now, if one places a conducting pathway between the poles of the battery, current will flow and work will be done in the conducting pathway. (This work can be mechanical if the conducting pathway is a motor, or chemical if the conducting pathway is an electrolytic cell.) Greater current flows represent faster chemical reactions in the battery and result in greater irreversibility losses. These irreversibility losses show up as a decrease in the voltage delivered by the battery, i.e., in the decreased work potential of each electron. The losses are therefore easily measured and can be expressed in terms of the voltage drop within the battery. The smaller the load the greater the efficiency, but the lower the amount of work done because few electrons are moving.

On the other hand, increasing loads also ultimately lead to very low work production, since the efficiency falls catastrophically as the voltage delivered to the load drops. In other words, the irreversibility losses within the battery constitute a larger and larger proportion of the energy released by the chemical reaction in the battery as the load increases. Thus it is a well-known axiom of electrical engineering that the rate of work done by a generating system is greatest when the voltage drop across the load is equal to the voltage drop across the generator's internal resistance. It follows from this simple axiom that *at maximum work output the energy harvested is 50% of the energy produced* (see Fig. 2).

As the ecologist H. T. Odum has pointed out (Odum and Pinkerton,

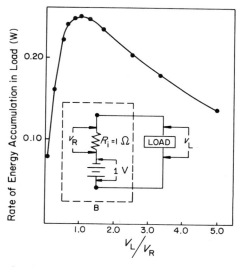

Fig. 2.   An example of the irreversibility losses that always occur when chemical reactions do work at finite rates. B is a battery in which the oxidation–reduction reactions release electrons to one pole and consume electrons from the other pole. The work potential of each electron is determined by the equilibrium free energy of the oxidation–reduction reactions and is expressed as the open-circuit (zero current) voltage across the battery, in this case, 1.0 V. When the current flow is finite, there are irreversibility losses which can be expressed in terms of the voltage drop across the internal resistance of the battery R_i, in this case, 1.0 Ω. As one increases the rate of reaction in the battery (by changing the load to allow more current to flow), the rate of energy accumulation in the load first rises to a maximum and then declines. The maximum energy storage in the load occurs when the current is such that the voltage drop across the internal resistance (V_R) is equal to the voltage drop across the load (V_L). At this reaction rate, exactly one-half of the free energy of the chemical reaction is dissipated as heat in R_i, that is to say the irreversibility loss is 50%.

1955), this axiom should apply to many biological systems and probably applies in some fashion to the process of photosynthesis. Since it is obviously to the advantage of the plant, at least in certain stages of its development, to produce as much photosynthetic product as possible, evolution has probably arranged that the load (in the form of metabolic processes using products of photosynthesis) be designed for maximum rates of biomass production and therefore for maximum rates of energy conservation under field conditions. This need for quite large irreversibility losses in photosynthesis may be largely taken care of by the great excesses of energy in the light quanta required to reduce a molecule of carbon dioxide. Indeed, it may be that this need is one of the reasons that evolution seems so inefficient. (Another reason, which is independent of the rate argument, is the fact that an energy-wasting, irreversible step is probably required to stabilize the products of any photochemical reaction by preventing immediate back-reactions.) Nevertheless, it is not at all certain that all of the irreversibility losses in photosynthesis are accommodated within the inefficient photochemical step, and we must entertain the possibility that there are major additional irreversibility losses in the "dark reactions."

Let us consider in more concrete terms the reasons why photosynthesis in the field actually does fall short of the 11% efficiency that might be possible if there were no irreversibility losses. In other words, why do some quanta absorbed by photosynthetically active pigments fail to play their part in transferring electrons from water to carbon dioxide when light intensities are high and photosynthesis is rapid? The bare skeleton of the photosynthetic process was shown in Fig. 1. Clearly photosynthesis can only reach its theoretical maximum efficiency if each reaction center is poised to receive each quantum of excitation energy as it arrives. That is to say, Q and X must be in the oxidized forms whereas Z and PC must be in their reduced forms at all times if each quantum is to be effective, a manifest impossibility if these substances are to function as electron carriers. Therefore, the efficiency of light harvesting is a function of the relative rates of arrival of quanta and rates of conversion of Z^+ back to Z, Q^- to Q, PC^+ to PC, and X^- to X. Clearly the energy conservation efficiency depends on the relationship between light intensity and the electron transport capabilities of the plant. These capabilities depend in turn on internal and external factors: the turnover rates of the carriers and the associated enzymes, the external supplies of reactants, notably carbon dioxide, and the rate of removal of photosynthetic products. At very low light intensities, when quanta are arriving at reaction centers infrequently, the reaction centers are all receptive or "open" and the actual efficiency approaches the theoretically possible efficiency. (In the electrical analogy the situation represents a very low internal resistance in the generator.) As the light intensity rises, the enzyme reactions within the plant and the uptake of carbon dioxide fall behind, no longer keeping all of the reaction centers active. Hence the efficiency of light utilization begins to fall.

The above arguments all involve theoretical computations based on idealized situations. But what are the actual efficiencies of energy conservation in real plants under real conditions? Photosynthesis at low light intensity (a condition for maximum efficiency) was studied for many years in an attempt to determine the minimum number of quanta required to reduce a molecule of carbon dioxide, the hope being that this information would contribute to the understanding of the mechanism itself. As a result of these studies, it is generally accepted that in practice fewer than 10 quanta are needed for one CO_2 (see Emerson, 1958). This value implies that photosynthesis in real plants can sometimes proceed with better than 80% of the efficiency that is theoretically possible. However, such efficiencies at very low light intensities are of little direct interest to agriculture since they are only observed when gross photosynthesis and respiration are of comparable magnitude and the experimental plants are growing very slowly. Of more relevance to agriculture are measurements made on maize fields at their period of maximum growth (when photosynthetic products are being made and used at very high rates). [See Fig. 3, taken from the work of Musgrave and Lemon (Lemon, 1965).] Far from being inefficient, it is apparent that maize, even in full sunlight, can sometimes conserve the energy of sunlight in products of photosynthesis with an efficiency greater than half of the theoretically possible efficiency. Indeed, in view of the fact that some irreversibility losses are unavoidable at high rates (as was pointed out above) and the fact that some respiration losses must always occur, the actual field efficiency of maize photosynthesis may already be approaching the upper limit when it reaches 5%.

Unfortunately, plants under most field conditions conserve much less than 5% of the energy of sunlight falling on them. One of the reasons may reside in their compromise design. Leaves of plants are exposed to very different light intensities during the day. Furthermore, the very leaves which were exposed to full sunlight at one stage in the plant's growth become shaded at a later stage. Therefore, all leaves are forced to choose between designs giving high efficiency at low light intensity and designs giving high efficiency at high intensity. Efficiency of energy conservation at low intensity requires a maximum interception of light and therefore very large arrays of light-trapping

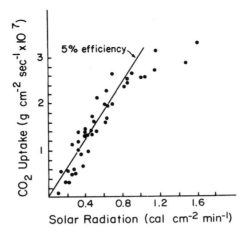

Fig. 3. Carbon dioxide uptake in a maize field at various light intensities. The highest intensities, 1.2 to 1.6 cal cm^{-2} min^{-1}, represent the maximum midday sunlight. Note that the energy conserved in the reduced carbon dioxide is close to 5% of the energy in the sunlight at all but the very highest intensities. (Reproduced from Lemon, 1965, by permission of the American Society of Agronomy and the Soil Science Society of America.)

bulk pigments (see Fig. 1). On the other hand, efficiency at high light intensity requires that a high proportion of reaction centers be receptive at all times. Since the light-trapping arrays must be very large to intercept light effectively, it would require an inordinate amount of enzyme machinery to handle all of the great flux of incoming quanta at high light intensities. Investments in such large amounts of photosynthesis enzymes to be used only when light intensity is high, that is to say at the very time when other factors than light utilization are most likely to be limiting growth, would probably be to the disadvantage of the plant.

None of the above considerations can fully explain the very poor year-round efficiencies of solar energy capture documented in Table I. In fact, the potential efficiency of utilization of light energy may be almost irrelevant if short growing seasons (due to inadequate water and low temperature), nutrient deprivation, or genetically controlled restriction of growth prevent photosynthesis. Consequently, we must now turn our attention to these other factors controlling productivity.

B. Water and Carbon Dioxide

Both carbon dioxide and water are needed for photosynthesis, but not in similar amounts. Carbon dioxide is required only as a substrate for photosynthesis, that is as one of the reactants, and it is therefore only consumed in proportion to the amount of photosynthesis products formed. In contrast, water serves both as a reactant and as the milieu in which photosynthesis takes place. Because photosynthesis occurs in an aqueous environment and the air from which carbon dioxide is obtained is often very dry, plants of necessity lose a great deal of water in the process of acquiring a little carbon dioxide.

This qualitative statement can be put in much more nearly quantitative terms. Let us consider the inevitable loss of water vapor from leaves. Both water vapor and carbon dioxide move into and out of a leaf by diffusing along a common pathway. Indeed, no pathway for the diffusion of carbon dioxide can fail to serve also as a pathway for the diffusion of water vapor, since no substance is known that is permeable to carbon dioxide and not to water vapor. The diffusion into and out of leaves is primarily through pores having regulated apertures, known as stomata which will be discussed later. The rate of diffusion of any gas is determined by the concentration differences, the nature of the diffusion pathway, and the mobility of the gas in the pathway. Thus, the rate of water loss through a stomatal pore can be expressed by:

$$\text{Outward diffusion of } H_2O = k_{H_2O} ([H_2O]_{inside} - [H_2O]_{outside}) \quad (2)$$

where $[H_2O]$ is concentration of water vapor in the air and where k_{H_2O} is a constant characteristic of the diffusion pathway and the mobility of water molecules in the air.

Similarly, the rate of uptake of CO_2 through the same stomatal pore can be expressed by:

$$\text{Inward diffusion of } CO_2 = k_{CO_2} ([CO_2]_{outside} - [CO_2]_{inside}) \quad (3)$$

where $[CO_2]$ is the concentration of CO_2 in the air and where k_{CO_2} is a constant characteristic of the diffusion pathway and the mobility of CO_2 molecules.

Therefore:

$$\frac{\text{moles of } H_2O \text{ lost}}{\text{moles of } CO_2 \text{ gained}} = \frac{k_{H_2O} ([H_2O]_{inside} - [H_2O]_{outside})}{k_{CO_2} ([CO_2]_{outside} - [CO_2]_{inside})} \quad (4)$$

Furthermore, since the two gases are diffusing along the same pathway:

$$\frac{k_{H_2O}}{k_{CO_2}} = \frac{\text{mobility of } H_2O}{\text{mobility of } CO_2} \quad (5)$$

The ratio of mobilities is easily calculated because the kinetic energies of the movements of the different kinds of molecules have the same distribution. Thus, on the average,

$$\tfrac{1}{2}m_{H_2O}\,(v_{H_2O})^2 = \tfrac{1}{2}m_{CO_2}\,(v_{CO_2})^2 \qquad (6)$$

where m_{H_2O} and m_{CO_2} are the weights of water and carbon dioxide molecules and v_{H_2O} and v_{CO_2} are the average velocities of the molecules. Thus:

$$\frac{\text{mobility of } H_2O}{\text{mobility of } CO_2} = \frac{v_{H_2O}}{v_{CO_2}} = \sqrt{\frac{m_{CO_2}}{m_{H_2O}}} = \sqrt{\frac{44}{18}} = 1.56 \qquad (7)$$

Substituting Eqs. (7) and (5) in Eq. (4) we find that,

$$= \frac{\text{moles of } H_2O \text{ lost}}{\text{moles of } CO_2 \text{ gained}} = 1.56 \,\frac{\text{inside} - \text{outside difference in } [H_2O]}{\text{outside} - \text{inside difference in } [CO_2]} \qquad (8)$$

Let us now compute the actual water use ratio, making the extremely favorable (and therefore unrealistic) assumptions that the leaf and the air are at the same temperature, say 30°C, that the relative humidity outside the leaf is 50%, and that the leaf is able to lower the internal CO_2 concentration to zero without lowering the external concentration at all.

Water vapor:

> Internal water vapor pressure (air saturated with H_2O at 30°C) = 31.8 mm Hg = 4.2×10^{-2} atm
>
> External water vapor pressure (half saturated) = 2.1×10^{-2} atm
>
> Difference = 2.1×10^{-2} atm

Carbon dioxide:

$$\text{External } CO_2 \text{ at 300 ppm} = 3 \times 10^{-4} \text{ atm}$$
$$\text{Internal } CO_2 = \text{zero}$$
$$\text{Difference} = 3 \times 10^{-4} \text{ atm}$$

From Eq. (8):

$$\frac{\text{moles } H_2O \text{ lost}}{\text{moles } CO_2 \text{ gained}} = 1.56 \times \frac{2.1 \times 10^{-2}}{3 \times 10^{-4}} = 109$$

Thus, under the stated favorable conditions, no plant could obtain carbon dioxide for photosynthesis without losing 109 times as much water.

The above exercise was designed to illustrate how plants are forced to buy carbon dioxide with water at a very poor rate of exchange. In fact, under field conditions, the rate of exchange is much worse (see Table II). Under field conditions, few if any plants operate with their internal CO_2 concentrations anywhere near zero. Very often, plants

TABLE II
Water Use by C_3 and C_4 Plants[a]

Plants	Moles of H_2O transpired/mole of CO_2 fixed
C_4[b]	
Foxtail Millet (*Setaria italica*)	475
Broom-corn Millet (*Panicum miliaceum*)	445
Sorghum (*Sorghum spp.*)	507
Sudan-grass (*Sorghum vulgare var. sudanense*)	508
Maize (*Zea mays*)	582
Tumbleweed (*Amaranthus graecizana*)	433
Pigweed (*Amaranthus retroflexus*)	508
Saltwort (*Salsola kali*)	523
Purslane (*Portulaca oleracea*)	468
C_3[b]	
Durum wheat (*Triticum durum*)	903
Common wheat (*Triticum aestivum*)	928
Barley (*Hordeum vulgare*)	863
Oats (*Avena sativa*)	972
Rye (*Secale cereale*)	1057
Rice (*Oryza sativa*)	1137
Bromegrass (*Bromus inermis*)	1628
Beet (*Beta vulgaris*)	628
Pigweed (*Chenopodium album*)	1097
Knotweed (*Polygonum aviculare*)	1130
Cotton (*Gossypium hirsutum*)	947
Potato (*Solanum tuberosum*)	958
Buffalo-bur (*Solanum rostratum*)	893
Sunflower (*Helianthus annuus*)	1038
Cocklebur (*Xanthium pennsylvanicum*)	692
Sagebrush (*Artemisia frigida*)	1090
Cabbage (*Brassica oleracea capitata*)	863
Turnip (*Brassica rapa*)	1023
Rape (*Brassica napus*)	1190
Ragweed (*Ambrosia artemisifolia*)	1520
Watermelon (*Citrullus vulgaris*)	962
Cucumber (*Cucumis sativus*)	1143
Cow-pea (*Vigna sinensis*)	1060
Bean (*Phaseolus vulgaris*)	1167
Alfalfa (*Medicago sativa*)	1407

[a] Calculated from Shantz and Premeisel, 1927.

[b] Other C_4 plants: sugar cane (*Saccharum officinarium*). Other C_3 plants: soybean (*Glycine max*), pea (*Pisum sativum*), sweet potato (*Ipomoea batatas*), tomato (*Lysopersicon esculentum*), strawberry (*Fragaria spp.*), tobacco (*Nicotiana tabacum*), and all other tree and shrub crops.

operate with internal CO_2 concentrations much closer to the external CO_2 concentration. Furthermore, the conditions producing minimum internal CO_2 tend to lower the external CO_2, or to raise the leaf temperature above the ambient temperature, thereby increasing the water vapor concentration difference. Nor is a relative humidity of 50% likely to be maintained in many agricultural regions as the sun warms the air. Therefore, under most practical conditions, the exchange rate quoted in the exercise needs to be multiplied severalfold.

We have not attempted to define the factors influencing the exchange rate more precisely, because plants use water for purposes other than to obtain CO_2, purposes that sometimes play a much larger role in determining water utilization than does the CO_2–H_2O exchange requirement. By far the most significant of these other purposes is evaporative cooling. The water economy of the plant can be assessed in terms of the energy budget of the plant, and evaporative cooling is a major item in the balance. Thus all of the energy of sunlight absorbed by a leaf must be accounted for by photosynthesis, reradiation, transfer to the air via convection and by heat of vaporization of the transpired water. Much work has been done in this area, and fairly reliable values are available describing the energy budget of single leaves or of arrays of leaves (Uchijima, 1975). As we have seen, even under the most favorable of conditions photosynthesis accounts for only a few percent of the energy of the sunlight falling on the leaf, and its contribution to the energy budget can be neglected under nearly all conditions. Reradiation of energy in the long infrared wavelengths and convective cooling both depend critically on how much warmer the leaf is than the surroundings and, of course, evaporative cooling depends on the relative humidity and on the wind speed. It is not possible to develop this complex subject adequately here. However, it would seem that over a wide range of conditions evaporative cooling accounts for much of the energy of the sunlight absorbed by plants (Uchijima, 1975). On the basis of this assumption, let us again calculate water use during photosynthesis.

If we know the proportion of the energy of the sunlight (β) accounted for by evaporative cooling, it is a simple matter to deduce the amount of water vaporized by the plant. The heat of vaporization of water at normal field temperatures is about 10.5 kcal/mole. Therefore

$$\text{water loss (in moles)} = \frac{\beta \times \text{absorbed light energy (in kcal)}}{10.5} \qquad (9)$$

Furthermore, if we know from other studies the efficiency with which the plant is conserving energy in the products of photosynthesis, we can also deduce the amount of CO_2 being reduced while this same amount of energy is being absorbed. As we have already pointed out, 114 kcal are conserved for every mole of CO_2 reduced to the carbohydrate level. Therefore

$$\text{gain of } CO_2 \text{ (in moles)} = \frac{\text{light use efficiency} \times \text{absorbed light energy (in kcal)}}{114} \quad (10)$$

By combining Eqs. (9) and (10) we find that

$$\frac{\text{moles of water lost}}{\text{moles of } CO_2 \text{ gained}} = \frac{10.8\,\beta}{\text{light use efficiency in photosynthesis}} \quad (11)$$

For example, let us assume that the maize plants of Musgrave and Lemon (see Fig. 3) were disposing of 80% of the absorbed light energy by evaporating water. Then $\beta = 0.8$ and, since these plants were conserving 5% of the energy in the form of reduced carbon dioxide, the transpiration ratio must have been $10.8 \times 0.8/0.05$ or 173. (It will be noted by comparing the results of these two exercises that the computed water costs of photosynthesis are of comparable magnitude whether we base the computation on the diffusion exchange rate or on the need for evaporative cooling. This is not happenstance but rather the result of looking at two sides of the same coin. Water used in exchange for CO_2 is at the same time being used for cooling. The opening and closing of stomata affect both the exchange rate and the amount of evaporative cooling. Thus, the amount of water used for evaporative cooling is also an expression of the exchange rate.)

The water use calculations in the two examples above were made by assuming situations more favorable than are usually encountered, and this explains the fact that water is rarely used so efficiently in the field. For instance, in the computations it was assumed that the diffusion pathway was simultaneously optimal in two respects: the diffusion resistance was high enough to permit the internal CO_2 concentration to fall almost to zero, while at the same time it was low enough to permit photosynthesis to proceed at a reasonable rate. Clearly the two requirements are to some extent contradictory. For maximum water economy at various rates of photosynthesis, or for maximum photosynthesis at various levels of water availability, different optimum diffusion resistances are required. The plant is therefore forced into compromises in order to keep the resistance of the diffusion pathway optimal for its overall well-being. As a consequence, plants have evolved a very subtle instrument of diffusion adjustment, the variable aperture of the stoma. Stomata close in response to water deficits and open in response to CO_2 deficits.

Although there is as yet only conjecture about the way in which water status is detected, and even less information about the way CO_2 status is detected, the mechanics of the opening and closing are well understood and have been thoroughly described elsewhere (Raschke, 1975) (see also Fig. 4). The mechanism can be described very briefly thus: a specialized cell known as a guard cell lies on each side of the stomatal pore. When the turgor of the guard cells is low, the two cells are closely appressed and the pore is closed. However, when they become turgid their ends expand in such a way that the pair is pushed apart, thus opening the pore. This increase in turgor is due to water uptake, which in turn is associated with an accumulation of potassium salts inside the guard cells (Fischer and Hsiao, 1968). Sometimes, perhaps usually, the salt is potassium malate (Allaway, 1973). Unfortunately, little is known yet about the processes that cause the accumulation and extrusion of potassium salts.

The responses of stomata have been studied for many years and a great deal is now known about them (Raschke, 1975). It has been shown (Raschke, 1965) that stomata can adjust very quickly to changes in the

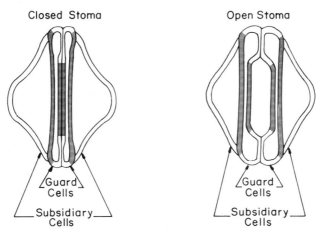

Closed Stoma   Open Stoma

Guard Cells   Guard Cells

Subsidiary Cells   Subsidiary Cells

Fig. 4. A diagrammatic representation of the mechanism of opening of stomata. Stomata open when the extensible ends of the dumbell-shaped guard cells are expanded, as in the figure on the right. The expansion is caused by an uptake of water, which itself is an osmotic consequence of the uptake of potassium salts. Expansion is restricted to the end regions of the guard cells since the cross-hatched areas are reinforced and relatively inelastic. The increase in volume of the ends pushes the guard cells apart at the middle to form an open pore. (Adapted from Raschke, 1970.)

external CO_2 concentrations in such a way as to keep the CO_2 flux almost constant (see Fig. 5). Stomata also open and close in response to water availability and water demands. Catastrophic dehydration may be prevented if the pores close when the leaf loses enough water to become flaccid. Certainly wilted plants stop losing water to the air almost completely. But the opening and closing of stomata in response to water potentials is much more delicately balanced than this gross wilting response would suggest, and closing does not necessarily depend on decreased leaf turgor. The hormone abscisic acid, which is formed in response to water stress (Wright, 1969) and to other stresses, can rapidly close stomata whether or not there is a water deficiency (Raschke, 1974). It is tempting to suggest that some quite delicate sensor of water status may control the level of abscisic acid, which in turn may contribute to the control of the stomatal aperture.

Clearly, stomatal regulations of water loss and CO_2 uptake must be

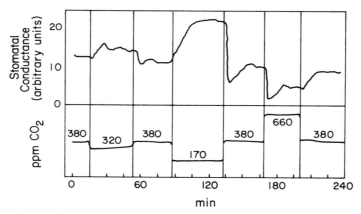

Fig. 5. Stomatal conductance (degree of opening) as a function of the concentration of CO_2 in the air. Measurements of conductance refer to rates of flow of air from a cup attached to the lower surface of a maize leaf through the leaf to a cup attached to the upper surface. Note that the stomata open and close in such a way that the amount of CO_2 entering the leaf is almost constant. Thus, if the concentration of CO_2 is doubled, the rate of flow halves. (From Raschke, 1965.)

It should be noted that the almost complete control of the CO_2 uptake observed in this experiment is much more precise than is usually encountered under natural conditions. This may be because the mass flow of air under pressure through a small opening such as a leaf stoma is especially sensitive to variations in the pore diameter. Thus the viscous flow employed in this experiment is proportional to the third power of the diameter, whereas the normal diffusion of CO_2 through the pore is proportional to the first power of the pore diameter. Under normal conditions of CO_2 diffusion in stationary air (rather than a mass flow of air), only about 75% of effects of variations in external CO_2 concentration on photosynthesis are compensated for by variations in the conductance of the maize stomata. (G. Farquhar, personal communication.)

closely related if the plant is to be well served by its diffusion control mechanism. There is some reason to believe that abscisic acid also plays an important role in this interrelationship. As Raschke has pointed out, stomatal responses to abscisic acid depend on the concentration of CO_2, and stomatal responses to CO_2 depend on the level of abscisic acid. Since water deficits cause abscisic acid to accumulate in leaves, it seems reasonable to suggest that "these interactions cause stomata to behave like 'adjustable control systems' capable of giving priority either to CO_2 assimilation or to water husbandry" (Raschke, 1976).

We must now ask ourselves how successful plants actually husband water. In order to use available water to best advantage, plants have evolved a number of strategies. Each of these strategies requires different anatomies and physiologies, and each makes different demands on the stomatal system regulating gas exchange. These strategies are described briefly below.

1. Avoidance of water stress by growing only when abundant water is available. In this category are rapidly maturing annuals that survive drought in the seed stage, a few herbaceous plants, a number of lower plants with vegetative tissues that survive dessication. Many common grasses with underground parts that become dormant and, by virtue of being underground, escape the worst heat and drying. In all of these plants, conservation of water through optimization of the water–carbon dioxide exchange is probably less important than speed of development. Evolution would certainly tend to favor a water-wasting, hurry-up approach since any plant saving the water in the soil saves it for its competitors. (Agriculture, with its monocultures and its concern with yield and productivity rather than with plant survival, is another matter. In monocultures, improved economy of water use should lengthen the period of water availability and therefore increase the total crop. Thus solutions to problems arrived at by natural selection may not be optimal under the unnatural conditions of agriculture.)

2. Closing stomata during water stress. Normally, the periods of greatest water stress coincide with periods of maximum sunlight and therefore with the greatest opportunity for photosynthesis. However, under severe conditions of water shortage almost all plants close their stomata and husband what water there is at the expense of photosynthesis. In addition to doing without photosynthesis, plants under these conditions may be subjected to very great temperature rises and, if they are to survive for prolonged periods without irreversible damage, their physiology and the very nature of their proteins probably must be modified. Herein lies a great potential for plant selection. A period of

drought need not (but too often does) lead to a total loss of crop, simply because some species and varieties cannot endure the consequences of temporarily decreased transpiration.

Large groups of plants have carried the stratagem to the extreme of keeping their stomata closed almost all day. This conserves a very great deal of water, because the relative humidity of the air is usually fairly high at night when the stomata are open. Such plants have learned to forgo evaporative cooling. The stratagem would still be a losing proposition, however, if such plants did not store carbon dioxide during the night to be used the next day for photosynthesis. Therefore, carbon dioxide is temporarily fixed in organic anions such as malate during the night for reduction by photosynthesis the next day (see Ranson and Thomas, 1960). Plants employing this strategem are known as CAM plants (for crassulacean acid metabolism). As might be predicted, CAM plants tend to be dry weather plants or to grow on droughty sites. Included in this category are Sedum and other members of the family Crassulaceae, pineapple and other members of the family Bromeliaceae, and, of course, the entire Cactus family. They are also sometimes known as "succulents" because of their fleshy leaves and stems (which may be fleshy in order to store the large amounts of organic acids formed during the night). Because the storage of carbon dioxide probably becomes a limiting factor, rather than the interception of light, their leaves are often reduced in area or (in the cacti) disappear altogether. Photosynthesis is then carried on by the stems. This reduction in surface area has the very real advantage of reducing the heat input in structures deprived of evaporative cooling. Nevertheless, CAM plants in desert situations must be exposed to rather high internal temperatures and their physiology presumably must be heat tolerant. The only CAM plant currently grown extensively as a crop is the pineapple.

3. Minimizing the internal carbon dioxide concentration. As we have seen, the purpose of a plant must be to obtain carbon dioxide while at the same time avoiding dessication and excessive temperature rise. The optimum solution to this problem in tradeoffs cannot be predicted easily, since it depends on the relative abundances of water and carbon dioxide and on the sensitivity of the plant to drying or heating. Many of these factors change with changing seasons and with the stage of development of the plant and are very hard to evaluate. However, under almost any circumstance it would seem to be to the advantage of the plant to increase its potential for carbon dioxide uptake if it can do so without increasing its water loss. Carbon dioxide uptake relative to water loss can be increased by increasing the external CO_2 concentration or by decreasing the internal CO_2 concentration. The first alterna-

tive is quite easily accomplished in the laboratory and without too much difficulty in enclosed houses. On a field scale it is quite impossible, since atmospheric mixing is too efficient (Allen *et al.*, 1974). Evolution has not been able to affect the availability of external CO_2 except to the extent that the design of the architecture of plants can minimize localized depletion of CO_2 within the canopy by assuring air mixing. On the other hand, evolutionary processes can and have devised ways of lowering the internal CO_2.

In order to explain the techniques used by certain plants to lower the concentration of CO_2 inside the leaves, it will be necessary to discuss a few details of the biochemistry of CO_2 fixation and reduction. In a majority of higher plants and algae, the first step in the assimilation of CO_2 is the addition of CO_2 to a five-carbon sugar phosphate, ribulose diphosphate, to give two molecules of phosphoglyceric acid (Wilson and Calvin, 1955).

$$
\begin{array}{c}
\text{CH}_2\text{OP} \\
| \\
\text{C}{=}\text{O} \\
| \\
\text{CHOH} \\
| \\
\text{CHOH} \\
| \\
\text{CH}_2\text{OP}
\end{array}
\;+\; \text{CO}_2
\;\xrightarrow[\text{carboxylase}]{\substack{\text{ribulose} \\ \text{bisphosphate}}}\;
\begin{array}{c}
\text{CH}_2\text{OP} \\
| \\
\text{CHOH} \\
| \\
\text{COOH} \\
+ \\
\text{COOH} \\
| \\
\text{CHOH} \\
| \\
\text{CH}_2\text{OP}
\end{array}
$$

Ribulose   two 3-phospho-
bisphosphate   glyceric acids

The phosphoglyceric acid formed is then reduced with electrons from water and dimerized to give the familiar six-carbon sugars. Plants that use this method of CO_2 fixation almost exclusively are known as C_3 plants, after the fact that the first product of photosynthesis is the three-carbon phosphoglyceric acid (PGA). Unfortunately, the enzyme that catalyzes the addition of CO_2 to ribulose diphosphate, ribulose diphosphate carboxylase, also catalyzes the addition of oxygen (Andrews *et al.*, 1973).

$$
\begin{array}{c}
\text{CH}_2\text{OP} \\
| \\
\text{C}{=}\text{O} \\
| \\
\text{CHOH} \\
| \\
\text{CHOH} \\
| \\
\text{CH}_2\text{OP}
\end{array}
\;+\; \text{O}_2
\;\xrightarrow[\substack{\text{carboxylase} \\ \text{(oxygenase)}}]{\substack{\text{ribulose} \\ \text{bisphosphate}}}\;
\begin{array}{c}
\text{CH}_2\text{OP} \\
| \\
\text{COOH} \\
+ \\
\text{COOH} \\
| \\
\text{CHOH} \\
| \\
\text{CH}_2\text{OP}
\end{array}
$$

Ribulose   Phosphoglycolic
bisphosphate   acid + 3-PGA

The two-carbon fragment, phosphoglycolic acid, is then oxidized in higher plants, contributing further to this phenomenon of extra, light-dependent O_2 uptake known as photorespiration. Thus CO_2 and oxygen compete at one step in photosynthesis. If oxygen wins the competition, carbon dioxide is produced instead of being consumed. As the concentration of CO_2 is lowered by photosynthesis, the oxygen reaction becomes more and more favored until the two processes are in balance, with CO_2 being consumed and produced at the same rate. The level of CO_2 concentration at which this balance is achieved is called the "CO_2 compensation point" and, of course, plants cannot lower the internal CO_2 concentration below this point. In C_3 plants such as tobacco the compensation point is the range of 50 ppm (Zelitch, 1969). Obviously plants that have to shut their stomata to conserve water operate, in effect, in closed chambers, and their rates of photorespiration tend to rise toward their rates of photosynthesis, at which point there is no longer any net gain of reduced carbon dioxide.

A number of species of plants, usually plants adapted to heat and considerable water stress, have developed a system that has the effect of concentrating CO_2 and thus diminishing photorespiration. To do so they have taken over a part of the CAM plan of first fixing CO_2 into malate, a four-carbon acid anion. As a consequence, these plants are called C_4 plants.

$$
\begin{array}{c}
\text{COOH} \\
| \\
\text{C}-\text{OP} \;+\; \text{CO}_2 \xrightarrow[\text{carboxylase}]{\text{PEP}}
\end{array}
\quad
\begin{array}{c}
\text{COOH} \\
| \\
\text{C}=\text{O} \\
| \\
\text{CH}_2 \\
| \\
\text{COOH}
\end{array}
\xrightarrow[2\text{H}^+]{2e^-}
\begin{array}{c}
\text{COOH} \\
| \\
\text{CHOH} \\
| \\
\text{CH}_2 \\
| \\
\text{COOH}
\end{array}
$$

Phosphoenol-pyruvic acid (PEP)   Oxaloacetic acid   Malic acid

These reactions have no counterpart in which oxygen replaces CO_2. Therefore, oxygen is not competitive and no photorespiration is associated with primary CO_2 fixation. Rather than accumulate organic acids (as do CAM plants), the C_4 plants promptly transfer the carbon dioxide in the malate to ribulose bisphosphate, where it joins the regular C_3 photosynthesis pathway. The manner of transfer somehow eliminates the oxygen competition which one would expect still to occur at the ribulose bisphosphate carboxylase level. This lack of competition is probably to be explained on the basis of the spatial separation of reactions (see Fig. 6). According to widely accepted theory (see Black, 1973), CO_2 is first encountered by the mesophyll cells, where it is fixed into malate by PEP carboxylase. This malate is then transported into the bundle sheath cells where it contributes its CO_2 to ribulose

A

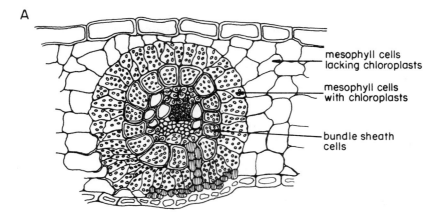

mesophyll cells
lacking chloroplasts

mesophyll cells
with chloroplasts

bundle sheath
cells

B

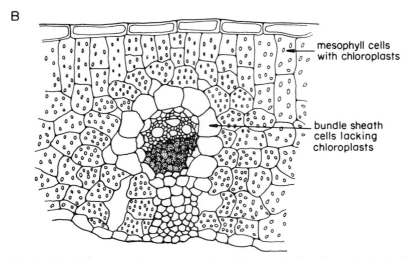

mesophyll cells
with chloroplasts

bundle sheath
cells lacking
chloroplasts

Fig. 6. (A) A diagrammatic representation of a vascular bundle in the leaf of a C_4 grass of temperate, dry lands, such as *Bouteloua pectinata* (Grama grass). The single row of large cells around the bundle is known as the bundle sheath. In this case the cells of the bundle sheath are filled with chloroplasts. All of the other chlorophyll-containing cells are in a ring of one or two cells around the bundle sheath. This arrangement has been called "kranz" anatomy from the German word for a wreath. Apparently the chloroplasts in the outer ring fix CO_2 while the chloroplasts in the bundle sheath reduce the already-fixed CO_2 to carbohydrate. (B) A vascular bundle in the leaf of a C_3 grass of humid, temperate regions such as *Poa* (bluegrass). In this case there are no chloroplasts in the bundle sheath, all of the chloroplasts being in mesophyll cells that fill the greater part of the space between the bundles. The mesophyll cells both fix CO_2 and reduce it to carbohydrate. (Adapted from Gould, 1968.)

diphosphate carboxylase. All of the remaining steps of photosynthesis seem to be carried out in the bundle sheath cells. Either the juxtaposition of the malate decarboxylase and the ribulose diphosphate carboxylase reactions or the existence of some specific mechanism for transfer between the two enzymes probably accounts for the elimination of O_2 competition. In effect, there must be a local high concentration of CO_2 in the vicinity of the carboxylating enzyme. In any event, C_4 plants have little if any photorespiration and, consequently, the CO_2 compensation point no longer reflects the balance between a rapid forward reaction and a potentially rapid backward reaction. Instead, the compensation point reflects the affinity of phosphoenolpyruvate (PEP) carboxylase for CO_2 and the quite slow respiratory production of CO_2. Thus C_4 plants typically have CO_2 compensation points below 10 ppm, and the concentration of CO_2 inside the leaves under field conditions could be reduced nearly to this level (Zelitch, 1969). By lowering the concentration of CO_2 in their leaves to a low level, C_4 plants can increase the inside–outside concentration difference and therefore can exchange CO_2 for water more efficiently than do C_3 plants (see Table II). However, it is by no means clear how often water use efficiency is determined by the theoretically attainable carbon dioxide–water exchange rates. The potential rate of exchange may become irrelevant when other uses of water predominate (such as essential evaporative cooling) or when photosynthesis is limited by growth conditions that have nothing to do with gas exchange capacities. Certainly the internal CO_2 levels in both C_3 and C_4 plants tend to be far above the compensation points, especially if water is readily available. This is obvious from the rather low water use efficiencies commonly observed in the field; given these observed efficiencies, one can reverse the exercise used above to illustrate CO_2–H_2O exchanges and thus determine the average CO_2 concentration difference across the diffusion barriers. These differences are sometimes surprisingly small, which means that internal CO_2 concentrations are often quite high. It does seem clear from Table II, however, that C_4 plants are regularly more efficient in their use of water than C_3 plants, presumably because they can afford to keep their stomata more nearly closed without inducing photorespiration.

In addition to being more economical with water, C_4 plants have another advantage over C_3 plants, namely, the virtual absence of photorespiration. Photorespiration releases CO_2 already reduced by photosynthesis and decreases net photosynthesis accordingly. In fact, C_3 plants often cannot use high light intensities efficiently because at high light intensities the lowered internal CO_2 concentration favors photorespiration. This seems to be the reason that C_3 plants respond well to augmentation of the external CO_2 supply (Gaastra, 1959), since higher external CO_2 concentrations cause higher internal CO_2 concentrations. The internal CO_2 then competes more favorably with O_2 in the reaction with ribulose bisphosphate and photorespiration is correspondingly diminished. However, it may be that the increased efficiency of C_4 plants at high light and low CO_2 is paid for by lower efficiency when the light intensity is low. If it is true that the mesophyll cells absorb light primarily for the purpose of concentrating CO_2, and thus foiling photorespiration as the current dogma would have it, then the efficiency of light utilization may suffer when the CO_2 supply is adequate and the light intensity is limiting (Björkman and Ehleringer, 1975). Probably the mechanism of photosynthesis in C_4 plants is not yet fully understood, since C_4 plants have not been universally successful in spite of their apparent advantages. In the hot, dry climates in which they seem to have evolved, they exist side-by-side with many species of C_3 plants that do not seem to be seriously handicapped and, for some obscure reason, very few C_4 plants are successful in cooler climates, either under cultivation or in nature.

Before leaving the topic of efficiency of water use, it might be useful to compare practical efficiencies in the field with the unattainable limits set in the examples we used in our illustration of the physical principles involved. In the exercises we deliberately used a number of simplifying assumptions that were far too optimistic. As a result, the computed efficiencies were gross overestimates. We assumed higher relative humidities in the atmosphere, lower CO_2 concentrations inside the leaf, and higher efficiencies of photosynthesis than are ever maintained over the growing period of the plant. In the field, the ratio of the number of water molecules expended to carbon dioxide molecules reduced depends, as might be expected, on the abundance of water, on the dryness of the atmosphere, and less obviously, on the soil nutrients. Nitrogen-deficient plants show decreased growth and therefore, by definition, decreased net photosynthesis. These undernourished plants idly export water from the soil while accomplishing little CO_2 fixation and thus have poor water use efficiency. Some actual ratios of evapotranspiration to dry matter production under field conditions follow. These ratios are expressed in moles of water used per mole of carbon dioxide reduced: grass in the Netherlands, 267 to 1810 depending on the time of year and level of fertilizer (Wind, 1954); Sudan grass in Alabama, 568 to 1019 depending on the soil moisture and nitrogen fertilizer (Weaver and Pearson, 1956); maize in North Dakota, 486 to

909, again depending on the soil moisture and nitrogen fertilizer (Carlson *et al.*, 1959); winter wheat in Nebraska, 942 to 4167 (Ramig, 1960). (See also Table II.)

Matters of water use efficiency are also discussed in Chapter 3 in this volume by Hanson and Nelson.

C. Temperature

The reactions involved in photosynthesis are of two kinds: photochemical and thermochemical. Photochemical reactions occur as a result of light absorption and the consequent dislodgement of electrons from their stable ground state orbitals. Such reactions have little dependence on temperature, since they do not depend on molecular collisions. On the other hand, thermochemical reactions do require collisions between molecules. Furthermore, for each particular thermochemical reaction there is a threshold collision energy below which no reaction can take place; if new bonds are to be formed, old bonds must first be broken and some minimum amount of energy is required to break the old bonds. This threshold energy is known as the activation energy of the reaction. Since temperature is an expression of the average kinetic energy of molecules, increasing temperatures represent molecules moving faster and faster. As they move faster, a larger proportion of them collide with energies sufficient to cause the reaction in question. The greater the necessary activation energy, the more the reaction depends on temperature and the more rapidly the reaction rate increases with increasing temperature. For statistical reasons that have to do with the distribution of the kinetic energies among the individual molecules, the rate of almost any simple thermochemical reaction can be expressed by the Arrhenius equation:

$$\text{Rate} = K \, e^{-(E_a/RT)}; \quad \ln \text{Rate} = \ln K - E_a/RT \qquad (12)$$

where E_a is the activation energy, K is the constant describing the rate if the activation energy E_a were zero, R is the gas constant, and T is the absolute temperature. This equation applies, of course, to all of the reactions of photosynthesis except the primary photochemical reactions of Photosystems I and II.

The implication that photosynthesis should go faster and faster ad infinitum as the temperature is raised flies in the face of common sense and common experience for two reasons. In the first place, the rate of net photosynthesis depends on a balance between forward and backward reactions (gross photosynthesis and respiration), both of which increase with temperature. Whenever the sum of respiration and photo-respiration increases more than gross photosynthesis increases, net photosynthesis will actually decrease with increasing temperature. But the rate of gross photosynthesis itself may fall with higher temperatures if these higher temperatures are injurious to the machinery of photosynthesis. As F. F. Blackman pointed out many years ago (1905), the inhibition of photosynthesis at high temperatures is time dependent. That is, a high temperature that seems to inhibit photosynthesis if the measurements are made over an hour or two may greatly increase photosynthesis if the measurements are completed before injury develops. Therefore the expression "temperature optimum," though meaningful and useful when applied to long-term effects on complex systems, is meaningless and misleading when we try to analyze the system in terms of the responses of the component reactions. Above all, it is important to keep in mind that the causes of increases with temperature below the "optimum" are usually unrelated to the causes of decreases with temperature above the optimum.

The most serious adverse effects of high temperature on photosynthesis in the field are likely to be associated with various kinds of injury, some reversible and some irreversible. Indeed, the seriousness of the adverse effect is directly related to the irreversibility of the injury. Since exposure of leaves to high temperature is often accompanied by exposure to severe water stress, and may result in part from the failure of evaporative cooling, it is not always clear whether desiccation or high temperature is primarily responsible for an observed injury. Whatever the immediate cause of injury, the different responses of different plants is striking. For instance, the tops of potato plants are completely killed when the air temperature and light intensity are not far from optimum for the closely related tomato. Selection of plants on the basis of their ability to withstand high leaf temperatures is an important factor in adapting plants to the climates of many agricultural areas, not only to avoid injury from high air temperatures but also to provide one of the attributes necessary for drought survival. As we already pointed out when discussing water use efficiency, there is a great need for physiological analysis of the differences between plants that result in differences in heat tolerance.

We do not wish to imply that high temperature injury is restricted to the photosynthetic machinery or, for that matter, that injury is the only cause of the decrease in photosynthesis. Undoubtedly, increases in respiration and photorespiration (Zelitch, 1971), the production of specific photosynthesis inhibitors, and the inhibition of growth itself contribute to high-temperature inhibition of productivity.

We must now turn to the extremely serious problems introduced by suboptimal temperatures. These problems play an important role in limiting photosynthesis in all of the temperate regions of the world, that is at all high latitudes and high elevations. The problems are also much more complex than one might imagine. It is of course true that all of the thermochemical reactions that comprise the overall process of photosynthesis are slowed at low temperatures; encounters between reacting molecules are then too infrequent and too low in collision energy. But this is only one of a number of reasons, and it is frequently not the major reason for the observed decrease in photosynthesis at low temperatures. A list of cold effects that ultimately lower the rate of photosynthesis would have to include the following:

1. Slower diffusion rates due to the slower movements of molecules and the decrease of permeability of membranes (increase in viscosity).

2. Direct inhibition of the reactions of the electron transport system and the CO_2 reduction pathway due to an insufficiency of "activation energy."

3. Inhibition of growth resulting in an inhibition of the utilization of the products of CO_2 reduction and a "feedback inhibition" of photosynthesis (Section II,D).

4. Inhibition of growth resulting in a failure to produce new photosynthetic machinery.

5. Inhibitions due to cold injury: (a) freezing; (b) chilling effects on membranes and enzymes; and (c) production of inhibitory substances.

Direct cold inhibition of the electron transport system can be demonstrated quite easily by isolating chloroplasts and studying their ability to reduce exogenous electron acceptors, such as the ferricyanide ion (the Hill reaction). As expected, the Hill reaction is slowed by lowering the temperature, about twofold for every 10°C. However, the electron transport of the Hill reaction is not as sensitive to cold as is the photosynthesis of the many plants from which the chloroplasts are isolated. In fact, electron transport reactions in chloroplasts from different plants probably do not differ nearly as much in their sensitivities to low temperatures as overall photosynthesis does in the whole plants. Consequently, it seems likely that the inhibition of photosynthesis at low temperatures is primarily due to effects on the CO_2 reduction pathway and on the regulators of that pathway.

Cold injury contributes far more to the failure of photosynthesis at low temperatures than is generally recognized. It is obvious that freezing kills the vegetative parts of plants, and that plants differ greatly in their resistance to freezing. In fact, the winter survival of perennial and biennial crops is one of the most important considerations in the success or failure of such crops in temperate regions. Freezing resistance seems to be associated partly with the preparation of tissues by partial dehydration and partly with factors inhibiting the growth of ice crystals through cell walls and membranes (George *et al.*, 1974). Gums and mucilages tend to prevent the formation and proliferation of ice crystals, probably by interfering with the regular deposition of water molecules on the ice crystal faces. Some woody plants seem to dehydrate their intercellular spaces so that there is no water continuum and therefore ice crystals cannot spread from cell to cell. However, even if ice crystals outside the cell do not grow inward and perforate membranes, their formation can severely stress the cells, either by rapidly withdrawing water from them (Hudson and Idle, 1962), by adhesion damage, or simply by expanding the intercellular spaces in the tissues and disrupting cell-to-cell contacts. For these reasons, too, it is important that there be a limited amount of free water between cells. It is unfortunate that we know so little about the factors contributing to tissue dehydration and the inhibition of ice formation in plants, or about the factors that make different plants so different in their abilities to prevent ice formation and to confine ice formation to the intercellular spaces.

Cold injury can take quite different forms, which may have nothing to do with ice crystal formation or with subfreezing temperatures. These types of chilling injury, which often occur far above the freezing point of water, are all too often overlooked. Were it not for the persistence of chilling injury, plants could photosynthesize and grow if the days were warm, whether or not the nights were cold. Unfortunately, most of our warm weather crops (maize, tomato, etc.) share with many warm weather weeds (*Xanthium*, *Amaranthus*, etc.) a complete inability to grow, night or day, when night temperatures are low. At least one of the effects of chilling seems to be a fairly direct and long-lasting inhibition of photosynthesis itself. Thus *Xanthium* plants kept for 96 hr at 5°–10°C lose almost all of their ability to carry on photosynthesis (Drake and Raschke, 1974). This inhibition lasts for several days. Chilling injury may also result in less dramatic partial inhibitions. Therefore, those who would study the low temperature growth of plants should keep the phenomenon of chilling injury in mind at all times and distinguish very carefully between transient and persistent temperature effects.

We need to know more about the causes of chilling injury in plants

(and in warm-blooded animals). There are phase transitions (liquid–
solid) and conformational changes in membranes and proteins associated with temperature changes (Lyons and Raison, 1970), and some
of these may be harmful to the organism. It seems that some membranes
can "freeze" at temperatures well above 0°C. Sometimes irreversible
damage to the membrane may result (Taylor and Craig, 1971), but it is
probable that more often the membranes simply malfunction because of
their changed properties and in malfunctioning distort metabolism in a
variety of deleterious ways. Resistance to this kind of chilling injury
may be related to a lowering of the freezing point of membranes associated with the incorporation of a more unsaturated liquid lipids
therein. On the other hand, some chilling injury may not be due, either
directly or indirectly, to membrane changes. Cold-sensitive enzymes
are known to exist, but it is not certain that these enzymes are cold-
sensitive *in vivo*. Perhaps some cold injury is simply the result of the
inhibition of essential reactions disposing of products that continue to
be formed at low temperatures. Perhaps some organisms need
functions which have threshold energy requirements regardless of
temperature. Such organisms might be incapable of closing down
metabolism at low temperatures without damage. In *Xanthium* at least,
chilling is associated with the accumulation of abscisic acid in the
leaves, which makes stomata close much more readily in response to
the internal CO_2 level (Raschke *et al.*, 1976), and this may in part
explain the photosynthetic inhibition caused by chilling. However,
kinetic analyses have shown that this is not the major source of inhibition by chilling. Furthermore, chilling injury inhibits photosynthesis
in subsequently isolated mesophyll cells where stomatal resistance to
CO_2 uptake is not involved.

D. Utilization of the Products of Photosynthesis

Even the simplest living thing performs many functions, all of which
must be coordinated if chaos is not to result. It is unthinkable that any
highly organized system such as a growing plant should have its production of substances uncoupled from its use of those substances. Thus
it is no surprise to find that the rate of photosynthesis is modified by
the availability of sinks for the photosynthetic products. Removal of
some of the leaves results in a higher rate of photosynthesis in the
remaining leaves (Wareing *et al.*, 1968). Similarly, diseased leaves reduce less CO_2 and the remaining healthy leaves on the plant compen-
sate by reducing more (Livne and Daly, 1966). Removal of developing

ears of corn (Moss, 1962) or of developing potato tubers (Burt, 1964) decreases photosynthesis. Grafting of a shoot with a high growth rate to a plant of lower growth rate increases photosynthesis in the leaves of the slow grower (Thorne and Evans, 1964), etc. Moreover, it may be that the commonly encountered "midday depression" of photosynthesis is, in part, a reflection of the saturation of available sinks. Part of the inhibition of photosynthesis encountered at low temperatures may also result from slowed utilization of photosynthetic products, since carbohydrates seem to accumulate under these conditions (Warren Wilson, 1966).

In spite of the inevitability of such controls and the vast literature reporting their existence, the subject remains controversial. This may be in part because the extent of control is critically dependent on many factors, especially on the growth potential relative to the photosynthesis potential. This in turn depends on a host of environmental and genetic factors. In part the controversy revolves around a confusion between the fact and the suggested mechanisms. The fact of control is incontrovertible, but none of the suggested mechanisms have been established. Perhaps there are many mechanisms of control, not all of which need to be due to "product inhibition" of photosynthesis. Coordination of the rates of production and utilization might be at a much subtler hormonal level. Furthermore, attempts to relate the inhibition of photosynthesis to an accumulation of carbohydrate in the leaf have foundered on one inconvenient fact: the chemical activities of carbohydrates and related substances in leaves may not be reflected by the total amount of carbohydrate present. For instance, there is no reason to believe that the amount of insoluble starch stored away in granules corresponds in any way to the concentrations of starch precursors present. Yet, if simple feedback inhibition accounts for the control of photosynthesis by product utilization, it is likely to be the concentration of the starch precursor that determines the rate.

Since photosynthesis is clearly limited under many circumstances by the use of photosynthesis products, any factor affecting growth or storage must influence the rate of photosynthesis. The environmental and genetic constraints on photosynthesis are therefore legion. Thus it is primarily through modifying the use of photosynthesis products that the nutrient satus of the plant determines the rate of photosynthesis and hence the water use efficiency (see Section II,B above). Nevertheless some kinds of deficiencies may affect photosynthesis directly. For example, manganese deficiency inhibits photosynthesis by inhibiting water oxidation and oxygen production (see Kok and Cheniae, 1966).

III. GROWTH STRATEGIES AND THE MAXIMIZATION OF YIELD

In the introduction we emphasized that plant productivity can be equated with net photosynthesis. With this obvious fact in mind, a number of workers have attempted to relate productivity to rates of photosynthesis when these rates were measured in parts of leaves, whole leaves, and whole plants. However, more often than not there is no discernible relationship between productivity and the rates of photosynthesis so measured. Thus Heichel and Musgrave (1969) have shown that photosynthesis rates in single maize leaves in the field differ widely, sometimes threefold, depending on the genetic constitution of the plants. Nevertheless, the widely different photosynthesis rates are not correlated at all with the widely different grain yields or with the size of the above-ground parts of the plants.

This apparent contradiction has its origin in semantics. Production of biomass is, by definition, a function of the rate of net photosynthesis *when the rate is expressed per plant*. The relationship becomes less direct or disappears when the rate is expressed on the basis of leaf area or chlorophyll content. Imagine, for instance, two small plants with equal leaf areas and identical photosynthetic apparatus. Let us further suppose that one of these plants stores almost all of its reduced CO_2 in the form of starch in a tuber, while the other plant diverts almost all of its reduced CO_2 into the manufacture of more photosynthetic apparatus (leaf surfaces, support structures, and feeder roots). At first, the plant storing starch and the plant building new photosynthetic apparatus will increase in biomass at the same rate. However, as soon as the new leaf surface begins to function, the plant that reinvests its photosynthetic products will forge ahead (see Blackman, 1919).

Let us now consider the effect of reinvestment on producitivity in more quantitative terms. If P is the dry weight of the photosynthetic apparatus of the plant complete with supporting stems and roots, R is the rate of photosynthesis expressed as a proportion of P in unit time, and if α is the proportion of the photosynthesis products invested in the production of more P, then the rate of increase of the total photosynthetic apparatus, dP/dt, is αRP. As in every case where the rate of formation of a substance is proportional to the amount already present, the result is a typical exponential (i.e., logarithmic) increase in P. Thus by integrating we obtain the expression [Eq. (13)]

$$P = P_0 e^{\alpha R t} \qquad (13)$$

where P_0 is the size of the photosynthetic apparatus when the observations are begun, that is, when $t = 0$. Furthermore, every increase in dry weight due to photosynthesis is partitioned between the formation of new P and the formation of stored material S in the tuber. It follows that the ratio of new P to S is equal to the ratio of α to $1-\alpha$ or $S = (P-P_0) [(1-\alpha)/\alpha]$ and the total weight of the plant [Eq. (14)]

$$P + S = P + (P-P_0) [(1-\alpha)/\alpha]$$

$$P + S = \frac{\alpha}{\alpha}P + \frac{1-\alpha}{\alpha}P - \frac{1-\alpha}{\alpha}P_0 \qquad (14)$$

$$P + S = \frac{1}{\alpha}P - \frac{1-\alpha}{\alpha}P_0$$

substituting Eq. (13) in this expression we obtain Eq. (15)

$$P + S = \frac{1}{\alpha} P_0 e^{\alpha R t} - \frac{1-\alpha}{\alpha} P_0 \qquad (15)$$

The effect of varying α in the growth rate of a plant is illustrated in Fig. 7.

We can see from this analysis that total growth of a plant depends almost equally on the rate of photosynthesis, R, and on the proportion of the photosynthesis products devoted to the making of new, photosynthetically useful plant parts, α, since the rate of compound interest that determines the growth rate does not depend on R but rather on the product of R and α. However, that is not the only effect of the plant's reinvestment policy. In the absence of specialized storage organs (and plants often lack such organs during much of their growing period), the reinvestment provides a sink for the products of photosynthesis, and in so doing may also increase R. Thus the growth potential of the plant contributes in at least two ways to the ultimate size of the plant, whereas the productive potential of the photosynthetic apparatus may contribute very little because it is not expressed. *Herein lies the reason that normal maize plants are larger than dwarf maize plants and the reason that sunflower plants are larger than wheat plants. It is also one of the reasons for the stunting of plants by stresses and deficiencies that are as likely to lower α as they are to lower R.*

So we come to another truism: anything that slows the production of new photosynthetic apparatus decreases the production of total biomass, whether or not the rate of photosynthesis is also decreased. The potential activity of the photosynthetic apparatus, that is the activity observable under experimental conditions with minimum internal and external constraints, will more often than not be irrelevant to the

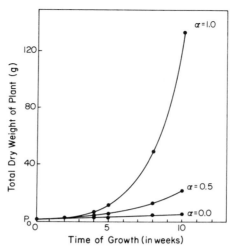

Fig. 7. Predicted rates of growth of plants when different proportions of their photosynthesis products are reinvested in new photosynthetic apparatus. Values were obtained by assuming equal rates of photosynthesis and no initial storage in nonphotosynthesizing tissues. The equation describing growth under these conditions is:

$$\text{Total weight of plant} = \frac{1}{\alpha}\, P_0 e^{\alpha R t} - \frac{1 - \alpha}{\alpha}\, P_0$$

where α is the proportion of photosynthesis products used to make new photosynthetic apparatus, and $1-\alpha$ is the proportion of photosynthesis products stored; R is the rate of photosynthesis, in this case 70 mg additional dry weight per gram of dry weight of photosynthetic apparatus per day; P_0 is the initial dry weight (1.0 g); e is the base of the natural logarithms (2.718 . . .); and t is the time of growth in days. It should be noted that the figure does not represent the growth of any particular plant, since in the real world both α and R have changing values as plants develop. The figure is only intended to illustrate the importance of α in determining the final size of a plant.

accumulation of biomass. Certainly no consistent relationship exists between photosynthesis rates observed in the laboratory and ultimate plant size. Therefore, we will have to pay great attention to the responses of plants to stresses and to patterns of growth and development if we are to understand the factors involved in the maximization of plant productivity.

Not only are patterns of development important in determining overall growth, they are also especially important if plants are to exploit changing seasons to their advantage. Very often, timing of the phases of development is more important than efficient use of light or water. For instance, there is an urgent need for rapid growth early in the spring if maximum use is to be made of the sunlight and water that are then relatively abundant. Annual plants, which develop from minute embryos in seeds, of necessity require a good deal of time to produce enough leaf surface to cover the ground and intercept the sunlight. For these plants, the advantage of early rapid growth may be so great that a strategy of total reinvestment of photosynthesis products and a very profligate use of water may be indicated. Perennial plants have an even better system. Using large reserves of nutrients and preformed minature branches in their winter buds, they are able to expand new leaf surfaces at a phenomenal rate as soon as the temperature permits growth. In just a few warm days trees can produce a virtually continuous overlapping surface of leaves. The point is that none of these considerations has anything to do with the biochemistry or physiology of the photosynthesis process itself. Nevertheless, such adaptations play a major role in determining the production of biomass. Since photosynthesis is prevented for much of the year by low temperatures or inadequate water, the need for a rapid response to warmer weather or more water may supercede all other considerations.

However, it is in the optimization of the yield of useful plant products that patterns of development are of overwhelming importance. Two crops with the same biomass may have very different yields. In selecting cultivars or in prescribing cultural practices, the agronomist must have in his sights improved yield, not increased biomass. Aside from purely subjective aesthetic considerations, the quality of yield includes more objective factors such as keeping ability and nutritive value. These qualities are determined by the genetics of the cultivar, by disease incidence, and by the maturity of the seed, fruit, or tuber. Only very indirectly are they influenced by the rate of photosynthesis, and they are almost as likely to be adversely influenced by increased photosynthesis, if it comes at the wrong time, as they are to be influenced favorably. On the other hand, the quantity of yield *does* depend on the rate of photosynthesis. Indeed, the photosynthesis per plant (i.e., the total biomass) and the partitioning of the products of photosynthesis between the useful and useless portions of the plant are the sole factors determining the magnitude of the yield.

Yield is the culmination of a sequence of stages of plant development, all of which are subject to genetic control, presumably mediated by hormones and by as yet unidentified agents of differentiation. In most crops, there is a stage of purely vegetative growth when almost all of the products of photosynthesis are used to make more photosynthetically active plant material. The purposes of this first phase are manifold: (1) to provide machinery for later production of the products to be stored in the yield-producing organ; (2) to get as much growing done as possible while water and nutrients are relatively abundant; and (3) to tower above less successful neighbors while stealing their light and water. The second phase involves the growth of yield-producing organs (seeds, etc.) using the already prepared vegetative plant. Actually, the growth of fruit and seeds, once it has started, seems to depend heavily on photosynthesis in the plant parts adjacent to the fruit or seed. Thus much of the carbon stored in some cereal seeds is said to come from CO_2 reduced in the floral parts and the flag leaf (Thorne, 1965). Meanwhile, the more remote leaves contribute little fixed CO_2 to the developing seed but instead close down their photosynthesis and ultimately senesce. This loss of photosynthetic potential is probably not as wasteful as it seems since the "superfluous" leaves have already played an essential role in developing the entire support system of stems and roots and in accumulating minerals and available nitrogen, a considerable proportion of which is ultimately translocated to the seeds. Furthermore, these superfluous leaves may be a heritage of a long history of weed supression. A large part of their function may be to compete with neighbor plants, as was suggested above. Indeed, it is probable that the success of modern high-yielding, short-strawed cereals can be attributed in some degree to the elimination of excess vegetative growth, since modern agricultural practices make competitive advantages over weeds less important.

IV. IMPROVING PRODUCTIVITY AND YIELD

Over the last few decades, we have acquired considerable understanding of the basic processes involved in photosynthesis. Unfortunately this understanding has had little impact on programs of crop improvement. The fault does not lie with the biochemist or with the agronomist, but rather with the nature of our knowledge. We know a great deal about the physics of light absorption, the photochemical oxidation–reduction reactions, the electron transport intermediates, and the enzymes of carbon dioxide reduction. But these basic processes are almost identical in all photosynthetic organisms, from the prokaryotic blue-green algae to the eukaryotic higher plants, and therefore have probably existed almost unchanged since early in the history of life on earth. This being so, the chances of our being able to modify them in a useful way are about the same as our chances of repealing the laws of physics. Most improvements in productivity will have to be made by modifying the things that control photosynthesis. But our knowledge of such things remains rudimentary.

Total net photosynthesis (productivity) is determined by the availability of light, CO_2, water, and nutrients; by the growth patterns of the plant that determine both the photosynthesis rate and the reinvestment rate; and by the responses of the plant to stress. We can do little about light and CO_2, except to a limited extent by varying the density of the stand and by modifying the architecture of the plant. Most of the improvement in productivity will therefore be made by changing water and nutrient supply, by changing patterns of development, or by changing responses to stress. Moreover, since it may become less expensive to adapt the plant to the environment than to adapt the environment to the plant, modifications of growth patterns and responses to stress will sometimes be more practical than modification of external supply factors. To alter these internal processes one usually has to alter the gene complement of plants through breeding.

Plant breeding has traditionally set as its goal bigger yields of better crops, but the reasons for the bigger and better crops have not always been asked. It is here that studies of the controls and limitations of photosynthesis can make their greatest contributions. Breeding for the end result of interactions of a multiplicity of unknown gene-controlled processes is inevitably a matter of unsystematic and very time-consuming trial and error. Identification of the components of yield in terms of specific physiological processes should take much of the randomness out of breeding, and might ultimately lead to the identification of the genes involved. Only to the extent that we can describe productivity in terms of the mechanisms that control photosynthesis and growth can we bring productivity improvement out of the dark ages of pure empiricism.

What kinds of new knowledge will be most helpful in directing breeding programs and in determining field practices? Obviously, if we are to go about increasing productivity in a systematic manner, we must recognize the attainable limits and analyze the reasons for not attaining the attainable. We must study the mechanisms of the processes which limit photosynthesis in the field, study the interactions between the limiting processes, and by studying the interactions come to an understanding of the compromises which go into optimization of yield. The following is a summary of some of the factors limiting dry matter production which might be investigated profitably:

1. Chief among the external constraints on productivity is the availability of water and the intimately related availability of CO_2. The availability of CO_2 for reduction depends on the external CO_2 supply (which we cannot change), on the permeability of the stomatal pores

(which is subject to internal regulation), and on the efficiency of the CO_2 fixation reactions. There is a great variability among crop species in stomatal behavior, but the degree of genetic variability within a crop species is unknown. Nor do we understand the problems of optimization of the water–CO_2 exchange well enough to seek appropriate genetic variability. However, the tools needed for an analysis of the system are at hand (Raschke, 1974) and the prospects of getting further information seem good. Unfortunately, the prospects for putting this information to work in improving water use efficiency in crops seem poor. As we have already pointed out, much of the water use by a crop canopy is involved in essential evaporative cooling. While stomatal control of water loss undoubtedly plays a major role in protecting individual plants and plant parts from damaging desiccation, it does not seem likely that stomata have much control over the amount of water ultimately lost by the canopy as a whole. Rather, the water use depends heavily on the absorbed radiation, which is not under the plant's control, and for that reason the amount of water lost from widely different crops is quite similar when these crops are subjected to the same insolation. Water use being relatively invariant, it follows that water use efficiency is determined to a large extent by the rate of carbon dioxide uptake.

There is great variability among crop species with respect to the efficiencies of the initial carboxylation reactions but, again, little evidence of genetic variability within a crop species. There are very few reports of intermediates between C_3 plants and C_4 plants, even though some C_3 and C_4 plants can hybridize (see Björkman, 1976). Apparently, the device of prefixing CO_2 in specialized cells employed by C_4 plants is incompatible with some other device or devices employed by C_3 plants. This implies that C_3 plants have their own advantageous tricks. The fact that C_3 and C_4 plants seem to compete on fairly even terms in hot, dry environments, and the fact that C_3 plants usually do better in cool climates, also suggest that C_3 plants have their own hidden advantages. We need a much greater understanding of the functions of C_3 and C_4 plants and the nature of photorespiration (which may be a good thing under some conditions) before we can contemplate changing the efficiency of the CO_2-fixing reaction by plant breeding.

2. The adequacy of nitrogen and mineral nutrition is a factor in productivity that is almost too obvious to need comment. However, nitrogen nutrition comes within the purview of this chapter for a very simple reason: the fixation of gaseous nitrogen by legumes demands much energy, both for the development of the bacteria-containing nodules

and for the subsequent reduction reactions therein. Nitrogen fixation in legumes therefore depends on photosynthesis (see Hardy and Havelka, 1976), which in turn depends on growth made possible by the fixed nitrogen. This interaction of photosynthesis, growth, and nitrogen fixation needs to be more fully investigated.

3. Low temperature affects photosynthesis directly by slowing all of the thermochemical reactions and indirectly by inhibiting growth. Low temperatures also cause injuries. The frost injuries and chilling injuries that prevent photosynthesis and growth are far more serious than the simple slowing of reactions due to a deficiency of activation energy. Breeding for resistance to chilling injury has an immense potential for increasing the productivity of many plants, especially those of cold-susceptible plants that start to grow too late in the spring (maize, tomatoes, etc.). Research aimed at discovering the nature of the inhibitions of photosynthesis caused by chilling injury should have a very high priority. Breeding for resistance to frost injury is also of utmost importance if we are to increase the productivity and widen the range of cultivation of perennial plants and winter crops.

4. The fraction of reduced CO_2 used in constructing new photosynthetic apparatus is decisive in determining productivity, sometimes even transcending such factors as the availability of water. (Under very dry conditions, a sunflower plant, if it survives at all, will still be larger than a barley plant.) Selection of plants with an appropriately high capacity for growth may have more of an effect on total photosynthesis and plant productivity than the selection of any other character. Synchronization of the growth and storage phases of development with changing seasons is also very important in determining productivity. For instance, an early stage of exponential growth, followed by a later stage in which storage predominates, will almost always give more productivity than a constant partitioning of photosynthetic products between growth and storage, especially if the conditions for a high growth rate are fleeting. For these reasons, the physiology of growth and development are as pertinent to the production of biomass as is the physiology of photosynthesis. This is especially true with respect to the yield of useful products. Optimum yield is hardly ever consistent with maximum productivity (forage crops being an exception) but yield is nevertheless productivity dependent. Therefore, yield has a double dependence on developmental events. When one considers that there is much more genetic variability available to influence patterns of development than there is to influence the fundamental process of photosynthesis, it becomes obvious that studies of growth and development

are much more important to the plant breeder than are studies of photosynthesis.

To reiterate, the well-tried agronomic approaches, breeding and selection of new cultivars to match new conditions and modifications of conditions to suit new cultivars, remain our best hopes—especially if the physiological phenomena associated with adaptation can be identified. To this end, we must study all aspects of stress physiology, in particular, the effects of chilling and desiccation. We must continue to study the internal factors which regulate photosynthesis and the use of photosynthesis products. It is also important to realize that the greatest opportunities for progress in breeding selection will arise whenever climatic changes or technological developments change requirements. After all, eons of selection by nature and millennia of selection by humans have already been expended in adapting plants to their environments. Therefore, it is not surprising that improvements have always come more easily when new situations arose. It likewise follows that the development of new plant uses for which our plants were not designed may provide an important route to increased plant productivity. However, a final word of caution is needed. The matching of crops to environment and environment to crops can become confining if, as is too often the case, breeding stations are restricted to major crop areas and specialize in breeding for a narrow range of conventional farm practices. The breeding of crops for areas in which they do not now succeed and for farm practices that are foreign to our society may ultimately be as important as making improvements in crops where they already do well. As we have already pointed out, it may be easier to breed crops for new conditions than to improve the adjustment of plants to familiar conditions. There is also a risk in fine adjustments of the closed selection system if maximum yields are obtained at the cost of plant versatility. We cannot guarantee delivery of constant conditions. Long-term changes in weather have the inevitability of death and taxes, and social systems have even less stability than the weather.

V. PHOTOSYNTHESIS AND THE CONSERVATION OF SOLAR ENERGY

The products of recent photosynthesis have always been used for many purposes: as food for man and animals; as fiber for the production of textiles, cordage, and paper; as lumber for construction; as raw materials for industrial chemistry; and, until very recently, as the sole source of fuel. How well can current photosynthesis fill these needs, especially if we turn back to the use of biomass for the production of a considerable part of the energy we use?

In the light of the constraints on photosynthesis we have already discussed, we can put some upper limits on photosynthesis in the United States. First let us consider the maximum possible primary productivity in terms of the conservation of light energy and in terms of efficiency of water use. It has been estimated that the sunlight falling on the United States has an average year-round energy content of 4000 kcal m^{-2} day^{-1} (Morse and Simmons, 1976). Since the area of the country is about 8×10^8 ha (8×10^{12} m^2), the total energy falling in a year is about 1.2×10^{19} kcal or 5.0×10^{22} J. We have seen that the very efficient maize plant can conserve about 5% of this energy under optimum conditions. However, optimum conditions only occur during a small part of the year. As we have also seen, the average yearly efficiency of photosynthesis in a good maize field, well-watered and well-fertilized, is rarely better than 0.5%. Thus, if we were by some miracle to cover the farms, mountains, deserts, and cities with good maize fields, the total energy conserved would be 6×10^{16} kcal (2.5×10^{20} J).

Assuming water rather than light to be the main factor limiting photosynthesis, one can make another independent calculation of an equally optimistic maximum. The average annual rainfall on the United States is probably 75 cm, and therefore 6×10^{18} g or 3.3×10^{17} moles of water fall each year. About one-third of this water either runs off or evaporates from regions devoid of vegetation. Therefore, only 2.2×10^{17} moles of water are available for evapotranspiration. If this amount of water were used with the efficiencies observed in well-fertilized fields, about $2.2 \times 10^{17}/500$ or 4.4×10^{14} moles of CO_2 would be reduced. The energy stored in the products of photosynthesis would then be about 5.0×10^{16} kcal (2.1×10^{20} J).

Still another optimistic assessment of total photosynthesis can be made by assuming a moderate yield of maize grain over the entire surface of the United States, 5 metric tons/ha. If the grain is one-third of the entire plant, then photosynthesis would be producing 15 metric tons/ha of dry matter. This yield, when multiplied by 8.0×10^8 ha, gives 1.2×10^{16}g, 4.8×10^{16} kcal, or once again 2.0×10^{20} J.

Obviously, these calculated yields represent unattainable goals that cannot be approached for a number of practical reasons. The calculations err because conditions for growth are suboptimal over most of the country. One need only look at the color of the plains and desert regions from an airplane during summer to see how far from the truth is the premise of ubiquitous, well-watered maize fields. Even if water were to be in sufficient supply, photosynthesis would often be limited by the supply of nitrogen or by unfavorable soil characteristics that make water and nutrients relatively inaccessible. A deficiency of nitrogen can double water loss for a given amount of biomass production. Almost any other condition unfavorable for growth has a similar adverse effect on water use efficiency.

What then is the real annual production of biomass in the United States? Lieth (1975) has estimated that net photosynthesis on the land masses of the world conserves on the average about 3000 kcal m^{-2} year^{-1} and it may be that the contiguous United States are not very different from the world average. We have no unproductive arctic tundras and only small areas of really unproductive desert but, on the other hand, there is no tropical rain-forest and the vegetation covering the greater part of the country is dormant during winter. Inspection of vegetation maps (Sharpe, 1975) and observed productivities of vegetation types (Lieth, 1975) suggest that 3000 kcal may be somewhat too high for the United States. An annual conservation of 3000 kcal/m^2 translates into 1.0×10^{20} J, or one-half of the photosynthesis we would expect with a uniform surface of productive maize fields. In view of the large areas of semiarid country, a mean equal to one-half of the best seems excessive. However, our purposes here is to set upper limits and for that reason we will use Lieth's average for purposes of discussion. But in accepting this high estimate we must recognize that inadequate water and low temperatures are largely responsible for the ceiling. Neither of these limitations is likely to disappear for our convenience. Therefore, large increases in continental photosynthesis cannot be obtained on command, even though some locally important increases may be possible in the more humid regions, where poor soil conditions or ill-adapted plants unnecessarily limit production.

We must now ask how well this annual biomass increment containing 1.0×10^{20} J can meet our current needs and how much might be left over for a renewed use of plants for fuel (see Fig. 8). In natural ecosystems the net productivity is, of course, zero; heterotrophic organisms consume autotrophic organisms and, except in bogs, nothing is left. If we insert ourselves into the ecosystem's energy flux, how much of the energy can be diverted to serve our purposes, that is how much can we channel through our economy without degrading the productive capacity of the system and without eliminating an unacceptable number of our fellow creatures who are inevitably our competitors for biomass? How much food is required for ourselves and our domestic animals, and how much primary productivity is required to produce this amount of food? How much wood, paper, and fiber do we need,

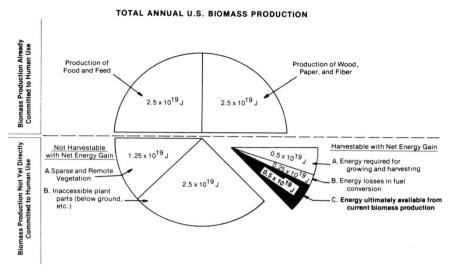

Fig. 8. An illustration of the considerations that determine the availability of fuel from plant products in the United States. The values in each category are very rough estimates, but are probably more often optimistic than pessimistic. In any event, the maximum amount of solar energy that might ultimately be harvested from plants for use as fuel is only a few percent of our current energy consumption of 8.0×10^{19} J.

and how much primary productivity does this need represent? Finally, how much of the remaining biomass is potentially harvestable for fuel and what is the net energy gain after the costs of harvesting the fuel?

Rough estimates of our food requirements can be arrived at by two independent methods that yield similar numbers. The energy content of the farm crops in the United States is approximately 6×10^{18} J. This does not include hay, pasture, and ensilage and, of course, it does not include any of the unharvested parts of the plants. The value of 6×10^{18} J calculated from data in the FAO Production Yearbook of 1975 therefore probably does not represent more than 25% of the primary productivity required to feed us if we continue to eat animals and animal products. Thus, our food bill in terms of the energy content of the necessary biomass must be 2.0–2.5×10^{19} J. Using entirely different data, G. A. Borgström (personal communication) has calculated that each of us, with our animal proxies, consumes about 16,000 kcal/day. This represents 3.0×10^{18} J/year for the whole population. However, there are very significant losses of food in handling, and neither we nor our domestic animals eat the greater part of the plant. Humans, pigs, and chickens eat only the grain, and not always all of that, while no domestic animal eats plant root systems. It could be argued that the part of the biomass not actually consumed—the straw, for instance—could be harvested for fuel. However, most of the parts of plants not now harvested are probably required to maintain soil productivity. Certainly their removal would increase soil erosion and the need for fertilizers, and would decrease water retention. Some additional crop removal may be possible, but total biomass production in agriculture must always be several times greater than our actual food consumption. Therefore, Borgström's value for calories consumed probably represents less than 20% of the required biomass, and once again we are confronted with a food bill approaching 2.5×10^{19} J if we express the bill in terms of the required primary productivity.

The need for forest productivity is much harder to evaluate. We use large amounts of lumber and paper annually, amounts that are easily determined. The difficulty comes when we try to assess the net photosynthesis required to yield this amount of useful product. If one makes a calculation based on the present yield of forest lands, there will be, by definition, nothing left over for other purposes. On the other hand, if we assume a new technology regularly harvesting a much larger proportion of the growth, even perhaps pulling up stumps and roots, we immediately encounter problems of forest renewal and the maintenance of forest productivity. As long as we demand trees large enough to be used for lumber (boards and plywood), we will probably have to devote most of our good forest lands to lumber production. Some gains in the efficiency of growth and harvesting pulpwood for paper may be made, but again these gains will be made on moderately productive and fully accessible land. Just as the best agricultural land is devoted to the production of food, so too must the best forest land be devoted to the production of wood. The net photosynthesis in forests is similar to the net photosynthesis on arable land, and the area of forest is similar to the area of arable land (1.9×10^8 ha). Therefore, the amount of photosynthesis devoted to the production of wood is probably similar to the amount of photosynthesis needed for the production of food, that is, another 2 to 2.5×10^{19} J. There is no immediate prospect of a major decrease in this commitment of land resources to conventional forestry.

It follows that about one-half of the photosynthesis going on in the country is already directed toward meeting existing needs. Furthermore, this one-half occurs on the most accessible and most productive areas. If we are to harvest biomass for fuel, we will have to use many scattered, slow-growing plants from remote places.

Assuming that one-half of the biomass being produced annually in the United States is not irreversibly assigned to other purposes, how much could be harvested for fuel production? The question has two parts: (1) what proportion of the biomass could be removed while maintaining productivity, and (2) what would be the net energy gain after subtracting the energy required for harvesting? These questions cannot be answered without a great deal of research yet to be done. Natural plant communities, especially those growing on marginally productive lands, are notoriously fragile, and any harvesting at all would inevitably cause major changes, probably in the direction of lower productivity. However, given enough knowledge and enough management effort, it might be possible to combine cropping with a sustained yield even in arid regions or rugged terrain. But management efforts are not without energy costs, and this brings us to our second question—net energy gain. Under most of the unfavorable conditions, the root systems of plants would likely be one-half or more of the total plant biomass. It does not seem likely that the root systems of shrubs or grasses could be harvested without expanding more energy than the roots contained. Moreover, root removal would make continuous biomass production impossible since there would be a period of very low productivity while the new crop was being established. For these reasons, fully one-half of the uncommitted biomass must immediately be dismissed from consideration. But not all of the remaining uncommitted biomass could be harvested with a net energy gain. At some low level of productivity plants become such a dilute commodity that more energy would be required to concentrate them than they contain. The same is true of very inaccessible plants growing on mountains or in lakes and streams. (It should be emphasized here that we are considering ALL photosynthesis—the biomass produced by every lichen, moss, alga, grass, and shrub.) It seems likely that only about one-half of the above ground parts of the plants growing on our currently unused lands could be harvested at all, if we insist on getting more energy back than we put in. This means that 25% of our unused biomass or about 12% of the total primary production in the country might be harvestable for fuel. A variable proportion of this harvestable biomass might find its way into useful fuel depending on how the fuel was used. Electricity-generating stations could burn plants directly, in which case plants would compete on almost equal terms with fossil fuels. However, almost any other fuel use (conversion to methanol, alcohol, or oils) would entail very significant energy losses. If we want to use biomass for any other purpose than direct heating—such as transportation or chemical syntheses—not much more than 5% of the energy conserved by photosynthesis in the United States would be available. However, to be optimistic again, let us assume that we use biomass primarily for electricity generation and space heating and that we are thus enabled to use as much as 10% of the energy conserved by photosynthesis, that is 1.0×10^{19} J.

Having guessed that the biomass containing 1.0×10^{19} J might eventually be gathered for fuel, let us now inquire into how much energy would have to be expended as a production cost. In making the estimate, we must remember that we have already discarded as unharvestable the least productive and least accessible regions, but we must also remember that we have preempted the most productive and most accessible regions for food and wood production. Pimentel *et al.* (1973) have estimated that maize can be grown on and collected from our best agricultural lands with an energy expenditure that is only about 30% of the energy content of the grain. If the stalks were also harvested, the energy expended would probably not be over 20% of the energy content of the crop. The return on marginal lands would be much less, since yields would decline with declining productivity much more rapidly than would the energy costs of production. Transport alone would become formidable if we attempted to harvest sparse vegetation. Furthermore, if productivity were to be maintained, the ashes from the power stations would have to be returned to the cropped areas. All of the fixed nitrogen in the harvested plants would be lost in burning and would have to be replaced on the fields—more nitrogen than this, in fact, since fertilizer nitrogen is less efficiently utilized than is nitrogen incorporated in plants. In view of these considerations, it seems inconceivable that a net return of over 50% of the energy contained in the harvested biomass could ever be attained.

Thus, the massive capital investments and total social reorganization necessary for full exploitation of photosynthesis would probably not yield us more than 5% of the energy in the nation's biomass production or about 5×10^{18} J. In order to evaluate the ultimate impact of "energy plantations" on our current energy problems, we must match this 5×10^{18} J against our current industrial uses of energy. In 1972, our annual consumption of oil provided us with about 36×10^{18} J; our consumption of natural gas, about 24×10^{18} J; and our consumption of coal, about 16×10^{18} J; giving a total energy consumption of about 80×10^{18} J (U.S. Energy Research and Development Administration, 1975). If our needs for food and forest products hold constant, if we build no more roads or cities on agricultural land, and if we do not increase our use of energy, we might, by making a supreme effort, someday replace 6 or 7% of our fossil fuel with fuel we grow. However, this is an optimistic estimate and, of course, no great and disruptive effort will ever be made for such a modest gain. Minor conservation efforts would do more to ameliorate our energy problems within days than would decades of national dedication to energy plantations or to any other scheme for energy acquisition based on current photosynthesis. Driving the "subcompact" automobiles used by other countries in the United States would save more energy than would be gained by harvesting every harvestable green thing.

Recent political events and our shrinking oil reserves have forced us into a belated recognition of the fact that energy resources are finite and poorly distributed. For the last century or more nature has seemed to thrust stored energy upon us in the form of gushing oil wells and pressurized hydrocarbon gases. The all-too-ready accessibility of the fossil products of photosynthesis has shaped our modern technology; we have developed a society that uses fossil energy reserves with abandon to harvest and consume yet more fossil energy reserves at an ever-increasing tempo. Until recently there has been little thought for tomorrow and no questioning at all of the real usefulness of the energy we so wantonly waste. An end to the bounty is now in sight. With this belated recognition that we cannot subsist forever on past photosynthesis has come a revival of interest in current photosynthesis, a renewable and truly inexhaustible (but not unlimited) resource. Cost analyses have shown that alcohol or other fuels could be made from vegetation at prices which, although higher than present petroleum costs, may not be prohibitive. However, the proponents of the use of biomass for industrial energy have looked at costs without looking at supply. Fuel production from organic wastes and from the by-products of agriculture and forestry are worthy goals if only to reduce pollution and indeed such production might make a significant contribution if our appetite for fuel were more modest. But to hold out current photosynthesis as a major source of the energy needed to fuel our power-drunk economy is to deal in illusions. Energy consumption in the United States is approximately equal to the total energy conserved by photosynthesis. Only a small fraction of the energy in biomass can be harvested with a net energy gain and much of that fraction is needed for other purposes. There may be other options open to us, if we are willing to curb our excessive appetite for energy. We can harvest solar energy with photovoltaic devices, and we may someday be able to do so with a 10% yield. Furthermore, such devices do not require water and therefore in no way compete with photosynthesis. We can explore the use of tides and, if we are willing to consider decentralization of our industry, we can reexplore the use of wind. Above all, we can conserve energy by building a less wasteful, more rational technology. The large-scale use of biomass for industrial energy is not an option. Indeed, the shoe is on the other foot. Agriculture needs inputs of energy from outside the system, not only so that bigger crops can be grown with the irrigation water and fertilizer that can then be provided, but also to avoid the necessity of feeding a part of the crop to four-legged tractors. Mankind has probably already passed the point of no return and may no longer be able to eat without using agriculture to turn fossil fuels into food.

REFERENCES

Allaway, W. G. (1973). *Planta* **110**, 63–70.
Allen, L. H., Desjardins, R. L., and Lemon, E. R. (1974). *Agron. J.* **65**, 609–620.
Andrews, T. J., Lorimer, G. H., and Tolbert, N. E. (1973). *Biochemistry* **12**, 11–18.
Björkman, O. (1976). In "CO$_2$ Metabolism and Plant Productivity" (R. H. Burris and C. C. Black, eds.), pp. 287–309. Univ. Park Press, Baltimore, Maryland.
Björkman, O., and Ehleringer, J. (1975). *Carnegie Inst. Washington, Yearb.* **74**, 760–761.
Black, C. C. (1973). *Annu. Rev. Plant Physiol.* **24**, 253–286.
Blackman, F. F. (1905). *Ann. Bot. (London)* **19**, 281–295.
Blackman, V. H. (1919). *Ann. Bot. (London)* **33**, 353–360.
Burt, R. L. (1964). *Aust. J. Biol. Sci.* **17**, 867–877.
Carlson, C. W., Alessi, J., and Mickelson, R. H. (1959). *Soil Sci. Soc. Am., Proc.* **23**, 242–245.
Drake, B., and Raschke, K. (1974). *Plant Physiol.* **53**, 808–812.
Emerson, R. (1958). *Annu. Rev. Plant Physiol.* 9:1–24.
Fischer, R. A., and Hsiao, T. C. (1968). *Plant Physiol.* **43**, 1953–1958.
Gaastra, P. (1959). *Meded. Landbouwhogesch. Wageningen* **59**, 1–68.
George, M. F., Burke, M. J., and Weiser, C. J. (1974). *Plant Physiol.* **54**, 29–35.
Gould, F. W. (1968). "Grass Systematics." McGraw-Hill, New York.
Hardy, R. W. F., and Havelka, U. D. (1976). In "Symbiotic Nitrogen Fixation in Plants" (P. S. Nutman, ed.), pp. 421–439. Cambridge Univ. Press, London and New York.
Heichel, G. H., and Musgrave, R. B. (1969). *Crop Sci.* **9**, 483–486.
Hill, R., and Bendall, F. (1960). *Nature (London)* **186**, 136–137.
Hudson, M. A., and Idle, D. B. (1962). *Planta* **57**, 718–730.
Kok, B., and Cheniae, G. (1966). *Curr. Top. Bioenerg.* **1**, 1–47.
Lemon, E. R. (1965). In "Plant Environment and Efficient Water Use" (W. H. Pierre *et al.*, eds.), pp. 28–48. Am. Soc. Agron. Soil Sci. Soc. Am., Madison, Wisconsin.
Lieth, H. (1975). In "Primary Productivity of the Biosphere" (H. Lieth and R. H. Whittaker, eds.), pp. 203–215. Springer-Verlag, Berlin and New York.
Livne, A., and Daly, J. M. (1966). *Phytopathology* **56**, 170–175.
Lyons, J. M., and Raison, J. K. (1970). *Plant Physiol.* **45**, 386–389.
Morse, F. H., and Simmons, M. K. (1976). *Annu. Rev. Energy* **1**, 131–158.
Moss, D. N. (1962). *Crop Sci.* **2**, 366–367.
Odum, E. P. (1971). "Fundamentals of Ecology." Saunders, Philadelphia, Pennsylvania.
Odum, H. T., and Pinkerton, R. C. (1955). *Am. Sci.* **43**, 331–343.
Pimentel, D., Hurd, L. E., Bellotti, A. C., Forster, M. J., Oka, I. N., Sholes, O. D., and Whitman, R. J. (1973). *Science* **182**, 443–449.
Ramig, R. E. (1960). Ph.D. Thesis, University of Nebraska, Lincoln.
Ranson, S. L., and Thomas, L. (1960). *Annu. Rev. Plant Physiol.* **11**, 81–110.
Raschke, K. (1965). *Z. Naturforsch., Teil B* **20**, 1261–1270.

Raschke, K. (1970). *Planta* **95**, 1–17.
Raschke, K. (1974). *Plant Growth Subst., Proc. Int. Conf., 8th, 1973* pp. 1151–1158.
Raschke, K. (1975). *Annu. Rev. Plant Physiol.* **26**, 309–340.
Raschke, K. (1976). *Philos. Trans. R. Soc. London* **273**, 551–560.
Raschke, K., Pierce, M., and Popiela, C. C. (1976). *Plant Physiol.* **57**, 115–121.
Sharpe, D. M. (1975). *In* "Primary Productivity of the Biosphere" (H. Lieth and R. H. Whittaker, eds.), pp. 147–166. Springer-Verlag, Berlin and New York.
Shantz, H. L., and Piemeisel, L. N. (1927). *J. Agric. Res.* **34**, 1093–1189.
Taylor, A. O., and Craig, A. S. (1971). *Plant Physiol.* **47**, 719–725.
Thorne, G. N. (1965). *Ann. Bot. (London)* [N.S.] **29**, 317–329.
Thorne, G. N., and Evans, A. F. (1964). *Ann. Bot. (London)* [N.S.] **28**, 499–508.
Uchijima, Z. (1975). *In* "Vegetation and the Atmosphere" (J. L. Monteith, ed.), Vol. 2, pp. 33–64. Academic Press, New York.
U. S. Energy Research and Development Administration (1975). "A National Plan for Energy Research, Development and Demonstration," Vol. I, Publ. No. ERDA-48. ERDA, Washington, D. C.
Wareing, P. F., Khalifa, M. M., and Treharne, K. J. (1968). *Nature (London)* **220**, 453–457.
Warren Wilson, J. (1966). *Ann. Bot. (London)* [N.S.] **30**, 383–402.
Weaver, H. A., and Pearson, R. W. (1956). *Soil Sci.* **81**, 443–451.
Wilson, A. T., and Calvin, M. (1955). *J. Am. Chem. Soc.* **77**, 5948–5957.
Wind, G. P. (1954). *In* "European Grassland Conference," Proj. 224, pp. 195–198. European Productivity Agency of the Organization for European Economic Cooperation, Paris.
Wright, S. T. C. (1969). *Planta* **86**, 10–20.
Yocum, C. S., Allen, L. H., and Lemon, E. R. (1964). *Agron. J.* **56**, 249–253.
Zelitch, I. (1969). *In* "Physiological Aspects of Crop Yield" (J. D. Eastin *et al.*, eds.), pp. 207–226. Am. Soc. Agron. and Crop Sci. Soc. Am., Madison, Wisconsin.
Zelitch, I. (1971). "Photosynthesis, Photorespiration, and Plant Productivity." Academic Press, New York.

Chapter 2

Nitrogen Fixation

Winston J. Brill

I. INTRODUCTION

There is great emphasis now for increased research on biological N_2 fixation, especially with the goal of energy conservation in the face of increased pressures for intensive agriculture. Two important documents, coming from meetings of international experts, have been published to stress the need for more research in this area (Evans, 1975; Brown et al., 1975).

53

The Biology of Crop Productivity
Copyright © 1980 by Academic Press, Inc.
All rights of reproduction in any form reserved
ISBN 0-12-159850-0

Nitrogen fixation is a key reaction for continued life on this planet, for it recovers the fixed N that is lost to N_2 via microbial denitrification in the soil. Most of the atmospheric N_2 that is fixed occurs in a limited number of bacterial species. These bacteria contain the enzyme nitrogenase, which catalyzes the reduction of N_2 to ammonium. Since the early 1900's, industrially fixed N has been making an increasingly larger contribution to the global fixed N pool. More people in the world, and particularly more of those people wanting to eat well-fatted beef, have raised the demand for food and feed, and therefore for more N fertilizer. Forty million metric tons of fertilizer N, with a value of about $9 billion, were used in 1974. Four times that amount of fertilizer N is predicted to be required for crop production by the year 2000 (Hardy and Havelka, 1975).

Most of the industrially fixed N is synthesized by the Haber–Bosch process, a reaction that requires very high temperatures and pressures as well as a source of H_2. Fuels required to satisfy this energy-intensive reaction are becoming more costly and increasingly difficult to obtain in many parts of the world. This situation is producing higher prices and actual shortages of food.

Recent advances in understanding biological N_2 fixation have stimulated many researchers to consider new applications of microbially fixed N in order to lessen our dependence on industrially fixed N. There also exists the hope that knowledge of the mechanism of N_2 fixation by nitrogenase may stimulate the development of catalysts that can lower the energy demand for industrially fixed N.

Even though few bacterial species fix N_2, they cover a wide range of genera and frequent diverse habitats. Many of these bacteria fix N_2 by themselves in soil or water, but a few species require a symbiotic relationship with a eukaryote host in order to fix N_2. The best-known examples of the latter category are species of *Rhizobium* that form N_2-fixing root nodules on legumes. Some bacteria, such as *Azotobacter,* require air in order to grow on N_2. Other bacteria, such as *Klebsiella pneumoniae,* can grow both aerobically and anaerobically on fixed N, but can only fix N_2 under anaerobic conditions. *Spirillum lipoferum* will fix N_2 only when the partial pressure of O_2 is very low. *Rhodospirillum rubrum* and *Rhodopseudomonas capsulata* are examples of N_2-fixing photosynthetic bacteria, and *Nostoc* and *Anabaena* are examples of blue-green algae (cyanobacteria) that fix N_2 and CO_2 with photosynthetically derived energy and electrons. It is important to understand the biochemistry, genetics, physiology, and biology of these bacteria if we are to take the greatest advantage of biologically fixed N, and translate basic work into field results.

II. BIOCHEMISTRY

Even though N_2 fixation is found in bacteria that are quite different in their properties, nitrogenase from these organisms is remarkably similar (Eady and Postgate, 1974). There is great interest in the detailed mechanism of nitrogenase activity because of the enzyme's use as a model for chemical catalysis. Very few laboratories are involved with this research aspect, but new biophysical techniques (e.g., Cramer et al., 1976) are being developed that should aid in this work. It will become apparent that an understanding of the biochemistry of nitrogenase is important if we wish to endow N_2-fixing ability on a plant or bacterium that normally is unable to fix N_2.

A. Nitrogenase

Several reviews on the biochemistry of N_2 fixation have been published (Hardy et al., 1971; Eady and Postgate, 1974; Burris and Orme-Johnson, 1974; Zumft and Mortenson, 1975; Winter and Burris, 1976). Nitrogenase is composed of two proteins, components I and II. Component I has a molecular weight of about 220,000 and contains 1–2 molybdenum atoms and about 24 nonheme iron atoms. Component II has a molecular weight of 60,000 and contains four nonheme iron atoms. An acid-labile sulfide seems to be associated with each iron atom. Every N_2 that is fixed requires approximately 12–24 ATPs—the exact stoichiometry is dependent on the ratio of the protein components, as well as on the availability of ATP and electrons (Shah et al., 1975). It is this high energy requirement that presumably is the reason that most organisms do not fix N_2.

Another important property of nitrogenase is that both components are very O_2 labile; therefore, all organisms that fix N_2 either do so under anaerobic conditions or they have some mechanism for keeping O_2 away from the nitrogenase. In Azotobacter, the method for protecting nitrogenase seems to involve the ability of this bacterium to have an extremely high respiratory activity, by which it rapidly reduces O_2 to water (Phillips and Johnson, 1961; Jones et al., 1973). Blue-green algae that fix N_2 aerobically contain nitrogenase in specialized cells called heterocysts (Fleming and Haselkorn, 1973). Nodules on legume roots contain a red protein, leghemoglobin, that keeps free O_2 from inactivating nitrogenase in the Rhizobium cells (Bergersen and Turner, 1975). Klebsiella pneumoniae does not fix N_2 aerobically and is not able to keep its nitrogenase from being inactivated by O_2 (Pengra and Wilson, 1958; St. John et al., 1974).

B. Mechanism

With the use of electron paramagnetic resonance (EPR) spectroscopy, it has been possible to deduce the role of each of the two components (Orme-Johnson et al., 1972). Component II must react with ATP before it can be reduced. Reduced component II can now reduce oxidized component I. The substrate, N_2, then is reduced by component I with concomitant ATP hydrolysis and ammonium formation. No free intermediates are formed during the reaction.

An EPR signal having a spectroscopic splitting value (g) of 3.65 has been observed in whole cells that fix N_2 (Davis et al., 1972). This signal is produced by component I. Evidence that the g = 3.65 signal is due to a part of the active site of component I comes from work with mutant strains that produce inactive component I proteins that are normal with respect to iron-staining abilities, mobilities on polyacrylamide gels during electrophoresis, and antigenic cross-reacting material (Shah et al., 1973). None of these mutant strains had the g = 3.65 signal; therefore, the signal is correlated with activity but not with any other component I property that was tested.

C. Molybdenum

Molybdenum is an unusual element to be found in an enzyme. It has been assumed that molybdenum in component I plays a key role in the active site of nitrogenase. Perhaps molybdenum is required for the simultaneous transfer of both electrons and protons (E. Steifel, personal communication). Evidence that molybdenum is a part of a cofactor comes from work on nitrate reductase from *Neurospora crassa* (Nason et al., 1971). Nitrate reductase, like nitrogenase, is a molybdenum-containing enzyme. A mutant strain of *N. crassa*, *nit-1*, was unable to reduce nitrate *in vitro*, but when acid-treated component I was added to the extract, nitrate reductase activity was restored. In fact, acidification of any molybdoprotein would yield a factor that could reactivate *nit-1 in vitro*.

It was assumed that some mutant strains of N_2-fixing bacteria that lack component I activity but synthesize a functional component II could be missing the molybdenum cofactor. When mutant strains of *A. vinelandii* and *K. pneumoniae* were screened for the ability to be reactivated *in vitro* upon addition of acid-treated component I, several extracts were reactivated (Nagatani et al., 1974; St. John et al., 1975). Strains that yielded these extracts were presumed to be lacking the molybdenum cofactor. It was difficult to purify the molybdenum cofactor in an active form since it could not be released from the denatured, acid-treated protein by standard techniques. However, when N-methylformamide was used to wash acid-precipitated component I, all of the molybdenum and all of the molybdenum cofactor activity was found in the supernatant solution (V. K. Shah, unpublished results).

Preliminary analysis of the molybdenum cofactor from component I indicated that it is a small peptide containing molybdenum and iron. The molybdenum cofactor, as well as the apoprotein lacking the cofactor, are still very O_2 labile. This molybdenum cofactor is probably an integral part of the active site; therefore, its exact structure is of great interest.

D. Acetylene Reduction

Nitrogenase, besides being able to reduce N_2 to ammonia, is also capable of reducing cyanide (Hardy and Knight, 1967), azide (Schöllhorn and Burris, 1966), acetylene (Dilworth, 1966), and a variety of other triple-bonded C—C, N—N, or C—N compounds (Hardy et al., 1971). The ability to reduce acetylene is commonly exploited by most investigators involved with work on N_2 fixation. This reaction of nitrogenase is the basis of the acetylene-reduction assay for estimating N_2 fixation (Burns and Hardy, 1975; Burris, 1974). Both of the nitrogenase components and ATP are required to reduce acetylene to ethylene, which is not further reduced. Acetylene is a gas that is quite soluble in water, whereas the product, ethylene, is not very soluble. The acetylene-reduction assay, therefore, requires that the sample being tested for N_2 fixation be placed in a closed vessel containing acetylene. After an incubation period, a sample of the gas phase is taken with a syringe and the sample is injected into a gas chromatograph, which quantitates the amount of ethylene formed. This assay (Burris, 1974; Burns and Hardy, 1975) is extremely sensitive and can readily be used in field studies where samples can be stored in gas-tight vials for subsequent analyses.

The major problem with the acetylene-reduction technique is that the ratio between N_2 fixed and acetylene reduced is not constant. One might first suspect that three acetylene molecules would be reduced for each N_2 fixed, since two electrons are required for acetylene reduction and six for N_2 reduction. The exact ratio of acetylene reduced to N_2 fixed is dependent on the ratio of the two nitrogenase components (Shah et al., 1975). When component II (the more labile component) is limiting, N_2-fixing capacity may be underestimated by the acetylene-reduction assay. Field studies have shown that the acetylene reduction:

nitrogen fixation ratio varies between two and eight (Hardy et al., 1973). In spite of the inability to quantitatively measure exact levels of N_2 fixation, the acetylene reduction assay has been extremely useful to biochemists, bacteriologists, ecologists, agronomists, and soil scientists.

E. Hydrogen Production

When nitrogenase is incubated in the presence of ATP but in the absence of N_2, its substrate electrons donated to the enzyme combine with protons to produce H_2 (Bulen et al., 1965). Since N_2 is ubiquitous, this situation may have no parallel in nature. However, even when N_2 is present, some of the electrons (perhaps as much as 50%) are used to form H_2. This reaction has no obvious benefit to the organism, but rather it seems to waste ATP and electrons.

Several organisms are able to minimize this waste by producing a hydrogenase that can recover the electrons or possibly synthesize ATP via oxidation of H_2 (Dixon, 1972). This hydrogenase presumably is a reason that A. vinelandii fixes N_2 more efficiently than K. pneumoniae and C. pasteurianum (Hill, 1976). These latter two organisms do not have an H_2-oxidizing hydrogenase.

Many nodulated legumes also produce H_2 when they fix N_2 (Schubert and Evans, 1976). These workers estimated that the annual soybean crop of the United States evolves quantities of H_2 equivalent in energy to 300×10^9 ft³ of natural gas. Some root nodules have a hydrogenase that oxidize H_2. This seems to be a property of the bacterium rather than of the plant, since R. japonicum forms soybean nodules that evolve, as H_2, about 50% of the electrons transmitted to nitrogenase (Schubert and Evans, 1976). On the other hand, some cowpea strains (capable of nodulating soybean as well as cowpea) of Rhizobium will only lose about 10% of the electrons from nitrogenase as H_2 in soybean nodules. It is possible that H_2-oxidizing nodules will produce higher-yielding plants. Very little is known about the genetics and regulation of these hydrogenases, but they may be important for increasing N_2 fixation and therefore warrant a great deal of attention.

III. REGULATION

A cell will rather use fixed N than fix its own N from N_2. Natural N_2-fixing systems do not reduce N_2 when sufficient fixed N is available. For instance, nodules are not formed on heavily fertilized legume fields

(Fred *et al.*, 1932). *Azotobacter vinelandii* does not synthesize any detectable nitrogenase when it is growing with excess ammonium (Davis *et al.*, 1972); the ratio between repressed and derepressed levels is greater than 10^4-fold (Shah *et al.*, 1972).

There are many obvious demands specifically made on an organism to fix N_2. First, nitrogenase comprises about 1–2% of the total cell protein in a bacterium such as *A. vinelandii*. The enzyme has a very high demand for iron, and also requires additional sulfur and molybdenum. Besides enzymes required to place the metals on nitrogenase, additional permeation reactions and synthesis of possible metal chelators all require a nitrogenase-specific energy input. The energy requirement of 12–24 ATPs for each N_2 fixed is an additional energy tax on the organism. These probably are the main reasons why nitrogenase synthesis is so tightly repressed by ammonium, a good N source for most bacteria.

It is surprising that feedback inhibition of N_2 fixation does not occur in *A. vinelandii*. It is known that the synthesis of both components stops when ammonium is added, but several generations of growth are required until the active components are diluted out in the cell's cytoplasm (Davis *et al.*, 1972). This seems to be quite wasteful, since ATP is used to fix N_2 when there is no need for this reaction in the presence of ammonium. On the other hand, nitrogenase in *R. rubrum* is immediately inactivated when ammonium is added to a N_2-fixing culture (Schick, 1971). When *R. rubrum* is exposed to air, nitrogenase also is rapidly inactivated, but can be activated again when O_2 is removed (Neilson and Nordlund, 1975). A constitutively made protein (activating factor) is required to reactivate nitrogenase (Ludden and Burris, 1976). It seems that component II but not component I is the moiety that undergoes this inactivation–reactivation process.

A. Glutamine Synthetase

Most of the work on the regulation of N_2 fixation has been concerned with repression of nitrogenase synthesis by a good fixed N source, such as ammonium. An indication of how this repression occurs, at least in *K. pneumoniae*, came out of work with *K. aerogenes*, a species that does not fix N_2 (Magasanik *et al.*, 1974). *Klebsiella aerogenes* is able to degrade histidine, proline, or tryptophan in the absence of ammonium; however, certain mutations in the gene that specifies glutamine synthetase did not allow growth on these amino acids (Prival *et al.*, 1973). This could be expected because glutamine synthetase is required for glutamate formation when cells grow on poor N sources such as amino acids. What was unexpected, however, was the finding that the histidine-degrading enzymes, the proline-degrading enzymes, and tryptophan permease were not formed in the presence of their respective inducers when ammonium was absent. This was the first evidence that glutamine synthetase, besides catalyzing the synthesis of glutamine, also plays a role in the regulation of enzyme synthesis for pathways that supply fixed N to cells that are growing on poor nitrogenous substrates.

Normally, glutamine synthetase synthesis is repressed when cells grow on ammonium, but is derepressed when fixed N is limiting growth. Further evidence for the regulatory role of glutamine synthetase was provided by the discovery that some mutations that caused derepressed synthesis of glutamine synthetase also allowed high levels of the histidine-degrading enzymes to be formed in the presence of excess ammonium—conditions that normally repress the synthesis of these enzymes even when histidine is present. It has been shown that glutamine synthetase actually plays a role in transcription of the gene specifying an enzyme required for histidine degradation (Tyler et al., 1974) and that the ability of glutamine synthetase to promote transcription is dependent on the level of adenylylation and presence of effectors on the enzyme.

Several approaches were used to determine if glutamine synthetase also plays a role in nitrogenase synthesis in K. pneumoniae. The glutamate analog, methionine sulfoximine, is an inhibitor of glutamine synthetase in Klebsiella (Brenchley, 1973). When this compound was added to a culture of K. pneumoniae growing in the presence of excess ammonium, growth ceased and the bacteria began to synthesize nitrogenase (Gordon and Brill, 1974). Presumably, methionine sulfoximine causes glutamine synthetase to be in the conformation that allows derepression of nitrogenase synthesis. Further evidence for the regulatory role of glutamine synthetase in nitrogenase synthesis was indicated by the finding that glutamine auxotrophs did not synthesize nitrogenase and that some revertants of such auxotrophs produced nitrogenase, even in the presence of ammonium (Tubb, 1974; Streich et al., 1974).

It is not known whether glutamine synthetase plays a role in nitrogenase synthesis in other N_2-fixing organisms. Methionine sulfoximine will derepress nitrogen synthesis in A. vinelandii (Gordon and Brill, 1974), S. lipoferum (Okon et al., 1976a), R. rubrum (Brill, 1975; Weare and Shanmugam, 1976), as well as the blue-green alga, Anabaena cylindrica (Stewart and Rowell, 1975). This does not necessarily prove that glutamine synthetase directly plays a regulatory role in these organisms. It is possible that glutamine or some metabolite requiring glutamine synthetase activity is responsible for repression.

B. Other Regulatory Mechanisms

Repression by fixed N is not the only process to prevent N_2 fixation in *K. pneumoniae*. When N_2-fixing bacteria find themselves in an environment that lacks molybdenum, obviously no active nitrogenase can be made. Such environments are common (Anderson, 1946; Evans et al., 1951; Lobb, 1953). Some inoculant companies sell rhizobia mixed with molybdenum salts to assure that molybdenum deficiency will not limit N_2 fixation. The situation of N starvation together with a molybdenum deficiency would seem to cause cells to waste energy by producing an inactive nitrogenase. To prevent this waste, *K. pneumoniae* has some type of regulatory mechanism by which synthesis of both nitrogenase components is prevented in molybdenum-deficient media (Brill et al., 1974).

Unlike *A. vinelandii*, *K. pneumoniae* will not fix N_2 aerobically (Hamilton and Wilson, 1955). It is possible that nitrogenase is synthesized under aerobic, N-limiting conditions but that it is rapidly O_2 inactivated. This does not seem to be the case, since no nitrogenase is synthesized, even in an inactive form (St. John et al., 1974). Therefore, nitrogenase synthesis also is regulated by O_2 in this organism. The interaction between the regulatory mechanisms of nitrogenase synthesis by ammonium, molybdate, and oxygen are expected to be quite complex and probably require a great deal more genetic work before detailed insights can be made.

C. Possible Applications of Regulatory Mutants

Ever since the first mutant strain having derepressed nitrogenase synthesis was reported, there have been many ideas for potential agronomic applications of such mutant strains (Gordon and Brill, 1972; Shanmugam and Valentine, 1975; Balandreau et al., 1976). Since most N_2-fixing bacteria fix only as much N_2 as they need for growth, no excess ammonium is excreted. If some fixed N becomes available, a certain amount of repression occurs and the contribution by N_2 fixation is decreased. However, derepressed mutant strains do not decrease the amount of nitrogenase synthesis when fixed N is available. Such strains that would survive in the soil could be expected to fix more N_2 than the wild type in an environment already containing fixed N.

There are several ways to obtain derepressed strains. Mutant strains that are unable to fix N_2 due to a defect in a regulatory gene frequently can be reverted so that they now are able to fix N_2. In some cases, such revertants are derepressed for nitrogenase synthesis (Gordon and Brill, 1972; Gordon et al., 1975). Another means for obtaining derepressed strains in K. pneumoniae is to isolate glutamate-requiring mutants (Shanmugam and Valentine, 1975), but the glutamate levels demanded for growth are so high that they make such strains impractical for most applications. Mutant strains have been described that hyperproduce one of the nitrogenase components (Shah et al., 1974); if the other component can also be hyperproduced, even more N_2 might be fixed, especially in a strain that is already derepressed for the synthesis of nitrogenase.

Because of the high demand for electrons and ATP for ammonium excretion by a N_2-fixing organism, the availability of the energy source could very well limit the value of any excreting strain. Perhaps the future will see ponds inoculated with excreting strains, and waste products converted into suitable energy sources. The pond contents could then be used as fertilizer. Alternatively, photosynthesis could be useful for ammonium excretion by blue-green algae. These organisms generally grow quite slowly, and most are limited to growing only on the surface of a body of water.

IV. GENETICS

A. *Klebsiella pneumoniae*

The genetics of N_2 fixation is a specialty that has only begun to make important advances during the last few years. Several reviews dealing with this topic have been published (Streicher and Valentine, 1973; Brill, 1975). The finding that gave the genetics of N_2 fixation a major boost was the discovery that the phage, Pl, could be used for transduction in K. pneumoniae (Streicher et al., 1971). This phage has been used by many geneticists for studying Escherichia coli. Klebsiella pneumoniae is closely related to E. coli, and even seems to have a gene order that is similar to that of E. coli (Matsumoto and Tazaki, 1971). By transduction and conjugation, it was shown that nif mutations are located in a region of the chromosome that is very close to the genes specifying histidine biosynthesis (his) (Streicher et al., 1971; Dixon and Postgate, 1971). Mutant strains of this organism were phenotypically characterized and ordered with respect to his by use of Pl transduction (Streicher et al., 1972; St. John et al., 1975).

One of the easiest techniques for detailed genetic analysis is deletion mapping in a system that has available many deletions ending within the region of interest. A method for obtaining localized deletions in E. coli makes use of the phage, Mu (Howe and Bade, 1975). This phage can integrate randomly in the chromosome. If a special mutant phage with a thermolabile repressor has integrated into the chromosome, the cell will live at low temperatures. However, when the temperature is raised, the lytic process begins and terminates by killing the cell. Deletions occur spontaneously at low frequencies. A population of cells containing the prophage with the temperature-sensitive repressor will be lysed when the temperature is increased. Some of the rare survivors will have spontaneously deleted the prophage and thus be resistant to the high temperature. In many of these resistant survivors, variable amounts of DNA adjacent to the prophage will be simultaneously deleted along with the prophage DNA.

Klebsiella pneumoniae normally is resistant to infection by Mu, but Mu-sensitive strains have been selected (Rao, 1976; Bachhuber *et al.*, 1976a) and are useful for generating deletions that have one end terminating within the *nif* region (Bachhuber *et al.*, 1976a). Genetic crosses with such strains have confirmed the order of mutations obtained by transduction and have now unambiguously ordered several hundred mutations (T. Malavich and D. MacNeil, unpublished results).

The latter technique used conjugation—transfer of DNA by mating two bacteria. The *nif* region of the chromosome was recombined into a drug-resistance transfer plasmid (R factor) that already allows conjugation to occur (Dixon and Postgate, 1971; Dixon *et al.*, 1976). Thus the *nif* genes on the plasmid could now be mobilized, by conjugation, from strain to strain. Deletions and point mutations have been obtained in the *nif* region on the plasmid (Bachhuber *et al.*, 1976b). Such plasmids are useful for merodiploid analyses that should yield the number of genes in the *nif* region as well as the possible function of the regulatory genes.

Enrichment of *nif* DNA should be possible by isolating the plasmids. With techniques such as restriction enzyme cleavage, *nif* DNA can be separated from the rest of the plasmid DNA. The isolation of *nif* DNA will be important for understanding some of the details of *nif* regulation through *in vitro* transcription and translation studies.

Because of the close relationship between E. coli and K. pneumoniae, genetic techniques that have become quite sophisticated for E. coli studies can readily be applied to studies of *nif* in K. pneumoniae. This, and the background work already achieved with *nif* in K. pneumoniae, will probably keep this organism as the model system for *nif* genetics for a number of years. Unfortunately, K. pneumoniae has not yet been shown to be of any potential agricultural importance. Therefore, it is not obvious that understanding nif in K. pneumoniae will be directly important for increasing crop production. There is a need to know how similar nif is in K. pneumoniae to nif in other N_2-fixing organisms that have, or potentially have, agricultural value.

B. *Azotobacter*

All species of Azotobacter fix N_2. These bacteria grow aerobically on N_2 with a generation time of 2 hr—the fastest of any bacterium utilizing N_2 as the sole N source. Because Azotobacter has an H_2-oxidizing hydrogenase, it wastes less energy while it fixes N_2 (Dixon, 1972). The efficiency of N_2 fixation is the greatest of all organisms studied (Mulder and Brotonegoro, 1974). Azotobacter has been used in the Soviet Union for many decades to increase crop production (Rubenchik, 1963). Several companies in the United States, as well as in other countries, are marketing Azotobacter inoculants. It seems, however, that the benefit to the plant is by plant-growth hormone production rather than N_2 fixation by the bacterium (Azcon and Barea, 1975; Brown, 1976). An advantage of this organism is that it can form cysts, which are dormant structures that can resist desiccation (Socolofsky and Wyss, 1962). Storage and shipping of cysts should be free of problems that are encountered with production and distribution of vegetative cells.

Many Nif⁻ mutant strains of A. vinelandii have been characterized by biochemical and serological techniques (Shah et al., 1973). Several of the nif mutations were mapped with respect to each other by transformation (Bishop and Brill, 1977)—a technique by which DNA from one cell can be added to another cell (Page and Sadoff, 1976). Preliminary data indicated that, unlike the nif genes in K. pneumoniae, A. vinelandii nif genes are not clustered in a small region. Regulatory genes are quite distant from the component I and II structural genes.

C. Photosynthetic Bacteria and Blue-Green Algae

Rhodopseudomonas capsulata is a photosynthetic bacterium for which a reproducible gene-transfer system is available (Marrs, 1974). Wall et al. (1975) were able to isolate Nif⁻ mutant strains of this organism, but have not demonstrated any linkage yet to other markers. The blue-green alga, Anacystis nidulans, has been used for transformation studies (Shestakov and Khyen, 1970; Orkwiszewski and Kaney, 1974), and C. P. Wolk has recently obtained interesting Nif⁻ mutant strains of *Anabaena cylindrica* (personal communication). These important systems require a great deal of work before useful genetic information will be obtained.

D. *Rhizobium*

Gene-transfer systems also are available for studying the genetics of infection and *nif* expression in *Rhizobium*. Many genetic systems have been reported (see review by Brill, 1975; Kowalski, 1970; Beringer and Hopwood, 1976; Meade and Signer, 1976). This symbiotic system obviously is much more difficult to analyze genetically than the free-living organisms. The infection process requires interactions between bacterium and legume, and no one has yet been able to get *Rhizobium* to grow on N_2 as the sole N source. Rapid progress on the genetics of N_2 fixation requires that plant-independent screening assays and selection techniques be developed. Some strains of *Rhizobium* fix N_2 and reduce acetylene asymbiotically in media having very low partial pressures of O_2 (e.g., Tjepkema and Evans, 1975). Such strains still require fixed N for growth, however. Perhaps agglutination of *Rhizobium* by isolated plant proteins required for the infection process (see Section V) will be useful in selecting or screening for mutant strains incapable of infection. If a bacterial cell-surface site is common to both infection and specific phage binding, then phage-resistant mutant strains might be useful for investigating the genetics of the infection process.

Several mutant strains of *R. japonicum* have been isolated that do not form a N_2-fixing symbiosis with soybean (Maier and Brill, 1976). After mutagenesis of a culture, survivors were selected for the ability to grow as well as the wild type in a variety of minimal and rich media. Several thousand colonies from such a culture were screened by use of an effectiveness assay. This assay (Wacek and Brill, 1976) involved surface sterilizing soybean seeds and then placing one seed to a vial containing sterile N-free medium and vermiculite. A portion of one colony was added to a seed and the vial was incubated for 2 weeks in a plant growth room. After this time, each vial was assayed for acetylene reduction. Colonies that did not allow the plants to reduce acetylene were tested further. One of these mutant strains made nodules that contained bacteria lacking active component II but containing active component I. Other interesting mutant strains did not make nodules at all or made small nodules that had no leghemoglobin. Such strains should be useful for identifying steps involved in the infection process as well as in establishment of effective nodules. No satisfactory techniques have yet been developed for mapping these mutations.

In order to understand the genetics of N_2 fixation in legumes, the contribution by the plant also has to be appreciated. For instance, leghemoglobin synthesis is coded by the plant (Cutting and Schulman, 1968; Dilworth, 1969). A variety of interesting phenotypes have been documented in clover (Bergersen and Nutman, 1957; Nutman, 1968), pea (Holl, 1975), and soybean (Weber, 1966; Vest, 1970; Vest and Caldwell, 1972). Some genes prevent nodulation, whereas other genes allow nodulation but not N_2 fixation. Dominance characteristics have been studied, but nothing is known about the initial biochemical defect caused by these genes. This is an area of research that requires much more effort, especially since indications of the plant's contribution to the symbiosis might be useful in breeding programs.

Is it possible to breed for superior N_2 fixation in legumes? One argument against this possibility is that CO_2 fixation may be limiting in the legume–*Rhizobium* system. When higher-than-normal CO_2 levels are used for growth, soybeans increase N_2 fixation dramatically, with a concomitant increase in seed yield (Hardy and Havelka, 1973). However, it is possible that photosynthetic ability is regulated by fixed N and that N_2 fixation could be regulated by some aspect of photosynthesis. Thus, it is conceivable that legume productivity can be increased by increasing N_2 fixation with genes specific for the symbiosis.

Wacek and Brill (1976) used the effectiveness assay to screen many cultivars of soybean and found that different cultivars exhibit a great variety of activities. What relationship might there be between 2-week-old plants with high acetylene-reducing activities and the N_2-fixing ability of a mature plant growing in a field? Some plants with low activities by the effectiveness assay also showed low acetylene-reducing activities in soil during the early weeks of growth. Such plants did increase their activity later in the growing season. The effectiveness assay, therefore, could be used to indicate plants or rhizobia that are late nodulating combinations.

Many cultivars that exhibited high acetylene-reducing activities by the effectiveness assay did not have high activities in the field. A probable explanation is that other parameters are limiting N_2 fixation in these plants. For instance, canopy size may limit energy flow to the nodule. It would be very interesting to determine if cultivars having high scores when tested by the effectiveness assay can be shown to have important genes that could be used for breeding better plants in the field.

The effectiveness assay could have application for rapidly testing commercial *Rhizobium* inoculants or preinoculated seeds to determine the quality of the inoculum. The assay has been used successfully on alfalfa, bean, cowpea, and clover, as well as on soybean. The effectiveness assay also has been used to screen for potentially superior strains of Rhizobium. Maier and Brill (1978) mutagenized a culture of R. japonicum and isolated stable mutant strains that were more active than the wild type when tested by the effectiveness assay. One strain produced approximately twice as many nodules as the wild type. A major problem with field application of "super" strains is that such strains might very well be outcompeted by rhizobia that are indigenous to the soil (Johnson et al., 1965; Ham et al., 1971). A potential way to overcome this problem might be to transfer the "super" genes into Rhizobium strains that are known to be successful in field situations.

E. Transfer of *nif* to Other Organisms

An event that served to stimulate thinking about many novel applications of N_2 fixation was the finding that the plasmid containing nif from K. pneumoniae could be transferred by conjugation to E. coli (Dixon and Postgate, 1972). Escherichia coli does not fix N_2, but when the nif-containing plasmid was introduced, the resulting strain was capable of growing on N_2. This experiment evoked the possibility that nif genes might also be transferred to nonlegume crop plants such as wheat or corn, allowing such plants to be productive without a requirement for N fertilizer. This would truly be a magnificent contribution! In support of this goal are reports that genes from E. coli can be expressed in plant cells in culture (Carlson, 1973; Doy et al., 1973; Ledoux and Huart, 1974) and that certain plant cells in culture can be induced to form a mature plant (Chaleff and Carlson, 1974).

The possibility of obtaining a plant that will fix N_2 via nif genes in its cells becomes more difficult to realize when consideration is given to the barriers that must be overcome. For instance, noone has yet created a mature plant containing bacterial genes. The tremendous energy requirement for N_2 fixation will make the plant sacrifice other energy-demanding processes. Perhaps this problem can be overcome by breeding for plants with greater photosynthetic capacities.

A major problem that has to be considered is the O_2 lability of nitrogenase. When nif genes on the plasmid were transferred to aerobic bacteria such as Agrobacterium and Rhizobium, the resulting hybrid strains were not capable of acetylene reduction or growth on N_2, even though transcription and translation of the nif genes presumably occurred (Dixon et al., 1976). The probable interpretation of these findings is that nitrogenase was synthesized but was rapidly inactivated by O_2. When the nif genes were transferred to Nif⁻ mutant strains of A.

vinelandii, N_2 fixation occurred aerobically (Cannon and Postgate, 1976), but it must be remembered that *Azotobacter* has a special mechanism for keeping O_2 away from nitrogenase (see Section II,A). It is not likely that an O_2-insensitive nitrogenase can be obtained by mutation, since (to our knowledge) natural selection has not yet turned out such a protein, even though one might guess that an O_2-insensitive nitrogenase would have tremendous selective advantage. The other way to keep O_2 away from nitrogenase would be by some means of compartmentation of the N_2-fixing apparatus, such as heterocysts in blue-green algae or root nodules in legumes. This would seem to be a difficult goal to achieve in the cereal plant.

Other potential problems that must be overcome to create a cereal that fixes N_2 due to incorporation of the *nif* plasmid include sequestering of the higher iron and molybdenum levels required for N_2 fixation. Nitrogenase synthesis must be derepressed by means other than glutamine synthetase. Also, if all of these problems have been overcome, sufficient levels of ammonia assimilatory enzymes need to be synthesized so that ammonium is prevented from reaching toxic concentrations.

V. NITROGEN-FIXING SYMBIOSES

Rather than being diverted toward as tenuous a target as the engineering of an N_2-fixing cereal, work should continue on the efficient legume–*Rhizobium* symbiosis. This is equivalent to what might be desired in the cereal plant, but the whole bacterium, rather than merely the N_2-fixation genes (*nif* genes), is incorporated in the legume. Nodules create a suitable environment by surrounding the rhizobia with leghemoglobin and by transporting photosynthate to, and fixed N away from, the nodules. The nodule also keeps the rhizobia in a stable environment that is quite resistant to drying and competition with other soil bacteria.

One of the more active research areas involves the attempt to understand why only *Rhizobium* forms N_2-fixing root nodules on legumes and why certain species of *Rhizobium* only nodulate specific legume plants (Fred *et al.*, 1932). For instance, *Rhizobium japonicum* infects soybean, *R. meliloti* is specific for alfalfa, and *R. trifolii* specifically nodulates clover. Lines of specificity are not always clearcut; for example, certain rhizobia nodulate both soybean and cowpea, whereas other strains nodulate only soybean.

A great deal of literature is concerned with the morphological events that lead up to an effective nodule (e.g., Napoli and Hubbell, 1975), but little is known about biochemical and genetic requirements for infection and nodule development. An important breakthrough that gave some insight into the mechanism of infection by *Rhizobium* was the finding that specific legumes have seed proteins (lectins) that bind only to the *Rhizobium* strains that infect the particular host plant (Bohlool and Schmidt, 1974; Dazzo and Hubbell, 1975; Wolpert and Albersheim, 1976). For instance, lectin from soybean seeds will bind to most strains of *R. japonicum*; however, certain strains of this species did not bind to the lectin (Bohlool and Schmidt, 1974). No explanation for these exceptions has been proposed. These lectins also are found on root hair tips—the initial site of infection (Dazzo and Brill, 1977).

The part of the bacterium that interacts with the lectin seems to be the polysaccharide O antigen that is part of the lipopolysaccharide on the outer surface of the cell (Wolpert and Albersheim, 1976). There is some evidence that the lectin cleaves the O antigen from the bacterial lipopolysaccharide (Albersheim and Wolpert, 1976). Why the lipopolysaccharide is modified and the stage at which this cleavage reaction occurs are important but unanswered questions.

An interesting finding is that the site on clover roots to which *R. trifolii* binds is antigenically related to the bacterial polysaccharide that binds to the lectin (Dazzo and Hubbell, 1975). It is not yet known whether this antigenic cross reactivity is found in other *Rhizobium*–legume symbioses, and the significance of this similarity is not yet understood, but analogies are known. For example, the surfaces of some pathogenic bacteria are structurally similar to the surfaces of mammalian cells (Zabriskie, 1967). As a result of this molecular mimicry, host responses that would normally eliminate an invading bacterium can sometimes be deceived.

Unlike free-living N_2-fixing bacteria, nitrogenase synthesis does not seem to be completely repressed by ammonium, since ammonium or another fixed N source is required for the rhizobia to express nitrogenase (Keister, 1975; Kurz and LaRue, 1975). The main target of regulation must occur at a stage of the infection process, because no nodules are formed on inoculated plants grown with sufficient ammonium or nitrate (Fred *et al.*, 1932). Hopefully, studies on the mechanism of infection will yield clues about the nature of the regulation of infection. Will it be possible to find or create symbioses that retain active nodulating ability, even in the presence of fertilizer N?

Rhizobium cells in the nodule are enclosed in plant-derived membranes (Bergersen and Briggs, 1958; Tu, 1974). Several types of leghemoglobin surround the bacteria (Fuchsman *et al.*, 1976). Direct evidence that the globin moiety of leghemoglobin is synthesized by the plant is that leghemoglobin-coding messenger RNA is found on polysomes isolated from nodular plant tissue (Verma et al., 1974). There are no indications as to the role of each different leghemoglobin or as to how the Rhizobium initiates synthesis of this O_2-binding protein. Perhaps insight into the mechanisms of recognition, the infection process, and the development of nodules will someday yield ideas that will have a direct benefit for agriculture.

In spite of the promises of basic research for increasing the productivity of legumes, a more obvious (and possibly more immediate) use of N_2 fixation induced by Rhizobium is the appreciation that most legumes have not been examined for possible application in agriculture. Some wild legumes could already be adapted to yield useful products under adverse conditions such as high salinity, arid soil, etc. Perhaps the mere addition of molybdenum will yield a soil that will readily support some of the more exotic, but useful, legumes. A good example of a plant that was used mainly as a garden crop, but that could be valuable for agriculture, is the winged bean. This legume has edible seeds, leaves, flower, and tuberous root—all with high protein levels (Schultes, 1975).

Legumes are not the only plants that can obtain all of their N from symbiotic N_2-fixing bacteria. Other nodulated plants include species of Alnus (alder), Casuarina, Myrica, Elaeagnus, Ceanothus, Purshia, and Coriaria (Bond, 1974). Such plants are woody, perennial, small trees or shrubs and cover a wide range of habitats. The organisms responsible for nodule formation and N_2 fixation seems to be of the bacterial genus, Frankia. Little is known about these nodulating bacteria; however, they do not induce leghemoglobin formation in the nodules.

Another nonlegume that has turned out to be especially interesting is a variety of Trema cannabina, a plant that sometimes grows between rows of tea. The bacterium isolated from nodules of Trema also will nodulate the legume, Vigna sinensis, and rhizobia isolates from V. sinesis and soybean were able to nodulate Trema (Trinick, 1976). This is the first indication that a Rhizobium can fix N_2 in a nonlegume. The features of Trema that allow this unusual symbiosis will be important to understand, especially if a research goal is to extend N_2 fixation by Rhizobium to nonlegumes. This work also points out the fact that leghemoglobin is not an absolute necessity for N_2 fixation with Rhizobium, since Trema nodules do not contain this protein. It is important to determine how such nodules protect the nitrogenase from being O_2 inactivated.

Some important N_2-fixing symbioses have a blue-green alga as the fixing organism. Examples of plants that obtain their fixed N through blue-green algae include *Gunnera, Azolla,* and Cycad species (Millbank, 1974; Becking, 1976). *Gunnera* contains N_2-fixing *Nostoc* in special glands on the base of the stem. *Azolla* is a floating fern that can play an important role in N fertilization of wet rice fields. The blue-green algae in this symbiosis is an *Anabaena* which is found in small pore cavities on the leaves.

The fact that N_2-fixing symbioses can be found in a wide range of plants should be incentive to search for more of these systems and possibly apply such symbioses for land reclamation, green manure, or for food and forage.

VI. ASSOCIATIONS

Besides the very tight symbioses discussed in the previous section, evidence is accumulating that looser associations are maintained between N_2-fixing bacteria and nonlegume plants. The rhizosphere of rice, for instance, can be populated with *Beijerinckia,* an N_2-fixing aerobe (Balandreau *et al.,* 1976). Other grasses that have been shown to harbor N_2-fixing bacteria include *Paspalum notatum* and *Digitaria decumbens* (Döbereiner and Day, 1976). The associated bacteria are, respectively, *Azotobacter paspali* and *Spirillum lipoferum.* Currently, there is some argument as to whether these bacteria actually contribute significant quantities of fixed N to their host plant. When it was discovered that *S. lipoferum* also can be found on corn roots (von Bülow and Döbereiner, 1975), several laboratories tested corn that had been inoculated with *S. lipoferum* for increased plant growth. The results so far show a variable increase in N content in inoculated plants (Barber *et al.,* 1976; Okon *et al.,* 1976b). Superior vegetative growth in some of these associations might be caused by release of plant growth hormones by the bacteria.

Perhaps further work will establish that other natural N_2-fixing associations exist. One of the problems with these systems is that the numbers of the associative bacteria and their N_2-fixing activities could be too low to contribute a significant N input to the plant. Another problem could be that the tight control of nitrogenase synthesis would allow the bacteria to fix sufficient N_2 for their use only and therefore not excrete any fixed N for the plant's use. A possible application of these associations could use mutant strains that excrete ammonium and thus allow the plant to utilize directly some of the N_2 fixed by the associated bacteria.

The genotype of the plant may be crucial for establishing a beneficial association between it and a N_2-fixing bacterium (Kass *et al.*, 1971; Döbereiner *et al.*, 1972; Neal and Larson, 1976). The best plants to be used to foster such associations would be ones that excrete carbon compounds to supply energy for the N_2-fixing bacteria on their roots. If a stable N_2-fixing association can be established in the laboratory, there is only a small possibility that the association would remain under field conditions. Competition with other bacteria for excreted plant carbon would be a major barrier. A method that may select for a stable association could utilize a plant that excretes carbon compounds. When this plant is grown in N-limited soil, N_2-fixing bacteria associated with the roots could be isolated. Ammonium-excreting strains derived from these bacteria could then be used to inoculate the plants. The physical intimacy required of such an association might be through concentration of the bacteria on the root by a mucilaginous sheath, as in the case of *A. paspali* (Döbereiner *et al.*, 1972), or through direct invasion into root cells, as in *S. lipoferum* (Döbereiner and Day, 1976).

A further association that needs to be mentioned is the incorporation of whole bacterial cells into plant cells. Carrot callus cells were grown on N-free medium with an inoculum of *A. vinelandii* (Carlson and Chaleff, 1974). The bacteria did not enter the carrot cells, but remained in the intercellular regions in the tissue. On the other hand, when spheroplasts of a mycorrhizal fungus were mixed with protoplasts of *A. vinelandii*, uptake of the bacteria by the fungus and acetylene reduction by these fungi has been reported (Giles and Whitehead, 1976). If this work can be confirmed, the possible applications of such associations are great.

VII. SUMMARY

Up to the early part of this century, natural deposits of nitrate in Chile were the major sources of fixed N in agriculture. In 1893, Sir William Crookes warned the British Association for the Advancement of Science that the deposits were being depleted. This gave scientists the incentive to consider production of fertilizer N by industrial means. Within a few years, several processes were in commercial operation. Now, three-quarters of a century later, we are being warned by experts that natural gas and oil, required for fertilizer production, are being depleted. Therefore, another direction is required to supply agricultural N for the future. Taking advantage of biological N_2 fixation should be an obvious part of that direction. Many advances are being made by the collaboration of agronomists, bacteriologists, chemists, geneticists, and biochemists. Interdisciplinary approaches must continue in this field and will yield a detailed understanding of N_2 fixation. We can expect applications of these discoveries to be used to sustain and improve efficient crop production.

REFERENCES

Albersheim, P., and Wolpert, J. S. (1976). *Plant Physiol. (Ann. Meet. Suppl.)* **57**, 79.
Anderson, A J. (1946). *J. Counc. Sci. Ind. Res.* **19**, 1–18.
Azcon, R., and Barea, J. M. (1975). *Plant Soil* **43**, 609–619.
Bachhuber, M., Brill, W. J., and Howe, M. M. (1976a). *J. Bacteriol.* **128**, 749–753.
Bachhuber, M., Malavich, T., and Howe, M. (1976b). *Am. Soc. Microbiol., Abstr. Annu. Meet.* **76**, 108.
Balandreau, J. P., Rinaudo, G., Oumarov, M. M., and Dommergues, Y. R. (1976). *Proc. Int. Symp. Nitrogen Fixation, 1st, 1975* pp. 611–628.
Barber, L. E., Tjepkema, J. D., Russell, S. A., and Evans, H. J. (1976). *Appl. Environ. Microbiol.* **32**, 108–113.
Becking, J. H. (1976). *Proc. Int. Symp. Nitrogen Fixation, 1st, 1975* pp. 556–580.
Bergersen, F. J., and Briggs, M. J. (1958). *J. Gen. Microbiol.* **60**, 61–65.
Bergersen, F. J., and Nutman, P. S. (1957). *Heredity* **11**, 175–184.
Bergersen, F. J., and Turner, G. L. (1975). *J. Gen. Microbiol.* **91**, 345–354.
Beringer, J. E., and Hopwood, D. A. (1976). *Nature (London)* **264**, 291–293.
Bishop, P. E., and Brill, W. J. (1977). *J. Bacteriol.* **130**, 954–956.
Bohlool, B. B., and Schmidt, E. L. (1974). *Science* **185**, 269–271.
Bond, G. (1974). In "The Biology of Nitrogen Fixation" (A. Quispel, ed.), pp. 342–378. North-Holland Publ., Amsterdam.
Brenchley, J. E. (1973). *J. Bacteriol.* **114**, 666–673.
Brill, W. J. (1975). *Annu. Rev. Microbiol.* **29**, 109–129.
Brill, W. J., Steiner, A. L., and Shah, V. K. (1974). *J. Bacteriol.* **118**, 986–989.
Brown, A. W. A., Byerly, T. C., Gibbs, M., and San Pietro, A. (1975). "Crop Productivity—Research Imperatives." Natl. Sci. Found., Washington, D. C.
Brown, M. E. (1976). *J. Appl. Bacteriol.* **40**, 341–348.
Bulen, W. A., Burns, R. C., and LeComte, J. R. (1965). *Proc. Natl. Acad. Sci. U.S.A.* **53**, 532–539.
Burns, R. C., and Hardy, R. W. F. (1975). "Nitrogen Fixation in Bacteria and Higher Plants." Springer-Verlag, Berlin and New York.
Burris, R. H. (1974). In "The Biology of Nitrogen Fixation" (A. Quispel, ed.), pp. 9–33. North-Holland Publ., Amsterdam.
Burris, R. H., and Orme-Johnson, W. H. (1974). In "Microbial Iron Metabolism" (J. B. Neilands, ed.), pp. 187–209. Academic Press, New York.
Cannon, F. C., and Postgate, J. R. (1976). *Nature (London)* **260**, 271–272.
Carlson, P. S. (1973). *Proc. Natl. Acad. Sci. U.S.A.* **70**, 598–602.
Carlson, P. S., and Chaleff, R. S. (1974). *Annu. Rev. Genet.* **8**, 267–278.
Cramer, S. P., Eccles, T. K., Kutzler, R. W., Hodgson, D. O., and Mortenson, L. E. (1976). *J. Am. Chem. Soc.* **98**, 1287–1288.
Cutting, J. A., and Schulman, H. M. (1968). *Fed. Proc., Fed. Am. Soc. Exp. Biol.* **27**, 768.

Davis, L. C., Shah, V. K., Brill, W. J., and Orme-Johnson, W. H. (1972). *Biochim. Biophys. Acta* **256,** 512–523.

Dazzo, F. B., and Brill, W. J. (1977). *Appl. Environ. Microbiol.* **33,** 132–136.

Dazzo, F. B., and Hubbell, D. H. (1975). *Appl. Microbiol.* **30,** 1017–1033.

Dilworth, M. J. (1966). *Biochim. Biophys. Acta* **127,** 285–294.

Dilworth, M. J. (1969). *Biochim. Biophys. Acta* **184,** 432–441.

Dixon, R., Cannon, F., and Kondorosi, A. (1976). *Nature (London)* **260,** 268–271.

Dixon, R. A., and Postgate, J. R. (1971). *Nature (London)* **234,** 47–48.

Dixon, R. A., and Postgate, J. R. (1972). *Nature (London)* **237,** 102–103.

Dixon, R. O. D. (1972). *Arch. Mikrobiol.* **85,** 193–201.

Döbereiner, J., and Day, J. M. (1976). *Proc. Int. Symp. Nitrogen Fixation, 1st, 1975* pp. 518–555.

Döbereiner, J., Day, J. M., and Dart, P. J. (1972). *J. Gen. Microbiol.* **71,** 103–116.

Doy, C. H., Gresshoff, R., and Rolfe, B. (1973). *Proc. Natl. Acad. Sci. U.S.A.* **70,** 723–726.

Eady, R. R., and Postgate, J. R. (1974). *Nature (London)* **249,** 805–810.

Evans, H. J. (1975). "Enhancing Biological Nitrogen Fixation." Natl. Sci. Found., Washington, D. C.

Evans, H. J., Purvis, E. R., and Bear, F. E. (1951). *Soil Sci.* **71,** 117–124.

Fleming, H., and Haselkorn, R. (1973). *Proc. Natl. Acad. Sci. U.S.A.* **70,** 2727–2731.

Fred, E. B., Baldwin, I. L., and McCoy, E. (1932). "Root Nodule Bacteria and Leguminous Plants." Univ. of Wisconsin Press, Madison.

Fuchsman, W. H., Barton, C. R., Stein, M. M., Thompson, J. T., and Willett, R. M. (1976). *Biochem. Biophys. Res. Commun.* **68,** 387–392.

Giles, K. L., and Whitehead, H. (1976). *Science* **193,** 1125–1126.

Gordon, J. K., and Brill, W. J. (1972). *Proc. Natl. Acad. Sci. U.S.A.* **69,** 3501–3503.

Gordon, J. K., and Brill, W. J. (1974). *Biochem. Biophys. Res. Commun.* **59,** 967–971.

Gordon, J. K., Garfinkel, D., and Brill, W. J. (1975). *Am. Soc. Microbiol., Abstr. Annu. Meet.* **75,** 175.

Ham, G. E., Frederick, L. R., and Anderson, I. C. (1971). *Agron. J.* **63,** 69–72.

Hamilton, P. B., and Wilson, P. W. (1955). *Ann. Acad. Sci. Fenn., Ser. A* **60,** 139–150.

Hardy, R. W. F., and Havelka, U. D. (1973). *Plant Physiol.* **51,** S35.

Hardy, R. W. F., and Havelka, U. D. (1975). *Science* **188,** 633–643.

Hardy, R. W. F., and Knight, E. (1967). *Biochim. Biophys. Acta* **139,** 69–90.

Hardy, R. W. F., Burns, R. C., and Parshall, G. W. (1971). *Adv. Chem. Ser.* **100,** 219–247.

Hardy, R. W. F., Burns, R. C., and Holsten, R. D. (1973). *Soil Biol. & Biochem.* **5,** 47–81.

Hill, S. (1976). *J. Gen. Microbiol.* **95,** 297–312.

Holl, F. B. (1975). *Euphytica* **24,** 767–770.

Howe, M. M., and Bade, E. G. (1975). *Science* **190,** 624–632.

Johnson, H. W., Means, U. M., and Weber, C. R. (1965). *Agron. J.* **57,** 179–185.

Jones, C. W., Brice, J. M., Wright, V., and Ackrell, A. C. (1973). *FEBS Lett.* **29,** 77–81.

Kass, D. L., Drosdoff, M., and Alexander, M. (1971). *Soil Sci. Soc. Am., Proc.* **35,** 286–289.

Keister, D. L. (1975). *J. Bacteriol.* **123,** 1265–1268.

Kowalski, M. (1970). *Acta Microbiol. Pol., Ser. A* **2,** 115–122.

Kurz, W. G. W., and LaRue, T. A. G. (1975). *Nature (London)* **256,** 407–409.

Ledoux, L., and Huart, R. (1974). *Nature (London)* **249,** 17–21.

Lobb, W. R. (1953). *N. Z. Soil News* **3,** 9–16.

Ludden, P. W., and Burris, R. H. (1976). *Science* **194,** 424–426.

Magasanik, B., Prival, M. J., Brenchley, J. E., Tyler, R. M., DeLeo, A. B., Streicher, S. L., Bender, R. A., and Paris, C. G. (1974). *Curr. Top. Cell. Regul.* **8,** 119–138.

Maier, R. J., and Brill, W. J. (1976). *J. Bacteriol.* **127,** 763–769.

Maier, R. J., and Brill, W. J. (1978). *Science* **201**, 448–450.

Marrs, B. (1974). *Proc. Natl. Acad. Sci. U.S.A.* **71**, 971–973.

Matsumoto, H., and Tazaki, T. (1971). *Jpn. J. Microbiol.* **15**, 11–20.

Meade, H., and Signer, E. (1976). *Am. Soc. Microbiol., Abstr. Annu. Meet.* **76**, 105.

Millbank, J. W. (1974). *In* "The Biology of Nitrogen Fixation" (A. Quispel, ed.), pp. 238–264. North-Holland Publ., Amsterdam.

Mulder, E. G., and Brotonegoro, S. (1974). *In* "The Biology of Nitrogen Fixation" (A. Quispel, ed.), pp. 37–85. North-Holland Publ., Amsterdam.

Nagatani, H. H., Shah, V. K., and Brill, W. J. (1974). *J. Bacteriol.* **120**, 697–701.

Napoli, C. A., and Hubbell, D. H. (1975). *Appl. Microbiol.* **30**, 1003–1009.

Nason, A., Lee, K. Y., Pan, S. S., Ketchum, P. A., Lamberti, A., and DeVries, J. (1971). *Proc. Natl. Acad. Sci. U.S.A.* **68**, 3242–3246.

Neal, J. L., Jr., and Larson, R. I. (1976). *Soil Biol. & Biochem.* **8**, 151–155.

Neilson, A. H., and Nordlund, S. (1975). *J. Gen. Microbiol.* **91**, 53–62.

Nutman, P. S. (1968). *Heredity* **23**, 537–551.

Okon, Y., Albrecht, S. L., and Burris, R. H. (1976a). *J. Bacteriol.* **128**, 592–597.

Okon, Y., Albrecht, S. L., and Burris, R. H. (1976b). *Plant Physiol. (Ann. Meet. Suppl.)* 57, 70.

Orkwiszewski, K. G., and Kaney, A. R. (1974). *Arch. Microbiol.* **98**, 31–38.

Orme-Johnson, W. H., Hamilton, W. D., Ljones, T., Tso, M.-Y. W., Burris, R. H., Shah, V. K., and Brill, W. J. (1972). *Proc. Natl. Acad. Sci. U.S.A.* **69**, 3142–3145.

Page, W. J., and Sadoff, H. L. (1976). *J. Bacteriol.* **125**, 1080–1087.

Pengra, R. M., and Wilson, P. W. (1958). *J. Bacteriol.* **75**, 21–25.

Phillips, D. H., and Johnson, M. J. (1961). *J. Biochem. Microbiol. Technol. Eng.* **3**, 277–309.

Prival, M. J., Brenchley, J. E., and Magasanik, B. (1973). *J. Biol. Chem.* **248**, 4334–4344.

Rao, R. N. (1976). *J. Bacteriol.* **128**, 356–362.

Rubenchik, L. I. (1963). "Azotobacter and its Use in Agriculture" (transl. from Russian). Isr. Program Sci. Transl., Jerusalem.

St. John, R. T., Shah, V. K., and Brill, W. J (1974). *J. Bacteriol.* **119**, 266–269.

St. John, R. T., Johnston, H. M., Seidman, C., Garfinkel, D., Gordon, J. K., Shah, V. K., and Brill, W. J. (1975). *J. Bacteriol.* **121**, 759–765.

Schick, H. J. (1971). *Arch. Mikrobiol.* **75**, 89–101.

Schöllhorn, R., and Burris, R. H. (1966). *Fed. Proc., Fed. Am. Soc. Exp. Biol.* **66**, 25.

Schubert, K. R., and Evans, H. J. (1976). *Proc. Natl. Acad. Sci. U.S.A.* **73**, 1207–1211.

Schultes, R. E. (1975). "The Winged Bean—A High Protein Crop for the Tropics," Report No. 17. Natl. Acad. Sci. Washington, D. C.

Shah, V. K., Davis, L. C., and Brill, W. J. (1972). *Biochim. Biophys. Acta* **256**, 498–511.

Shah, V. K., Davis, L. C., Gordon, J. K., Orme-Johnson, W. H., and Brill, W. J. (1973). *Biochim. Biophys. Acta* **292**, 246–255.

Shah, V. K., Davis, L. C., Stieghorst, M., and Brill, W. J. (1974). *J. Bacteriol.* **117**, 917–919.

Shah, V. K., Davis, L. C., and Brill, W. J. (1975). *Biochim. Biophys. Acta* **384**, 353–359.

Shanmugam, K. T., and Valentine, R. C. (1975). *Proc. Natl. Acad. Sci. U.S.A.* **72**, 136–139.

Shestakov, S. V., and Khyen, N. T. (1970). *Mol. Gen. Genet.* **107**, 372–375.

Socolofsky, M. D., and Wyss, O. (1962). *J. Bacteriol.* **84**, 119–124.

Stewart, W. D. P., and Rowell, P. (1975). *Biochem. Biophys. Res. Commun.* **65**, 846–856.

Streicher, S. L., and Valentine, R. C. (1973). *Annu. Rev. Biochem.* **42**, 279–302.

Streicher, S. L., Gurney, E. G., and Valentine, R. C. (1971). *Proc. Natl. Acad. Sci. U.S.A.* **68**, 1174–1177.

Streicher, S. L., Gurney, E. G., and Valentine, R. C. (1972). *Nature (London)* **239**, 495–499.
Streicher, S. L., Shanmugam, K. T., Ausubel, F., Morandi, C., and Goldberg, R. B. (1974). *J. Bacteriol.* **120**, 815–821.
Tjepkema, J., and Evans, H. J. (1975). *Biochem. Biophys. Res. Commun.* **65**, 625–628.
Trinick, M. J. (1976). *Proc. Int. Symp. Nitrogen Fixation, 1st, 1975* pp. 507–517.
Tu, J. C. (1974). *J. Bacteriol.* **119**, 986–991.
Tubb, R. S. (1974). *Nature (London)* **251**, 481–485.
Tyler, B., DeLeo, A., and Magasanik, B. (1974). *Proc. Natl. Acad. Sci. U.S.A.* **71**, 225–229.
Verma, D. P. S., Nash, D. T., and Schulman, H. M. (1974). *Nature (London)* **251**, 74–77.
Vest, G. (1970). *Crop Sci.* **10**, 34–35.
Vest, G., and Caldwell, B. F. (1972). *Crop Sci.* **12**, 692–693.
von Bülow, J. F. W., and Döbereiner, J. (1975). *Proc. Natl. Acad. Sci. U.S.A.* **72**, 2389–2393.
Wacek, T. J., and Brill, W. J. (1976). *Crop Sci.* **16**, 519–522.
Wall, J. D., Weaver, P. F., and Gest, H. (1975). *Nature (London)* **258**, 630–631.
Weare, N. M., and Shanmugam, K. T. (1976). *Arch. Microbiol.* **110**, 207–213.
Weber, D. R. (1966). *Agron. J.* **58**, 43–46.
Winter, H. C., and Burris, R. H. (1976). *Annu. Rev. Microbiol.* **45**, 409–426.
Wolpert, J. S., and Albersheim, P. (1976). *Biochem. Biophys. Res. Commun.* **70**, 729–737.
Zabriskie, J. B. (1967). *Adv. Immunol.* **7**, 147–188.
Zumft, W. G., and Mortenson, L. E. (1975). *Biochim. Biophys. Acta* **416**, 1–52.

Chapter 3

Water: Adaptation of Crops to Drought-Prone Environments*

Andrew D. Hanson and Charles E. Nelsen

*The authors' research reported in this chapter was carried out under U. S. Energy Research and Development Administration Contract EY-76-C-02-1338.

I. INTRODUCTION

A. Water Availability as a Constraint on Crop Production

1. Aims and Scope of Review

The various biophysical, physiological, genetic, agronomic, and ecological aspects of plant–water relations have been thoroughly reviewed in recent years (see listing below). This review will attempt a limited synthesis of these aspects, drawing mainly from research on drought resistance in grain crops, and emphasizing the progress— theoretical and practical—that could result from collaboration between physiologists, geneticists, and plant breeders. A central theme will be research and development aimed at fitting crop plants to fluctuating, drought-prone environments, in a world situation where less reliance can be placed on the continued availability of cheap and convenient sources of fossil fuel energy.

Valuable recent texts, reviews, and symposium contributions on aspects of plant–water relations are classified in a necessarily arbitrary way as follows: (1) *Biophysics:* Cowan and Milthorpe (1968), Cram (1976), Dainty (1976), D. M. Gates (1968), Lewin (1974), Tanner (1968), Weatherley (1970). (2) *Physiology:* Begg and Turner (1976), Boyer (1976a,b), Boyer and McPherson (1975), Hellebust (1976), Hsiao (1973), Hsiao *et al.* (1976), Passioura (1976), Raschke (1975), Slatyer (1969), Vaadia (1976). (3) *Genetics and Breeding:* Atsmon (1973), Eslick and Hockett (1974), Finlay (1971), Grafius (1971), Hurd (1971, 1976), O'Toole and Chang (1978), Reitz (1974), Sprague (1969). (4) *Agronomy:* Arnon (1972a,b), Campbell (1974), Hsiao and Acevedo (1974), Jensen (1968), Poljakoff-Mayber and Gale (1972), Ritchie (1974), Viets (1971, 1972). (5) *Ecology:* Evenari *et al.* (1971), Fischer and Turner (1978), Walter and Stadelmann (1974).

2. General Considerations

It is clear that water—in terms of direct deficits (droughts), as well as water surfeits (flooding and waterlogging) and poor irrigation water quality (salinity)—is a major constraint on the use of solar energy for food, feed, and fiber production in almost all agricultural regions of the world. In each region, the climate, the soil types, the availability, quality, and management of irrigation water, the drainage practices, the cropping systems, human labor, and the level of technological development interact with each other and with economic and political factors in determining the extent to which production of any crop will be directly limited by water. While all these biological and institutional interactions are as old as agriculture itself (e.g., Arnon, 1972a; Evenari et al., 1971) the rapid, simultaneous industrialization and development of scientific agriculture in today's developed countries has increased the impact of technology on all other factors. The application of industrial technology to agriculture has proved very successful in industrial countries, and in the modified form of the "green revolution," also in less-developed countries (LDCs). In essence it has purchased a degree of control over the environment for crop production, particularly with respect to water, soil fertility, and pest management. The price has been an ever-increasing rate of expenditure of fossil fuel energy, perhaps in some cases to the extent that " . . . agriculture should be redefined as the human activity that converts fossil fuel into food by means of solar energy, plants and animals." (de Wit, 1975). There is now widespread feeling that (1) developed countries cannot long continue to raise agricultural production by increasing fossil fuel energy inputs (Council for Agricultural Science and Technology, 1973; Steinhart and Steinhart, 1974a), and (2) that LDCs must produce the bulk of their own food, and that the wholesale import of industrial agricultural systems cannot solve their production problems (Crosson, 1975; Steinhart and Steinhart, 1974a; Wortman, 1975). It follows that the broad agricultural research and development aims of both developed and less-developed countries should coincide: to stabilize and increase production of food, feed, and fiber, and to do so with the most efficient utilization of resources, particularly fossil fuels. Such aims require massively increased attention to plant-environment interactions, especially in applied plant breeding.

As mentioned briefly above, this review will consider water availability as a constraint on crop production, mainly from the standpoint of research on drought stress in grain crops, especially stress on cereals grown in the dryland farming systems of semiarid areas. There are several reasons for this choice. First, by narrowing the field of discussion to drought stress in cereals, it becomes easier to define productivity objectives for contrasting types of agricultural systems, and to consider some specific research strategies implied by these objectives. Second, by further narrowing consideration to semiarid areas and dryland farming practices, attention is focused on the more severe aspects of drought stress. Most of the land devoted to production of wheat (the world's largest cereal crop) is in the dry, drought-prone areas of North America, the Soviet Union, India, the Near East, and Australia. In these zones, drought causes occasional total crop failures, and water is almost always a major environmental constraint on yield. Third, the general adaptation of wheat, barley, and sorghum to the erratic rainfall patterns of semiarid regions, taken with the large amount of genetic, physiological, and agronomic information available on such crops, provide good starting points for multidisciplinary research aimed at a better understanding of how to fit a crop to its environment. It seems likely that data and concepts based on plant–environment interactions in semiarid regions will also be applicable to the drought stresses encountered by crops grown under irrigation in dry regions (e.g., maize) and by rainfed crops of more humid regions (e.g., upland rice).

B. Added Fossil Fuel Energy

1. Industrial Countries

The agriculture of the United States and other industrialized countries is now heavily dependent on fossil fuel energy. The components of this agricultural energy use (variously termed added energy, support energy, purchased energy, and energy subsidy) have been extensively analyzed. They include irrigation, field operations, production and application of fertilizers, pesticides, and herbicides; grain drying; and construction and use of farm machinery (Heichel, 1976; Pimentel et al., 1973; Steinhart and Steinhart, 1974a; U.S. Department of Agriculture, 1974). Although on-farm energy use accounts for only about 3% of the total energy consumption in the United States (CAST, 1973; Steinhart and Steinhart, 1974a), agriculture cannot be insulated indefinitely from the consequences of future oil and natural gas shortages and the accompanying high energy costs. Proven oil and natural gas reserves, within the United States and worldwide, will be largely depleted within 30 to 50 years at present consumption rates (U.S. Energy Research and Development Administration, 1975; Newland and Price, 1975). Coal, the only alternative energy source that is feasible at present, is not as environmentally desirable as oil, nor is it as easy to use in agricultural applications.

Figure 1A illustrates the success of fossil fuel use in wheat production. The combined effects of mechanized soil and water management and field operations, of fertilizer and chemical application, and of cultivar improvement have increased yields by 100% within 30 years in the United States. Three additional points are illustrated by Figs. 1A and 1B.

1. General farm energy use increased fourfold during the 1940–1970 period, although wheat yields only doubled. Furthermore, the wheat

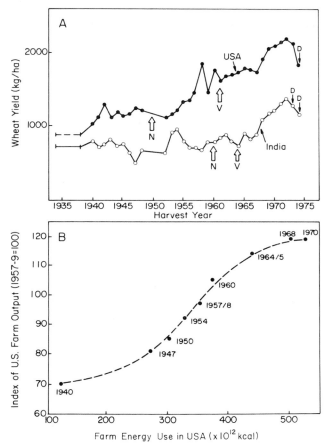

Fig. 1.   Trends in wheat yields (kg/hectare harvested), and energy demand for food production. (A) Wheat yields in the United States and India, 1934–1974. Arrows designated N show approximate dates for the start of widespread inorganic fertilizer (especially nitrogen) application; arrows designated V show approximate release dates for new, high-yielding (short-strawed, disease-resistant) varieties; arrows designated D pinpoint recent years of widespread drought in the wheat-growing regions. (Yield data from Production Yearbooks, F.A.O., United Nations; N and V for the United States refer particularly to the Palouse region.) (B) Total farm output of the United States, 1940–1970, as a function of the on-farm energy use which includes fuel, electricity, fertilizer, farm machinery, tractors, and irrigation (Data from Steinhart and Steinhart 1974b, reprinted by permission of the publisher, Duxbury Press.)

yield plateau reached about 1970 (Fig. 1A) coincides roughly with the flattening out of general farm output (Fig. 1B); since the mid-1960's the increments in production have been far smaller than in earlier years, despite the continued growth in farm energy use. Even given adequate, stable energy resources, it seems probable that further massive energy intensification would not produce spectacular yield increases.

2. Much cultivar improvement has emphasized fitness (i.e., high yield) for the improved growing conditions made possible by high fossil fuel energy inputs. This is figuratively shown by the relative dates for introduction of fertilizer (mainly nitrogen) application and the release of adapted, short-strawed varieties (e.g., Gaines) capable of responding favorably to increased nitrogen application. Such varieties were developed in response to, and specifically for, farming practices that depended on increased energy input. A secondary point illustrated by Fig. 1A concerns the time to develop and release new varieties of crops. Even when the yield-limiting characteristics can be readily identified and bred for (short straw and a high grain/straw ratio in this case) it can take many years to incorporate these characteristics into the adapted genetic background required of an improved crop variety for release in a given region.

3. There are very large year-to-year fluctuations in wheat yield. While these are partly institutional in origin (e.g., total wheat acreage changes, shortfalls in fertilizer supply) and also reflect disease outbreaks, the timeliness of water availability (as stored soil moisture, rainfall, and irrigation) is the primary factor involved in determining yields in the U.S. wheat belt. Rainfall and the water status of plants and soils also have a secondary influence on disease development and on the wheat acreage planted and harvested. In years of widespread drought (e.g., 1974), average wheat yields are greatly depressed. Since they represent whole-country mean yields, the data of Figs. 1A and B tend to underemphasize the yield reduction caused by dry weather in the most drought-prone dryland farming areas. In dry years in such areas an economic crop may never be made and consequently will not be harvested. Since the yields of Fig. 1A are given on the basis of area actually harvested, this method of yield reporting underestimates the severity of yield reduction caused by drought.

2 Less Developed Countries (LDCs)

The choice of India as an LDC, for comparison with the United States from the standpoint of wheat yields, is based on similarities in land resources in their respective wheat-growing areas, and on a comparable total area of wheat harvested (varying between 18 and 24 $\times$ 10^6 ha in the United States between 1955 and 1973, and steadily increasing from 11 to 19 $\times$ 10^6 ha in India during the same period). Comparison of the

United States and Indian data of Fig. 1A illustrates basic similarities and differences.

1. The rise in Indian wheat yields during the 1960's reflects the expansion of irrigation, the increased use of chemical fertilizer and pesticides, and the introduction of high-yielding dwarf varieties that responded well to these conditions (e.g., Sonora 64, Lerma Rojo 64A, and Inia 66S). This successful Green Revolution Agriculture resembles the situation described above for the United States insofar as the enhanced yields came partly from varieties developed specifically for an environment modified by increased fossil fuel energy input. Increases in irrigation and chemical fertilizer use again tended to precede the availability of dwarf varieties. One difference between the United States and India is that the Indian wheat yield increases have been more dependent on expanded irrigation (Gavan and Dixon, 1975).

2. Despite the fact that Green Revolution Agriculture is using some high-energy crop production technology, current fossil fuel energy use in Indian farming is far below that in the United States. Very large output increases can be made in India with small added fossil fuel inputs (in terms of electricity for irrigation schemes, production of fixed nitrogen, and pesticides) for two main reasons. First, the farming systems are still very much on the rising part of an input–output curve like that of Fig. 1B. Second, the intensive human labor of small farms can deploy small fossil fuel inputs very effectively, and about 75% of the Indian labor force is engaged in agriculture compared with less than 5% in the United States. Based on considerations of this type, several authors have concluded that limited, strategic application of high-energy technology could continue to increase grain yields in LDCs if institutional constraints can be overcome (Brown and Pariser, 1975; Lipton, 1975; Mellor, 1976; Wortman, 1975). The possible limitations imposed on such development by within- and between-country competition for declining oil reserves are unpredictable. It is clear, however, that the absolute energy demand for sustained agricultural development in LDCs is modest compared to the current energy budgets of industrial countries.

3. The year-to-year fluctuations in Indian wheat yields are at least as large as those in the United States. As in the United States, although plant diseases and institutional factors help produce the fluctuations, droughts are the principal cause. The lack of stability of yield has been, and continues to be, of even greater significance to India than to the United States.

C. Productivity Objectives and Future Research

1. Objectives

The preceding survey of wheat yields in relation to energy inputs and to water stress shows clearly the enduring significance of droughts for the production of cereals. Future advances in meteorology may enable the prediction of droughts with sufficient timeliness and accuracy to permit cropping plans to be modified accordingly (Jackson et al., 1975). Appreciable improvements in long-term stability of grain production could be achieved by this route. Another possibility for increasing yields and yield stability in the face of droughts of different types and durations lies in massive investment in various assured irrigation and associated soil management technologies (Jackson et al., 1975; Mellor, 1976). This route is limited both by the availability of suitable water resources and by the energy costs inherent in obtaining, storing, and distributing water. Overall, it is clear that water availability will always be a primary constraint on grain yields and that, on a world scale, the problem is as much one of improving stability of grain yield under water stress as it is one of maximizing yield potentials in the absence of such stress, given finite resources of water, land, and energy. The following four objectives, for the United States and India, are presented as within the range of the potential applications of research on plant–water relations to plant breeding and agronomy: (a) Improved stability of wheat yield, in both dryland and irrigated conditions in the face of climatic fluctuations. (b) Holding the wheat yields per hectare in the United States at the current level, even though the area planted to wheat increases moderately, and the on-farm energy use per unit of cultivated land area remains static or is reduced to 1960 levels. (c) Continued steady yield increases in dryland and irrigated farming systems in India to attain the level of about 2000 kg/ha, with minimal reliance upon fossil fuel-dependent technology. (d) The attainment of (a), (b), and (c) within 30 years. The declining quality and quantity of fossil fuel reserves and steadily inceasing population pressure combine to impose this time constraint.

2. Cooperative Research

Many thousands of generations of cereal crops have been subjected to the selection pressures of traditional agriculture, which have emphasized consistent and reliable yield rather than high yield (Harlan, 1975). As outlined above, the spectacular increases in yield achieved in the last one-half century by scientific agriculture have been made possible partly through technology per se, and partly by selecting (during

at most 200 generations) for high yield in environments that are partially controlled by fossil fuel technology. The world's major plant
breeding efforts have been directed toward developing disease and
insect resistance, capacity to respond favorably to fertilizers and irrigation, and qualities required for increasingly energy-intensive farming
systems. There has been far less conscious emphasis placed on systematic breeding for characteristics that permit the crop plant to cope
with environmental stresses, although this has now begun. Examples of
such research on cereals include investigations of winter hardiness
(Grafius, 1974; Olien, 1974; Shearman et al., 1973); aluminum tolerance (Kerridge and Kronstad, 1968; Reid, 1971); and rooting patterns
in relation to drought resistance (Hurd, 1974).

There has been little attempt to breed for drought resistance for two
main reasons. First, there is a dearth of basic knowledge of what the
factors responsible for drought resistance are, leading to an inability to
recognize and select for them. It is only recently that our knowledge on
plant–water relations has increased to the point where there is a reasonable expectation of practical applications within the forseeable future. Second, there has not been great pressure to improve drought
resistance, since other avenues have led to satisfactory advances in
yield. The pressure for development of drought resistance is only now
becoming intense because the alternative, simpler avenues to higher
yields have already been explored.

What are the reasons for believing that plant breeding can play a
crucial role in achieving objectives of the kind outlined? First, yield
stability was more important during the vast bulk of crop evolution
than was high yield, and therefore there is probably considerable unexploited variation in the world's germplasm banks of cereals and their
wild progenitors, with respect to many environmental stresses (e.g.,
Zohary et al., 1969). Many types of drought stress resistance must be
represented in these banks. Second, there is a growing possibility that
we will be able to increase the available genetic variation through
interspecific and intergeneric wide crossing (e.g., Jensen, 1976) and
somatic hybridization (e.g., Carlson and Polacco, 1975). Third, the
major cereals have been genetically analyzed, and thus the data base for
an investigation of the inheritance of drought resistance has been laid.
If, as seems probable, components of drought resistance prove to be
quantitative traits, then genetic theory is still sufficiently developed to
handle such traits in cereal breeding programs (Sprague, 1969).

What type of research effort is necessary to realize the potential for
breeding plants resistant to drought stress? It is essential to use our
growing knowledge of plant–water relations to define factors involved

in drought resistance step by step, reducing the scope of our concepts from the whole crop, through the individual plant, to the cellular and subcellular levels. Once identified, the mode of inheritance of these factors or components must be investigated. The resultant advances in the physiological genetics of higher plants should furnish breeding programs on drought resistance with the information on what to breed for, and on how to select for it. Clearly, this research effort must be multidisciplinary.

Certainly, there are many severe drought situations in which no amount of genetic improvement in drought resistance can prevent cereal crop failure. However, under both irrigated and dryland conditions, average cereal yields fall far short of maximum yield potential, largely because of moderate drought stresses. It is in this intermediate area that the opportunities for breeding are greatest. It may well be necessary in many cases to trade a very high potential for yield in well-irrigated, fertile conditions for a high degree of drought resistance, although definitive evidence on this point is lacking (Sections III,E,2 and V,B). If such a trade-off proves to be necessary to provide a hedge against crop failure in dry seasons, at least separate and irreconcilable plant breeding aims can be defined for specific types of environment, and some of the element of chance will be taken from breeding programs and farming alike.

In Section II, problems concerning the identification of components of drought resistance are reviewed, and the potential use of such defined components in plant breeding programs is outlined. Sections III and IV cover selected recent approaches to the study of plant–water relations that have a bearing on the mechanisms involved in drought resistance, beginning with whole plant studies and ending with cellular biochemistry.

II. THE INTERFACE BETWEEN FIELD AND LABORATORY

A. Identification of Components of Drought Resistance

1. Overall Strategy for the Analysis of Drought Resistance

We use the term *drought resistance* in this review in a broad sense to describe the sum or end result of the features of a plant's life cycle, morphology, physiology, and biochemistry that contribute positively to the ability to survive and reproduce in conditions of limited water availability. The term *component* is also used in a broad sense, to describe any subset of the overall phenomenon of drought resistance. In this sense, components cover all levels of structure and function from yield-limiting, drought-sensitive growth stages to primary gene products related to drought resistance. *Drought sensitivity* is taken as the inverse of drought resistance. The important related concept of *water use efficiency* (dry weight produced per unit of water used) is excluded from our broad working definition of drought resistance, and is considered separately in Section III,F,2. We use *adaptation* to denote satisfactory agronomic performance in the type of environment specified.

Because drought resistance is a complex character, and cannot be expected to be controlled by only a few genes, it must be broken down into components before physiological and genetic investigation is begun. The conceptual stages of such a breakdown and analysis for any crop are as follows:

1. Broad definition of the effect of drought throughout the crop's life cycle and qualitative description of the strategies available for coping with drought.

2. Identification of measurable, favorable and unfavorable characters that determine responses to specific types of drought stress, especially at critical growth stages.

3. Investigation of the physiological responses to drought under controlled environmental conditions, and development of quick, reliable tests to identify the component(s) controlling drought resistance.

4. Survey of the existing natural variation in these characters (components) available in world germplasm collections of the crop species and its wild relatives.

5. Study of the modes of inheritance of the characters and the development of a program based on physiological test criteria to breed pure lines or populations with resistance to specific types of drought, with field testing to validate the selection criteria adopted.

In cereal breeding, analogous approaches have already proved successful in the areas of disease resistance, winter hardiness, protein quality, photoperiod insensitivity, and plant architecture. In principle, the application of physiological genetics to the components of drought resistance should lead to the identification of characteristics that are increasingly close to primary gene products. By basing selections in a plant breeding program on characteristics as close as possible to primary gene products, the complexities introduced by multigenic inheritance and interallelic interactions are minimized, and can be recognized for what they are when they do occur (Sprague, 1969). Such an approach also allows valuable characteristics to be detected and exploited, even when they occur in very poor genetic backgrounds.

2. Field Data Required

a. What is Needed? The main current constraint on application of physiological genetics to drought resistance is the dearth within a crop species of genotypes showing clear differences in their response at specific growth stages to reasonably well-defined drought stresses. The range of natural variability in response to drought simply has not been systematically assessed in cereals or in any other crop. In retrospect, much of the potential variability must already have been released in dryland cereal breeding programs by crosses between adapted and nonadapted parents, and subsequently lost when only relatively adapted progeny were continued to later generations. It is only through research on both drought-sensitive and drought-resistant types that genetic differences amenable to physiological definition can be recognized. In short, valuable materials for future research—the poorly drought-adapted plants—are now discarded from breeders' nurseries. Some of this poorly adapted material must be retained for comparison with adapted elite lines. Caution is necessary here, however, because poor dryland adaptation can result from many causes besides high sensitivity to water stress, for example, susceptibility to endemic diseases.

Heading and maturity dates not matching the pattern of soil moisture availability in a given area can also result in poor dryland adaptation. In these cases there are obvious relationships with drought resistance. Because they are obvious, they can be handled by field screening techniques in breeding programs. Physiological investigations must take into account these aspects of drought resistance in assessing the performance of any genotype. The most valuable poorly adapted lines for physiological research, however, may be those that have high yield potential under conditions of ample moisture but that, for no obvious reasons, show consistently low yields in drought-prone environments. A failure to account for poor performance of a line in drought conditions could indicate the presence, at some stage of growth, of a gross developmental lesion, and could open this lesion to analysis by physiological genetics.

Of the two following subsections, the first describes techniques for the analysis of genotype–environment interactions, and their application to investigation of drought resistance; and the second discusses the potential use of recurrent selection in an evolutionary approach to develop plant populations of contrasting drought resistance. Field-oriented research of the type reviewed in these sections is a prerequisite for further progress in breeding for drought resistance.

b. Regression Analysis. When coupled with field observations of the growing crop, regression analysis can be of use in identifying those genotypes representing the extremes of adaptation to drought (e.g., Finlay and Wilkinson, 1963; Finlay, 1964, 1971). Essentially, the technique involves growing many genotypes in replicated yield trials in a range of environments. In one study (Finlay and Wilkinson, 1963), 277 diverse barley varieties were grown at three dryland locations in South Australia for several seasons; the sites differed with respect to soil type, but moisture was the most important yield-limiting environmental variable. The mean yield of all varieties at each site and season (site mean yield) was used as a quantitative measure of the environment, enabling designation of individual site/season combinations as low-yielding or high-yielding environments. A linear regression for the yield of each variety on the site mean yield was calculated for each site and season. The regression coefficient (b, phenotypic stability) and mean variety yield across all environments were used together to characterize the genotype–environment interactions and to identify dryland-adapted genotypes. In the calculations of means and regressions, yields were expressed on a logarithmic scale in order to induce a high degree of linearity in the regressions. Such a transformation was necessary to handle the wide range of genotypes and the extremes of environment involved and is not an integral part of the technique.

In Fig. 2, the regression lines for three contrasting varieties are reproduced. It should be noted that the average phenotypic stability for the group of varieties is $b = 1.0$ (broken line). When $b > 1.0$, a variety shows less than average stability, and when $b < 1.0$, a variety has higher than average stability under the drought-prone conditions of the experiment. The U.S. barley variety Atlas shows a near-average phenotypic stability ($b = 0.90$), with a high mean yield across all environments and a high yield potential. It can thus be considered stable and generally adapted to the variable dryland environments. In contrast, the British variety Provost has a high yield potential in favorable (high moisture) environments, but yields are severely reduced in low-yielding drought environments; the b value is thus very high ($b = 2.13$) and the mean yield across all environments lower than that of Atlas. Provost is not adapted to the low-yielding, drought environments. A third type of behavior is shown by the Hungarian variety Bankuti Korai, which yields well in low-yielding environments, but is unable to exploit more favorable conditions; the b value is therefore very low ($b = 0.14$) and the mean yield across all environments is also low.

What are the strengths and weaknesses of the regression analysis approach when trying to identify contrasting genotypes for physiological study of drought resistance? The main strength is that it provides a conceptual framework for the interpretation of genotype–environment interactions, especially when the ranges of both genotypes and environments are wide. For example, Fig. 2 suggests clearly that Atlas and Provost could provide an interesting pair for comparisons (similar high yield potential, very different phenotypic stability in water-limited environments). An additional practical strength is that by use of the average yield of a large number of varieties to grade complex natural environments, a first cut with regard to classifying varietal behavior in drought-prone conditions can be made without detailed analysis of interaction of edaphic, climatic, and biological components of the environment. Some data on the environment are, however, indispensable. It must be certain that a single environmental variable (rainfall) was the principal determinant of grain yield, that this variable ranged only from suboptimal to optimal levels (and did not become supraoptimal), and that major disease problems did not arise (Knight, 1970). The two former conditions were met in the work reported by Finlay and Wilkinson (1963), and the semiarid climate of South Australia presumably minimized disease development in the exotic varieties studied. Two groups (Singh et al., 1973c; Hanson et al., 1977) have made use of the Finlay and Wilkinson (1963) data to identify barley varieties of differing drought resistance suitable for physiological investigations.

The major weakness of regression analysis is its lack of resolving power with respect to the sequence of developmental steps that interact with each other and with the environment to determine yield. The variety Bankuti Korai (Fig. 2) supplies a simple example. It is yield stable and low yielding because it evades drought by very early heading and maturity; regression analysis alone is incapable of distinguishing the drought evasion of Bankuti Korai from a drought endurance strategy that might be adopted by a later-maturing variety. In general, there must be many alternative developmental strategies open to genotypes that can give similar end results in terms of the dual criteria of phenotypic stability (low b value) and satisfactory mean yield across all environments. Regression analysis cannot be expected to pinpoint many examples of comparable genotypes differing only by the presence or absence of limited genetic lesions that cause poor drought resis-

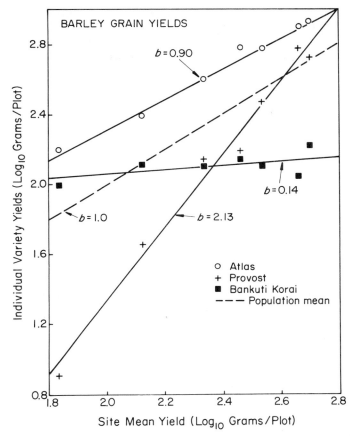

Fig. 2. Regression lines, showing the relationship of individual grain yields of three varieties and population mean of 277 varieties of barley grown at different dryland sites in southern Australia. Linear regression coefficients (*b*) are indicated. (Data from Finlay and Wilkinson, 1963, reproduced by permission of the *Australian Journal of Agricultural Research.*)

tance. It can only readily identify genotypes with good or poor strategies with respect to seed yield in drought-prone conditions. Within the good category there will be found many developmental ways to achieve high, stable yield (Finlay, 1971). Within the poor category will be found many ways to genetic oblivion!

Other weaknesses inherent in regression analysis can be eliminated by modifying the statistical treatment of the yield data, by taking supplementary field data, and by controlling water availability. These improvements will be described below.

An improvement to the Finlay and Wilkinson technique involves the recognition of deviation from the regression lines as an important component of phenotypic stability in a fluctuating environment (e.g., Eberhart and Russell, 1966). The slope of the regression line can be viewed as the first index of stability, and the unexplained deviations from the regression line (i.e., those not accounted for by r^2, the coefficient of determination) as a second index. Of two varieties with similar b values, that with the lower r^2 would be considered less stable. It is possible that varieties with unexplained deviations (low r^2) may provide very interesting material for physiological investigation. This can be illustrated by reference to a highly simplified model for wheat yield (Table I and Fig. 3). In this model, there are six idealized wheat varieties differing in their drought resistance at various growth stages. They are grown in a series of environments in which drought stress is experienced at one or more growth stages. The regression analysis technique is then applied to the final grain yields. The major assumptions in the model are as follows:

1. There is an orderly sequence of development of wheat grain yield components with time; the growth stages during which the components are determined do not overlap.

2. Buffering effects due to compensation between yield components are small.

3. The effects of drought stress on each yield component are multiplicative in their effect on final yield.

4. All six varieties have the same maximum yield potential (100 units) when no drought stress occurs.

5. The varieties show differences in the effect of a given drought stress on each yield component, ranging from no effect (= 100% development of that yield component) to an 80% reduction (= 20% development of that yield component).

Of these assumptions, (1) and (2) are great oversimplifications, while (3), (4), and (5) are more reasonable. Despite obvious shortcomings, such a model is useful in illustrating the kinds of considerations that must go with an analysis of the effect of drought on crop yield. Table I shows the growth stages at which drought is imposed, the yield components that are affected, the relative drought sensitivities of the six varieties, and the final grain yields. Figure 3 presents regression lines and b and r^2 values for three varieties only: F, the most drought resistant at all growth stages; A, the least drought resistant at all growth stages; B, a variety resistant at all growth stages except one. It is clear that varieties F and A show up in the regression analysis as relatively

TABLE I
Description of a Model for Regression Analysis of Grain Yield in Wheat Subjected to Drought Stress

Code number	Growth stage subjected to drought stress — Description	Yield component affected	Grain yield (% of maximum) following drought stress at specified growth stage in wheat varieties A through F — A	B	C	D	E	F	Mean yield of all cultivars A to F (% maximum)
—	None	None	100	100	100	100	100	100	100
1	Establishment and early vegetative growth	Fertile tiller number/m²	50	20	80	50	80	100	63.3
2	Head initiation	Spikelets/head ⎫ seeds/ head	50	80	80	60	70	90	71.7
3	Boot to heading	Fertile florets/spikelet ⎭	50	80	80	70	60	80	70.0
4	Heading to maturity (grain fill)	Seed weight	50	80	20	80	50	70	58.3
3,4	—	—	25	64	16	56	30	56	41.2
2,3,4	—	—	12.5	51.2	12.8	33.6	21	50.4	30.3
1,2,3,4	—	—	6.3	10.2	10.2	16.8	16.8	50.4	18.5
2,3	—	—	25	64	64	42	42	72	51.5

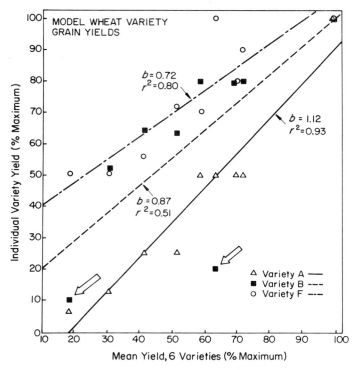

Fig. 3. Finlay and Wilkinson-type regression analysis applied to three of the model wheat varieties subjected to the hypothetical drought stresses described in Table I. Variety A is uniformly and moderately susceptible to drought at all stages from establishment and early vegetative growth to grainfill; Variety F is highly drought resistant at all stages; Variety B is drought resistant at all stages except establishment and early vegetative growth, at which it is highly susceptible. Open arrows indicate those instances in which drought occuring during establishment and early vegetative growth caused sharp yield reductions in variety B. Linear regression coefficients (b) and coefficients of determination (r²) are indicated.

stable and unstable, respectively, using the b value criterion. Variety B appears to be intermediate between F and A, based on the b value alone. However, inspection of the deviations from regression lines (r² values) shows that, while the deviations are quite small for F and A, they are large for B. Specifically, two points for B (arrowed on Fig. 3) lie far from the others. In this model, these points are explained by the high sensitivity of B to drought at just one growth stage. It follows that if genotypes such as B exist in the real world, they are likely to be characterized more by low r² values than by high b values—and that supplementary data on trial site conditions during the growing season could provide clues as to which growth stage was so drastically affected.

It is probable that many low r^2 values would, in practice, be due to specific, limited disease or pest damage to certain varieties or to certain parts of a nursery site. However, varieties like B would be so useful for physiological and genetic studies that the search for them is worthwhile.

As originally proposed, the Finlay and Wilkinson technique relied on the year-to-year climate fluctuations of a semiarid region to provide the range of environments. This dependence on weather necessarily extends the time scale of the experimental observations to several or even many seasons. Useful data can be obtained in a single season by selecting sites in various parts of a region in which there is a characteristic increase in rainfall from one part to another, such as eastern Oregon. Another approach, applicable to spring cereals, is the use of early and late planting dates to obtain an extra environment at each location (Eberhart and Russell, 1966). A more direct method is to control soil moisture by irrigation in semiarid areas; within limits, the timing, length, and severity of drought stress can be regulated in this way (e.g., Day and Thompson, 1975). Since only a single location is then required, soil type is eliminated as a variable and it becomes feasible to use detailed on-site measurements of plant and soil water status as criteria for timing of irrigations. A method for inducing controlled drought stress under field conditions where precipitation may be high has been developed for spring cereals in eastern England— troughs are laid between the crop rows and intercept up to 60% of the rainfall (Rackham, 1972).

The value of supplementary field data (on rainfall, soil type and moisture, disease, heading, and maturity dates) in interpreting regression analysis data has already been emphasized. In general, the more data that are logged, the more it becomes possible to ascribe poor yield performance at given sites to specific causes. Additionally, field observations of the growing crop made during or shortly after a drought episode improve the chances of spotting differences in injury development or recovery rates at a specific growth stage. Such differential responses would tend to be far less obvious from grain yield data alone, due to the strong tendency for component compensation to occur in the buffered yield system of grain crops (Adams, 1967; and Section III,C,2). To a limited extent, measurements of the components of yield on the genotypes in a mature nursery that has experienced drought can provide after-the-event data on the stage(s) at which drought stress occurred, and on the relative sensitivities of the genotypes (R. F. Eslick, personal communication). As an example, in spring barley the apical meristems lay down the spikelet primordia of the heads soon after stand establishment, and the maximum possible number of primordia in favorable conditions is genetically determined. In a season when severe drought stress occurs soon after establishment, primordium production will be curtailed and spikelet development slowed (Husain and Aspinall, 1970). Such a drought stress would tend to result in shorter heads (i.e., a small number of grains per head), and general reduction in head length would characterize such a droughted trial nursery. Genotypes within such a nursery would be ranked for drought resistance (at the head initiation stage) by arranging them in order of relative reduction of grain number per head (= grains per head in drought-stressed nursery/maximum possible grains per head × 100%). Similar types of relative drought sensitivities at other growth stages could be inferred from reductions in plant height and seed weight. Such data for a large number of genotypes and locations could be handled and interpreted using variations of the regression analysis technique (Stroike and Johnson, 1972).

In summary, regression analyses can identify and categorize the genetic variation available in drought resistance strategies, and can be used to evaluate nursery material at various stages in a plant breeding program. Regression analysis has some resolving power with respect to components of drought resistance, but this power is limited because the technique tends to emphasize the overall strategy of the line or variety, i.e., the general genetic background in which the components occur. Some genetic approaches that help to eliminate the pitfalls of working with components of drought resistance expressed in different varieties are covered briefly in Section II,A,2,c and in Sections II,B,1,a and b. These approaches seek either to minimize or to assess genetic background effects.

c. Recurrent Selection with Simultaneous Opposing Selection Pressures. Recurrent selection is a powerful and widely used tool in practical plant breeding (Allard, 1960), which could be used in an evolutionary approach to develop, for physiological studies, pairs of populations differing in their responses to drought stress (Reitz, 1974). Briefly, recurrent selection aims to concentrate genes scattered through a population by the following four steps: (1) evaluation of potential parents for a character; (2) intercrossing parents with the desired level of expression of the character; (3) evaluation and selection of progeny for expression of the character; and (4) use of the selection from (3) as parental material for further cycles of crossing and selection. Application of this method to investigation of drought resistance in self-pollinated crops such as wheat or barley would involve the initial establishment of a large and genetically variable panmictic population from a series of crosses between varieties or lines (composite cross-type population, e.g., Suneson, 1956). Incorporation of male-sterile plants into the composite cross population would facilitate intercrossing and enable a more rapid approach to a common gene pool for the population (e.g., Eslick and Hockett, 1974; Wiebe, 1968). After the establishment of an intercrossing population, simultaneous heavy selection pressure could be applied in the field both for resistance and for susceptibility to drought at a given growth stage. Comparisons could be made between a large number of lines developed from single seeds of plants drawn randomly from the intercrossing population. These lines could be tested simultaneously in well-irrigated conditions and in conditions

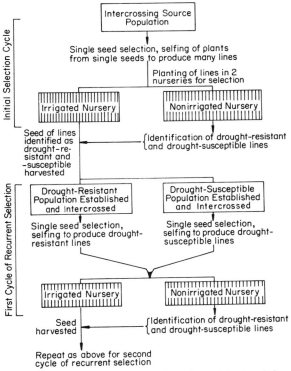

Fig. 4. Schematic method for developing drought-resistant and drought-susceptible populations by recurrent selection, based on field testing under well-irrigated and water-limited regimes.

where irrigation was withheld at a critical stage. Those lines showing the greatest and the least yield reduction (or other symptom of stress) could be identified, and used to create two separate populations (drought-susceptible and drought-resistant), for further cycles of inter-crossing and field selection (Fig. 4). While this method of obtaining a pair of contrasting populations with some shared genetic background is time consuming, it has the advantage of being suitable for achieving progress when the character under selection is under complex genetic control. Complex genetic control and the associated low heritability might reasonably be expected for the first identified physiological components of drought resistance.

3. Development and Application of Physiological Tests

a. Requirements for Physiological Tests. When a component of drought resistance at a given growth stage can be defined in physiological terms, laboratory testing methods can be developed for assessing the genetic variation of the component. Genetic analysis coupled with physiological tests can then give information on the mode of inheritance of the component (Hurd, 1976; Sullivan, 1971; Williams et al., 1969; and Section II,B,1). At this point, physiological screening tests for drought resistance, combined with field testing, can be incorporated into a plant breeding program. An ideal physiological screening test for a component of drought resistance would be: (1) highly correlated with drought resistance (e.g., good grain yields) under field conditions where drought stress occurred at the growth stage or stages at which the component is expressed; (2) rapid, accurate, and capable of handling hundreds to thousands of samples per season; (3) applicable at an early stage of development; and (4) nondestructive.

The extent to which these requirements are met determines the levels at which physiological testing can be utilized in a breeding program for drought resistance. The question of application is considered below (Section II,A,3,b). Two points should be emphasized at this stage regarding the development and use of physiological tests. First, they can only be helpful when they assess a component of drought resistance that is likely to be of value in the soil and climatic conditions for which the crop is being bred. Breeding for a component of drought resistance expressed solely at the seedling stage will be of little use to a cereal normally planted in adequate soil moisture conditions, but which commonly experiences soil and atmospheric droughts during heading and grainfill stages. Second, when physiological testing is applied to segregating populations, the appropriate selection intensity for a component of drought resistance can only be judged by simultaneous field testing for other characters. Since extreme drought resistance and a high yield potential in favorable conditions may be, to some extent, mutually exclusive (Section III,E,2), some trading-off between drought resistance and yield potential may be essential. In any case, drought resistance is only one of many desirable features of a crop, and most of these can only be assessed in field trials.

b. Levels at Which Physiological Tests for Drought Resistance Could Be Applied in a Plant-Breeding Program. As shown in Fig. 5, there are essentially three levels at which drought resistance tests can be inserted in a breeding program. Major factors influencing the deployment of tests are their cost, the time required to make them, and whether they involve total destruction of the plants. The most effective and economical use of tests, especially destructive ones, is at the level of selection of parents for crosses (level A, Fig. 5). Even with expensive, lengthy, and destructive tests requiring many replications, a wide range of germplasm can be screened for one or more components of drought resistance. Parents can then be chosen on the bases of intense expression of desired components and/or of potential physiological complementation (Wallace *et al.*, 1972). After crossing selected parents, selection of progeny could rely entirely on field screening, and

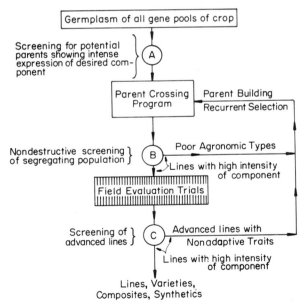

Fig. 5. Outline of a generalized plant breeding program, indicating points (A,B,C) at which physiological tests for components of drought resistance could be applied.

yield testing at a number of drought-prone locations, to identify superior genotypes.

If the test is nondestructive and capable of dealing with large numbers of individual plants, especially seedlings, it can be applied to segregating F_2 or F_3 populations (level B, Fig. 5). In this case, individual plants can be selected and their progeny evaluated in subsequent field tests. Destructive tests can be used to screen segregating populations, but selection between families derived from F_2 individuals must be substituted for selection between individual plants. This interposes an additional generation between crossing and selecting, which by consuming time and greenhouse or field space detracts from the advantages of physiological testing.

A compromise between testing only potential parents and screening segregating populations is use of tests at level C (Fig. 5), i.e., on advanced lines that have already been selected in the field for drought resistance and other agronomic characters. Screening at this level permits a judicious choice to be made among adapted lines before their release as varieties, etc. During the field testing and selection of these elite lines, severe drought stress may not have occurred and the more drought-susceptible lines might not have been eliminated. If this is the case, such susceptible lines could be caught at level C.

The loops on the right hand side of Fig. 5 are intended to show that drought-resistance genotypes identified at any stage in the breeding program can be returned to the crossing phase (for recurrent selection or parent building). Such recycling of material is a valuable procedure that would be made possible by the use of controlled screening tests for components of drought resistance. Physiological testing for components enables their detection in individuals, families or lines that are otherwise unadapted to field conditions, and which would therefore have been eliminated on the basis of field screening alone. By continually returning such genotypes to the parental crossing population, and by retrieving their drought-resistant progeny, it is possible to effect stepwise progress toward an adapted genetic background for the component of drought resistance under selection.

B. Exploitation of Genetic Variation in Components of Drought Resistance

1. Genetic Analysis of Drought Resistance

a. Population Genetics Studies and Diallel Crosses. When suitable physiological screening tests are available, genetic studies involving F_2 and backcross populations of crosses between contrasting parents could be made on components of drought resistance. Instances in which such methods have been applied to physiological characters include the inheritance of winter hardiness in wheat (Gullord, 1974) and of aluminum tolerance in barley (Reid, 1971).

Further information on the pattern of inheritance of physiological characters can be obtained from the analysis of a diallel cross, in which a number of contrasting genotypes are crossed in all possible combinations. For traits under simple genetic control, such pairwise crossings are powerful methods for the analysis of gene function and structure (Srb et al., 1965). For quantitatively inherited characters, diallel analysis is a useful genetic tool in practical plant breeding, as it identifies suitable parental combinations for crossing purposes. A study of the inheritance of possible components of drought resistance in sweet corn (Williams et al., 1969) illustrates the potential of diallel cross analysis. These authors crossed a series of six lines having varying degrees of drought resistance, and made simple physiological tests on the parents and on F_1, F_2, and F_1 backcross generations. They obtained data on the genetic control of germination in high osmotic potential, and of the recovery from heat and severe wilting treatments. As the authors indicated, although such traits may be useful, measurable components of drought resistance at certain growth stages, the results of such genetic analyses require confirmation by field testing of the selected resistant or susceptible lines from the crosses. A further example of the application of diallel analysis to physiological characters comes from freezing hardiness in winter wheat (Gullord, 1974). Using controlled stress-testing conditions in conjunction with a six- and a four-parent diallel it was shown that freezing hardiness was controlled by partially dominant genes which were mostly additive in their effect.

After a diallel cross, when testing is done in the F_2 or subsequent generations, the influence of the genetic background on the expression of a trait can be assessed (Sprague, 1969). Comparisons within and between F_{2---n} families are an approach to assessing the average value of a trait (e.g., a component of drought resistance) when it appears in various backgrounds.

b. Isogenic Analysis. Isogenic analysis could be applied as a precise theoretical tool for the investigation of specific components of drought resistance and is of equal interest to the physiologist and the breeder. In principle, isogenic lines (lines homozygous for a^1a^1 and a^2a^2) differ from each other only at the a locus—the genetic background against which the component governed by a is expressed is thus constant. By comparing the drought resistance of a^1a^1 and a^2a^2 phenotypes, the a locus component can be directly evaluated; such a situation is ideal for the physiological and biochemical characterization of the a locus component. Further information about the expression of the a gene and the role of its products in drought resistance can be obtained by incorporating a^1a^1 and a^2a^2 into several different background genotypes.

Isogenic lines can arise through mutations or they can be developed by crossing procedures (Wiebe, 1968). Two methods of developing isogenic lines (backcrossing or crossing followed by selfing, with selection for heterozygosity) are outlined schematically in Fig. 6. It is clear from this figure that isogenic lines take several years to develop, and that their properties depend on the method used to produce them.

Awns of wheat heads (Fig. 7) are active photosynthetic organs, and occur mainly in varieties adapted to warm, dry regions; awnless wheat varieties are generally confined to the more temperate zones. The expression of awns is frequently under single-gene control. Varieties with the awned characteristic generally outyield awnless ones under drought conditions, due to their higher average seed weights (Arnon, 1972b). The awned characteristic is thus a simple example of the type of component of drought resistance whose existence could be inferred from visual comparisons of stable and unstable genotypes, identified by a regression analysis of yields in drought-prone sites (Section II,A,2,b). More definitive data on the value of awns in drought-prone conditions have been obtained by the development of isogenic awned and awnless lines of several wheat varieties (Tables II and III). Table II shows clearly that, on the average, ten awned lines, developed from a cross between two adapted varieties, significantly outyielded the corresponding awnless lines in drought seasons in Texas by as much as 13.5% in a very dry year (1950). There was no significant effect of awns on yield in favorable years. Table III confirms the advantage of the awned characteristic in three different varietal backgrounds, under warm and dry Californian growing conditions. The physiological basis for the value of awns in drought conditions lies partly in their continued photosynthetic contribution to grainfill while the lower leaves and flag leaf are "burning up" (Evans et al., 1972; McDonough and Gauch, 1959). It may also involve favorable modification of the microclimate in the crop canopy (Ferguson, 1974).

There are several hundred near-isogenic pairs of lines of grain crops presently available (for barley, see Moseman et al., 1972). Among this backlog of material there are almost certainly some valuable experimental tools. However, application of isogenic analysis to any newly

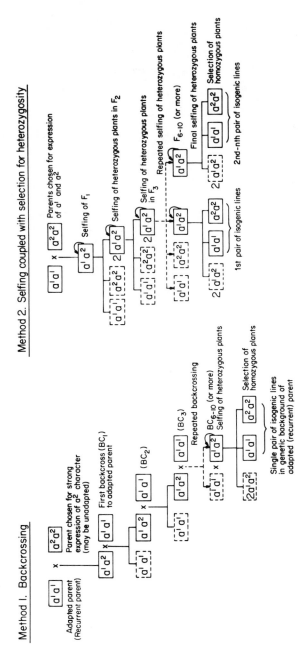

Fig. 6. Two conventional methods of developing pairs of isogenic lines, applicable in wheat or barley to a character in which the heterozygous plants can be recognized. Broken lines in boxes around genotypes indicate plants that are discarded. Method 1 (isogenics developed by backcrossing) places a gene (in this case a²) into a specific genetic background, usually an adapted variety (in this case a variety homozygous for a¹). Method 2 (isogenics developed by selfing) can give rise to many isogenic pairs (a¹a¹ and a²a²) in a range of genetic backgrounds. Whether any of these genetic backgrounds are adapted will depend on the choice of parents in the initial cross and on any selection imposed during the selfing stages.

103

Fig. 7. Heads of an awned and an awnless variety of wheat. Awns (also known as beards) are prolongations of the lemma of each flower.

TABLE II

Mean Yields of Ten Paired Awnless and Awned Isogenic Lines of Wheat Grown under Rainfed Conditions in Texas, 1947–1952

Year	Drought during grainfill	Mean yield, bu/acre[a]		Yield advantage of awned lines (%)
		Awnless lines	Awned lines	
1947	Yes	24.8	27.0[b]	+4.4
1948	No	31.6	32.5	+2.8
1950	Yes	15.6	17.7[b]	+13.5
1952	No	27.4	26.9	−1.8

[a] Test weight about 59 lb/bu.

[b] Designates yield advantages of awned over awnless lines significant at the 1% level. The ten paired isogenic lines in this study were developed from a cross between an awned (Kanred) and an awnless (Clarkan) variety. Expression of awns in this cross is controlled by a single gene, and heterozygous plants are recognized by the presence of short awns. The initial cross was followed by selfing with selection for heterozygosity for ten generations (see Fig. 6, method 2). (Data from Atkins and Norris, 1955, by permission of the American Society of Agronomy.)

TABLE III

Mean Yields of Near-Isogenic Awned and Awnless Wheat Lines Based on Three Varieties, Grown in California, 1946–1959[a]

Variety type	Number of paired tests	Mean yield (lb/acre) Awnless lines	Awned lines	Yield advantage of awned lines (%)
Baart	75	2292	2538	10.7
Onas	40	2496	2652	6.3
Ramona	43	1908	2028	6.3

[a] The near-isogenic lines were produced essentially by backcrossing for 10 to 14 generations (see Fig. 6, method 1), and were tested over many years in a semiarid climate. (Data from Suneson and Ramage, 1962, by permission of the Crop Science Society of America.)

identified potential components of drought resistance has certain limitations (Eslick and Hockett, 1974; Sprague, 1969). First, there is the definite possibility of transferring substantial chromosome segments associated with the locus of interest during development of isogenic pairs; this possibility is highest when the backcross method (Fig. 6, Method 1) is used. Such extraneous genetic material could markedly affect results and conclusions. Second, the development of isogenic pairs is time consuming and relies on accurate identification of contrasting genotypes in each generation. This identification is quite straightforward for visible features (e.g., awns in wheat), but many other components of drought resistance would probably require physiological or biochemical screening methods. If these methods could not distinguish between individual homozygous and heterozygous plants, progeny testing would be necessary, further prolonging the time scale of the operation. Third, isogenic analysis is, by definition, best fitted to the study of components controlled by single loci or small linkage groups. If complex plant characters such as drought resistance prove impossible to break into several simpler, identifiable components, then isogenic analysis is inapplicable.

Compromises are possible between complete isogenic analysis to assess the value of a component of drought resistance and simple reliance on comparisons between varieties. Isogenic populations (near isogenics) are one such compromise (Eslick and Hockett, 1974); they are obtained by crossing a^1a^1 and a^2a^2 parents and bulking homozygous F_2 or F_3 lines. A second compromise involves the use of only the first two steps of the backcross method (Fig. 6, Method 1), using several sources of a possible component of drought resistance crossed with one adapted line. The progenies of the first backcrosses will have an average of 75% of the genome of the adapted recurrent parent. Testing these BC_1 plants themselves (or their progeny obtained after selfing) would give data on the value of a suspected component of drought resistance that could be of immediate use to breeding programs, and could also indicate whether detailed isogenic analysis might be fruitful.

2. *Breeding for Drought Resistance*

The preceding parts of Section II have laid emphasis on the interdependence of physiology, genetics, and breeding in dealing with drought resistance. Physiological approaches themselves need small breeding programs to obtain suitable material for study and to test the validity of their conclusions (e.g., recurrent selection techniques and isogenic analysis). Genetic investigations rely on physiological tests to identify characters. Applied breeding programs for drought resistance would require supporting satellite programs in both physiology and genetics. Given appropriate physiological tests for the components of drought resistance, and data on their modes of inheritance, breeding for drought resistance on a systematic basis becomes possible. Below, we briefly outline three breeding methods that have proven useful in dealing with complex physiological characteristics, and that have potential for the development of drought-resistant crops. Because physiology, genetics, and breeding converge on this topic, most of the principles have been outlined earlier in the text (e.g., Figs. 4–6). The reader is referred to Allard (1960) for more detailed explanations of conventional breeding methods.

With the conventional *pedigree method* of breeding, two parents are chosen for desired characteristics, such as general adaptation and quality in one parent and intense expression of a component of drought resistance in the other (exotic) parent. The parents are hybridized, and the resulting F_1 and subsequent self-pollinated generations are grown and evaluated agronomically and physiologically (see Fig. 5). In the F_2 generation, single plants that show desirable gene combinations are selected and the parent–progeny relationship recorded. The selected F_2 individuals are advanced to give F_3 families; differences between families become apparent in the F_3 generation, and selection is mainly between families. In the F_4 and later generations, selection within superior families predominates. Variations on the pedigree method include the use of third or third and fourth parents when all the characters for which improvement is sought do not occur in any two parents. The use of pedigree breeding for a complex physiological trait—winter hardiness in wheat—is demonstrated by Gullord (1974).

Recurrent selection was outlined in Section II,A,2,c (see Fig. 4). This breeding strategy is essentially a way of circumventing the limitation imposed by selfing on the association of desired plant characters. For example, when a population of a wheat hybrid (e.g., between an adapted line and an exotic line with a complex drought-resistance character) is driven to homozygosity by several generations of selfing, desirable genes controlling the drought resistance characteristic may not be fixed in the combinations sought by the breeder to enhance plant performance. By intercrossing selected sib progeny (i.e., those lines in which a reasonable level of drought resistance is detectable), recurrent selection offers an opportunity for concentrating the genes that control the complex character—drought resistance—after they have been scattered by segregation and assortment to individual lines that move towards homozygosity as the generations are advanced. In general, lines that emerge from a recurrent selection program may contain a higher intensity of the complex character under selection than the lines that entered the program, but may tend to lack other adaptive features that would maximize yield and quality.

Parent building (see Fig. 5) is another breeding strategy that aims to avoid the isolating syndrome that begins and is maintained by selfing and the lack of intermating. Following a cross between, for example, an adapted line and an exotic line with an intense expression of a drought resistance component, inbreeding is allowed to occur for several generations. Those genotypes combining as many of the desired features (of drought resistance and adaptation) as possible are selected. These selected genotypes are then recycled through the crossing program, making appropriate crosses either to the original parents or to different adapted or exotic parents (or to each other) in order to accumulate the adaptive features they lack. Parent building differs from recurrent selection (and classical backcross breeding) by combining cycles of crossing, backcrossing, and inbreeding; it provides a continuing opportunity for rare recombinations to occur while keeping adaptation in focus.

III. OVERVIEW OF ENERGY FLOW, WATER STRESS, AND PLANT STRATEGIES

A. Introduction

The means by which terrestrial plants control water use and combat water stress are complex and, in most cases, little understood. Stomatal action and plant hydraulics are being investigated with interesting results, but much is still to be learned about water stress effects at the whole plant, tissue, cellular, and subcellular levels. The intricate nature of the many plant processes, and our ignorance of what is being optimized by each process, make it necessary first to break down these processes into identifiable components (Section II,A,1). An attempt can then be made to understand the interactions of components and control systems of each process. In Section III, we present an approach to plant–water relations in which water is treated as a constraint on the use of solar energy. This energy is followed as it enters the plant system and interacts with the many control systems in the plant. Such a conceptual approach is helpful in identifying gaps in our knowledge of plant processes and their controls, and thus helps form a framework for analysis of drought resistance.

B. A Model Illustrating Water as a Controller of Energy Flow through a Plant

Energy flows from the sun in the form of electromagnetic (wave) energy to the photosynthetic machinery in green plants, where it is converted to chemical bond energy. The chemical bond energy is then used to build and maintain a system. That is, it is used to make structural material (carbohydrates, proteins, etc.) as well as to assemble and maintain the structure. This chemical energy is eventually degraded and converted to heat through the respiration of the plant (or through respiration of consumers and decomposers), and is radiated to space (Morowitz, 1970; H. T. Odum, 1971; Odum and Odum, 1976). The total energy flow through a particular plant over time depends on many factors. Some factors within the plant are genetic controls over size or over length of life (e.g., annual growth habit). Some external factors with a controlling influence are water, temperature, day length, and nutrient availability. Each factor can be viewed as operating a valve or "work gate" (as defined by H. T. Odum, 1971, p. 44) controlling the flow of energy through the plant system. The following example illustrates this concept. On any open area of soil, a fairly predictable amount of solar energy will fall during one growing season. Consider the case where *all* requirements for growth are present, with the exception of water. A viable seed placed in these conditions will not germinate and no energy will flow through the plant system. If water becomes available to the seed, germination and growth will occur, and subsequently energy from the sun will begin to flow through and maintain this system. Furthermore, complete removal of water at any time will reduce the energy flow through the system to zero. Water can thus be viewed as acting at one or more valves to control the energy that flows through the system. Figure 8 shows a simplified energy diagram depicting such a situation. Symbols, taken from H. T. Odum, are briefly described here. For a more detailed discussion see H. T. Odum (1971) or Odum and Odum (1976).

1. The circles indicate any energy source located outside the system being considered. In this approach, which reduces all inputs to the plant to a single common denominator—water and CO_2, as well as the sun—can be represented as energy sources (H. T. Odum, 1971).

2. The tank symbols represent the storage of any type of energy in the system. It can be storage of energy in the form of water in the soil, in chemical bonds, or in order (e.g., specific DNA sequences).

3. The bullet-shaped symbol indicates the chloroplast, which has the ability to produce concentrated (chemical) energy from dilute wave (solar) energy.

4. The pointed, multiplier boxes (valves or work gates) leading to the storage tanks represent points of interaction where the flow of solar energy through the system is controlled by, for example, water.

5. The arrows, pointing to the ground, indicate the loss of energy from the system to the sink at every reaction or transformation step

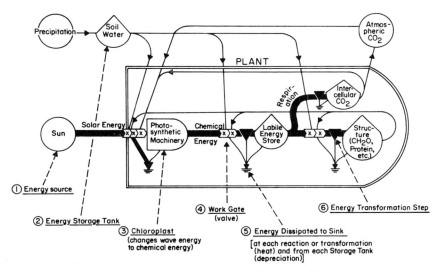

Fig. 8. Water as it controls energy flow through a plant. Water (and other requirements) act at work gates to control the flow of solar energy through a plant system. Limited water implies limited total energy flow. Symbols, after H. T. Odum (1971), are described in the text. The wide energy flow lines distinguish the principal paths of solar energy flux. The narrow lines show the smaller energy fluxes associated with the control functions of water and CO_2, as well as some minor pathways of solar energy flow.

(heat) and from every energy storage (depreciation). This loss of energy from the system is required by the second law of thermodynamics (Lehninger, 1973; Morowitz, 1968, 1970; H. T. Odum, 1971).

6. The solid, inverted triangles represent energy transformation steps, such as a transformation of chemical to heat energy in the case of respiration, or chemical to order in the case of a specific DNA sequence. An energy transformation is implicit in the definition of a chloroplast and therefore is not shown in the diagram. Note that some energy is lost (to the sink) at every transformation step.

Figure 8 shows three stages at which water controls the flow of energy through the plant. The first stage is at the photosynthetic apparatus. In higher plant photosynthesis, water is the ultimate source of electrons for the reduction of CO_2, and must thus be considered as a reactant. It is not known if reductions in the chemical activity of water play a significant role in changing photosynthetic metabolism, as the reductions that occur under even severe moisture stress are quite small (see Hsiao, 1973, and Section IV,A,3). In addition to any direct effect, as water becomes less available decreasing cell volumes will increase solute concentrations. These changes in concentration of some or all cell solutes may have (as yet undetermined) effects on enzyme action or organelle function (Boyer, 1976a,b; Weatherley, 1970, 1976). Of course, as water stress increases and as guard cell turgor is lost, stomatal conductance will decrease and photosynthesis will be affected by lowered CO_2 concentration in the leaf. Raschke (1975, 1976) discusses "hydropassive" and "hydroactive" closure of stomates which affect both photosynthesis and transpiration. Boyer (1976a) lists many references describing depressive effects of water stress and/or stomatal closure on photosynthesis.

The second stage where water exerts a controlling influence over energy flow through the plant is at the level of labile energy storage. The labile energy store consists predominantly of the metabolic pools of recent assimilates that are constantly being added to by photosynthesis, and withdrawn from by all the energy-requiring processes of the plant. The labile energy store can be loosely viewed as 1 day's photosynthate. At this stage, concerned with the fuel of the plant, water deficit may—as above—modify cellular activity via an effect on organelle or enzyme function caused by a change in chemical potential or solute concentration (Weatherley, 1970, 1976). Such cellular effects are currently speculative. Abscisic acid and proline accumulation are both possible end results of this type of cellular effect, and are discussed in Section IV. On an organism level, however, plants are known to alter their distribution of daily photosynthate in response to changes in water availability. Passioura (1976) and Passioura and Ashford (1974) discuss how a wheat plant influences its long-term water status by the way it partitions its assimilate (i.e., labile energy storage) between shoot and root. Hurd (1974) shows that selection of wheat for high yield under moisture stress is also selection for larger root systems. This can be interpreted as the result of an increased fraction of the labile energy being supplied to the root in times of water stress.

The third stage at which water controls energy flow through the plant is structural. Water is essential to both tissue expansion (growth) and, in most cases, structural rigidity (turgor). Many have discussed the relationships between tissue water potential, solute potential, matric potential, and turgor pressure in relation to expansive growth and turgor maintenance (for example, see Acock, 1975; Barrs, 1968; Barrs and Kramer, 1969; Boyer, 1967, 1969; Burström, 1965; Hsiao et al., 1976; Weatherley, 1970; and Section IV,A,1). In mature leaves where turgor maintenance is of primary importance, water will affect solar energy flow in at least two ways. First, as turgor is lost, structural integrity is impaired and the plant may be subject to increased mechanical damage due to wind or other factors. Second, as water stress increases, the chance of cavitation occurring in xylem vessels increases. Salisbury and Ross (1969, p. 128) suggest that larger vessels are inherently more prone to cavitate. Newman (1976) also discusses these possibilities and suggests that if bubbles occur randomly, they would be most common in the widest vessels that carry the largest volume of water. As he points out, the loss of function of the largest vessels decreases water flow to an extent proportionately greater than the cross-sectional area affected. This is because the conductivity to longitudinal volume flow is a function of the fourth power of the radius of the xylem vessel, while cross-sectional area is a second-power function of the radius. As the largest xylem vessels lose the ability to carry water, resistance to water flow to a particular leaf or part of the plant will increase dramatically. For a given atmospheric evaporative demand, a leaf in this condition might be unable to maintain a flow rate to keep leaf water potential (Ψ_w) at a high value, the Ψ_w would drop below that level needed to maintain viability, and the leaf would die. It is possible that in cereal leaves that die back from the tip rather than abscise, this process could be one means of controlling leaf surface area during water stress. The phenomenon of cereal leaf dieback from the tip toward the base during water stress has been discussed by Hanson et al. (1977) and by Kozlowski (1976). (Could dieback represent a controlled loss of transpiring surface during water stress with the regulatory mechanism being a variable xylem vessel diameter?) From the discussion of leaf shedding by Kozlowski (1976) there seems little doubt that this phenomenon is a means of controlling transpiration as well as plant water status in many species during water stress.

In young, growing tissue there are additional structural effects of water stress besides those described above for mature tissue. Effects of water stress on growing tissue are well documented (e.g., Boyer, 1969, 1970, 1974; Bunce, 1977; Campbell, 1974; Cleland, 1967; Hsiao, 1973; Hsiao et al., 1976; Ritchie, 1974). In general, growth by cell enlargement is considered to be the plant process most sensitive to water stress. Since leaf growth and increased leaf surface area are a direct means of increasing solar energy capture, water deficit effects on growth directly control total energy flow through the plant.

Two additional points should be made concerning Fig. 8. First, note that energy flow is used to further increase the flow of energy through the plant. The easiest way to envision this is to consider that solar energy is used to make more leaves, which can then intercept an increased amount of solar energy, which then flows through the plant making more leaves in a continuously growing loop (Good and Bell, Ch. 1, this volume). If all environmental growth controllers are in plentiful supply (water, nutrients, etc.), energy flow to growth will at first proceed exponentially [until halted by genetic factors, or until photosynthetic energy inputs are matched by maintenance and other energy costs (H. T. Odum, 1971)]. This is an example of positive feedback in a plant system. The concepts of system building and maintenance by energy flows, positive feedback loops, and competition for available energy between systems cannot be covered here, and the interested reader is directed to Morowitz (1968), H. T. Odum (1971), Odum and Odum (1976), and E. P. Odum (1971, Chap. 3).

Second, the respiration (maintenance) branch of the energy flow from the labile energy storage could be shown as feeding back to all parts of the plant. Respiratory maintenance performs the function of keeping an ordered state orderly against the tendency of all ordered states to decay toward disorder (Morowitz, 1968; H. T. Odum, 1971; Odum and Odum, 1976), and thus could be shown as an input to all energy storage in the plant.

C. Decision Points in Plant Development in Relation to Water Stress

1. Examples of Decision Points

The majority of crop plants are grown as annuals and, like all annuals, have a relatively long period of growth before they set seed. That is, annuals invest the energy acquired during a growing season into a single payoff; this sequence has been left more or less unchanged during the evolution of cereal crops from their wild annual progenitors. The payoff is, of course, genetic survival through viable seed. If, for any reason, the parent plant does not survive and set seed, that particular fraction of the gene pool is lost from the population.

Few higher plants, and no crops, are capable of surviving severe desiccation (except at the seed stage). The homeohydric nature of crops is a major constraint on reaching the goal of genetic survival. Because crops must control their water status at high levels and within narrow limits to maintain viability, they must have a genetic memory of the water availability patterns of the environment in which they evolved. This genetic memory would consist of the responses of the plant to water stress encoded in the genetic material as a result of selection pressures over evolutionary time, and is probably most important in environments in which water becomes progressively less available as the growing season advances. Crops grown in areas of ample rainfall throughout the growing season may have no need to "remember" about long-term water availability, or the memory may indicate that water availability is always adequate. Dryland crops, however, which sometimes grow exclusively on stored soil moisture, may be completely dependent on this genetic memory of water availability for successful seed set.

Plants continually face times when they must make decisions for future growth and development based on currently available information. They must take stock of their current situation and plan their energy budgets for the future. Campbell (1974) discusses the ability of a wheat crop to determine early in the season how much moisture is available and, on this basis, to adjust the number of heads (i.e., the maximum number of viable seeds) per unit land area. Passioura (1976) describes how the dual root system of temperate cereals can exercise control, based on available water, on the rate of growth of the shoot. When water is available such that the upper soil is wet, nodal roots develop and provide ample water to the shoot, resulting in rapid growth. When the upper soil is dry, little or no nodal root growth takes place, and the few deeply penetrating seminal roots supply subsoil stored water to the shoot. In this case, the high resistance to flow in the seminal roots is thought to cause first a slight drop in leaf water potential, thus decreasing stomatal aperture. This in turn reduces both CO_2 uptake and the flow of water through the plant resulting in slowed growth. Passioura points out that such a plant does not show obvious symptoms of water stress (i.e., wilting or leaf death); it is only smaller.

Through small size the plant controls its water status and the use of stored ground water.

The importance of each decision point in the life cycle can be loosely viewed as being proportional to the observed sensitivity to a stress episode occurring while that decision is being made. Campbell, (1974), Jensen (1968), Ritchie (1974), and Slatyer (1969) discuss the effects on yield of stresses at various stages in the growth of crop plants. Based on their discussions, Fig. 9 shows the effect on the yield of a hypothetical cereal crop when water stress is experienced at different times in its development. The relative yields are intended only to indicate, and not to quantify, the impact of a stress at the various growth stages. The specific mechanisms by which a crop assesses water availability at each growth stage are not well understood, but the effects of these assessments become apparent in grain yield. Jensen's discussion (1968) includes simple models for yield of determinate and indeterminate crops. Taking actual water use divided by water use if soil water is not limiting for three growth stages, and a power function relating growth stage and susceptibility to water stress, he models the effect of stress on yield for sorghum with good results. He points out that stress effects on yield can be multiplicative for determinate crops (such as a grain crop),

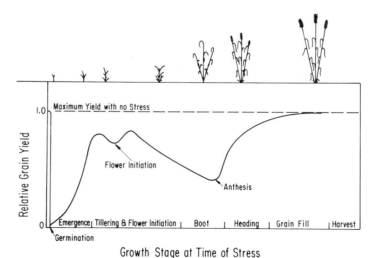

Fig. 9.   Relative reduction of yield due to an episode of water stress at various growth stages of a hypothetical grain crop. Yield changes are not meant to be quantitative, but only indicative of the effects of stress at each growth stage. General curve constructed from data and discussions of Campbell (1974), Day and Thompson (1975), Jensen (1968), Ritchie (1974), and Slatyer (1969).

and that economic yield may not be linearly related to total water use if stress conditions are encountered. His model demonstrates the need to know susceptibility to stress at the decision points and can be expanded to more than three growth stages.

Jensen designates the boot to milk stage as the most sensitive growth stage (i.e., the decision point) for sorghum. In a more general sense, Ritchie (1974) concludes that crop plants are most sensitive when reproductive organs are formed and when pollination occurs. For wheat, Campbell (1974) discusses two stages of critical importance. One is the jointing stage, when the decision is made as to how many tillers will be kept to produce heads, and the other is the boot stage, when the plant decides how many kernel positions per head to produce. Although stress later in development can result in shrunken kernels, this problem is partially or even wholly reversible if the stress is short. Slatyer (1969) reviews data for several cereals and concludes that damage is greatest when any tissue is in a stage of rapid development and growth; this would include floral initiation, anthesis, and fertilization.

2. Flexibility after Decision Points

Because water stress can be a short-term or intermittent problem, it would be advantageous to have as much flexibility or plasticity in yield components as possible after each decision is passed. (For definitions of yield components in cereals, see Table I). At the tissue or organ level, Campbell (1974) depicts wheat as "producing more tillers than it will actually use, producing more flowers than it expects to fertilize and producing more positions for kernels on the head than it produces kernels." If stress is encountered or becomes more severe in the future, unused parts will abort. This overinitiation at each stage could be considered somewhat wasteful, but it allows for the maximum number of possibilities at future decision points if conditions improve (Adams, 1967). Slatyer (1969) also discusses the developmental plasticity of cereals at several stages. He quotes evidence of others to state that in barley, if stress at floral initiation is mild and relatively brief, upon relief of stress floral initiation rate is more rapid than in controls. The stressed plant can catch up so that yield is little reduced. Sorghum displayed plasticity when stress was imposed during floral initiation, apparently delaying the completion of initiation for about 10 days until the stress was relieved. Sorghum also showed the ability to withstand stress after floral initiation was completed. Stress resistance was achieved by ceasing inflorescence elongation during the period of stress (14, 24, and 28 days), then continuing elongation after stress relief, with flower emergence taking place 10, 24, and 30 days later than the controls, respectively. For wheat and possibly oats, Slatyer (like Campbell) points to the variable number of florets per spikelet as an aspect of plasticity. Tillering also adds to plasticity at decision points, primarily because flowering of tillers is progressive over time and thus can protect a plant from short periods of water stress. This may be particularly important, since anthesis and fertilization have little plasticity due to their brief, sensitive nature. Day and Thompson (1975) demonstrated plasticity in four barley varieties by withholding irrigation water at three growth stages (jointing, flowering, and late grainfill) in the field. Grain yield was not significantly different from the controls for any treatment in three of the four cultivars. The barley demonstrated plasticity through varying the number of heads per unit land area, number of seeds per head, seed weight, and by altering the numbers of days required to reach maturity.

Flexibility at the cellular level is another option open to plants (see Sections IV,A,1 and 2). In this connection, Weatherley (1970) discusses two hypothetical cells, one with a high elastic modulus, the other with a low modulus. At a given water potential (Ψ_w) below full turgor, the stiff cell (high elastic modulus) will have a smaller change in cell volume (i.e., less concentration of solutes), but will lose more turgor than the cell with the low elastic modulus. This stretchy cell (low elastic modulus) will maintain more turgidity, but will have its solutes more concentrated since the cell volume change is greater. The stiff cell is subject to mechanical or physical damage due to loss of turgor, while the stretchy cell is possibly more prone to adverse effects on the function of enzymes or organelles due to the greater decrease in its osmotic potential. Weatherley concludes that the cell that will sustain more damage will depend on the "physiological importance of the displacements involved." He is, of course, correct, but from the data to be considered in Section IV,A,2 one might infer that as water becomes limiting, turgor maintenance may be in general more important to the plant. Data from Elston *et al.* (1976) appear to support this conclusion. They show that the change in turgor pressure divided by the change in relative water content is lowest in beans grown in the driest field conditions. That is, the turgor pressure change for a given change in water content is less in plants grown in water stress conditions, presumably due to changes in cell wall properties.

D. Sensing, Control, and Feedback in Plant–Water Relations

Positive feedback was introduced in the section on energy flow through plants (Section III,B). Implicit in the topic of decision points in growth and control of plant water status (Section III,C) is the idea of negative feedback. The investigation of plant control systems and feedback loops has only recently begun, despite their universal occurrence. Because the concepts involved have increasingly broad application, they are reviewed briefly below, drawing on the atypically simple example of turgor control in giant algae. In almost all other plant processes the situation remains far more ethereal. More detailed treatments of control theory in biology are given by Cram (1976), Jones (1973), and Toates (1975).

In simple control systems, one possible desired end is homeostasis. The maintenance of the output from the system at a constant level in the face of perturbations from within and from without that system is the goal in this case. Figure 10 shows the components of a simple negative feedback control system. 1. The reference or desired value that is the input to the whole system. 2. The sensor (or transducer) that compares the desired value and the output value. The negative sign on the feedback loop at the sensor indicates that the output value is subtracted from the input (reference) value. 3. The output from the sensor (transducer) is termed the error signal and is an indication of how different the desired value and the actual value are. 4. The error signal is the input to an effector (or transfer function), which performs an action in some way proportional to the error signal. 5. The output of the effector is the output signal or actual state of the system. 6. A feedback loop connects the output value and the sensor so that the sensor may perform its function of comparing the desired value and actual system output.

If the output is not equal to the desired value, the system will tend to correct the situation; the larger the error signal, the stronger the reaction of the system. If the output is less than the desired value, the error signal will be positive and the output will be increased. Conversely, if

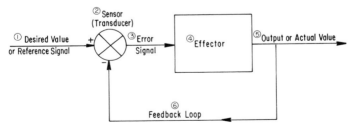

Fig. 10. A simple, negative feedback control system. (1) desired value, (2) sensor, (3) error signal, (4) effector, (5) output value, and (6) feedback loop are described in the text. The feedback loop will tend to correct fluctuations in output value back toward the desired value.

the output is greater than the desired value, the error signal will be negative and the output will decrease. Note that the actual input to the effector is the error signal. That is, the effector acts on the amount the system output is in error from the desired value and not on the desired value itself.

Gutknecht (1968) and Hastings and Gutknecht (1974) describe what appears to be a negative feedback control system in giant algal cells (*Valonia*). The goal of this system is maintenance of a constant turgor potential (Ψ_p). (See Section IV,A,1 for a discussion of water potential parameters.) These cells are often exposed to varying osmotic potentials in the aqueous medium that will affect turgor. The desired turgor pressure is apparently maintained in the cell by controlling the osmotic potential (Ψ_s) of the vacuole at a level about 1 to 1.5 bars more negative than Ψ_s for the external medium. The lower Ψ_s inside the cell causes water to passively move into the cell down a water potential gradient. As water moves into the cell, the protoplast swells and presses against the cell wall until a Ψ_p of +1 to 1.5 bars is generated to exactly offset the difference in Ψ. If the external osmotic potential is now lowered, water will tend to flow out of the cell, and Ψ_p will drop below the desired level. After a time delay of about 20 to 30 mins, active ion uptake is increased to adjust the Ψ_s of the vacuole below that of the altered medium. Once again, water will flow into the cell and reestablish the Ψ_p of 1 to 1.5 bars. Conversely, if the external solution is then diluted, so that water flows into the cell causing Ψ_p to increase above 1 to 1.5 bars, the active ion uptake will decrease below a level required to counter the ion leakage out through the membrane. Vacuolar ion concentration will now decrease, water will flow out of the cell, Ψ_p will return to the desired value, and the ion uptake rate will again be increased to offset membrane leakage and maintain Ψ_p at 1 to 1.5 bars. In this example, the desired value is the 1.5 bars of turgor pressure, the output is actual turgor pressure (a function of the difference between the medium Ψ_s and the vacuolar Ψ_s), and the effector is the net rate of active ion uptake (i.e., rate of active ion flow into the cell minus membrane leakage rate). The nature of the sensor or transducer is unknown, but it is hypothesized to be located at the plasmalemma–cell wall interface. There, it transforms a change in Ψ_p into a signal (error signal). The error signal itself is also unknown but, based on the apparent time delay of 20 to 30 mins, may be chemical in nature. Note that this system can respond only to slow changes in medium osmotic potential, on a time scale of hours.

In his review of stomatal control, Raschke (1975) describes a more complex system that appears to involve at least one CO_2 negative feedback loop and three H_2O control loops (two negative feedback and one open-loop control). He also describes the effects of light level and temperature changes on these control systems. Because time delays exist in these systems, oscillations in stomatal aperture are predicted to occur and have been observed (see Barrs, 1971; Cowan, 1972; Raschke, 1970). Such oscillations are inherent in real control systems, and many investigators have taken them as signs of instability in the biological systems being considered. Raschke (1975) and Cowan (1972) suggest, however, that oscillations may sometimes be advantageous. They may aid in more quickly adjusting stomatal aperture to optimal values. These optimal values themselves change for two related reasons. First, the goals of high CO_2 concentration in the leaf and low water loss from the leaf are always at odds. Second, CO_2 entry and transpiration are differentially affected by changes in environmental parameters. In other words, oscillations may serve to optimize CO_2–H_2O input–output ratios.

Control systems exist in all biological processes. Toates (1975) discusses several control systems that exist in animal physiology. H. T. Odum (1971) and Odum and Odum (1976) discuss control systems as they relate to ecology. In plant physiology, models on water movement have appeared that relate to control theory implicitly (Boyer, 1974; Fiscus, 1975; Gutknecht, 1968; Hastings and Gutknecht, 1974) or explicitly (Cowan, 1972; Raschke, 1966). In general, control theory will apply to any study of the phenotypic changes undergone by plants as they adapt to growth in stress conditions. The general phenomenon of stress hardening (see Boussiba et al., 1975; Carceller and Soriano, 1972; Hegarty, 1970; Henckel, 1964) suggests that plants sense changing conditions and may generate error signals that can change the system output or reference value, or can cause a switch to a new control system, thus affecting growth temporarily or permanently.

E. Strategies and Goals in Plant–Water Relations

1. Examples of Strategies and Goals

The controls discussed above are essentially tactics by which the plant attains its goals, the most important goal being genetic survival. In order to guide the tactical control systems and associated adaptive changes, natural selection must have caused plants to develop strategies during evolution. Recently, Passioura (1976) has discussed plant strategies and goals from the standpoint of water availability. He recognizes that strategies and goals cover an enormous range of time scales, and suggests that short-term strategies imply lesser goals, and long-term strategies imply greater goals. Table IV combines and expands his Tables I and II, and relates time scale to environmental process or stress, plant strategy, and possible plant goal. An example of a short-term strategy implying a lesser goal is regulation of leaf turgor by stomata. Closing stomata can result in turgor maintenance during drought stress, but extended closure and negative carbon balance will obviously be antagonistic to the long-term goal of genetic survival. Therefore, turgor maintenance during long-term stress is probably accomplished by shedding leaves or by an alteration in the shoot–root ratio.

Plant strategies come in many forms. Avoidance of stress can be seen in plants that may emerge, flower, and set seed during brief periods of water availability. Certain annuals avoid cold or water stress by their chosen life cycle. Desert annuals practice water stress avoidance to the extreme; viable seeds germinate after a heavy rain and complete their life cycle in the very short time during which moisture is available (E. P. Odum, 1971). Kozlowski (1976) discusses several species that combat water stress by losing, and then regrowing, some or all leaves as stress is imposed and then relieved. Hurd (1974) discusses deep rooting and root–shoot ratios as they relate to water availability in cereals, as do Passioura and Ashford (1974). However, Hurd (1974) and Ferguson *et al.* (1970) point out that little is known about root growth as a strategy for surviving water stress. Ehleringer *et al.* (1976) discuss increasing leaf pubescence and decreasing leaf size in desert shrubs as a means of providing a more favorable energy balance as stress is increased seasonally. Regulation of leaf size, number, color, and thickness, as well as cuticular characteristics, are all strategies that plants can use to adapt to changes in environmental conditions. Raschke (1960), D. M. Gates (1968), and Poljakoff-Mayber and Gale (1972) discuss energy balances, leaf temperature, and transpiration in relation to leaf size and other factors. Hurd (1976) discusses leaf rolling as a strategy for the reduction of transpiration during stress. He also suggests that, for wheat and barley, awns appear to have a multiple role in increasing grain yield during drought stress, as was already discussed in Section II,B,1,b.

The use of these and other strategies probably increases the environmental range in which a species may live. The expression of a specific adaptive strategy is the result of genotype–environment interactions, with the adaptive limits set by the genotype and the actual expression determined by the environment. Bradshaw (1974) discusses phenotypic plasticity in fluctuating environments. If environmental changes occur slowly relative to generation times, the changes will

TABLE IV
Environmental Input and Plant Strategy Time Scales in Relation to Importance of Plant Goal[a]

Time scale	Environmental conditions	Plant strategy	Possible goal
Seconds to hours	Cloud cover changes Wind speed changes Rain or irrigation	Stomatal adjustments Changes in hydraulic resistances	Turgor maintenance Optimization of transpiration ratio (H_2O_{out}/CO_{2in})
Hours	Diurnal changes in evaporative demand	Stomatal adjustments Geometric adjustments (photonasty, rolling)	Reduction of water loss to minimum, particularly under conditions of little or no photosynthesis
Days to weeks	Rundown in soil water Day length changes	Cellular conditioning (hardening) Root and shoot growth (relative and actual) Alteration of leaf area ($\uparrow$ or $\downarrow$) Morphological and/or physiological changes	Maintenance of plant water status Maximum solar energy capture Alteration of energy distribution at proper time to new process (e.g., flowering)
Weeks to months	Seasonal evaporative demand Seasonal water supply Total growing season insolation	Growth habit (e.g., leaf number and size, leaf area duration, length of life cycle, viable seed number)	Maximum genetic survival

[a] Environmental input time scales compared with plant strategy time scales and theoretical plant goals. Except for genetic survival, real plant goals are hypothetical. Short-term environmental inputs are associated with short-term strategies and lesser goals; long-term inputs, with long-term strategies and goals.

have a selective pressure on the gene pool and will result in an adaptive response that closely follows these changes (e.g., annual life habit). However, if environmental fluctuations occur rapidly with respect to generation time, selection for increased phenotypic plasticity (wide adaptability) will be the result. If fluctuations are high, plasticity will be high; if fluctuations are low, plasticity will be low.

2. A Dilemma—Adaptability versus Maximum Yield Potential

Viewed from the above standpoint it is probable that few crop varieties grown in the developed countries today retain very wide adaptability. As the amount of irrigation, herbicides, pesticides, fertilization, and cultivation increases, the environment encountered by the crop fluctuates less and increasingly tends toward an optimum, stable environment. This control over environmental fluctuations has made possible the development of varieties selected for maximum economic yield. The question arises though, as to how much of the gain in yield potential has been achieved through a reduction in adaptability. The total insolation on a field over a growing season is fairly constant. If all other conditions for growth are ideal, the energy flowing through the plant will be at a maximum (see Fig. 8). This maximum value will flow into structure and maintenance, and a maximum yield (part of the structure) will be realized. If conditions are held near optimal levels for many generations, can the fraction of energy channeled into desired structure (i.e., economic yield) be increased by selection that reduces the fraction of the total energy that flows into structure or maintenance and is not needed as long as conditions are optimal? Consider a situation where a fraction of the maximum energy available went to the production of a chemical or structural component that enabled the plant to outcompete a second plant or to resist the attack of a pathogen or insect. The environment is then manipulated to remove the competition and/or pest and the now unnecessary energy drain is bred consciously or unconsciously out of the plant, increasing the fraction of the energy partitioned to the desired yield structure. Pictured this way, it is probably advantageous to control environmental perturbations and undesirable effects of competition, disease, and pests so that the fraction of the total energy flowing to the desired economic yield can be truly maximized by complete removal of all unnecessary structural and maintenance pathways (energy costs). Of course, this hypothetical higher-yielding plant would quickly succumb to environmental stresses that were again allowed to come to bear on it, resulting in yield reduction to a level below that of its original parent. Such may be the case with the dwarf wheat and rice varieties of the Green Revolution. These crops were specifically bred for short stature to prevent lodging under high-fertility, irrigated conditions. The shortening of the straw and reduction in the numbers of lower leaves gave rise to a significant increase in economic yield (Arnon, 1972b; MacKey, 1973); this yield increase might be viewed as resulting from increased partitioning of energy to the grain at the expense of vegetative structure. Dwarf varieties tend to have less extensive root systems, possibly because of the reduction in the number of lower leaves that supply assimilates to the root (MacKey, 1973); this increases the susceptibility of such varieties to water stress and low soil fertility regimes. In addition, the short stature and reduction of basal leaves reduce the ability of dwarf types to compete with weeds, and make more rigorous weed control essential (Jennings, 1976). It is thus apparent that dwarf varieties tend to be inherently more prone than tall varieties to drought and to weed infestations when energy-subsidized control of the environment (irrigation and herbicide application) is relaxed. This may reflect the results of breeding for maximum energy flow to economic yield at the expense of energy flow to advantageous vegetative structure.

General energetic principles indicate the above manipulations are possible for a given energy flow; reduction of energy costs in one component of a system increases the energy available for a second. Yield might be increased at the cost of wide adaptability. How applicable this situation is to the real world has not been defined, but it should be. Because of the complexities of a whole plant (for examples, see Minchin and Pate, 1973; Penning de Vries, 1975), complete studies of energy flow and distribution are not available. However, those individuals studying adaptability in plant breeding hint at the answer. Reitz (1974) states that "In many cases, survival of periods of [water] stress is the key to the success of the species, and this may lead to characteristics negatively correlated with productiveness." Olien (1974), in a discussion on winter hardiness in cereals, concludes that "Breeders seem to select against these components [of hardiness] in developing other needed characteristics such as high yield" Finlay and Wilkinson (1963) conclude that "a breeding program designed to produce a variety with still higher mean yield over all environments will almost certainly fall short of the ideal, but as yet there is no way of predicting what sort of compromise will be reached between yield potential and phenotypic stability."

Conceptually, crop yield increases in response to selection may have resulted from three distinct manipulations of energy flow. First, yield increases may have resulted from increased *total* energy flow through the plant, thus more closely approaching a potential maximum. Second, increases may have been realized by shutting off the energy flow to adaptive features without the genetic loss of such features. Third, adaptive features may have been deliberately or incidentally bred out of the gene pool. If yield increases are a result of this third manipulation, a return to a less controlled, less stable environment could be difficult if the return is desired, or disastrous if the return is unplanned.

F. Illustrative Models of Plant Strategies to Survive Water Stress

1. Descriptions of Model Strategies

To define any one of the myriad strategies that plants have developed to achieve their goals in the face of water stress is a formidable task. The approach outlined earlier (Section III,B), in which water is viewed as one controller of energy flow through the plant, is complicated by interactions involving other controlling factors in the leaf, stem, and root. Just within the leaf, the close interrelationships between water use, CO_2 assimilation, leaf temperature, air temperature, nutrient and hormone delivery, nitrogen metabolism, and respiration are apparent. Others could be added to this list of interdependent functions. Despite this complexity, some simplified examples will be presented to clarify the types of strategy open to plants for surviving periods of water stress. Five situations, including an unstressed control, are considered. They can be viewed as ranging from short-term to long-term strategies for survival under water stress. The energy flow concepts presented in Fig. 8 will be used and enlarged upon. One day's photosynthate (labile energy storage) will be considered to be on hand at stress initiation for use by the plant. This energy store will be called the relative energy reserve (RER), 100% being the labile energy storage in viable tissue in well-watered conditions. Variations in viable leaf surface area (VLSA) will be the increases or decreases occurring in viable leaf surface area in the situation being considered. Strategies will be treated in a nonoverlapping fashion, but it is obvious that real plants may use more than one strategy, or may shift strategies at different growth stages. Figure 11 shows a simplification of Fig. 8 with values added to represent energy flow (in kcal m^{-2} day^{-1}). (An approximation of 4.5 kcal/g dry wt can be used to convert to structure for terrestrial plants.) These energy values are realistic for a crop grown in the temperate zone (E. P. Odum, 1971, pp. 39, 42, and 44). Unless otherwise indicated, for each strategy considered, the water stress imposed is assumed to be severe

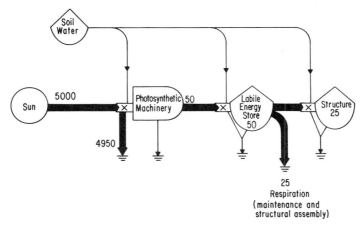

Fig. 11. A simplified diagram of solar energy flow for a well-watered crop. Figure 8 has been simplified and energy values have been added for insolation, gross photosynthesis, respiration, and net photosynthesis. Numerical values, derived from E. P. Odum (1971), are in kcal m^{-2} day^{-1}. Energy losses associated with the work gates and with depreciation from the storage tanks are ignored.

enough to reduce assimilation to 10% of the well-watered value, primarily by stomatal closure (i.e., from 50 to 5 kcal m^{-2} day^{-1}). Since respiration costs also include energy to assemble new structures as well as to maintain existing ones, in situations where growth stops, respiration rates will arbitrarily be reduced by 20% (from 25 to 20 kcal m^{-2} day^{-1}). Unless otherwise indicated, stomata are considered either open or closed, with no intermediate values possible. Finally, leaf temperature effects and other consequences of reduced transpiration are ignored. Schematic plants are drawn in Fig. 12 to give a qualitative impression of each situation.

In the well-watered control (Fig. 12A), relative energy reserve will remain at 100% and the viable leaf surface area will increase linearly in this model.

Figure 12B depicts a plant whose strategy is based on a genetic memory that indicates that any water stress encountered is likely to be very short (e.g., on the order of a noon-day wilt). The strategy here is to shut the stomata to retain (or recover) turgidity, and to wait out the situation until water uptake by the root is again sufficient to supply transpiration requirements. During the water stress, the plant lives off the labile energy storage, keeping total viable leaf surface area at 100% until the stress has passed. This plant has the ability to use all its labile storage for maintenance energy costs, but not to mobilize reserves from other

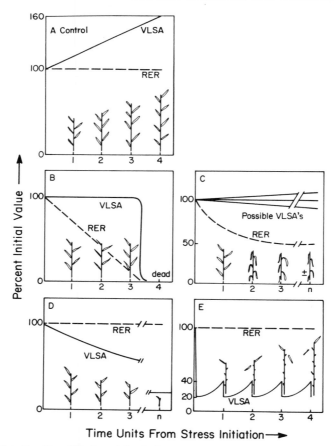

Fig. 12A to E. Simplified models of plant strategies to combat water stress. Except in the well-watered control (model A), stress is imposed in all models at time = 0. Plant responses are determined by strategies based on genetically programmed expectations of short stress only (model B) through prolonged stress (model E). RER is the relative energy reserve (% change in the labile energy storage where the well-watered, nonstressed value = 100%). VLSA is the viable leaf surface area increase or decrease as a percent of the area at time = 0. Schematic plants visually demonstrate various responses as described in the text.

structural material. If growth stops, and stress is long, its energy reserve of 50 kcal/m² will last 3.3 time units (days in this case) [−20 kcal (respiration) + 5 kcal (photosynthesis) = −15 kcal m⁻² day⁻¹; 50/15 = 3.3 days]. At the end of that time, its leaf viability will fall sharply to zero, due to its inability to initiate any other strategy. If stress is short (i.e., less than 3.3 time units), it will be ready to resume rapid growth

with maximum leaf surface area still available. Relative energy reserves, which had been declining steadily, will rise to 100% and
maximum growth will then be resumed. Recently emerged seedlings
tend to show strategies of this type. Seedlings have poorly developed
roots, a limited labile energy supply (especially if seed reserves are
small), and no other reserves to mobilize (e.g., from root, leaf, or stem
storage); they can withstand only fairly short stresses.

The plant of Fig. 12C has a strategy for handling water stresses of
somewhat longer duration than those that B can survive. In this example, the stomatal apparatus is capable of controlled partial closure,
without shutting completely. As a result, during water stress leaf water
potential (Ψ_w) will decrease to a level commensurate with the new flow
rates (transpiration), resistances to water flow, and soil water potentials. The model assumes that stomatal and nonstomatal effects cut
photosynthesis by 50% when stress is imposed. Some turgor is maintained by an osmotic potential in the leaf still lower than the new Ψ_w
(this could involve osmotic adjustment at some metabolic cost). The
new assimilation rate of 25 kcal m^{-2} day^{-1} is just able to offset the
original maintenance costs. Many scenarios can be envisioned for this
"cliff-hanger." Cessation of growth would free the respiratory flux of 5
kcal m^{-2} day^{-1} associated with structural assembly. This energy flow
could be rechannelled, possibly for some resumption of root growth to
increase water uptake. A second possibility is that the 5 kcal could go
toward a resumption of slow total growth [see data of Boyer (1970) and
Hsiao *et al.* (1976)]. Of course, reduced leaf water potential might at
some point become detrimental, causing increased respiration resulting
in zero or negative assimilation (negative carbon balance). If the balance
goes negative, the labile energy storage will decay toward zero and leaf
area will be lost. Experimental data on respiratory behavior during
water stress are scarce. Boyer (1970) reports that respiration decreases
during water stress in corn, soybean, and sunflower. Hsiao (1973), discussing respiration and water stress, concludes that the respiratory
response is ill defined, since increases and decreases have been reported. In the strategy of Fig. 12C the plant attempts to continue photosynthesis at reduced rates to keep some energy reserves available for
the maintenance of vital parts, at the cost of lowered leaf water potential and at the risk of loss of some photosynthetic area due to desiccation, or to some other problem associated with trying to operate at low
Ψ_w and/or low turgor. This plant maintains some part of VLSA longer
than does B, but it will eventually succumb if stress worsens or is
extended. Note that the RER in C is shown as decaying to 50% of the
original value. This is a response to the change in input to the labile

storage (a change in the assimilation rate). This type of strategy could be very widespread since the options available are many, depend on stress level, and may include osmotic adaptation (Hsiao *et al.*, 1976), cell wall changes (Bunce, 1977; Hsiao *et al.*, 1976) and the other physiological changes involved in drought hardening (Boussiba *et al.*, 1975; Henckel, 1964). Possible real examples of this strategy are given by Boyer (1970). Data from the International Rice Research Institute (1975) for upland rice show that a variety (Saovina) that had apparently poor stomatal control was the only cultivar of several that exhibited severe drought-stress symptoms in a field trial that survived. In this case it is possible that those rice varieties with good stomatal control starved to death, as envisioned in example 12B.

In the strategy of Fig. 12D, the plant recognizes some signal of on-coming water stress and alters its development accordingly. Photosynthesis is reduced (to the arbitrary 5 kcal m^{-2} day^{-1}), and leaf senescence begins in an orderly fashion such that nutrients are salvaged and translocated to growing points, storage areas, and other viable tissue. A steady reduction in leaf and transpiring areas occurs, but the remaining viable parts of the plant are held at a relatively high water status. The relative energy reserve of those viable parts is maintained at 100% by the prolonged use of the limited water, and by the supply of nutrients from the senescing leaves. The mobilization and redistribution of nutrients allows an increased life span of the vital parts of the plant, e.g., the meristems, some roots, and possibly some leaf area. Strategies of this type have been developed by plants in areas where rainfall is low or comes only at one season, such as semiarid grasslands and tropical savannas (see E. P. Odum, 1971, pp. 388–392). Many grasses and cereal crops have evolved in these ecosystems and may exhibit strategies of this type. The strategy of closing the stomata and hanging on, slowly shedding leaves, while waiting for rain, is described by Passioura (1976) in his discussion on the control of water flow in cereals. This strategy does have the drawback of provoking loss of some photosynthetic area rather quickly through planned senescence. Overreaction by the plant will occur if stress is short but, in the climatic conditions in which such a plant evolved, a reduction in transpiring surface to reduce water loss is more important, in general, than maintenance of total photosynthetic area (which can be replaced when water again becomes freely available).

Plants used to desert conditions of prolonged drought or perpetual low levels of water availability have usually developed radical strategies in order to survive. Fig. 12E shows a hypothetical plant that sheds all but the youngest leaf as water becomes limiting. The plant then maintains its water status by dropping each older leaf as a new one emerges, keeping up *slow* growth while limiting water use. Total viable leaf surface area under stress may fluctuate between something like 20% and 40% if the total number of leaves under favorable conditions arbitrarily equals 5, while relative energy reserve stays at 100% for the limited leaf area retained. Size of the leaf, as well as volume and cuticular characteristics, can also become important. Kozlowski (1976) discusses some desert species that have strategies that resemble the one described here. This strategy differs from 12D in that older tissue is continually replaced by young tissue and some of the available solar energy is always used (the solar energy flow through D will approach zero as the above-ground material totally senesces). The plant of Fig. 12E always anticipates limited water availability and can fine-tune its leaf area to make full use of what little water is available.

2. *Implications of Models for Real Plant Situations*

1. The relationship between strategy time scales and importance of goals (Passioura, 1976) is clearly very significant. Control of water status via stomatal closure is quick and advantageous if water deficit lasts for hours, but if stress lasts for days its usefulness in achieving the major goal has been lost. Passioura (1976) voices concern that major attention has been focused on short-term strategies at the cost of investigating slower, but possibly more important, long-term strategies such as control of leaf area. He feels that the long-term control mechanisms, which sense and integrate the short-term inputs and responses, thus guiding the total system towards its major goal, are the least understood and most important strategies of the plant.

2. The possibility that a tradeoff exists between adaptability and maximum growth or yield must be considered from the viewpoint of plant strategies. A plant bred for maximum yield under favorable conditions might stubbornly refuse to lose photosynthetic area if prolonged stress did occur. Leaf area has a positive feedback effect on assimilation rate (see Fig. 8), and any tendency to lose leaf area might lead to a decrease in maximum yield potential, the already established goal of this plant. Conversely, a plant adapted to handle drought situations may elect to begin losing leaf area at the first signs of stress. This latter strategy may help control water availability and/or plant water status, and aid in survival through a prolonged stress. With the return of favorable conditions, replacement of leaf area could then occur. Such a tendency to overreact may limit the maximum yield potential under generally favorable conditions, but it would be of benefit in suboptimal situations.

3. How do these strategies tie in with the different but related concepts of drought resistance and water use efficiency (or its inverse, transpiration ratio)? The strategies B to E described here are arranged in order of increasing drought resistance, which we take as the ability to survive and set seed in conditions of limited water availability. Strategy B is susceptible and succumbs quickly. Strategy C tries to cope but is susceptible at some level of stress due to decreasing Ψ_w. At the first signs of stress, D begins to mobilize its defenses to protect at least parts of itself at the expense of some amount of leaf area. It does not grow during stress, but it does not die either. Strategy E continues to survive and even grow and reproduce in the harshest environment. No mention has been made of water use efficiency. It must be remembered that water use efficiency is the ratio of carbon fixed to water lost through evapotranspiration (Reitz, 1974). Defined as such, it may have little or no bearing on resistance or susceptibility to water stress. Like any ratio, water use efficiency can be raised or lowered by changing the amount of carbon fixed, water used, or both values in the same direction or in opposite directions. As Ritchie (1974) points out, once leaf area index approaches or exceeds 3 in conditions of ample water supply, water use approaches potential evapotranspiration and any crop uses essentially the same amount of water. In dryland conditions, it is the timing of peak water demand and the ability to survive drought, not water use efficiency, that determines which crops can be grown (Viets, 1971). The ability to make large amounts of dry weight per unit of water used is only useful if ample water is available, or if vegetative growth is held sufficiently in check to permit attainment of the major goal of reproduction. In CAM (crassulacean acid metabolism) plants, a high water use efficiency is usually tempered by a slow growth rate. In corn, a water use-efficient C_4 plant, no such tempering exists, and as a result corn is a rather drought-sensitive crop (Reitz, 1974; Viets, 1971). Evolution has endowed the CAM plant (as well as some C_4 and C_3 plants) with a strategy in which it limits the positive feedback loop involving leaf area to such an extent that in the best of seasons it is still prudent. In the worst of seasons it survives to reproduce. The evolution of corn, on the other hand, must have been under conditions of ample water availability, which led to a large positive feedback and thus rapid growth. Corn cannot be grown in areas suitable for dryland wheat or barley production, despite its better water use efficiency than the small grains, which are C_3 plants (Viets, 1971). The less water use-efficient plant can still be the most drought resistant. Put simply, water use efficiency is a useful feature for a crop as long as moisture is freely available. When water is not freely available, the concept of water use

efficiency is not applicable, and drought resistance becomes more important in determining the yield of the crop.

4. That water use and drought resistance are complex is evident from the space that we have taken to examine even the oversimplified strategies presented here. The complexity of the situation and our ignorance of what is being optimized at each step call for an identification of the components of drought resistance and an analysis of the interaction of these components in the control systems of the plant.

IV. REVIEW OF SOME RECENT APPROACHES TO THE STUDY OF PLANT–WATER RELATIONS

A. Control of Turgor and Cell Expansion

1. *Water Relations and Cell Growth*

Water status is commonly evaluated macroscopically in the following way, to characterize the net interactions of plant cells with water. Water potential (Ψ_w) of growing and nongrowing cells is partitioned into three major components, usually assigned units of pressure

$$\Psi_w = \Psi_s + \Psi_m + \Psi_p \tag{1}$$

where Ψ_s is solute potential, Ψ_m is matric potential, and Ψ_p (turgor potential) is a hydrostatic component developed at the plasmalemma–cell wall interface. Both Ψ_s and Ψ_m have negative values, while Ψ_p is positive. In many treatments, Ψ_m is assumed to be small and to remain constant within the Ψ_w range of biological importance.

In nongrowing cells the volume (V) has an absolute upper limit and can change only slightly. Small changes in V ($d\,V/V$) have a relatively small physical effect on Ψ_s

$$d\,\Psi_s = -\Psi_s\,d\,V/V \tag{2}$$

and a much larger effect on Ψ_p

$$d\,\Psi_p = \epsilon\,d\,V/V \tag{3}$$

where ϵ is an elastic coefficient (with units of pressure) that is itself a function of V, tending to ∞ as maximum cell volume is approached (Dainty, 1976).

Growing cells present a very different situation; V increases continuously. Equation (2) is still applicable, but pressure changes cannot be described by Eq. (3) alone because the cell wall yields (plastic deformation) in response to turgor pressure above a minimum threshold value. Cell enlargement rate (relative to initial cell volume) can be described by

$$dV/Vdt = E_g \left(\Psi_p - \Psi_{pth} \right) \tag{4}$$

where t is time, Ψ_{pth} is the threshold of minimum turgor pressure below which the cell wall does not yield, and E_g (gross extensibility) is a coefficient that describes plastic deformation per unit turgor pressure increment above Ψ_{pth} (Hsiao et al., 1976).

This physical approach to cell water relations is inadequate to describe living cells because many critical variables (Ψ_s, V, ϵ, E_g, and Ψ_{pth}) are subject to metabolic modification. An example of such metabolic control of water relations in the giant algal cell Valonia was discussed above (Section III,D). Some interesting recent data indicate that analogous control mechanisms may operate to adapt higher plant cells to drought stress. Metabolic control of Ψ_s (osmoregulation or osmotic adaptation), ϵ, E_g, and Ψ_{pth} are thus candidates for genetically determined components of drought resistance, and changes in these parameters may be aspects of the elusive phenomenon of drought-hardening.

2. Higher Plant Cell–Water Relations during Drought Stress

Nongrowing cells apparently seek to maintain a turgor pressure sufficient to ensure structural rigidity. A certain positive turgor pressure (at near constant volume) may thus be the desired output in these cases (Brown et al., 1976; Campbell, 1974; Hsiao et al., 1976; Weatherley, 1970). In contrast, growing cells subjected to water stress seem to set continued expansion growth (increase in volume) as the goal, and may adjust turgor pressure itself and/or cell wall characteristics to achieve this (Acevedo et al., 1971; Boyer, 1970; Bunce, 1977; Greacen and Oh, 1972; Hsiao et al., 1976; Meyer and Boyer, 1972).

For nongrowing cell situations, examples of metabolic adaptations to water stress are given by Brown et al. (1976) for mature leaves of cotton plants, and by Hsiao et al. (1976) for fully expanded sorghum leaves. Mature leaves of cotton plants preconditioned by eight periods of soil moisture stress were compared with leaves of well-irrigated plants. Solute potentials of bulk leaf tissue at incipient plasmolysis were −36 and −27 bars, respectively, suggesting that there had been a substantial decrease in Ψ_s (osmotic adjustment) in the leaf cells of preconditioned plants, which enabled preconditioned leaves to retain structural and functional integrity longer during an episode of increasing soil moisture stress. This drought-hardening effect was apparently reflected in stomatal behavior during a period of water witholding. In pre-stressed (osmotically adjusted) leaves, Ψ_w fell from -15 to -30 bars before any increase in the stomatal resistance (R_s) of the lower leaf surface occurred. In previously well-irrigated plants, R_s began to increase sharply as Ψ_w fell below -20 bars, and stomata were essentially closed at Ψ_w values below -25 bars. In fully expanded leaves of field-grown sorghum, seasonal changes in Ψ_w and Ψ_s have been found (Hsiao et al., 1976). In leaves of unirrigated plants, Ψ_w declined gradually from about -10 bars at the time of panicle initiation to about -16 bars at harvest maturity. This was matched by a parallel decrease in Ψ_s from about -14 to -20 bars; Ψ_p was maintained essentially constant through the season. In leaves of irrigated sorghum, Ψ_w and Ψ_s were always higher (less negative) than in the unirrigated crop, but similar downward trends in both Ψ_w and Ψ_s were again found as the season advanced, with Ψ_p fairly constant. In irrigated plants, the Ψ_p value maintained (about 5 bars) was close to that in unirrigated plants. In these experiments, the seasonal osmotic adjustment was taken to occur in response to water stress arising from two sources: soil water depletion and increases in internal liquid flow resistance due to age and increased height.

For growing cell situations, examples of two distinct types of metabolic control of water status are provided by Hsiao et al. (1976) for expanding corn leaves, and by Bunce (1977) for elongating soybean leaves. In expanding leaves of field-grown corn plants, a diurnal oscillation in Ψ_s occurred that maintained a positive turgor pressure and enabled leaf elongation to continue throughout the day. In these experiments, metabolic osmotic adjustment was strongly implicated, because the decrease in Ψ_s that occurred during the day could not be ascribed to dehydration. This possibility was frequently not excluded in earlier studies of Ψ_s in relation to water stress (e.g., Walter and Stadelmann, 1974). For elongating leaves of soybean, Bunce (1977) demonstrated changes in both Ψ_{pth} and E_g that tended to permit continued growth during water stress. In these experiments, plants were grown in three different environments (field, greenhouse, and growth chamber), and under three different watering regimes in the growth chamber. In all cases, the young leaves of plants in the drier environments required less turgor pressure for elongation (lower Ψ_{pth}) and showed a greater increase in elongation rate per unit increase in turgor (higher E_g). No significant osmotic adjustment was found; the continued leaf elongation under water stress was apparently achieved by changes in cell wall properties alone. Hsiao *et al.* (1976) demonstrated similar changes in Ψ_{pth} and E_g in elongating leaves of drought-stressed sorghum plants.

The metabolic basis of osmotic adaptation of plants to drought stress is not yet known, although it apparently involves the generation of internal osmotica (e.g., small sugar molecules, organic acids). This contrasts with the situation in many salt-stressed plants [e.g., barley (Greenway and Rogers, 1963) and beans and cotton (Gale *et al.*, 1967)] in which Ψ_s is lowered at least partly by uptake and accumulation of ions. Hellebust (1976) and Cram (1976) have reviewed the small amount of available literature on the internal osmotica of higher plants. Potassium salts of organic acids and sugars are the major components of Ψ_s, but essentially nothing is known of the contribution of these and other metabolites to changes in Ψ_s provoked by water stress.

The dynamic chemical structure of the growing cell wall is only just beginning to be understood (Northcote, 1972). Although the chemical changes underlying modifications of E_g and Ψ_{pth} have been studied in the elongation growth of fairly simple experimental objects, no clear picture of the interrelationship between growth physics and macromolecular chemistry has yet emerged. Advances in these areas using simple experimental objects like cultured cells, cotton fibers, and coleoptiles seem essential for an understanding of the growth of a complex structure such as a leaf in a fluctuating environment.

In summary, the genetic and metabolic control of Ψ_s, ϵ, E_g, and Ψ_{pth} during water stress is an area in critical need of basic research. In interpreting the current and future literature in this area, some caution is necessary, for two principal reasons. First, the water relations of leaves are far more complex than those of single cells, major factors being the high degree of cellular differentiation and the presence of both intracellular (symplastic) and extracellular (apoplastic, bound) water phases (Acock, 1975; Boyer, 1967; Dainty, 1976). Extracellular water may constitute 10 to 30% or more of total leaf water in various species and may vary during the course of development within a species, but some theoretical treatments and many practical methods do not take this into account. The common practice of determining Ψ_s on frozen and thawed tissue entails mixing of intra- and extracellular water phases. When the extracellular water fraction is small and constant, the dilution effect on Ψ_s may be negligible. However, when it is large, and if it varies, the errors in estimating Ψ_s may be important, particularly if Ψ_s is then subtracted from Ψ_w to give an estimate of Ψ_p [see Eq. (1)]. Leaves are necessarily treated in water relations models as homogeneous populations of cells in which the mesophyll (the greatest bulk of tissue) is assumed to be the major determinant of Ψ_w or Ψ_s. This approximation may be reasonable in well-irrigated plants, but during water stress marked gradients of Ψ_w can develop within the tissue. The water-stressed leaf therefore cannot really be considered to be homogeneous, and true Ψ_w and Ψ_s values for stressed leaves may be even more elusive than for unstressed ones. Useful working hypotheses can, however, definitely be made using approximations to Ψ_w and Ψ_s.

Second, there are important differences in measurement techniques used for Ψ_w and Ψ_s. In some cases, both Ψ_w and Ψ_s are determined psychrometrically, the latter after freezing and thawing the same tissue sample. In other cases, both Ψ_w and Ψ_s are determined with a pressure bomb on the same sample. Alternatively, Ψ_w may be determined with a pressure bomb on an intact leaf, and Ψ_s on a small sample after freezing and thawing by psychrometry or freezing point depression, or on expressed sap (with or without freezing and thawing). In all cases Ψ_p is calculated by difference [see Eq. (1)]. Because Ψ_p is often small compared with Ψ_w and Ψ_s, neither of which can be determined with high precision, estimates of turgor pressure are difficult to make. Reproducible Ψ_p values require careful design and skillful execution of experiments.

3. Perception and Transduction of Water Stress

Several recent reviews have considered how water stress might be perceived by a sensor or receptor and transduced to a signal capable of triggering metabolic responses like those outlined above and those discussed in Section IV,B, below (Cram, 1976; Hsiao, 1973; Hsiao et al., 1976; Raschke, 1975). Because in both growing and nongrowing plant cells only small volume changes (10 to 15%) need occur to provoke striking metabolic consequences, a sensor for turgor pressure at the cell wall–cell membrane interface seems the most reasonable possibility. Direct effects of the chemical activity of water on cellular mechanisms seem less probable, but they cannot be ruled out. Water in plant cells, especially at functional membrane and protein sites, is essentially in interfaces where bulk effects are less important than specific surface interactions (Lewin, 1974; Viaud, 1972). The small decrease in the chemical activity of bulk cell water that occurs in the normal range of Ψ_w reduction may not describe changes in the solvent–solute–functional site interactions that occur in protoplasm. Biophysical research in this area is seriously lacking.

Abscisic acid (ABA) has now been shown to be one chemical signal generated during water stress that can cause a wide range of physiological and metabolic responses (Hsiao, 1973; Milborrow, 1974; Raschke,

1975). There is evidence that in plant cells and organs *de novo* ABA synthesis, metabolism, and compartmentation are all involved in production of the signal in response to water stress and in control of the length and intensity of the response provoked (e.g., Hiron and Wright, 1973; Loveys *et al.*, 1975; Milborrow and Robinson, 1973; Raschke *et al.*, 1976; Raschke and Zeevaart, 1976; Zabadal, 1974). Two adaptive responses relevant to drought resistance that can be provoked by ABA are stomatal closure (Raschke, 1975) and leaf abscission (Milborrow, 1974). No evidence is available regarding the sensor (transducer) involved in the perception of water stress and the triggering of ABA accumulation, although accumulation may begin when Ψ_p reaches zero (Beardsell and Cohen, 1975; Wright, 1977).

A number of authors have reported enhanced rates of ethylene production by water-stressed plants (e.g., Ben-Yehoshua and Aloni, 1974; El-Beltagy and Hall, 1974; Guinn, 1976; McMichael *et al.*, 1972; Wright, 1977). Whether a causal role can be ascribed to this stress-induced ethylene production in the abscission or senescence of leaves and other organs during water stress is not established, and its relationship to ABA is unclear. On the basis of the very limited evidence available, it seems possible to view ethylene production from water-stressed tissue as another signal capable of effecting adaptive physiological responses.

B. Intermediary Metabolism during Water Stress: Proline Accumulation

1. Types of Metabolic Response to Stress

Investigations of plants stressed by flooding the roots or by salination of rooting media have provided some examples of both deleterious and protective metabolic responses to the stress imposed. These responses can be loosely viewed as positive and negative feedback situations, respectively (section III,D). If the imposition of a stress enhances the rate of a pathway whose end product is toxic at high concentrations [e.g., ethanol production in flooded roots (Crawford, 1969), diamine production in the leaves of salinated plants (Gollek, 1973; Smith, 1971)], then the harmful effect of the stress is amplified and the plant may succumb primarily from accumulation of substrate quantities of toxic products. If stress imposition stimulates the rates of pathways that either prevent the accumulation of toxins [e.g., malate production as an end product of glycolysis in flooded roots (McManmon and Crawford,

1971)], or that lead to products of protective value in combatting the stress [e.g., betaine accumulation in salt-stressed plants (Storey and Wyn Jones, 1975; Wyn Jones et al., 1974)], then the stress effects are minimized and plant survival becomes more probable. There is thus some precedent for minus and plus aspects of the intermediary metabolism of plants under stress, and therefore good reason to search for the operation of such pathways in drought-stressed plants. If we could identify them, it would be of great value in developing laboratory screening tests for components of drought resistance (Section II,B).

Hsiao (1973) has thoroughly reviewed the effects of water stress on plant metabolism. Only one metabolic response—the accumulation of free proline—will be covered here. Proline accumulation, a very common response to water stress, has been the subject of considerable recent study (Stewart, 1980; Stewart and Hanson, 1980). It has been suggested that proline synthesis or accumulation is of adaptive (protective) value to drought-stressed plants and might thus be a component of drought resistance.

2. Physiology of Proline Accumulation

Free proline accumulates in the attached and detached leaves of almost all crop species when they are subjected to moderate drought stress in laboratory experiments. Field-grown crops also accumulate proline in their leaves under drought conditions. Crops in which proline accumulation occurs to various degrees include barley, wheat, corn, sorghum, forage grasses, soybeans, kidney beans, jack beans, alfalfa, turnip, radish, sunflower, tobacco, pepper and tomato (e.g., Barnett and Naylor, 1966; Chu et al., 1974; Kemble and MacPherson, 1954; Pálfi and Juhász, 1971; Pálfi et al., 1974; Singh et al., 1973a,d; Stewart et al., 1966; Waldren and Teare, 1974). Characteristically, free proline accumulates in stressed leaves to 10 to 100 times the level found in the leaves of well-watered plants. No other amino acids show such large increases during water stress, and many tend to decline in concentration (Barnett and Naylor, 1966; Singh et al., 1973a). In severely stressed leaves, proline is typically the major free amino acid and may account for up to 30% of the total soluble nitrogen (protein and nonprotein) in the leaves. Proline accumulation begins within a few hours after the onset of moderate stress (a fall in Ψ_w of about 10 bars) and can continue at a high rate for several days in attached leaves. The highest proline concentrations found in viable drought-stressed leaves are of the order of 50 mM, and thus are too low to be of major osmotic significance—unless the bulk of the proline accumulated is confined to a small cellu-

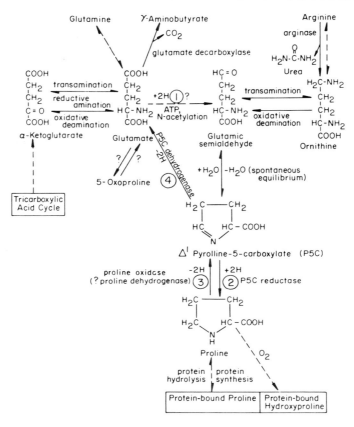

Fig. 13. Some possible interrelationships in pathways of biosynthesis and degradation of proline and related amino acids in plants. Broken arrow lines indicate interconversions which involve more than one enzyme. Bidirectional arrows designate reversible conversions, unidirectional arrows show irreversible ones. Question marks identify poorly characterized steps. Enzyme preparations which catalyze reactions in the major pathways of proline synthesis and oxidation [(1) to (4)] have been obtained from plants. Their sources and characteristics are summarized below.

(1) Formation of glutamic semialdehyde (details uncertain) (Swiss chard leaves: Morris *et al.*, 1969). Glutamic and N-acetylglutamic acid converted to corresponding semialdehydes by leaf extracts. An intermediate phosphorylation step implicated by requirements for ATP and Mg^{2+}. NADH and NADPH effective electron donors. (2) Δ^1-Pyrroline-5-carboxylate reductase (dark-grown peanut seedlings: Mazelis and Fowden, 1969; tobacco leaves: Noguchi *et al.*, 1966). [See also (3), below.] NADPH preferred electron donor. Tobacco enzyme reported to be partially localized in chloroplast fraction; chloroplast fragments able to utilize photosynthetically generated NADPH for P5C reduction. (3) Proline Oxidase (etiolated shoots of corn, wheat, barley, soybean, mung bean: Boggess *et al.*, 1978; spinach leaves: Huang and Cavalieri, 1979). Enzyme associated with mitochondria, O_2-dependent, probably linked to mitochondrial electron transport via

lar compartment. When water stress is relieved, free proline levels decline rapidly in viable tissue (Singh et al., 1973a; Stewart, 1972a), but remain high in drought-killed, desiccated tissue (Hanson et al., 1977).

During water stress, roots of intact plants can accumulate proline (Singh et al., 1973a), whereas excised roots apparently cannot (Singh et al., 1973b; Stewart et al., 1966). Taken with the observation that detached barley leaves accumulate proline at a rate 5 or 10 times higher than attached leaves subjected to a comparable water deficit (Boggess and Stewart, 1976), it seems possible that nitrogenous compounds (not necessarily proline itself) may be transferred out of the leaves during water stress. C. T. Gates (1968) and Tully et al. (1979) have supplied data that support this possibility. A priori, it appears that a reasonable goal for a drought-stressed plant would be to mobilize nitrogen from the most expendable organs—the mature leaves—and to store and utilize this nitrogen in vital organs, such as the crowns and roots in cereals. Tully et al. (1979) were able to show that wilted barley leaves exported up to 25% of their total organic nitrogen before translocation ceased; however, little of this nitrogen appeared to move in the form of proline.

3. Regulation of Metabolic Pathways Involved in Proline Accumulation

Figure 13 shows the major pathways associated with proline metabolism, and summarizes biochemical data available for plants on four key reactions. With respect to proline accumulation during water stress, most work has been done using tracer studies of detached leaf blades of barley seedlings and excised bean and tobacco leaves. It is clear from Fig. 13 that potential causes of free proline accumulation during water stress include the following: (1) decreased incorporation of proline into protein; (2) release of proline (and closely related amino acids) by protein hydrolysis; (3) conversion of free glutamine and glutamate pools to proline; (4) conversion of free arginine and ornithine pools to proline; (5) increase in the rate of de novo synthesis of

---

Fig. 13 (continued).   FAD. More likely to be in the in vivo catalyst of proline oxidation than L-proline dehydrogenase (Boggess et al., 1978). L-proline dehydrogenase (wheat germ: Mazelis and Creveling, 1974; dark-grown peanut seedlings: Mazelis and Fowden, 1971). Enzyme partially purified from acetone powders. Reaction product not identified at P5C. NAD$^+$ preferred electron acceptor. Wheat germ enzyme acts also as a P5C reductase, using NADPH or NADH. (4) Δ^1-Pyrroline-5-carboxylate dehydrogenase (etiolated barley shoots: Boggess et al., 1975; pea and corn plants, castor bean endosperm and pumpkin cotyledons: Stewart and Lai, 1974). NAD$^+$ preferred electron acceptor. Localization partially in mitochondrial fraction.

proline from α-ketoglutarate (and amino groups) via glutamate and Δ^1-pyrroline-5-carboxylic acid (P5C); and (6) decrease in the rate of proline oxidation (conversion via P5C to glutamate and α-ketoglutarate). Although decreased protein synthesis and increased proteolysis during water stress play some part in proline accumulation (e.g., Barnett and Naylor, 1966; Stewart, 1972b), the amount of proline accumulated is considerably greater than could be released by net protein breakdown (e.g., Kemble and MacPherson, 1954; Singh et al., 1973a). Furthermore, proline accumulation occurred when leaf protein content was still slowly increasing during moderate water stress (Singh et al., 1973a). Changes in free glutamate, glutamine, ornithine, and arginine pools are also generally far too small to account for observed increases in proline content (e.g., Boggess and Stewart, 1976; Singh et al., 1973a). An increase in net de novo synthesis of proline [i.e., (5) and/or (6) above] must therefore be invoked. There is good evidence that net de novo synthesis is the main source of the free proline accumulated during drought stress. Endogenous carbohydrate or applied sugar is necessary for rapid proline accumulation in darkness (Singh et al., 1973b; Stewart, 1972b; Stewart et al., 1966), which is consistent with a demand for α-ketoglutarate and reducing power for de novo synthesis. More direct evidence comes from experiments with labeled glutamate, which show increased incorporation into proline in wilted tissue (Barnett and Naylor, 1966; Boggess et al., 1976a,b; Morris et al., 1969). The net de novo synthesis of proline is apparently due both to increased proline synthesis via glutamate and P5C, and to slowed proline oxidation (Boggess et al., 1976a,b; Stewart et al., 1977) rather than to either process alone. It has been proposed that the increased rate of proline synthesis in wilted barley and tobacco leaves could be explained by a failure in a feedback control system that operates in turgid tissue (Boggess et al., 1976a). The apparent stimulation of proline biosynthesis in wilted barley leaves would seem to act on P5C formation rather than on P5C reduction to proline, because the incorporation of labeled P5C or ornithine into glutamate is not increased by wilting in short-term experiments (Boggess et al., 1976b). On relief of water stress, free proline is rapidly oxidized to glutamate and CO_2, converted to other amino acids, and incorporated into protein (Stewart, 1972a).

If proline accumulated during water stress is derived mainly from α-ketoglutarate via glutamate and P5C, then approximately one hexose molecule is consumed to provide each α-ketoglutarate carbon skeleton for proline synthesis. Maximum net proline synthesis rates in detached barley leaves are about 1.5 μmoles/g initial fresh weight/hr, corresponding to a hexose consumption rate of the same value. Carbon dioxide production from comparable barley leaves is about 9 μmoles/g initial fr. wt./hr, corresponding to 1.5 μmoles hexose oxidized to CO_2/g initial fr. wt./hr (A. D. Hanson, unpublished results). It is clear from this rough calculation that proline accumulation in stressed tissue can be a major metabolic activity in terms of carbon flux and consumption of the reducing equivalents generated by hexose oxidation.

4. Possible Adaptive Value of Proline Accumulation during Water Stress

Several workers have suggested that proline may serve as a storage compound for reduced carbon and nitrogen during stress, and that the stored proline could serve as a ready source of reducing power, carbon skeletons and amino groups during recovery following relief of water stress (Fig. 13). The high solubility (1.6 g/ml of H_2O at 25°C) of proline, its highly reduced nature, and its inability to undergo transamination reactions would tend to fit proline (rather than other amino acids) for such a storage role. There is, however, only indirect experimental evidence that proline accumulated during water stress is effective in enhancing the recovery phase (Blum and Ebercon, 1976; Singh et al., 1973c; Stewart, 1972a).

It is also possible that proline is itself a protective substance that minimizes the damage sustained in dehydrated cells (Schobert, 1977), or that the diversion of carbon, nitrogen, and reducing power flux to proline synthesis mitigates the effects of deleterious pathways (e.g., those leading to the accumulation of NH_3). In the latter case, the goal during water stress could be viewed as maximizing the rate of proline synthesis, rather than the accumulation of proline for its own sake. No unequivocal direct evidence supports either of these possibilities, although the first receives a little support from comparative plant physiology and from experiments in which exogenous proline was supplied to stressed plants. Certain halophytes (Goas, 1965; Stewart and Lee, 1974) growing in their natural habitats contain high levels of proline in the shoots. A similar situation has been reported for barley (Chu et al., 1976)—a salt-tolerant crop—in which salination with 10 bars of NaCl caused proline to accumulate in seedling leaves under conditions in which the plants remained turgid and continued to grow slowly. In these cases, the presence of high levels of free proline in the shoots of growing plants cannot be viewed as a short-term response to a fairly sudden stress like wilting; some long-term benefit of a high free proline content might be inferred. Similarly, analyses of the free amino acids of the desert plants creosote bush (Saunier et al., 1968) and Prosopis sp. (Carman, 1973) show the presence of high proline contents under favorable growing conditions for the species. In the case of *Prosopis* sp., it is interesting that high levels of the proline analog pipecolic acid (and its 4- and 5-hydroxylated derivatives) were also present. Favorable effects of exogenous proline on survival during drought have been reported for mature plants of wheat (Tyankova, 1966) and *Carex setifolia* (Hubac and Guerrier, 1972) and for germinating *Brassica campestris* seeds (Hubac, 1967). Unfortunately, however, the favorable effects observed in these studies cannot be assigned specifically to an increase in the internal proline levels in the treated plants, because internal proline levels were not determined and no other amino acids were supplied.

5. Proline Accumulation as a Screening Method for Drought Resistance in Plant Breeding

As is evident from the preceding section, there is as yet no firm basis for taking proline accumulation to be an adaptive, protective part of a plant's overall strategy for coping with drought. The widespread occurrence of proline accumulation as a major metabolic activity during water stress warrants further research on proline as a possible component of drought resistance, but too little is currently known to make proline accumulation tests useful screening methods. A previously proposed screening test is discussed below.

Using ten of the barley cultivars studied by Finlay and Wilkinson (1963), Singh *et al.* (1972) reported a correlation between the phenotypic stability index (*b* value, see Section II,A,2,b) and the capacity of seedling leaves to accumulate proline in response to severe osmotic stress. A threefold range in proline accumulation was found among the varieties, although they apparently did not differ significantly in their internal water status, as judged by Ψ_w determined on whole leaves. Varieties with the most stable grain yield accumulated the highest levels of proline. Further work (Singh *et al.*, 1973c) indicated that barley varieties that accumulated more proline tended to survive extreme water stress more readily at the seedling stage. These results led to the proposals (1) that proline accumulation might provide a reliable, nondestructive laboratory screening test for drought resistance in cereal breeding programs (Singh *et al.*, 1972), and (2) that the varietal differences in proline levels reflected genetically controlled differences in metabolic response to the same degree of internal water stress (Ψ_w), as distinct from genetically controlled differences in the regulation of internal water status during stress (Singh *et al.*, 1973c).

Recent investigations on barley by Hanson *et al.* (1977) and wheat by Dedio (cited in Hurd, 1976) have shown that proposal (2) is probably invalid, due to technical errors made by Singh *et al.* in Ψ_w determinations. Hanson *et al.* and Dedio found that proline levels in leaves of different cultivars were more closely related to the water status of the individual drought-stressed leaves than to the cultivar. Significant cultivar differences in proline accumulation rates were observed, but could be fully accounted for in barley by respective differences in the rates of decline of water status during stress (Hanson *et al.*, 1977). Proline level is thus essentially an indicator of the degree of water stress, and those cultivars able to maintain a higher water status under a given environmental water stress (i.e., probably the most drought resistant) therefore tend to show the lowest rates of proline accumulation.

It thus appears unlikely that selection for proline accumulation potential, as proposed by Singh *et al.* (1972), would result in genetic advance toward drought resistance; it might well achieve an opposite effect. Further, the use by Singh *et al.* of the phenotypic stability index *b* alone as a criterion of drought resistance with which to compare proline accumulation was misleading. Some highly stable varieties, such as Bankuti Korai (see Fig. 2), achieve this stability by always setting seed quickly, and thus have a very low yield potential in favorable environments. Even supposing that a proline accumulation test might permit selection for a low *b* value in drought-prone conditions (which now seems improbable), then if the low *b* value was accompanied by very low yield potential the selection would be purposeless. The above complexities probably explain reported failures to confirm a simple positive correlation between field drought resistance ratings and proline accumulation in a number of cereal crops (e.g., Blum and Ebercon, 1976; IRRI, 1975).

V. CLOSING REMARKS

A. Limitations of Conventional Plant Breeding and of Component Analysis Approaches to Drought Resistance in the Development of Drought-Resistant Crops

1. Conventional Plant Breeding

The first and major limitation of a conventional approach, relying on field screening, in breeding for drought resistance lies in the very large element of chance inherent in trying to select for characteristics under complex genetic control, which show strong interactions with the environment. Drought conditions tend to vary widely in timing and severity from year to year (and from site to site). If several genetically distinct components are involved in drought resistance, selection in the conditions of any one drought year will concentrate genes that were valuable just for the type of drought that occurred in that year. It is obvious that continual annual changes in the direction of selection pressure are almost inevitable with field screening for drought resistance, which makes genetic advance very difficult.

A second limitation of field screening methods is that certain components of drought resistance may be impossible to select for in single plants, in head rows, or even in small plots. A clear hypothetical example is that of a dryland cereal genotype with an exceptionally favorable matching of its seasonal pattern of soil moisture depletion to the evaporative demand occurring at various times during the growing season. An entire field of such a genotype would tend to show higher yields in conditions of limiting soil moisture, and would be classified as drought resistant. A single plant or small plot of this genotype, growing in competition with other genotypes in a nursery, would not appear outstanding. Its neighbors would deplete the soil moisture inefficiently in its behalf.

A third drawback of field testing for drought resistance was considered in Section II,A,3,b. In the case either of potential parents or of progeny from crosses, desirable components of drought resistance may be obscured by gross problems of adaptation to the local environment, such as high susceptibility to the prevailing disease and insect pests.

Very large crossing programs that include a wide range of adapted and nonadapted genotypes can, and have, partially overcome these limitations by sheer weight of numbers. As an example, the Centro Internacional de Mejoramiento de Maiz Y Trigo (CIMMYT) program on spring wheat has given rise to many lines that show good performance in both dryland and irrigated conditions. These lines have sufficient resistance to major diseases and enough tolerance of other environmental variables that they can be successfully grown in many parts of the world. The important point is not the progress that has already been made by such approaches, but whether they can continue to prove fruitful. It seems probable that most of the simple advances, based on a combination of selection for phenological and morphological characters and on intuition, have been or are now being made. The chance of further progress by the same route is therefore obviously declining. To cope with what has now become a low probability of producing and recognizing a more drought-resistant genotype, the number of crosses and the amount of field space would have to be increased enormously.

2. Component Identification and Analysis

A practical limitation on the search for components of drought resistance is that such an approach has the status of a high-cost research project from which no economic return can be guaranteed. However, a clear distinction must be drawn between the costs involved in breeding for drought resistance and for resistance to biological factors such as diseases and insect pests. The latter requires a continual effort to keep pace with the evolving pathogen. Because water stress is immutable, the identification of heritable components of drought resistance in crops is an investment of enduring value. A second, more theoretical limitation is that although a component analysis approach depends basically upon a sound understanding of plant processes contributing to drought resistance, in practical application it must rely on correlations between physiological or biochemical tests and genotype–environment interactions. Because such correlations are never perfect, to account for 80% of the variation involved would be a very satisfactory achievement for a correlation between field and laboratory. There is clearly still a considerable margin for error in reliance on a laboratory test as a screening method, particularly when tests cannot be properly replicated (as in the nondestructive sampling of a single plant from a segregating polulation). A third limitation is in reconciling the conflicting requirements of several desired types of laboratory test. Technical testing requirements may be incompatible with the objective of screening single plants nondestructively; for example, each type of test conducted might require two leaves. For this reason (in addition to the genetic problems associated with selecting simultaneously for several different characters) it is probable that, at most, only two or three tests could be applied together in screening individual plants or small populations. A larger number of tests could be used in choosing parents for crossing.

In summary, if heritable components of drought resistance can be identified, and suitable screening procedures developed, progress in breeding for them will probably be neither simple nor rapid. The progress to be expected from this route, however, seems better than that from continuing to make large numbers of crosses and to select on the basis of field performance alone.

B. Are High Yield Potential and Drought Resistance Mutually Exclusive?

The relationship between high economic yield and adaptability to drought was considered in Section III,E,2. Very general energetic considerations seem to lead to the same conclusion as that reached in the course of practical plant breeding: some compromise between yield potential and adaptability may be inevitable. Two additional points will be raised here. First, should major emphasis in breeding programs for drought resistance continue to be placed on maximum yield in the better environments? It is clear from Fig. 1 that wheat yields in farmers' fields in the United States and in India fall far below the yield potential of wheat in favorable, intensively farmed environments; average yields in the Netherlands exceed 5000 kg/ha and yields of over 7000 kg/ha in well-managed irrigated plots are common in CIMMYT nurseries in Mexico. It would seem that if some sacrifice in yield potential is necessary to achieve greater drought resistance, it may be a worthwhile tradeoff in the suboptimal moisture conditions in which most of the world wheat crop is produced.

Second, we have until now considered breeding for drought resistance only from the standpoint of the individual plant. A crop is a population, and whether it is self- or cross-pollinated it can be regarded as having a common gene pool. The land races of self-pollinated crops developed over millenia by and for traditional agriculture (where stability counts more than high yield potential) were definitely more heterogeneous than the pure line varieties of wheat, rice, and barley that currently produce much of the world's small grain supply. The same is true of heterogeneity in cross-pollinated crops, which were also highly heterozygous. This purely circumstantial, historical evidence that genetic diversity in a crop (achieved either by mixtures of genotypes or by heterozygosity) leads to stability in varying environments is supported by considerable experimental evidence and practical experience (e.g., Allard and Bradshaw, 1964; Finlay, 1964). This way of achieving stability in productivity (termed "populational buffering" by Allard and Bradshaw) has not been widely exploited in self-pollinated crops, although multilines (mechanical mixtures of several comparable genotypes with specific genetic differences) are certainly not a new idea. Such mixtures of homozygotes might provide a means for incorporating different components of drought resistance into a crop, by developing related lines each carrying a high intensity of only one of several favorable components. This might be achieved more easily than incorporating several components into a single genotype and might minimize any reduction in yield potential due to the simultaneous presence of many components of drought resistance in any one genome.

ACKNOWLEDGMENTS

We wish to thank Dr. E. H. Everson for much valuable assistance in preparing Section II, and our other colleagues for their critical reviews of the manuscript.

REFERENCES

Acevedo, E., Hsiao, T. C., and Henderson, D. W. (1971). *Plant Physiol.* **48**, 631–636.
Acock, B. (1975). *Aust. J. Plant Physiol.* **2**, 253–263.
Adams, M. W. (1967). *Crop Sci.* **7**, 505–510.
Allard, R. W. (1960). "Principles of Plant Breeding." Wiley, New York.
Allard, R. W., and Bradshaw, A. D. (1964). *Crop Sci.* **4**, 503–507.
Arnon, I. (1972a). "Crop Production in Dry Regions," Vol. I. Leonard Hill, London.
Arnon, I. (1972b). "Crop Production in Dry Regions," Vol. II. Leonard Hill, London.
Atkins, I. M., and Norris, M. J. (1955). *Agron. J.* **47**, 218–220.
Atsmon, D. (1973). *In* "Agricultural Genetics" (R. Moav, ed.), pp. 157–176. Wiley, New York.
Barnett, N. M., and Naylor, A. W. (1966). *Plant Physiol.* **41**, 1222–1230.
Barrs, H. D. (1968). *In* "Water Deficits and Plant Growth" (T. T. Kozlowski, ed.), Vol. I, pp. 235–368. Academic Press, New York.
Barrs, H. D. (1971). *Annu. Rev. Plant Physiol.* **22**, 223–236.
Barrs, H. D., and Kramer, P. J. (1969). *Plant Physiol.* **44**, 959–964.
Beardsell, M. F., and Cohen, D. (1975). *Plant Physiol.* **56**, 207–212.
Begg, J. E., and Turner, N. C. (1976). *Adv. Agron.* **28**, 161–217.
Ben-Yehoshua, S., and Aloni, B. (1974). *Plant Physiol.* **53**, 863–865.
Blum, A., and Ebercon, A. (1976). *Crop Sci.* **16**, 428–431.
Boggess, S. F., and Stewart, C. R. (1976). *Plant Physiol.* **58**, 796–797.
Boggess, S. F., Paleg, L. G., and Aspinall, D. (1975). *Plant Physiol.* **56**, 259–262.
Boggess, S. F., Aspinall, D., and Paleg, L. G. (1976a). *Aust. J. Plant Physiol.* **3**, 513–525.
Boggess, S. F., Stewart, C. R., Aspinall, D., and Paleg, L. G. (1976b). *Plant Physiol.* **58**, 398–401.
Boggess, S. F., Koeppe, D. E., and Stewart, C. R. (1978). *Plant Physiol.* **62**, 22–25.
Boussiba, S., Rikin, A., and Richmond, A. E. (1975). *Plant Physiol.* **56**, 337–339.
Boyer, J. S. (1967). *Plant Physiol.* **42**, 213–217.
Boyer, J. S. (1969). *Annu. Rev. Plant Physiol.* **20**, 351–364.
Boyer, J. S. (1970). *Plant Physiol.* **46**, 233–235.
Boyer, J. S. (1974). *Planta* **117**, 187–207.
Boyer, J. S. (1976a). *Philos. Trans. R. Soc. London, Ser. B* **273**, 501–512.
Boyer, J. S. (1976b). *In* "Water Deficits and Plant Growth" (T. T. Kozlowski, ed.), Vol. 4, pp. 153–190. Academic Press, New York.
Boyer, J. S., and McPherson, H. G. (1975). *Adv. Agron.* **27**, 1–23.
Bradshaw, A. D. (1974). *Brookhaven Symp. Biol.* **25**, 75–94.
Brown, K. W., Jordan, W. R., and Thomas, J. C. (1976). *Physiol. Plant.* **37**, 1–5.
Brown, N. L., and Pariser, E. R. (1975). *Science* **188**, 589–593.
Bunce, J. A. (1977). *J. Exp. Bot.* **28**, 156–161.
Burström, H. (1965). *Protoplasma* **61**, 294–301.

Campbell, G. S. (1974). "Proceedings, Eastern Washington Fertilizer and Pesticide Conference." Washington State University, Pullman.

Carceller, M. S., and Soriano, A. (1972). *Can. J. Bot.* **50,** 105–108.

Carlson, P. S., and Polacco, J. C. (1975). *Science* **188,** 622–625.

Carman, N. J. (1973). Ph.D. Thesis, University of Texas, Austin.

Chu, T. M., Aspinall, D., and Paleg, L. G. (1974). *Aust. J. Plant Physiol.* **1,** 87–97.

Chu, T. M., Aspinall, D., and Paleg, L. G. (1976). *Aust. J. Plant Physiol.* **3,** 219–228.

Cleland, R. (1967). *Planta* **77,** 182–191.

Council for Agricultural Science and Technology. (1973). "Energy in Agriculture," A report by a Task Force of the Council for Agricultural Science and Technology. Dept. of Agronomy, Iowa State Univ. Press, Ames.

Cowan, I. R. (1972). *Planta* **106,** 185–219.

Cowan, I. R., and Milthorpe, F. L. (1968). In "Water Deficits and Plant Growth" (T. T. Kozlowski, ed.), Vol. 1, pp. 127–193. Academic Press, New York.

Cram, W. J. (1976). In "Transport in Plants" (U. Lüttge and M. G. Pitman, eds.), Vol. II, Part A, pp. 284–316. Springer-Verlag, Berlin and New York.

Crawford, R. M. M. (1969). *Ber. Dtsch. Bot. Ges.* **82,** 111–114.

Crosson, P. R. (1975). *Science* **188,** 519–524.

Dainty, J. (1976). In "Transport in Plants" (U. Lüttge and M. G. Pitman, eds.), Vol. II, Part A, pp. 12–35. Springer-Verlag, Berlin and New York.

Day, A. D., and Thompson, R. K. (1975). *Agron. J.* **67,** 430–433.

de Wit, C. T. (1975). *Span* **18,** 2–4.

Eberhart, S. A., and Russell, W. A. (1966). *Crop Sci.* **6,** 36–40.

Ehleringer, J., Björkman, O., and Mooney, H. A. (1976). *Science* **192,** 376–377.

El-Beltagy, A. S., and Hall, M. A. (1974). *New Phytol.* **73,** 47–60.

Elston, J., Karamanos, A. J., Kassam, A. H., and Wadsworth, R. M. (1976). *Philos. Trans. R. Soc. London, Ser. B* **273,** 581–591.

Eslick, R. F., and Hockett, E. A. (1974). *Agric. Meterol.* **14,** 13–23.

Evans, L. T., Bingham, J., Jackson, P., and Sutherland, J. (1972). *Ann. Appl. Biol.* **70,** 67–76.

Evenari, M., Shanan, L., and Tadmor, N. (1971). "The Challenge of a Desert." Harvard Univ. Press, Cambridge, Massachusetts.

Ferguson, H. (1974). *Agric. Meterol.* **14,** 25–29.

Ferguson, H., Brown, P. L., and Fryrear, D. W. (1970). In "Evaporation in the Great Plains" (Great Plains Agric. Counc. Res. Comm.), Publ. No. 50, pp. 255–274. Kansas State University, Manhattan.

Finlay, K. W. (1964). *Barley Genet. 1, Proc. Int. Symp., 1st, 1963* pp. 351–359.

Finlay, K. W. (1971). *Barley Genet. 2, Proc. Int. Symp., 2nd, 1969* pp. 338–345.

Finlay, K. W., and Wilkinson, G. N. (1963). *Aust. J. Agric. Res.* **14,** 742–754.

Fischer, R. A., and Turner, N. C. (1978). *Annu. Rev. Plant Physiol.* **29,** 277–317.

Fiscus, E. L. (1975). *Plant Physiol.* **55,** 917–922.

Gale, J., Kohl, H. C., and Hagan, R. M. (1967). *Physiol. Plant.* **20,** 408–420.

Gates, C. T. (1968). In "Water Deficits and Plant Growth" (T. T. Kozlowski, ed.), Vol. 2, pp. 135–190. Academic Press, New York.

Gates, D. M. (1968). *Annu. Rev. Plant Physiol.* **19,** 211–238.

Gavan, J. D., and Dixon, J. A. (1975). *Science* **188,** 541–549.

Goas, M. (1965). *C. R. Hebd. Seances Acad. Sci., Ser. D* **261,** 2724–2726.

Gollek, B. (1973). "Structure and Function of Plant Cells in Saline Habitats." Wiley, New York.

Grafius, J. E. (1971). *Barley Genet. 2, Proc. Int. Symp.,* 2nd, *1969* pp. 346–355.
Grafius, J. E. (1974). *Mich., Agric. Exp. Stn., Res. Rep.* **247**, 16–20.
Greacen, E. L., and Oh, J. S. (1972). *Nature (London) New Biol.* **235**, 24–25.
Greenway, H., and Rogers, A. (1963). *Plant Soil* **18**, 21–30.
Guinn, G. (1976). *Plant Physiol.* **57**, 403–405.
Gullord, M. (1974). Ph.D. Thesis, Michigan State University, East Lansing.
Gutknecht, J. (1968). *Science* **160**, 68–70.
Hanson, A. D., Nelsen, C. E., and Everson, E. H. (1977). *Crop Sci.* **17**, 720–726.
Harlan, J. R. (1975). "Crops and Man." Am. Soc. Agron., Madison, Wisconsin.
Hastings, D. F., and Gutknecht, J. (1974). *In* "Membrane Transport in Plants" (U. Zim-
    merman and J. Dainty, eds.), pp. 79–83. Springer-Verlag, Berlin and New York.
Hegarty, T. W. (1970). *Hortic. Res.* **10**, 59–64.
Heichel, G. H. (1976). *Am. Sci.* **64**, 64–72.
Hellebust, J. A. (1976). *Annu. Rev. Plant Physiol.* **27**, 485–505.
Henckel, P. A. (1964). *Annu. Rev. Plant Physiol.* **15**, 363–386.
Hiron, R. W. P., and Wright, S. T. C. (1973). *J. Exp. Bot.* **24**, 769–781.
Hsiao, T. C. (1973). *Annu. Rev. Plant Physiol.* **24**, 519–570.
Hsiao, T. C., and Acevedo, E. (1974). *Agric. Meteorol.* **14**, 59–84.
Hsiao, T. C., Acevedo, E., Fereres, E., and Henderson, D. W. (1976). *Philos. Trans. R. Soc.
    London, Ser. B* **273**, 479–500.
Huang, A. H. C., and Cavalieri, A. J. (1979). *Plant Physiol.* (in press).
Hubac, C. (1967). *C. R. Hebd. Seances Acad. Sci., Ser. D* **264**, 1286–1289.
Hubac, C., and Guerrier, D. (1972). *Oecol. Plant.* **7**, 147–165.
Hurd, E. A. (1971). *In* "Drought Injury and Resistance in Crops" (K. L. Larson and J. D.
    Eastin, eds.), pp. 77–88. Crop Sci. Soc. Am., Madison, Wisconsin.
Hurd, E. A. (1974). *Agric. Meterol.* **14**, 39–55.
Hurd, E. A. (1976). *In* "Water Deficits and Plant Growth" (T. T. Kozlowski, ed.), Vol. 4,
    pp. 317–353. Academic Press, New York.
Husain, I., and Aspinall, D. (1970). *Ann. Bot. (London)* [N. S.] **24**, 393–407.
International Rice Research Institute (1975). Annual Report for 1974. IRRI, Los Baños,
    Philippines.
Jackson, W. A., Knezek, B. D., and van Schilfgaarde, J. (1975). *In* "Crop Productivity—
    Research Imperatives" (A. W. A. Brown *et al.*, eds.), pp. 201–274. Michigan Ag-
    ricultural Experiment Station, East Lansing.
Jennings, P. R. (1976). *Sci. Am.* **235**, 180–195.
Jensen, C. J. (1976). *Int. Assoc. Plant Tissue Cult. Newsl.* **18**, 2–7.
Jensen, M. E. (1968). *In* "Water Deficits and Plant Growth" (T. T. Kozlowski, ed.), Vol. 2,
    pp. 1–22. Academic Press, New York.
Jones, R. W. (1973). "Principles of Biological Regulation." Academic Press, New York.
Kemble, A. R., and MacPherson, H. T. (1954). *Biochem. J.* **58**, 46–49.
Kerridge, P. C., and Kronstad, W. E. (1968). *Agron. J.* **60**, 710–711.
Knight, R. (1970). *Euphytica* **19**, 225–235.
Kozlowski, T. T. (1976). *In* "Water Deficits and Plant Growth" (T. T. Kozlowski, ed.), Vol.
    4, pp. 191–231. Academic Press, New York.
Lehninger, A. L. (1973). "Bioenergetics." Benjamin, Menlo Park, California.
Lewin, S. (1974). "Displacement of Water and Its Control of Biochemical Reactions."
    Academic Press, New York.
Lipton, M. (1975). *Span* **18**, 17–18.
Loveys, B. R., Brien, C. J., and Kriedemann, P. E. (1975). *Physiol. Plant.* **33**, 166–170.

McDonough, W. T., and Gauch, H. G. (1959). *Md., Agric. Exp. Stn., Bull.* **A-103**, 1–15.
MacKey, J. (1973). *Proc. Int. Wheat Genet. Symp., 4th, 1973* pp. 827–842.
McManmon, M., and Crawford, R. M. M. (1971). *New Phytol.* **70**, 299–306.
McMichael, B. L., Jordan, W. R., and Powell, R. D. (1972). *Plant Physiol.* **49**, 658–660.
Mazelis, M., and Creveling, R. K. (1974). *Phytochemistry* **13**, 559–565.
Mazelis, M., and Fowden, L. (1969). *Phytochemistry* **8**, 801–809.
Mazelis, M., and Fowden, L. (1971). *J. Exp. Bot.* **22**, 137–145.
Mellor, J. W. (1976). *Sci. Am.* **235**, 154–163.
Meyer, R. F., and Boyer, J. S. (1972). *Planta* **108**, 77–87.
Milborrow, B. V. (1974). *Annu. Rev. Plant Physiol.* **25**, 259–307.
Milborrow, B. V., and Robinson, D. R. (1973). *J. Exp. Bot.* **24**, 537–548.
Minchin, F. R., and Pate, J. S. (1973). *J. Exp. Bot.* **24**, 259–271.
Morowitz, H. J. (1968). "Energy Flow in Biology." Academic Press, New York.
Morowitz, H. J. (1970). "Entropy for Biologists." Academic Press, New York.
Morris, C. J., Thompson, J. F., and Johnson, C. M. (1969). *Plant Physiol.* **44**, 1023–1026.
Moseman, J. G., Wiebe, G. A., Hockett, E. A., and Ramage, R. T. (1972). *Barley Newsl.* **15**, 82–89.
Newland, E. V., and Price, G. G. (1975). *Span* **18**, 4–6.
Newman, E. I. (1976). *Philos. Trans. R. Soc. London, Ser. B* **273**, 463–478.
Noguchi, M., Koiwai, A., and Tamaki, E. (1966). *Agric. Biol. Chem.* **30**, 452–456.
Northcote, D. H. (1972). *Annu. Rev. Plant Physiol.* **23**, 113–132.
Odum, E. P. (1971). "Fundamentals of Ecology." Saunders, Philadelphia, Pennsylvania.
Odum, H. T. (1971). "Environment, Power, and Society." Wiley, New York.
Odum, H. T., and Odum, E. C. (1976). "Energy Basis for Man and Nature." McGraw-Hill, New York.
Olien, C. R. (1974). *Mich., Agric. Exp. Stn., Res. Rep.* **247**, 1–7.
O'Toole, J. C., and Chang, T. T. (1978). *Int. Rice Res. Inst.*, Research Paper No. 14.
Pálfi, G., and Juhász, J. (1971). *Plant Soil* **34**, 503–507.
Pálfi, G., Köves, E., Bito, M., and Sebestyén, R. (1974). *Phyton* **32**, 121–127.
Passioura, J. B. (1976). In "Transport and Transfer Processes in Plants" (I. F. Wardlaw and J. B. Passioura, eds.), pp. 373–380. Academic Press, New York.
Passioura, J. B., and Ashford, A. E. (1974). *Aust. J. Plant Physiol.* **1**, 521–527.
Penning de Vries, F. W. T. (1975). In "Photosynthesis and Productivity in Different Environments" (J. P. Cooper, ed.), pp. 459–480. Cambridge Univ. Press, London and New York.
Pimentel, D., Hurd, L. E., Bellotti, A. C., Forster, J. J., Oka, I. N., Scholes, O. D., and Whitman, R. J. (1973). *Science* **182**, 443–449.
Poljakoff-Mayber, A., and Gale, J. (1972). In "Water Deficits and Plant Growth" (T. T. Kozlowski, ed.), Vol. 3, pp. 277–306. Academic Press, New York.
Rackham, O. (1972). In "Crop Processes in Controlled Environments" (A. R. Rees et al., eds.), pp. 127–138. Academic Press, New York.
Raschke, K. (1960). *Annu. Rev. Plant Physiol.* **11**, 111–126.
Raschke, K. (1966). *Planta* **68**, 111–140.
Raschke, K. (1970). *Planta* **91**, 336–363.
Raschke, K. (1975). *Annu. Rev. Plant Physiol.* **26**, 309–340.
Raschke, K. (1976). *Philos. Trans. R. Soc. London, Ser. B* **273**, 551–560.
Raschke, K., and Zeevaart, J. A. D. (1976). *Plant Physiol.* **58**, 169–174.
Raschke, K., Pierce, M., and Popiela, C. C. (1976). *Plant Physiol.* **57**, 115–121.
Reid, D. A. (1971). *Barley Genet. 2, Proc. Int. Symp., 2nd, 1969* pp. 409–413.

Reitz, L. P. (1974). *Agric. Meteorol.* **14**, 3–11.
Ritchie, J. T. (1974). *Agric. Meteorol.* **14**, 183–198.
Salisbury, F. B., and Ross, C. (1969). "Plant Physiology." Wadsworth, Belmont, California.
Saunier, R. E., Hull, H. M., and Ehrenreich, J. H. (1968). *Plant Physiol.* **43**, 401–404.
Schobert, B. (1977). *J. Theor. Biol.* **68**, 17–26.
Shearman, L. L., Olien, C. R., Marchetti, B. L., and Everson, E. H. (1973). *Crop Sci.* **13**, 514–519.
Singh, T. N., Aspinall, D., and Paleg, L. G. (1972). *Nature (London), New Biol.* **236**, 188–190.
Singh, T. N., Paleg, L. G., and Aspinall, D. (1973a). *Aust. J. Biol. Sci.* **26**, 45–56.
Singh, T. N., Aspinall, D., Paleg, L. G., and Boggess, S. F. (1973b). *Aust. J. Biol. Sci.* **26**, 57–63.
Singh, T. N., Paleg, L. G., and Aspinall, D. (1973c). *Aust. J. Biol. Sci.* **26**, 65–76.
Singh, T. N., Aspinall, D., and Paleg, L. G. (1973d). *Aust. J. Biol. Sci.* **26**, 77–86.
Slatyer, R. O. (1969). In "Physiological Aspects of Crop Yield" (J. D. Eastin *et al.*, eds.), pp. 53–83. Am. Soc. Agron. and Crop Sci. Soc. Am., Madison, Wisconsin.
Smith, T. A. (1971). *Biol. Rev. Cambridge Philos. Soc.* **46**, 201–241.
Sprague, G. F. (1969). In "Physiological Aspects of Crop Yield" (J. D. Eastin *et al.*, eds.), pp. 375–387. Am. Soc. Agron. and Crop Sci. Soc. Am., Madison, Wisconsin.
Srb, A. M., Owen, R. D., and Edgar, R. S. (1965). "General Genetics." Freeman, San Francisco, California.
Steinhart, J. S., and Steinhart, C. E. (1974a). *Science* **184**, 307–316.
Steinhart, J. S., and Steinhart, C. E. (1974b). "Energy Sources, Use and Role in Human Affairs." Wadsworth, Belmont, California.
Stewart, C. R. (1972a). *Plant Physiol.* **50**, 679–681.
Stewart, C. R. (1972b). *Plant Physiol.* **51**, 508–511.
Stewart, C. R. (1980). In "Physiology and Biochemistry of Drought Resistance in Plants" (L. G. Paleg and D Aspinall, eds.). Harcourt Brace Jovanovich Group, New York (in press).
Stewart, C. R., and Hanson, A. D. (1980). In "Adaptations of Plants to Water and High Temperature Stress" (P. J. Kramer and N. C. Turner, eds.). Wiley, New York (in press).
Stewart, C. R., and Lai, E. Y. (1974). *Plant Sci. Lett.* **3**, 173–181.
Stewart, C. R., Morris, C. J., and Thompson, J. F. (1966). *Plant Physiol.* **41**, 1585–1590.
Stewart, C. R., Boggess, S. F., Aspinall, D., and Paleg, L. G. (1977). *Plant Physiol.* **59**, 930–932.
Stewart, G. R., and Lee, J. A. (1974). *Planta* **120**, 279–289.
Storey, R., and Wyn Jones, R. G. (1975). *Plant Sci. Lett.* **4**, 161–168.
Stroike, J. E., and Johnson, V. A. (1972). *Nebr., Agric. Exp. Stn., Res. Bull.* **251**, 1–48.
Sullivan, C. Y. (1971). In "Drought Injury and Resistance in Crops" (K. L. Larson and J. D. Eastin, eds.), pp. 1–18. Crop Sci. Soc. Am., Madison, Wisconsin.
Suneson, C. A. (1956). *Agron. J.* **48**, 188–191.
Suneson, C. A., and Ramage, R. T. (1962). *Crop Sci.* **2**, 249–250.
Tanner, C. B. (1968). In "Water Deficits and Plant Growth" (T. T. Kozlowski, ed.), Vol. I, pp. 73–106. Academic Press, New York.
Toates, F. M. (1975). "Control Theory in Biology and Experimental Psychology." Hutchinson, London.
Tully, R. E., Hanson, A. D., and Nelsen, C. E. (1979). *Plant Physiol.* **63**, 518–523.
Tyankova, L. A. (1966). *C. R. Acad. Bulg. Sci.* **19**, 847–850.

U. S. Department of Agriculture. (1974). "The U. S. Food and Fiber Sector: Energy Use and Outlook." Committee Print, Committee on Agriculture and Forestry, US Senate, US Govt. Printing Office, Washington, D.C.

U. S. Energy Research and Development Administration (1975). "A National Plan for Energy Research, Development, and Demonstration," Vol. I, ERDA-48. ERDA, Washington, D.C.

Vaadia, Y. (1976). *Philos. Trans. R. Soc. London, Ser. B* **273**, 513–522.

Viaud, P. R. (1972). *Cryobiology* **9**, 233–239.

Viets, F. G. (1971). In "Drought Injury and Resistance in Crops" (K. L. Larson and J. D. Eastin, eds.), pp. 57–76. Crop Sci. Soc. Am., Madison, Wisconsin.

Viets, F. G. (1972). In "Water Deficits and Plant Growth" (T. T. Kozlowski, ed.), Vol. 3, pp. 217–239. Academic Press, New York.

Waldren, R. P., and Teare, I. D. (1974). *Plant Soil* **40**, 689–692.

Wallace, D. H., Ozbun, J. L., and Munger, H. M. (1972). *Adv. Agron.* **24**, 97–146.

Walter, H., and Stadelmann, E. (1974). In "Desert Biology" (G. W. Brown, ed.), Vol. 2, pp. 31–101. Academic Press, New York.

Weatherley, P. E. (1970). *Adv. Bot. Res.* **3**, 171–206.

Weatherley, P. E. (1976). *Philos. Trans. R. Soc. London, Ser. B* **273**, 435–444.

Wiebe, G. A. (1968). *U. S., Dep. Agric., Agric. Handb.* **338**, 96–104.

Williams, T. V., Snell, R. S., and Cress, C. E. (1969). *Crop Sci.* **9**, 19–22.

Wortman, S. (1975). In "Crop Productivity—Research Imperatives" (A. W. A. Brown *et al.*, eds.), pp. 43–61. Michigan Agricultural Experiment Station, East Lansing.

Wright, S. T. C. (1977). *Planta* **134**, 183–189.

Wyn Jones, R. G., Owen, E. D., Qureshi, R. H., and Aslam, Z. (1974). In "Plant Analysis and Fertilizer Problems No. 7" (J. Wehrmann, ed.), p. 589. German Society of Plant Nutrition.

Zabadal, T. J. (1974). *Plant Physiol.* **53**, 125–127.

Zohary, D., Harlan, J. R., and Vardi, A. (1969). *Euphytica* **18**, 58–65.

INTERACTION OF PLANTS AND OTHER ORGANISMS

Chapter 4

Plant Viruses

Albert Siegel and V. Hari

I. INTRODUCTION

The viruses comprise one of the several groups of pests that frequently have the effect, when present, of reducing agricultural productivity. Viruses can be defined as transmissable, obligate, intracellular parasites that differ from other forms of life in having no intrinsic metabolism and only one type of nucleic acid, either DNA or RNA. All of the major groups of cellular organisms can accommodate the replication of viruses, so that there are viruses that multiply in animal, plant,

155

The Biology of Crop Productivity
Copyright © 1980 by Academic Press, Inc.
All rights of reproduction in any form reserved
ISBN 0-12-159850-0

fungal, protist, or bacterial cells. Although there is usually considerable specificity in the virus–host interaction, there are some viruses that can replicate in the cells of two different major groups, such as plants and animals. This chapter will concern itself primarily, but not exclusively, with those viruses that replicate in plants and that, as a consequence, are frequently responsible for causing disease and lowering the yield of agricultural plant crops. Several more complete introductions to this topic are available among which are those by Matthews (1), Gibbs and Harrison (2), Kado and Agrawal (3), and Smith (4).

Diseases and other conditions caused by viruses have been known and described since earliest recorded history. However, it was not until the reports by Iwanowski (5) and Beijerinck (6) in 1892 and 1898, respectively, that it was realized that the causal agent of a transmissable plant disease, tobacco mosaic, was unique in that it could pass through a bacteria-retaining filter. Soon thereafter, it was discovered that foot and mouth disease of cattle was also caused by a "filterable" agent (7). Thus, it was established that agents smaller than bacteria could cause disease, and the term "virus" was adopted as a name for these agents. The work of several scientists (8–11), highlighted by Stanley's purification of the tobacco mosaic virus in 1935, gave physical reality to virus and demonstrated that they were composed, at a minimum, of protein and nucleic acid. The concept that it is deoxyribonucleic acid (DNA) that comprises the essential genetic material of bacteria and, by inference, all living things was provided by Avery and co-workers (12) in 1944 and was confirmed for bacterial viruses by Hershey and Chase (13) in 1952. This was followed in 1956 by the realization that viral ribonucleic acid (RNA) could also function as genetic material when Gierer and Schramm (14) and Fraenkel-Conrat (15) demonstrated that the tobacco mosaic disease could be induced by inoculation of a plant with the chemically isolated RNA portion of tobacco mosaic virus particles.

One modern view of viruses holds that they are essentially bits of nucleic acid genetic material that lack the coding capacity for independent replication. In order to replicate, reliance is placed on the metabolic and/or replicative machinery specified by a host cell's genetic material. In almost all cases, the viral genetic material is packaged together with protein molecules and sometimes also with lipid-containing membranous material to form a virus particle. This particle serves as a vehicle for the transfer of nucleic acid from host to host, and the nucleic acid is protected from degradation by enzymes likely to be encountered in the environment.

II. DAMAGE DONE BY VIRUSES TO PLANT CROPS

There is no doubt that plant viruses cause extensive damage and reduce the value of many economically important plant crops. Virus diseases almost always cause an outright reduction in yield of grain, fruit, or other agricultural or horticultural products and, in many cases, there is also a loss in crop quality. Thus, in addition to lower yield, tomatoes from tobacco mosaic virus-infected plants are frequently malformed or may have internal browning. Lettuce from lettuce mosaic virus-infected plants is discolored. Potatoes from tobacco necrosis virus-infected plants contain black discolored areas. As a consequence, virus disease leads not only to loss of yield, but frequently to reduced marketability.

Upon infection, viruses generally multiply locally and then spread to invade either specific tissues or, more commonly, the whole plant. Once established, the virus remains in the plant indefinitely. Therefore, there is rarely recovery from a plant virus disease. In view of this feature, virus diseases constitute a different type of hazard to perennial and vegetatively propagated crops (e.g., tree crops, potato) than they do to annual or biennial crops (e.g., small grains, sugar beet). We present below examples of the type and extent of damage that can be caused to both types of plant crops by virus disease.

Most annual crops are subject to attack by a number of different viruses, which sometimes leads to significant loss in available food supply. For instance, virus diseases have, at times, seriously reduced the rice harvest in areas where this crop is a dietary staple. The Hoja Blanca disease of rice, characterized by the appearance of white leaves on infected plants, was first reported in Columbia in 1935, and sometime later in Panama (1952), Cuba (1954), Venezuela (1956), and the United States (1957). Losses directly attributable to this disease vary from year to year and place to place. In 1958 many rice fields in Columbia were completely lost (16), and in 1956 losses were estimated at 25% in Cuba and 50% in Venezuela (17). Tungro, another disease of rice found primarily in the Phillipines and other parts of Asia, is estimated to have reduced the yield by 30% in Luzon province. Other virus diseases of rice—among which are rice dwarf, yellow dwarf and stripe— also pose continuous threats to bountiful yield (18). Rice is by no means the only annual crop that finds itself host to a diverse group of viruses. The same is true for almost all of the other grass, vegetable, and floricultural crops. Wheat is subject to numerous virus diseases, one of which is wheat soil born mosaic. This disease caused complete crop failure of susceptible wheat varieties for many years in Illinois (19), and in 1957 347,000 acres in Kansas alone were affected, leading to an estimated loss of some 2,000,000 bushels of wheat (20). Among the vegetable crops, Broadbent (21) has recently estimated that at least 20% of the worldwide tomato crop is lost to tobacco mosaic virus.

The economic loss caused by virus disease to perennial crops is compounded, because not only is there reduced crop yield in a single year, but sometimes also the loss of trees or other valuable stock. Even when virus disease is such that stock is not killed outright, replanting frequently becomes necessary, due to the accumulation of a number of different virus diseases and the consequent annual reduction of yield. Among other tree and vegetatively propagated crops, virus diseases cause serious damage to peach, pear, apple, cherry, cacao, coconut, citrus, and potatoes.

An impressive example of a devastating virus disease affecting a perennial crop is plum pox (22). The disease is called Sarka in central Europe, where it has caused substantial economic loss. The disease was first reported in Macedonia in 1915–1916, and by 1952 had affected an estimated 16 million plum trees in Yugoslavia, where plum accounts for 80% of all fruit grown. Plum growing has been abandoned in many regions of Yugoslavia and Bulgaria as a consequence of the disease, which is now widespread in Europe. It has been reported in, among other places, Italy, the Soviet Union, Switzerland, Turkey, and England. Other examples of serious virus causing tree diseases are the cadang-cadang disease of coconut (probably caused by a viroid), which results in the destruction of millions of trees of this important crop (23), and the cacao swollen shoot disease, which claims an average annual loss of about one-fifth of the crop (24). Virus diseases of other vegetatively propagated crops are also of considerable importance. Potatoes, for instance, are subject to yield loss from a large number of different virus diseases, among which are those caused by potato aucuba virus, tomato black ring virus, beet curly top virus, potato leaf roll virus, potato mop-top virus, potato paracrinkle virus, potato spindle tuber viroid, tobacco rattle virus, potato stunt virus, potato virus A, potato virus S, potato virus X, potato virus Y, and potato yellow dwarf virus (4). Some viruses are of economic importance in reducing the yield and/or marketability of a number of different crops. Cucumber mosaic virus, for instance, not only affects the cucumber crops, but causes diseases of varying intensities in a wide range of crops—among which are delphinium, columbine, watercress, violets, buckwheat, spinach, beet, geranium, muskmelon, summer squash, winter squash, watermelon, euphorbia, cowpea, lupin, celery, carrot, periwinkle, aster, calendula, zinnia, primula, lobelia, tobacco, tomato, pepper, petunia, potato, hops, lettuce, penstomen, privet, passion fruit, lilly, onion, banana, manila hemp, and maize (4).

III. TYPES OF PLANT VIRUSES

Viruses have in common the properties by which they are defined, that is, they are obligate intracellular parasites that differ from cellular organisms in lacking intrinsic metabolism and in containing only one type of nucleic acid, either RNA or DNA, rather than both. However, they are far from constituting a homogeneous group, there being different kinds of viruses that are distinguishable from each other by a number of properties. We shall review here the properties of the different virus groups, because their essential features may be of use in the design of rational control measures.

Some of the properties that have been used to classify viruses are (1) the type, size, and organization of the nucleic acid genome; (2) the size and morphology of the virus particle; (3) the vector responsible for transmission of the virus from host to host; and (4) the mode of replication, when this is well understood. The manner in which these properties might differ among viruses, in general, and plant viruses, in particular, is provided below.

A. Nature of the Genetic Material

The genetic material of all cellular organisms is DNA, which ordinarily exists in a double-stranded configuration (25). Viruses, on the other hand, may contain other types of nucleic acid as genetic material, and these are detailed below, together with a classification based on this property (26).

Class I—like cells, these viruses contain double-stranded DNA as genetic material.

Class II—viruses contain single-stranded DNA with, as far as is known, the same polarity as messenger RNA.

Class III—viruses have a double-stranded RNA genome.

Class IV—viruses have a single-stranded RNA genome that is of the same polarity as the viral messenger RNA.

Class V—viruses also have a single-stranded RNA genome, but one that is complementary in base sequence to the viral messenger RNA.

Class VI—consists of the RNA tumor viruses known, so far, only for

vertebrates. They contain single-stranded RNA and have a DNA intermediate in their replication cycle.

Class VII—added to the original classification (26) and consists of a
group of entities so far unique to plants. These are designated viroids
and consist of small, naked, single-stranded RNA molecules, which are
reported not to be translated into protein (27,28).

Most plant viruses belong to Class IV, that is, they contain single-
stranded RNA, most of which can be translated into virus-specific proteins by the host cell's protein synthesizing machinery. Plant viruses
are also known that contain double-stranded DNA (Class I); single-
stranded DNA (Class II) (29); double-stranded RNA (Class III); negative
single-stranded RNA (RNA that is complementary to messenger RNA)
(Class V), and small, naked, single-stranded RNA (Class VII). The fact
that most plant viruses contain RNA as genetic material is of significance in attempts to develop rational chemotherapeutic control programs because, as has already been mentioned, cellular genetic material is DNA. Therefore, attempts can be made to interfere with viral
RNA replication specifically without at the same time damaging the
host's vital apparatus for DNA replication. This subject will be dealt
with in more detail in section VI of this chapter.

B. Genome Organization

Another criterion in classifying plant viruses is genome organization. Some Class IV plant viruses have genomes that are packaged in
the virion as a single unsegmented strand of RNA, while others have
segmented genomes such that the complete genetic specification is
distributed among two to four RNA strands. These split genome viruses
usually have the different pieces of their genome packaged not in the
same virus particle but rather in two, three, or four nucleoprotein particles, depending on the particular virus (30). Thus, in many cases, several different particles must be present in order for successful initiation
of infection to take place.

C. Morphology

Still another property that provides a basis for virus classification is
the shape and architecture of the virus particle. Virus particles are
usually composed either of a free nucleocapsid or of a nucleocapsid
combined with accessory materials, consisting mostly of a protein containing phospholipid membrane. The nucleocapsid is a structured

aggregate of many protein molecules (either identical or of a few different kinds) and the one to several strands of the nucleic acid genome. The protein molecules are usually arranged to form either a tightly wound helix or a polyhedron with icosahedral symmetry. In the former case, the nucleocapsid assumes the shape of a stiff or flexuous rod. In the latter, there is a superficial resemblence to a sphere, although the protein molecules are actually arranged according to crystallographic rules or, in the same sense, geodesic dome constructions (31). In addition to the rods and polyhedral forms, some nucleocapsids assume a bacilliform shape (an elongated structure with hemispherical ends), in which the protein molecules are arranged in a pattern that is a modification of that found in the polyhedral forms.

Most of the plant viruses consist of free nucleocapsids, although there are important groups that have more complex virus particles. Examples of viruses that have naked nucleocapsids are the rod-shaped tobacco mosaic virus—composed of one molecule of single-stranded RNA with a molecular weight of 2.1×10^6, packed in a helical arrangement, together with 2100 identical protein molecules, each with a molecular weight of 17,500—and the polyhedral turnip yellow mosaic virus, also consisting of one 2×10^6 molecular weight RNA molecule. However, in the latter case, the genome is surrounded by the 180 identical protein molecules that comprise the polyhedron. Lettuce necrotic yellows and potato yellow dwarf are examples of viruses that have a bacilliform shape and a complex structure, consisting of a coiled flexuous rod-shaped nucleocapsid surrounded by a protein-containing membrane (32).

D. Method of Disease Transmission

Viruses can only be successful if they can spread from one host to another, and there are a number of ways this is accomplished in the case of the plant viruses. Sometimes the only known method of disease transmission is by direct contact. That is, disease is transmitted to a new host mechanically either by a diseased plant rubbing against a healthy one, or by accidental transmission when man or animal first touches a diseased plant and then a healthy one. Another method involves transmission from one generation to another through seed, or from one plant to another via pollen (33). In most cases, however, plant virus diseases are spread by rather specific vectors. These are usually insects, but may be, in specific cases, arachnids (34), fungi (35), or nematodes (36). The most common insect vectors are aphids (37) and leafhoppers (38), but some virus diseases are transmitted by either white flies, mealy bugs, beetles (39), dipterans, psylla, fleas, thrips, or others. The type of vector involved in transmitting specific viruses provides another criterion for classification.

Before describing some of the different plant viruses and virus groups, it is well to briefly discuss plant virus nomenclature. Several attempts have been made to systematize plant virus nomenclature but these, in general, have not been widely adopted. Instead, the viruses are named according to the host from which they were first isolated and the nature of the symptoms caused by the disease. Thus, tobacco mosaic virus was first isolated from a tobacco plant, with disease symptoms consisting of a mosaic of light green and dark green areas on its leaves. Despite the name, however, many strains of this virus have been isolated from species other than tobacco, and a number of virus strain combinations give rise to symptoms other than a mosaic. This same type of situation exists to a greater or lesser extent for many plant viruses.

It has become convenient to apply a cryptogram to viruses, both as an aid to their classification and as a shorthand means of listing some of their properties (40,41). The cryptogram in common use has four pairs of symbols, the two members of a pair being separated by a slash and the pairs by a colon. The four pairs of symbols, respectively, indicate the following properties:

1. The first pair indicates the type and strandedness of the genome. Thus, for instance, R/1 indicates that the viral nucleic acid is single-stranded RNA, and D/2 means that it is double-stranded DNA.

2. The second pair indicates the molecular weight of the genome in 10^6 units and the percentage nucleic acid in an infective particle. Thus, 2.1/5 signifies that the genome has a molecular weight of 2.1×10^6 and that this constitutes 5% of the mass of the virus particle. When the genome is segmented and all of the parts of the genome occur in one particle, then the total weight of nucleic acid is given preceded by a summation (Σ) sign. When pieces of the genome occur in separate particles, the information is given separately for each particle, with plus signs between the pairs of symbols.

3. The third pair indicates the shapes of the virus particle and nucleocapsid. The symbols employed are S for essentially spherical, E for elongated with the ends not rounded, U for elongated with the ends rounded, and X for complex or none of the above. Thus, U/E means that the virus particle is elongated with rounded ends and contains an elongated nucleocapsid.

4. The fourth pair indicates the type of host in which the virus replicates and the transmission vector. The symbols for the type of host are A for algae, B for bacterium, F for fungus, I for invertebrate, M for mycoplasma, P for pteridophyte, S for seed plant, and V for vertebrate. The symbols that have so far been adopted for vectors are Ac for mite or tick; Al for whitefly; Ap for aphid; Au for leaf, plant, or treehopper; Cc for mealy bug; Cl for beetle; Di for fly or mosquito; Fu for fungus; Gy for mirid, piesmid, or tingid bug; Ne for nematode; Ps for psylla; Si for flea; Th for thrips; Ve for vector known but not of those listed; and O for spreads without a vector via a contaminated environment.

Additional symbols used are an asterisk * when a particular property is unknown and parenthesis, ( ), when the enclosed information is doubtful or unconfirmed. When the entire cryptogram is bracketed, [ ], then the information is about a virus group. The cryptogram [R/1 : 4-6.5/5 : E/E :S/Ap] is for a virus group, all of whose members contain single-stranded RNA (R/1), in which the genome constitutes 5% of the virus particle—but may vary from 4–6.5×10^6 for different members of the group (4–6.5/5), which has both an elongated virus particle and nucleocapsid with straight ends (E/E), and which replicates in seed plants and is transmitted by aphids (S/Ap).

The codification of the different plant viruses is now being accomplished under the aegis of the International Committee of the Taxonomy of Plant Viruses, an arm of the Section on Virology of the International Association of Microbiological Societies. The groups of plant viruses deemed to be well enough understood to receive sanction as official entities are listed here (41).

Class I. Groups containing double-stranded DNA.
  A. Caulimovirus (cauliflower mosaic virus group) [D/2: 4.5/16: S/S: S/Ap]. The particles are ca. 50 nm in diameter and contain DNA.
Class II. Group containing single-stranded DNA.
  A. Geminivirus [D/1: 0.75/29: S/S: S/Au,Al]. Small particles, 19–20 nm in diameter, seen predominantly in pairs.
Class III. Groups containing double-stranded RNA.
  A. Plant reovirus group [R/2: Σ 10 to 16/11 to 22: S/S: S,I,V/Au]. This group resembles animal and insect reoviruses in having a segmented, double-stranded RNA genome, all parts of which are packaged into single particles of about 70 nm in diameter. Members

of this group, such as clover wound tumor virus and rice dwarf virus, multiply both in their plant host and in their insect (leafhopper) vector.

Class IV. Groups containing single-stranded RNA that is identical in base sequence to messenger RNA.

A. Nondivided Genome.

1. Helical symmetry (rigid or flexuous rod-shaped).

a. Tobamovirus (tobacco mosaic virus group). [R/1: 2/5: E/E: S/O]. Rigid rods with dimensions 300 × 18 nm.

b. Potexvirus (potato virus X group) [R/1: 2.2/6: E/E: S/O (Fu)]. The virions are flexuous rods 480–580 nm long and ca. 13 nm in diameter. This group, like the tobamovirus group, frequently causes mosaic symptoms.

c. Carlavirus (carnation latent virus group) [R/1: */6: E/E: S/Ap]. The particles of viruses belonging to this group are almost straight and have dimensions of 650 × 12 nm. The term latent indicates that there were few, if any, symptoms on the host from which the virus was first isolated.

d. Potyvirus (potato virus Y group) [R/1: 3.5/5: E/E: S/Ap]. This is the most common group of plant viruses known at present, containing many separately named viruses, all of which have long, flexious virions 730–790 × 11 nm. Many of these induce diseases with mosaic symptoms and characteristic "pinwheel" type cytoplasmic inclusions.

e. Closterovirus (beet yellows virus group) [R/1: 4.3/5: E/E: S/Ap]. The particles of this group are very long (1200–2000 nm). They induce diseases characterized by yellowing and phloem necrosis.

2. Isometric virions.

a. Tymovirus (turnip yellow mosaic virus group) [R/1: 2/37: S/S: S/Cl]. Virus preparations characteristically contain two types of particles, with and without nucleic acid. Both types have a diameter of 25–30 nm, but those lacking nucleic acid are noninfectious.

    b. Luteovirus (barley yellow dwarf virus group) [R/1: 2/*: S/S: S/Ap]. Particles of this group of viruses have a diameter of about 25 nm and may persist in the vector, aphids, for several weeks after acquisition. The diseases induced have not been mechanically transmitted from plant to plant.

    c. Tombusvirus (tomato bushy stunt group) [R/1: 1.5/18: S/S: S/*]. Particles of this group are 30 nm in diameter and usually cause necrotic symptoms.

    d. Tobacco necrosis satellite virus. [R/1: 0.4/20: S/S: S/Fu]. This virus is small, 17 nm in diameter, and can only replicate in the presence of tobacco necrosis virus. Tobacco necrosis virus is similar in some respects to the tombusvirus group.

    e. Southern bean mosaic virus group [R/1: 1.4/21: S/S: S/Cl]. Particles of this group have a small genome packaged in 28-nm polyhedra. The host range is restricted primarily to legumes.

    f. Maize chlorotic mottle virus group [R/1: 3.2/(36): S/S: S/Ve/Au]. These viruses have particles about 30 nm in diameter and a host range restricted to the Graminae.

B. Divided genome.

  1. Helical symmetry (rod-shaped).

    a. Tobravirus (tobacco rattle virus group) [R/1: 2.3/5 + 0.6 to 1.3/5: E/E: S/Ne]. The genome is bipartite, divided between rod-shaped particles of two different lengths. The longer particle, or its nucleic acid, can initiate infection. However, in the absence of the short particle, the infection consists only of replicating nucleic acid. No nucleoprotein virions are formed. The shorter particle is incapable of initiating infection, but its presence is necessary to support virion production, because its nucleic acid contains the coding sequence for the capsid protein.

    b. Hordeivirus (barley stripe mosaic virus

group) The particles are 110–160 nm long and 20–25 nm in diameter. There are two to four components to the genome of which two to three are required for infectivity.

2. Isometric.

a. Cucumovirus (cucumber mosaic virus group) [R/1: 1.3/19 + 1.1/19 + 0.8/19: S/S: S/Ap]. The genome consists of four different nucleic acid molecules distributed among three identical capsids, 30 nm in diameter. The two largest nucleic acid molecules are present singly in capsids, while the two smallest are present together in the third. Either the three nucleocapsids or the three largest nucleic acid molecules are necessary for initiation of infection. The smallest nucleic acid molecule is a monocistronic messenger RNA for the capsid protein. This is one of the most common groups of viruses found to infect plants in temperate regions.

b. Bromovirus (brome mosaic virus group) [R/1: 1.1/23 + 1.0/22 + 0.7/21: S/S: S/*]. This group has many similarities to the cucumovirus group, except that virions are somewhat smaller in diameter (25 nm) and their natural vector is not known.

c. Comovirus (cowpea mosaic virus group) [R/1: 2.3/34 + 1.5/28: S/S: S/Cl]. The virions are 25–30 nm in diameter and are of three types, either without nucleic acid or containing either a larger molecule (2.3×10^6) or a smaller molecule (1.5×10^6) of nucleic acid. Both nucleic acid containing particles are necessary for infection.

d. Nepovirus (tobacco ringspot virus group) [R/1: 2.4/43 + 1.4 to 2.1/30 to 40: S/S: S/Ne]. This group of viruses bears some resemblance to the comoviruses in that there are two separately encapsidated parts to the genome. However, among other differences between them, members of this group are characteristically transmitted by nematodes rather than by beetles. A peculiar feature of infection by this group is that plants that survive an early severe infection may recover and later show little sign of disease even though still infected.

    e. Ilarvirus (isometric labile ringspot virus group). Viruses of this group are common in fruit trees and perennial crops of temperate regions. The particles are of two or more kinds, and are unstable in leaf sap unless chelating or reducing agents are added. The particles contain from 15–25% RNA and have diameter of 20–35 nm.

   3. Bacilliform.

    a. Alfalfa mosaic virus group [R/1: 1.1/16 + 0.8/16 + 0.7/16: U/U: S/Ap]. Viruses of this group generally have particles of four distinct lengths, with rounded ends and of the same diameter. The three largest particles are necessary for infection.

Class V.   Groups containing single-stranded RNA that is complementary to messenger RNA.

    A. Plant rhabdovirus group [R/1: 4/2: U/E: S,I,V/Ap,Au]. Viruses belonging to this group—such as lettuce necrotic yellows, potato yellow dwarf, and sowthistle yellow vein virus—resemble the vertebrate and insect rhabdoviruses in structure and morphology. The virions are complex structures, having an outer lipoprotein membrane and an inner helical nucleoprotein core that contains the RNA that must be transcribed before translation can occur.

Class VII.   Group Containing nontranslatable single-stranded RNA.

    A. Viroids are naked circular RNA molecules that are the smallest disease agents known (about 350 nucleotides). They are peculiar in that they may not code for a protein.

There are, in addition, other groups of plant viruses that are not yet characterized to the point where it is feasible to include them in a descriptive classification scheme such as that presented here. Among these are such economically important viruses as the lipid-containing tomato spotted wilt and carrot mottle viruses, and the bacilliform cacao swollen shoot virus. The characterization and description of plant viruses lags behind that of the vertebrate and bacterial viruses, because there are far fewer workers in the field of plant virology than in other fields of virology, despite that fact that plant viruses present a continuing threat to our food and fiber crops. Several years ago, the Commonwealth Mycological Institute and the Association of Applied Biologists undertook to publish descriptions of the different plant viruses, and they have now produced 200 such descriptions (29a).

IV. EPIDEMIOLOGY OF PLANT VIRUS DISEASE

In this section we will consider briefly the physical and biological factors that influence the spread of plant virus disease, a subject that has been considered more fully by others (42–45). Virus particles must be introduced into living cells of a plant in order for it to become infected. This is usually accomplished by a living vector, which may be an insect, an arachnid, a nematode, or a fungus or, in some cases, direct physical contact resulting from agricultural practices whereby plants are manipulated by hands or tools. Several aspects of the epidemiology of plant virus disease shall be treated: (a) sources of the virus inoculum for a crop, (b) the nature of virus–vector relationships, (c) spread of virus disease into a crop, and (d) spread of virus disease within a crop.

A. Sources of Virus Inoculum

The most common sources of virus for a new crop or plantation are the planting material itself—plant and crop debris from a previous season, weed plants, neighboring fields or household gardens, and vectors that retain the virus for long periods of time.

Many plant viruses, although distributed in high concentration throughout a plant, either do not enter or are inactivated in developing seeds, and thus are not transmitted from one generation to another via seed. However, there are a significant number of virus diseases that are seed transmitted to a greater or lesser extent, either by the virus surviving in the embryo, in the storage tissue of the seed, or in the seed coat or fruit. In the latter two cases, where the virus is not passed through the embryo, infection occurs in young seedlings when germination takes place in the presence of surrounding virus particles. Even in cases where seed transmission of a virus disease may occur infrequently, it can still present a serious crop hazard, because a source of inoculum is provided for spread throughout a field. It has been demonstrated, for

instance, that a very low percentage of seed transmission can give rise
to a heavy infection of lettuce mosaic virus in California lettuce fields
in years when the aphid vector of the disease is active (46). Attempts
are now made to ensure that less than 0.1% of commercial seed will
give rise to infected seedlings. A problem of greater magnitude is present for vegetatively propagated crops, because planting stock derived
from virus-infected plants is also usually diseased. Thus, great pains
are sometimes taken to ensure a source of virus-free planting stock.
Among the herbacious, vegetatively propagated crops that are subject
to severe yield reduction when virus-diseased stock is used as planting
material are potatoes, sugarcane, and the different types of berries. In
addition, almost all of the tree and shrub crops are at risk from the
introduction of virus disease when a new plantation is established.

Not only are viruses spread by means of planting materials, the vectors of virus disease may also be carried to new locations along with the
planting materials. As an example, it is postulated that the nematode
vector of the grapevine fan leaf virus has been spread throughout the
world from Europe in the soil surrounding the roots of grapevine planting stocks (2).

The debris left from the harvesting of a virus-infected crop may
sometimes present a source of virus inoculum for a crop planted the
following season. The roots and stubble of cereals are usually left in the
soil and may, under appropriate conditions, prove to be a source of
virus to infect a newly planted crop. Vegetative propagules as well as
seedling volunteers arising from infected seed scattered during harvesting may, at times, also endanger a new planting. For example,
mosaic-infected cotton rattoons in the Sudan are frequently infested
with white flies, the vector of the disease, which then become viruliferous and transmit the disease to newly germinated cotton plants. Overlapping crops also present a ready virus inoculum for the later crop. It
has been demonstrated in Canada that winter wheat, which has been
planted and germinated before the completion of spring wheat harvesting, becomes infected with wheat streak mosaic as a result of the mite
vector being blown from virus-infected mature spring wheat plants to
the newly germinated winter wheat plants (47).

Weeds that grow within, adjacent to, or even at some distance from
agricultural crops constitute another inoculum source of a large
number of economically significant plant viruses (48). Many viruses, as
well as their vectors, have fairly wide host ranges, including weeds.
The green peach aphid, *Myzus persicae*—an important vector for about
70 different viruses—provides an example of a vector that can feed on a
large number of different species. Weeds play an important role in the

population increase of this vector in the Salinas Valley of California, where it can feed on at least 27 species of 13 different families. It frequently transmits virus from the weed reservoir to commercial crops. Examples of viruses with wide host ranges among both weed and crop plants are the beet curly top virus (49) and cucumber mosaic virus (4). Lettuce necrotic yellows virus is commonly spread to lettuce crops from the weed *Sonchus oleraceus* by an aphid vector (50), and common mosaic of cotton is frequently introduced to a cotton field by white flies that had been feeding on malvaceous weeds (51). Weeds also play an important role in the survival of nematode and fungal vectors for a number of important virus diseases.

B. Virus–Vector Relationships

As has already been pointed out, most viruses are transmitted from one host plant to another by a living vector, which can be an insect, a mite, a nematode, or a fungus.

Both sucking (aphids, leafhoppers, white flies, thrips, mealy bugs) and biting (beetles, grasshoppers) insects are known to be plant virus vectors. Among these, aphids transmit more different viruses than do the other insect groups and are, therefore, a major factor in the spread of plant virus disease. The specificity of the virus–vector relationship is variable, with many viruses having only a single known aphid vector, while other viruses can be transmitted by a number of different aphid species. In like manner, some aphid species are known to transmit only one or a few different viruses, whereas others, such as *Myzus persicae*, can serve as a vector for many. One of the features that make aphids such efficient agents of disease spreading is their tremendous reproductive potential. It is primarily only the winged forms that serve as vectors under field conditions.

Several types of virus–vector relationships have been defined for aphids as well as for some of the other insect vectors. These are classified as either nonpersistent (52,53) or stylet-borne, circulative, and propagative (54). The nonpersistent, or what is in most cases synonymous, stylet-borne, refers to a virus–vector relationship in which the vector acquires the virus after a short feeding period on an infected host plant (2–5 min), can transmit the virus to a healthy plant immediately after acquisition, and then rapidly (minutes) loses the ability to infect. The ability to infect is also lost upon molting. It might seem at first sight that in this type of transmission the virus is carried passively from one plant to another on the mouthparts of the vector. This is probably not the case, since several viruses are not transmitted by sucking insects, although they are not easily inactivated and are known to come into contact with insect mouthparts because there are clear signs that they are ingested (55,56). Other evidence that transmission is not a simple transfer comes from the fact that different strains of a virus may differ in transmission efficiency and from peculiar interactions among different viruses. Thus, potato aucuba mosaic virus is transmitted by aphids only when either potato virus Y or A is also present (57). Recent work does much to resolve some of the puzzling observations concerning the nonpersistent or stylet-borne viruses by demonstrating that the insect must obtain not only virus particles from a diseased plant in order to become infectious, but also a separable, as yet uncharacterized, transmission factor (58,59).

The persistent or circulative type of virus–vector relationship refers to the situation in which viruliferous insects remain infective through a molt, inferring that the virus is present either in the midgut or hemolymph. The time of feeding for acquisition of virus is usually longer than in the nonpersistent relationship and, following acquisition, there is a latent period of hours to days before the virus can be transmitted to a new host. Once the insect becomes infective, it remains so for an extended period of time (days to weeks). An example of a persistent vector–virus relationship is sowthistle yellow vein virus in its aphid vector *Hyperomyzus lactucae* L. The latent period is 8 days when the aphid is maintained at 25°C, following which infectivity is retained for as long as 52 days (60). Some other persistent viruses are pea enation mosaic virus in *Acyrthosiphon pisum* and *Myzus persicae*, beet western yellows virus in *Myzus persicae*, and barley yellow dwarf virus in *Rhopalosiphon padi*. The persistent virus–vector relationships are of two types. In one type, the virus does not multiply in the vector, while in the other, it does. The first situation is called circulative; the second, propagative. Among the aphid-transmitted viruses, pea enation mosaic virus is circulative (61), whereas sowthistle yellow vein virus and lettuce necrotic yellows virus are propagative. Not only do the propagative viruses multiply in their insect vectors, but in some cases the virus is transmitted to progeny through the eggs of viruliferous vectors, a process called transovarian transmission. This process is more common among leafhopper-transmitted virus, but it also occurs with certain aphid–virus combinations (62).

Intermediate between the nonpersistent and the persistent virus–vector combinations is a group that has characteristics of both and is called semipersistent. Most of these probably are not retained through a molt, and can be considered as stylet-borne virus that for some reason persist for a longer period than do most other stylet-borne viruses.

The leafhoppers are probably second in importance to the aphids as vectors of plant virus disease. Many of the viruses transmitted by the leafhoppers belong to Classes III and V, double-stranded RNA and negative single-stranded RNA viruses, respectively. The nonpersistent mode of transmission is unknown, the virus–vector relationship being either semipersistent, circulative, or propagative. The first viruses shown to multiply in their insect vector were the leafhopper-transmitted rice dwarf and clover wound tumor viruses (63,64). These viruses were also the first in which transovarian transmission was demonstrated (65,66).

Mites act as vectors for the transmission of a number of plant virus diseases, among which are currant reversion disease, wheat spot mosaic, wheat streak mosaic, and rye grass mosaic (46). Mites cannot fly, and presumably they spread disease slowly by crawling from one plant to another or more rapidly by wind dispersal.

Nematodes of the genera *Xiphinema*, *Longidorus*, and *Trichodorus*, together with certain fungi, are responsible for the transmission of the soil-borne viruses. The first two genera transmit the polyhedral Nepo viruses—such as tomato black ring spot virus, raspberry ring spot virus, arabis mosaic virus, and cherry leaf roll virus—whereas *Trichodorus* is a specific vector for the tobraviruses, such as the tobacco rattle and pea early browning viruses. Once acquired, viruses persist in nematodes for long periods of time (months), although there is no evidence of virus replication, transovarian transmission, or retention through a molt (67).

A number of viruses are transmitted by soil fungi. Of particular importance are the species of *Olpidium* which transmit tobacco necrosis, tobacco stunt, and cucumber mosaic viruses; *Spongospora subterranea*, which transmits potato mop top virus; and *Polymyxa graminis*, the vector for the economically important soil-borne wheat mosaic virus (35). There are apparently two methods of transmission. One is exemplified by the relationship between tobacco necrosis virus and *Olpidium*, where the virus becomes firmly attached to zoospores and probably infects plants at root sites where the fungus enters (68). There is a more intimate relationship between virus and vector in the other method, exemplified by the soil-borne wheat mosaic and potato mop-top viruses (35). Here, the fungus probably acquires the virus while growing in an infected host, and the virus is held internally, in the cytoplasm, rather than on the surface. Infection again takes place when zoospores germinate and invade the roots of healthy plants. The virus remains viable in resting fungal spores, and can remain infectious for an extended period of time.

C. Spread of Virus Disease into a Crop

Virus disease can be introduced into a crop in a number of ways. Among these are the planting material and debris or vectors left from a previous crop. In addition, many crops are affected by viruses carried into a field from an outside source by vectors. The flying leaf-sucking insects, especially aphids, are of particular importance in this regard. The reproductive capacity of aphids is great, and when conditions are favorable more than a million individuals can be produced per day in a single acre planted with beans (44). Estimates for other crops are equally large (69). It is perhaps not too surprising, then, that correlations have been found between the size of the vector populations and the spread of particular virus diseases. For example, the annual spread of potato virus diseases in the Netherlands is more rapid and more extensive in years when conditions are favorable for rapid aphid population buildup than when the reverse is the case (70). The annual spread of potato viruses Y and leaf roll in England could also be correlated with the numbers of the specific aphid, Myzus persicae, caught in traps (71). As was previously mentioned, the aphid Myzus persicae is capable of transmitting a large number of different viruses, including beet yellows, beet mosaic, and beet mild yellowing viruses. These viruses, as well as the aphid, overwinter in sugar beet crops kept for a second year to produce seed, in fodder beet, in mangold, and in many perennial weed host plants. Viruliferous winged forms of the aphid are produced in the spring. These leave to feed on the newly planted beet crop and, in the process, infect it with several of the beet viruses. Similarly, in Europe, bean leaf roll virus is transmitted between and within bean and pea crops by the pea aphid, Acyrthosiphon pisum.

Long-distance spread of many insect-transmitted viruses can occur, and it is known that airborne vectors may be carried hundreds of kilometers by wind. In addition, the activity of vectors is greatly affected by such factors as air movement and temperature. Mites, for instance, cannot fly but, nevertheless, can be carried passively by wind. As a result, the distribution and spread of wheat streak mosaic virus is very much dependent on the speed and direction of the wind (72). Frequently, a gradient of virus disease can be observed, with the highest proportion of infected plants being close to a virus source and the proportion decreasing with distance. The nature of such a gradient is affected by the type of vector involved and by climatic conditions. For instance, viruses spread by leafhoppers have shallower gradients under mild weather conditions than those spread by aphids, mites, mealy bugs, nematodes, or fungi, because the leafhoppers are strong fliers. The shallow type of gradient is also the type most often observed for the persistent viruses, because these are best spread by aphids that feed for a relatively long time, most frequently after longer flights. In contrast, the gradients for nonpersistent viruses are likely to be rather sharp, because of the short time that the vectors remain infectious.

Not only do air currents and wind play an important role in the long-distance spread of plant virus disease, but other climatic factors may also be of considerable importance. In the southwestern United States, for instance, the beet leafhopper overwinters in desert areas that usually receive seasonal winter rainfall. As water becomes scarce in the late spring, however, there is a migration of this population to the newly planted irrigated beet fields, with consequent introduction of beet curly top virus to the beet crop. Aphids usually produce primarily wingless individuals with little potential for movement under favorable conditions. However, when conditions become unfavorable, winged individuals that can fly are produced and migrate to more favorable areas, spreading virus disease in the process.

The rapidity of virus spread is influenced by whether or not a virus introduced into a field from an outside source will spread from the newly infected plants to other plants in the same field. If it does not, then only scattered plants will be infected, the number being proportional to the number of infective vectors entering the crop. Such a situation exists in Australia, in the case of lettuce necrotic yellow virus which is transmitted to lettuce plants from the weed *Sonchus oleraceus* by an aphid vector which, however, does not colonize lettuce. Thus, spread within the lettuce crop is negligible (73). The more common situation is that the vector that introduces a virus into a crop will also serve to disperse the virus to other plants in the same field.

More detailed information concerning epidemiology and disease gradients is available in a recent monograph (74).

D. Spread of Virus Disease within a Crop

A number of factors are known to affect the nature and rapidity with which virus disease will spread within a crop. Among these are the species, cultivar, and health of the host plant; the spacing of the plants; whether or not a cover or intercrop is present; and the color of the soil and foliage.

Young, tender plants are more susceptible to infection than are older plants, because many aerial vectors are attracted to younger plants for feeding. Therefore, crops that are young when vectors are abundant are more likely to experience rapid spread of virus disease than fields planted earlier or later. Furthermore, adequately fertilized, vigorously growing plants are more likely to become infected. In one early study, it was demonstrated that 30% of large cauliflower seedlings became infected with cauliflower mosaic virus, whereas only 15% and 5% of the less vigorous middle- and small-sized plants, respectively, became infected (75).

The agricultural practice of intercropping frequently affects virus disease spread. Thus, it has become a frequent practice to protect the sugar beet seed crop from the spread of sugar beet yellow virus by growing it for the first year with a ceral cover crop.

Aphids are attracted by colors of the red to yellow portion of the spectrum and, thus, peanut plants surrounded by red soil are more likely to be aphid infested than are plants surrounded by a bed of blue-green leaves. This is also the probable reason why gladiolus and squash plants are less affected by aphid-transmitted viruses when the soil on which they are grown is covered by reflecting aluminum foil (76).

V. INTRACELLULAR REPLICATION OF VIRUSES

As pointed out previously, most plant viruses have a single-stranded, translatable RNA genome combined with a capsid that is either rod shaped, polyhedral, or bacilliform. Our limited knowledge of the intracellular behavior of plant viruses is derived mostly from experimental work with such Class IV viruses. Therefore, the following discussion will pertain primarily to these, although available information concerning other plant viruses and viroids will also be summarized.

A. Early Events of Replication

Viruses are obligate, intracellular parasites and, thus, before replication can proceed virus particles must gain entrance into a viable cell. The precise mechanism of virus entry is incompletely understood, but it is known that infection can be initiated either through the mediation of a living vector—insect, arachnid, nematode, or fungus—or through mechanical wound sites that can be created by gentle abrasion of the plant surface. Plants that are exposed to a virus in the absence of injury or vector fail to become infected. Once inside a living cell, or during the process of entry, the genome is released from the virus particle. The mechanism of such "uncoating" is another process that is as yet poorly

understood. A number of chemical methods have been developed for
the *in vitro* separation of intact viral RNA from capsid protein, but
these methods are not of a type likely to occur inside a living cell
(77,78). The uncoating process frequently can be bypassed, because in
many cases infection can be initiated with the RNA genome alone, as
well as with complete virus particles, but usually with a loss in the
efficiency of inoculation. Once the genome is released from the capsid,
or in cases where infection is initiated with free viral RNA, the virus
genome is both translated into protein products and replicated. The
final step then follows, and consists of assembly of virus particles from
newly synthesized genomes and capsid proteins.

B. Replication of Viral RNA

The precise mechanism of plant virus RNA replication has not been
fully elucidated, and can only be presumed at the present time, based
on parallels that exist between phenomena that occur in bacterial, animal, and plant cells infected with Class IV viruses. New forms of RNA
appear in infected bacterial and animal cells and are termed replicative
form (RF) and replicative intermediate (RI). The former, upon extraction, is a double-stranded structure consisting of the viral genome (+
strand) and its complement (− strand), and the latter is a similar structure with single-stranded tails. These forms are almost certainly altered
during the usual extraction procedures, but they do represent structures that are unique to infected cells. Replicative form (RF) and RI
have also been identified in extracts of tissues infected with a number
of plant viruses, among which are tobacco mosaic, turnip yellow
mosaic, brome mosaic, cowpea mosaic, alfalfa mosaic, pea enation
mosaic, and barley stripe mosaic viruses (79–87). The RF, as expected,
has an estimated molecular weight just twice that of the single-
stranded genome. Where tested, the RF has proved not to be infectious,
but it becomes so after separation of the strands (86). In the case of the
split-genome viruses, double-stranded forms are present for each of the
major genomic RNA species (82–84). The double-stranded forms, as
their names imply, are presumed to be intermediates in the synthesis of
viral RNA, and evidence has accumulated to indicate that this is indeed
so. The current notion is that the viral RNA is used as a template by a
virus-specific replicase enzyme to synthesize the complementary negative strand. The negative strand is then used as template either by the
same or a modified replicase enzyme to synthesize new virus RNA
molecules, the system being such that considerably more viral RNA is

synthesized than is the negative strand. In support of this hypothesis, it has been observed that negative strands are synthesized preferentially early in a synchronous infection, whereas later the concentration of negative strand remains constant and the synthesis of viral RNA accelerates (88). The presence of two RNA double-stranded forms in infected tissue does not necessarily mean that both forms function as intermediates in viral RNA synthesis. Available evidence based on pulse-chase experiments with radioactive RNA presursor indicates that the RI form is the more likely candidate (89). Additional experimentation is needed, however, before this matter can be clearly resolved.

It is generally thought that all of the RNA synthesized in a healthy cell is transcribed from a DNA template. However, in the case of many of the RNA viruses, a different mechanism must be involved in the synthesis of viral RNA, because it has been demonstrated that this synthesis is not diminished when DNA-dependent RNA synthesis is inhibited. Thus, the presence of the double-stranded RF and RI forms suggests that the mechanism of viral RNA replication is in some respects similar to that of DNA, at least as far as each strand acting as a template for the other's synthesis is concerned. Since reports of DNA-independent RNA synthesis in healthy tissue are rare, the presumption is that cells do not ordinarily possess an enzyme apparatus for RNA replication and, thus, that enzymes with such specificity must be coded for by the viral RNA genome and must be unique to RNA virus-infected cells. Indeed, the first such enzyme was identified in extracts of RNA phage-infected bacteria. It was found to be specific for the bacterial viral RNA and would act only with low efficiency when supplied with other RNA templates. The enzyme was further found to be multimeric—consisting of four subunits, three of which were normal cell constituents, and the fourth a virus-coded polypeptide (90).

A determined search has been made in extracts of infected plant tissues for similar enzyme activity. Membrane-bound DNA-independent RNA synthetic activity has been found in extracts of tissue infected with among others, tobacco mosaic (91,92) turnip yellow mosaic (93,94), brome mosaic (95), tobacco ringspot (96), and cucumber mosaic (97) viruses. These particulate enzymes are attached to a template, are not stimulated by additional RNA, and, in at least in two cases, a double-stranded RNA product is produced similar to that found to be present in vivo (92,98). In the case of brome mosaic and broad bean mottle viruses, which are split-genome viruses, the in vitro products correspond to the different genomic RNA species. Extracts of tissue infected with these viruses incorporate RNA precursor first into a double-stranded form and then into single-stranded forms (99–101), a sequence of events in line with the proposed viral RNA synthetic mechanism.

The demonstration by Spiegelman's group and others (90) that the RNA of the bacterial virus Qβ could be replicated *in vitro* by a soluble enzyme extracted and purified from infected cells prompted a number of plant virus workers to attempt the solubilization and further purification of the enzyme(s) involved in plant virus RNA replication. Two features, in particular, of the bacterial system are of interest for comparative purposes. The first is the remarkable specificity of the Qβ-induced enzyme. It will accept as template Qβ RNA and very few others, even at reduced efficiency. The second is the fact, as was already mentioned, that the Qβ RNA replicase consists of four polypeptides, three of which are normal host constituents, the fourth being coded for by the viral RNA. Soluble enzymes with replicase activity have been obtained, usually with the aid of nonionic detergents, from extracts of plants infected with cucumber mosaic (102), tobacco ringspot (96), turnip yellow mosaic (103), tobacco mosaic (104,105), brome mosaic (106), and tobacco necrosis (107) viruses. None of these enzymes have been completely purified as yet, but estimates made of their molecular weights from either sedimentation or gel filtration behavior cover the wide range from 12,000 for a tobacco mosaic virus-induced activity (105) to 400,000 for the turnip yellow mosaic virus enzyme (103). Size estimates for enzymes induced by an individual virus also vary widely, with that for tobacco mosaic virus ranging from 12,000 (105) to 160,000 (104). Suggestive evidence indicates that the brome mosaic virus and turnip yellow mosaic virus enzymes may be multimeric (102,108). Most of the soluble enzymes thus far investigated appear to lack the type of template specificity that seems to be demanded for an authentic viral RNA replicase. The brome mosaic virus enzyme (109), the turnip yellow mosaic virus enzyme, and the cowpea mosaic virus enzyme (109a) however, exhibit appreciable specificity for the inducing viral RNA. The *in vitro* product of most of the solubilized enzymes is primarily double-stranded RNA, with only the complement being synthesized to the RNA supplied as template. It is apparent from the foregoing that a good deal of work remains to be done before the viral RNA replicative process is understood well enough for use in the design of rational control measures. One of the problems that has hindered work in this area has been the discovery that the extracts of some plants contain a DNA-independent RNA synthetic activity, even in the absence of apparent virus infection (110). As a consequence, it has been proposed by one group of investigators that some plant viral RNAs may be replicated by this host enzyme rather than by a virus specified replicase (110a).

Little is known of the RNA replication mechanisms of the Class V (containing single-stranded negative RNA) and the Class III (containing double-stranded RNA) plant viruses except for the presumption that they are in principle, the same as that of the Class IV viruses, although the details may differ. The RNA of the plant rhabdoviruses (Class V, e.g., lettuce necrotic yellows and potato yellow dwarf viruses) is not infectious, because upon infection it must first be transcribed into information bearing RNA (+ strand) by an enzyme contained in the virus particle before the infection process can proceed (111). The double-stranded RNA plant viruses, such as clover wound tumor and rice dwarf viruses, are similar to the animal reovirus group in having their genomes split into 10–12 pieces all packaged in a single virus particle (112). As with the rhabdoviruses, the double-stranded RNA animal viruses have been shown to contain an RNA synthesizing enzyme which, upon infection, transcribes the double-stranded RNA into messenger RNA (113). It is presumed that plant viruses are the same in this regard.

The replication mechanism of viroid RNA (Class VII) is under active investigation at the present time. The nucleotide sequence has been completely determined for several viroid strains (114) and the data confirm the unlikelihood that viroid RNA codes for a protein. However, the suggestion has been made that a complementary strand may perform this function (114a). The recent finding that viroid RNA can assume a circular configuration (114) heightens interest in this intriguing group of pathogens.

The site of intracellular replication has, as yet, been definitively determined for very few of the plant viruses, but the work done so far demonstrates that viral RNA replication is definitely localized within the cell and that the localized area is different for the different viruses. Thus, the evidence is clear that replication of turnip yellow mosaic virus takes place near the outer chloroplast membrane (98). The replication of the brome mosaic and maize dwarf mosaic virus RNAs are also probably chloroplast associated (108,115). Replication of cowpea mosaic virus RNA apparently takes place within vesicular cytopathological structures, located in the cytoplasm of infected cells (116), and that of pea enation mosaic virus within the nucleus (117). Two different sites may be involved in the replication of tobacco mosaic virus RNA. Earlier cytological and autoradiographic evidence implicated the nucleolus as the probable site (118–120), but later it was shown that both the double-stranded viral RNA forms and a virus-specific RNA replicase activity were associated with cytoplasmic membranes (91,92) and did not appear to be present in the nucleus.

C. Translation of Viral RNA

Eukaryotic cells differ from prokaryotic cells with respect to the nature of the messenger RNAs their translation apparatuses will accept. Prokaryotic cells have no difficulty in translating several different individual proteins from a single polycistronic messenger RNA, whereas eukaryotic cells are generally adapted to translate monocistronic messenger RNAs. Thus, the genome of the small RNA bacteriophages functions as a messenger RNA for the three proteins encoded on a single strand of RNA (121). The known RNA viruses with eukaryotic hosts, with the exception of the viroids and certain satellite viruses, all have more than one cistron. This is because they must code for at least one capsid protein and a replicase enzyme or part of one. The problem presented by the necessity of translating a multicistronic viral genome in a eukaryotic host has been solved in a number of unique ways in the different groups of RNA viruses. For instance, the RNA of poliovirus, an animal picornavirus, is translated into a giant polyprotein that is then snipped by host enzymes into a number of proteins with different functions in poliovirus biogenesis (122,123). At least two different strategies for translation are evident in the plant viruses that have been examined. The split-genome viruses have reduced the problem by having their genomes divided into mono-, or at most dicistronic, fragments. In the well-studied case of brome mosaic virus, the genome is divided into four pieces of RNA, with the two largest being monocistronic messengers for proteins that have as yet unknown function (124). The third largest piece of the genome is dicistronic, but only one of the two cistrons is translated *in vitro* (125) into a protein whose function is again not clearly defined, but is suspected of participating in the RNA replicative process (108). The fourth and smallest piece of the genome is derived from the third, dicistronic piece and contains the same information as its untranslated portion. Its function, in contrast to the other portions of the genome, is clearly defined; it proves to be a highly efficient monocistronic messenger for the viral capsid protein.

Most of the plant viruses with undivided genomes employ still a different strategy. Processing of the virion RNA into smaller fragments is necessary for translation of the entire genome. Tobacco mosaic virus provides a well-studied example. Part of its RNA is translated into two closely related proteins which differ only in that one is somewhat larger than the other (125a). The rest of the RNA is processed to yield at least one monocistronic RNA for capsid protein (126–128). Probably a second subgenomic RNA is also generated during infection which acts as a messenger for a fourth protein (130). The same phenomena probably also occurs during turnip yellow mosaic virus infection (129). The generation of a highly efficient messenger for capsid protein may be a general phenomenon for most of the Class IV plant viruses, whether their genomes are segmented or not. In the case of the segmented groups, the capsid messenger is generated from a dicistronic portion of the genome and is encapsidated during intracellular virus particle assembly, although this is not required for initiation of new infection. In the tobravirus group, the gene for the capsid protein is located on the shorter of the two nucleic acid molecules constituting the genome (131,132). In the case of tobacco mosaic virus, as was just mentioned, the capsid protein messenger RNA is generated from the undivided viral RNA during the infection process. In most strains of tobacco mosaic virus, this monocistronic RNA is not encapsidated. However, the cowpea strain constitutes an exception to this rule, where nucleoprotein short rods containing the capsid protein messenger, in addition to the long viral RNA-containing rods, are formed (133,134). In the case of the tymoviruses, the usual case appears to be that capsid messenger RNA is packaged, incidentally, in the same nucleoprotein particles that contain the viral RNA (129). Other virus groups have not yet been investigated in detail in this regard, but there is suggestive evidence that a capsid messenger RNA may also be generated during Poty virus group infection (135).

Several approaches have been used by investigators in attempts to gain information from which the events of infection may be deduced. One of these has been to detect new functional activities in extracts of infected tissue and then to attempt to purify these so that they may be better characterized. This is one of the approaches used in attempts to identify and characterize a postulated virus RNA-coded replicase enzyme. However, another approach has been to identify the appearance of unique macromolecules in infected cells and then to determine what, if any, function they may have. By this method, it was discovered that a low-molecular weight RNA component was present in tobacco mosaic virus-infected tissue (89) which, on further analysis, proved to be that portion of virus RNA (126) which coded for capsid protein (127,128). Again, by this method, several unique protein components have been found to be synthesized in tobacco mosaic virus-infected tissue (136), prominent among which are two large proteins with approximate molecular weights of 160,000 and 110,000. Although, several investigators have confirmed the presence of these components

(137–139), their function in the replicative process remains to be determined. There is a strong suspicion that one of these is the RNA replicase, or part of it (104). In the same way, a new protein with a molecular weight of 35,000 has been observed in extracts of brome mosaic virus tissue, and there is a suggestion that it might be involved in the RNA replicative process (108).

D. Virus Assembly

Although knowledge of the intimate details of the viral replicative process is still rudimentary, it is quite evident that the biosynthesis of viral RNA and protein components are independent processes. A number of studies have shown that, although reciprocal controls may be present, one can proceed without the other, and both processes can occur without the production of virus particles. Perhaps the best evidence for the conclusion that nucleic acid synthesis can proceed without the concommitant synthesis of viral capsid protein comes from the demonstration that the long rod of the split-genome tobacco rattle virus can initiate an infection in which the long rod RNA replicates but no synthesis of capsid protein occurs. Failure of capsid protein synthesis in this case results from the fact that the gene for this protein is not contained in the piece of genome used to initiate infection but, rather, on another piece (131). Evidence that capsid protein synthesis can proceed without viral RNA synthesis comes from the several viruses in which empty capsids are produced during infection along with infectious nucleocapsids. Turnip yellow mosaic virus is a good example, because it has been demonstrated that cells infected with this virus continue to produce empty capsids when viral RNA synthesis is inhibited (140). The fact that both viral RNA and capsid protein synthesis can occur in infected cells without the production of infectious virus particles is demonstrated by the defective strains of tobacco mosaic and tobacco necrosis viruses in which infection is maintained and synthesis occurs of both viral nucleic acid and a mutationally altered capsid protein that is unable to participate in virus particle formation (141,142).

The foregoing details concerning the independent synthesis of the different viral components have been presented in order to emphasize that the appearance of new virus particles represents a final assembly process, the mechanism of which, as it occurs intracellularly, has not yet been determined. The requirements for successful assembly are not difficult to set forth: (1) Control of synthesis of the two basic viral components must be such that they are made in the approximate proportions that they occur in the virus particles. (2) Either RNA and capsid proteins must be synthesized in close proximity to each other, or some mechanism must exist to bring the two together after they have been synthesized. (3) Either viral RNA is the only RNA species available for coaggregation with viral protein to form new virus particles, or specificity must be present under *in vivo* conditions so that the capsid protein coaggregates only with viral RNA and not with other RNA species. (4) Either the assembly process is such that it occurs spontaneously under the specific conditions of the cell compartment in which it occurs, or it is mediated by enzymes that do not appear in the final product.

The specifics of *in vivo* assembly, although not yet known completely for any plant virus, can be discussed in terms of known information about the infection process and *in vitro* phenomena. Of particular interest in this regard is the knowledge of the *in vitro* conditions under which the separated components of a number of different viruses will spontaneously aggregate into infectious virus particles (143–145). A number of features of the *in vitro* assembly processes of the several plant viruses that have been examined in some detail are of particular interest. Whereas the *in vitro* assembly of a number of viruses can as yet be carried out under what are clearly nonphysiological conditions, mild conditions, perhaps similar to those which might occur intracellularly, have been discovered for the assembly of other viruses. Thus, it is not unreasonable to suppose that for some viruses the process may occur spontaneously, when the concentrations of the viral components reach appropriate levels in a localized area within the cell. On the other hand, the assembly of some viruses might not take place efficiently without an appropriate catalyst, and some of the plant viruses would certainly appear to have sufficient, as yet unaccounted for, genetic information for such enzymes.

There is clearly specificity in the initial interaction between the capsid protein and nucleic acids of some viruses. Tobacco mosaic virus is the best-studied case in this regard, there being a recognition site on the viral RNA for a disklike aggregate of capsid protein. Following the initial interaction, there is addition of capsid protein, or capsid protein aggregates, to both sides of the initially interacting disk to complete the nucleoprotein rod (146). It is likely that the same sequence of events occurs *in vivo*, although the specificity of the reaction does not appear to be perfect, because a small proportion of the rods that are formed contain host, rather than viral, RNA (147). Evidence is lacking at the present time for the same type of specificity between capsid protein and RNA in the polyhedral viruses, and it is possible that a somewhat different *in vivo* assembly principle is operative with these (32).

The intracellular site of virus assembly has been established with certainty for very few viruses. Evidence is presented that the assembly of turnip yellow mosaic virus occurs near or in the outer chloroplast membrane (98,148), and that of tobacco mosaic virus someplace in the cytoplasm (149). Structures unique to infected cells are sometimes seen in electron micrographs, and it is suspected that these might be sites of both synthesis of components and assembly in the viral infections in which they occur (i.e., 150,151).

VI. CONTROL MECHANISMS

Considerable progress has been made in the past several decades in the development of both general and specific chemical and biological agents for the control of several of the plant pests. Although specific treatments have not yet been developed for the inactivation of plant viruses during their active phase of replication, without at the same time inflicting unacceptable damage to the host crop, several control measures, which in one way or another serve to prevent losses which can occur as a consequence of virus infection, have been adopted. The type of control measures that have been adopted in specific instances have depended to a large extent on the nature of the crop, the disease symptoms, and the disease vector. The type of control measures applicable to perennial crops can, in general, be distinguished from those more suitable to annual crops.

The nature of the disease and the capital invested in the crop are important considerations in adopting control measures for perennial and vegetatively propagated crops. An example of an extreme type of virus disease to be combated is that in which valuable trees are killed, often resulting in a serious investment loss (e.g., tristeza in citrus, swollen shoot disease in cacoa, and cadang-cadang coconut palm disease). A different situation is encountered in vegetatively propagated crops, such as potato and strawberry, which accumulate chronic, but not usually devastating, virus diseases with a consequent annual reduction in yield. Control measures are usually based on the principle of avoiding either virus infection or, in some cases, the consequences of virus infection. The avoidance of virus disease is generally accomplished by taking pains to establish a virus-free planting and then to keep it virus free as long as possible. At the same time, attempts may be made to minimize the consequences of infection, generally, by using cultivars tolerant to virus replication, tolerance implying that no serious damage to the host accompanies what can sometimes be massive virus multiplication.

The practice of taking pains to insure that virus-free stock is used when establishing a planting of perennial or vegetatively propagated crops usually permits at least several harvests without virus-induced yield reduction (152). In order to establish a commercial planting with a virus-free clone, it is first necessary to obtain a virus-free line and then to propagate and increase it under controlled conditions that protect it from infection (153). A virus-free line for commercial propagation can sometimes be selected when not all plants in a particular area are infected. Sometimes a line can even be established from a virus-free portion of an infected plant. It is not uncommon, for instance, for the shoot tip of a rapidly growing stem to have temporarily "outgrown" an otherwise systemic virus infection. In addition, moreover, the shoot and/or root apices of a number, but not all, of virus–host combinations prove to be free of virus, or else escape from infection when excised and cultured to regenerate mature plants. Sometimes, advantage is taken of the peculiarities of the host. Many citrus species, for instance, not only give rise to seedlings that originate from zygotes but, frequently, also from the diploid maternal cells of the nucellus. The nucellar seedlings have the same genotype as the cultivar from which they were derived and are seldom virus infected (154).

Situations exist in which no virus-free material can be found or recovered by the means discussed above. In such cases, heat therapy will sometimes be successful (155,156). This practice has a long history. The first report was in 1889 by Kobus, who observed that sugar cane ratoons from sereh-diseased canes would give rise to better growth if immersed in water at 50°C for 30 min before planting. A number of plants have been freed from diverse viruses by the expedient of either heating dormant plant parts in water at rather high temperatures, just below lethality, or by growing infected plants at 35°–40°C (or as hot as they can just tolerate) for an extended period of time (weeks). Sometimes only part of a heated plant will be freed of the virus, and in such cases virus-free stock for propagation has been successfully obtained by culturing the meristem tip from a heated plant.

Attempts have been made to employ chemotherapy, either to control virus disease or to obtain virus-free stock for vegetative propagation. These attempts have involved the use, primarily, of nucleic acid base or nucleoside analogs (cf. 140,157). They have not proved successful, probably because the agents tested interfere with normal cellular processes as well as with viral replication. As pointed out elsewhere, however, the fact that most plant viruses have an RNA genome should provide a point of chemotherapeutic attack, because the RNA replicative process is unique to virus-infected cells and is not known to occur in healthy tissue.

One of the problems encountered in propagating virus-free stock for distribution is to establish that the plants or plant parts are actually virus free. This is not always as simple a task as it might at first sight appear, due to a number of different reasons. Symptoms may, in some cases, take a long time to appear, or the presence of a yield-reducing virus may not always be apparent. As a consequence, a variety of procedures to test for the presence of virus (usually refered to as indexing) have been adopted, the most appropriate being dependent on the particular host–virus system under study. In the case of trees, where no herbaceous host is available, it is sometimes the practice to index stock by grafting to young trees of a species that is particularly susceptible and in which symptoms of virus disease develop rapidly. This is an example of a tedious and expensive way to test for the presence of virus, and is the method of choice only when less expensive procedures, usually based on mechanical transfer of infection to indicator plants, are unavailable. However, even such procedures are still based on the maintenence and growth of living materials and are, by nature, time consuming and expensive. Therefore, other methods of indexing are continuously being sought. One such method that has been adopted by a number of certification jurisdictions tests for the presence of virus in potato tuber extracts by serological methods (cf. 158).

Once a virus-free planting has been established, steps need to be taken to prevent or slow the accumulation of viruses. Again, dependent on the host–virus system involved, the value of the foundation stock, and the value of the crop, different methods are appropriate. Maintenance of a clone in sterile soil and in an insect-free enclosure is expensive but, nevertheless, appropriate for virus-free type specimens from which material is taken for propagation of planting stock. In a number of instances it has become the practice to grow a crop for seed material (potatoes) in an area not especially conducive to high yields, but which has the advantage of being inhospitable to the insect vectors for a number of virus diseases (159). The knowledge of vectors can be of importance in attempts to supress virus disease or to prevent its spread. Thus, for valuable crops it may be appropriate to combat the vector when means are available for this purpose. One example is the sterilization of soil in order to kill nematode and fungus vectors of several damaging virus diseases, particularly those affecting small fruits. Finally, man and his tools can sometimes be important vectors of virus disease, especially in crops that require handling in procedures such as grafting and transplanting. Proper sanitation can eliminate this cause of disease spread.

The control of virus disease in annual crops is based on somewhat, but not altogether, different principles. A practice that is usually more feasible for annual than for perennial crops is selection of disease-resistant varieties, combined with appropriate breeding procedures, to introduce virus resistance or tolerance into commercial, high-yielding varieties (160). Resistance to virus disease may be of several types. Plants may have a genotype that makes them immune to infection by a particular virus. This is usually a species characteristic, but it may sometimes also apply to a particular cultivar of a species that is otherwise generally susceptible to infection. Practical resistance to disease may also result from a particular type of response, such as hypersensitivity of the host to a virus. In this type of reaction, infection remains localized in cells surrounding a site of infection and does not spread to the rest of the plant. Frequently, such localization is accompanied by the death of small areas of infected tissue. This results in minimal damage to the plant, so long as the number of infections does not become great. A third type of disease resistance results from tolerance to infection, in which virus generally multiplies to fairly high levels, with the host plant showing little sign of infection under certain environmental conditions. Vigilance must be practiced when reliance is placed on host genetic factors to protect a crop from viruses, as well as from other disease agents, because of the ever-present danger of the evolution and selection of agents that will be virulent for formerly resistant cultivars.

There has been no well-documented case for the *de novo* appearance of a virus and, although there has been much speculation concerning the origin of viruses, the question of how they arose still remains unanswered. When a virus disease evidences itself in a crop, therefore, a source must be present for the responsible infecting virus particles. Therefore, a number of control measures, based on the elimination or neutralization of such sources, have been developed. For such control measures to be effective, the sources must be identified, and an understanding gained of the vector(s) that spread the virus from the source to previously uninfected plants, and of the conditions conducive to such spread. Among more common sources of infection are seeds (33), since many, but not all, plant viruses can be transmitted to a greater or lesser extent through seed; weeds, because many plant viruses have more than one host; volunteers remaining from a previous crop or out of phase crops of the same species (such as winter and spring wheat); alternate crop hosts in neighboring fields, an example of which is the home vegetable garden, which can harbor a variety of viruses damaging to crop plants; vectors such as nematodes (36) and fungi (35) with resistant stages, in which viruses can be harbored for an appreciable period of time (161); certain leafhoppers, in which some plant viruses multiply and are transmitted vertically by transovarian passage (38); and finally man, where he becomes the inadvertant carrier of a virus that can infect and cause disease in crops requiring handling, an example being the introduction of tobacco mosaic virus into tobacco, tomato, and other crops from smoking and chewing tobacco, almost all of which harbors the virus (21). When the source of virus for infection can be identified, it can be eliminated or controlled by practices such as indexing of seeds where seed transmission is a problem; elimination of weed hosts when this is feasible, separation of household gardens from crop-growing areas; interruption of an infection cycle by controlling harvesting and planting dates, in order to ensure a host-free period during the year (162); separation of the first-year plots of a biennial crop from second-year plots; soil testing to determine whether virus-containing nematodes and fungi are present, and if they prove to be, either avoiding or sterilizing the plot (163); and appropriate sanitation measures, where man is found to be the culprit.

Control measures that serve to limit the spread of virus infection once it is introduced into a crop area have also been adopted. The effectiveness of such control measures depends, as is true for all other control measures, on the virus–host system, the vector, climatic conditions, agronomic practices, and other, sometimes unknown factors. Frequently, a slight change in agronomic practice will alter the relationship between vector and host plant so that virus spread from an infection source is slowed considerably. Among such changes that have proved effective in specific cases are a slight shift in planting date, time of cultivation, density of planting, or including a barrier or cover crop. Other methods are also designed to reduce vector efficiency, and include the introduction of predators and/or parasites of vectors to reduce their number, and the judicious use of insecticides. However, these are usually effective only in specific, well-tested cases (cf. 164), because in many situations insecticides will have either no effect or will actually increase the rate of virus spread by, for instance, the preferential elimination of a vector predator.

The control measures discussed so far, which include most of those adopted to date, attempt in one way or another to interfere or prevent the spread of virus from one plant to another. However, there are other stages of the virus life cycle that should be considered in planning for the development of rational and economically advantageous control measures. These include the intracellular replication period in the host, and the spread of virus from one cell to another within the host. Some limited success has been achieved in blocking intracellular virus replication and in preventing virus spread within the host in selected instances, usually by the expedient of the selection and breeding of host plants with some form of resistance or tolerance to virus disease (160). Another ploy that has been found advantageous in a limited number of cases is the deliberate inoculation of a crop with a mild, latent, or masked strain of a virus, in order to protect the crop against a drastic loss that might otherwise be induced by a potent strain of the virus.

As more becomes known about the events of intracellular virus replication, it is likely that control measures may be developed based on one or another or the steps in this process. The steps of virus replication, what little is known about them, and possible control points are outlined below:

1. The virus must gain entry into a cell. The manner in which this is accomplished is not precisely known, and probably differs considerably among the various host–virus systems. What has been established is that plants do not become infected merely by being exposed to high concentrations of virus particles. Either there must be some mild type of wounding in the presence of virus, in the case of mechanical transmission (165), or the intervention is by a vector. Most vectors cause infection of host plants by in some way facilitating the entry of virus particles into cells, usually as a concomitant of feeding. In the case of fungus vectors, infection occurs when virus-containing zoospores germinate leading to hyphal invastion of root cells (166). Whatever the mode of viral entry into cells, it is presumed at present that the wound, although it may create trauma, does not kill the cells which become infected initially, because viruses can only replicate in living cells. Recently, it has been found possible to infect plant protoplasts with a number of different viruses, usually by merely suspending them together in the same medium. However, it is frequently necessary to add a polycation such as poly-L-ornithine, probably to alter the viral surface charge so that it will better interact with the protoplast cell membrane (167). It may be that both mechanical inoculation and vector transmission serve to bring virus particles close to cell membranes, where the likelihood is increased that interaction leading to infection will take place. The nature of the interaction of the cell membrane that leads to

entrance of the virus particle or its genetic material into the cell, however, is still poorly understood. Control measures that have the primary effect of blocking virus entry into cells have not been widely adopted. It has been reported, however, that some crops may become protected from aphid transmission of viruses when sprayed with an oil–water emulsion (168,169).

2. The genetic material of the virus must be released from its capsid protein. Very little is known about how this occurs, although it has been estimated to take about 2 hr under defined conditions in the few host–virus systems where it has been studied (170). No control measures are presently available to interfere with this process.

3. The viral genetic material must be translated. Most plant viruses contain single-stranded translatable RNA. Because the amount of genetic information is limited, its translation probably makes use of the host protein synthesizing machinery. Except for the possibility that the virus messenger RNA may be appreciably different in some respects from that of the host, it is unlikely that control measures based on blocking RNA translation can be devised that will not at the same time do serious injury to the host. It has been found in several cases, however, that viral RNA is processed before translation (128,171). If this type of RNA processing proves unique to viral RNA, and is not carried out by the same enzymatic apparatus as that involved in host RNA processing, then this step might prove amenable to specific blocking as a control measure.

4. The viral RNA must be replicated. We have pointed out that replication of RNA is a process unique to infected cells. It does not occur in healthy cells where, as far as is now known, all RNA is transcribed from a DNA template by several specific DNA-dependent RNA-polymerizing enzymes. The process by which plant viral RNA is replicated is not completely understood, but it is known that RNA structures appear as a consequence of infection that contain both viral RNA and its complement (86). Presumably then, during the replication of viral RNA, the complementary strand is synthesized and this is then used as a template for synthesizing new viral RNA molecules. The problem concerning the nature of the enzymes responsible for the virus-specific RNA synthesis is a subject of active investigation at the present time. It has been demonstrated that proteins with RNA replicating activity appear in infected cells, presumably as translation products of the viral genome, but their precise mechanism of function remains to be elucidated (cf. 103,172).

It would appear that the process of viral RNA replication should offer an ideal point of attack for a specific chemotherapeutic program, designed to control plant virus disease, because this biochemical process does not occur in healthy tissue. As more is learned about it, it should be possible to devise specific inhibitory controls that would not at the same time have ill effects on the host.

5. Assembly of the viral genome and other constituents to form new virus particles must occur. Tobacco mosaic virus was the first virus to be resembled from its constituent nucleic acid and capsid protein components (143). More recently, the *in vitro* mode of assembly of this as well as several other viruses is becoming understood in some detail (32,146). It is likely that much that is being learned about the *in vitro* mode of assembly may also apply to assembly *in vivo*. Therefore, it is not unreasonable to suppose that agents that block assembly without at the same time interfering with host metabolic process might be good candidates for the chemotherapeutic control of virus infection. However, such agents, if found, might not always be effective, because several cases are now known in which assembly does not take place due to the absence of functional capsid protein. Such infections, nevertheless, are maintained and cause disease, although it may be that the efficiency of transmission of infectivity in such cases is greatly reduced. Agents that may interfere with assembly are not known at the present time, nor, for that matter, have they been sought.

The foregoing analysis of the steps of the virus life cycle that might be amenable to control in blocking virus disease refers to the type IV viruses—those that contain single-stranded translatable RNA. The same type of analysis with appropriate modification applies to the other RNA-containing viruses. Plant rhabdoviruses containing single-stranded complementary RNA (type V) have a virion enzyme that transcribes the genome into messenger RNA once the virus has entered a cell. This transcriptive process is unique to infected cells, and is a step that should be amenable to control. The same comment applies to the double-stranded RNA viruses (type III), which are also packaged with an enzyme that transcribes the genome into messenger RNA upon infection. The viroids are an example of an entity whose life cycle is just beginning to be understood and for which it is still difficult to predict the parts of its life cycle that might be most sensitive to control measures. The few DNA-containing plant viruses (types I and II) might be most difficult to control during their replicative process without at the same time doing serious damage to the host. Thus, it would seem that for these viruses it might be best to consider other stages of the life cycle as points of control—such as entrance into the cell, uncoating, assembly, and transmission.

VII. USES OF VIRUSES TO BENEFIT AGRICULTURE

It might seem odd to discuss possible means by which viruses might serve to benefit agriculture, having just completed a consideration of the available and prospective methods for control of what are commonly considered plant pests. However, virus infection does not always lead to economic loss. There are a number of instances where a virus-induced leaf variegation and/or flower break adds considerable value to certain ornamentals. For example, several plant virology texts include reproductions of seventeenth century tulip cultivars whose characteristic striping pattern no doubt resulted from virus infection (1,2).

Although this chapter concerns itself with plant viruses, mention will be made of the fact that increasing use is being made of animal viruses to benefit agriculture as specific biological control agents for insect and other animal plant pests. It is convenient to divide the animal viruses into those that have vertebrate hosts and those that are more or less specific to invertebrate hosts. Among the latter (173), the greatest interest is focused on insect viruses and their possible use as specific agents to control insect pests of agricultural crops. Insect viruses fall into many of the same taxons as do vertebrate viruses. Prominent among these are the cytoplasmic polyhedrosis viruses and the iridoviruses. The cytoplasmic polyhedrosis viruses resemble the double-stranded RNA-containing viruses of vertebrates and plants in genomic constitution, structure, and morphology. They differ in being uniquely and characteristically embedded (or occluded) in crystalline inclusions, the polyhedra, composed of virus-specific proteins. Another group of viruses, the baculoviruses, are also occluded in proteinaceous structures. Thus far, they are of a type only described for insect hosts. Because of their specificity and larval toxicity, ease of spread, and other features, they are being used increasingly to protect agricultural crops from damage by insect pests (174–176). In like manner vertebrate viruses have been used in a number of instances for pest control, notably in Australia to increase sheep and cattle pasture carrying capacity by inducing disease in competing rabbits (177).

However, in addition to improvement of the aesthetic value of certain horticultural crops and the use of animal viruses to control plant pests, recent advances in the understanding of genetic material and how it may be manipulated both *in vivo* and *in vitro* offer a basis for predicting the possibility of employing viruses as vehicles for introducing specific desired capabilities into agronomic crops. There are several lines of speculation, based on current knowledge of nucleic acid biochemistry and of the molecular biology of viruses, plants, and other organisms as to how such genetic engineering might be successfully applied in the not too distant future. For example, one approach to the problem would be to convert a viral RNA into an exogenous plasmid and to incorporate genetic information specifying a desired characteristic into such a plasmid.

Proposed methods for synthesizing such a construct are based largely, but not completely, on currently available knowledge and technology. The problem might be approached by starting with a seed-transmitted virus. Following mutagenization, hereditable varients that are still seed transmitted, that induce little, if any, host disease, and in which nucleoprotein virus particles are not produced would be selected. The infectious entity would be naked nucleic acid. Such variants would, in essence, be maternally inherited RNA plasmids, whose generation appears to be within the realm of possibility because of the following considerations.

1. It is known that some viruses are seed transmitted to different degrees, depending on the host, and it seems likely that this characteristic would be subject to selection if it were desirable to increase its frequency (178).

2. A number of host–virus systems are known, in which the infected host suffers only a marginally detectible reduction in productivity, but in which, nevertheless, considerable virus replication occurs. The effects of certain virus strains are so slight that it is becoming an accepted agronomic practice in certain circumstances to inoculate a growing crop deliberately with a "mild" or "masked" strain of a virus in order to protect it from the ravages of a more potent strain with which it might come into contact (21).

3. A number of instances are known in which viral RNA replicates and maintains infection in the absence of nucleoprotein virus particle production. This is the normal mode for the viroid (179) and for infection induced by the long rods of the bipartite tobacco rattle virus. The short rods contain the gene for capsid protein (180). In the case of tobacco mosaic and tobacco necrosis viruses, variants have been selected that produce nonfunctional capsid protein and, thus, fail to produce nucleoprotein virions (181).

Assuming success in generating virus-derived maternally inherited plasmids, we argue, by analogy to known systems, that it may be possible to introduce into such plasmids specified genes that would bestow upon their hosts particular, desired agronomic characteristics. The following considerations are presented as a suggested mechanism by which such economically beneficial plasmids might be synthesized. Although definitive evidence for the mode of viral RNA replication is still to be obtained, it is not stretching the imagination too far to suppose that it is mediated by a viral-coded RNA replicase enzyme that recognizes specifically and initiates synthesis at the 3' ends of the viral RNA and its complement. The length of the RNA synthesized is then determined by the length of the RNA strand being used as template (cf. 182). If replication of the RNA were to take place in the absence of virus assembly, as it would with the type of plasmids selected, there would no longer be a compelling reason for the newly synthesized RNA to be of a size appropriate for proper packaging into a virus particle. Thus it could gain or lose length as long as the replicase-recognizing region remained unaltered. The feasibility of altering the length of a replicating RNA has already been demonstrated by the successful isolation of mini-RNAs after appropriate selection procedures have been applied to *in vitro* replicating RNA of the bacterial virus Qβ (183). The shortening of replicating RNA may also have occurred *in vivo* during the generation and selection of the satellite tobacco necrosis and tobacco ringspot viruses (184,185).

If the length of an RNA plasmid can be altered, then the incorporation of new genetic information, without destroying replicative capacity, should also be possible—either by replacement of some nonessential internal nucleotide sequences or by internal addition to the existing RNA. This might be accomplished by following and extending the technology that has been developed for the insertion of appropriate genes into bacterial DNA plasmids. This is a rapidly developing field and it is difficult to predict the precise procedures that would be successful in synthesizing the desired plant RNA plasmids. One approach would be to transcribe both the virally derived RNA plasmid and the messenger RNA of the desired gene into full-length, double-stranded DNA, employing an avian oncornavirus reverse transcriptase enzyme, and then to combine the two DNAs by using bacterial restriction endonucleases and the techniques for recombinant DNA formation to accomplish the necessary snipping and splicing. Finally the combined DNA could be retranscribed into what would hopefully be a RNA plasmid that contains and could express both the newly inserted gene and the old gene for an RNA replicating enzyme. Techniques for performing some of the foregoing construction have been developed and employed in a manner most closely resembling the above suggestions by Maniatis *et al.* (186), among others. They incorporated the DNA reverse transcript of globin messenger RNA into a bacterial DNA plasmid. Obtaining the reverse transcript of a virally derived RNA plasmid might not prove insurmountable, because methods for making long reverse transcripts (of the size of poliovirus) have been developed (187).

The ability to produce beneficial RNA plasmids depends to a considerable extent on the successful isolation, from plants or other organisms, of appropriate messenger RNAs. A number of specific messenger RNAs have been isolated from animals, and although work with plants lags behind somewhat, several plant messenger RNAs have also been isolated (188,189). It is likely, therefore, that as more is learned about the molecular biology of plant systems, other specific messenger RNAs will become available.

One scenario has been presented for the use of viruses as a vehicle for the introduction of desired information into a plant. It may be that one or another aspect of this proposed scheme might present insurmountable obstacles. However, this should not discourage attempts to develop some such procedure for crop improvement, because other experimental courses of action are available. Two will be mentioned briefly. One would employ the genome of one of the plant DNA-containing viruses (190), about which information has only been available for a short time, to generate beneficial DNA plasmids in much the same manner as has already been suggested for the RNA viruses. The other would substitute a beneficial messenger RNA for the capsid protein gene of one of the split genome viruses (30). In a number of cases, such RNA strands, which contain the gene for capsid protein, have been shown to be highly efficient monocistronic messenger RNAs (125,133,191) which, when present, may usurp a considerable proportion of the protein synthetic capacity of a cell. In order for this latter project to be successful, one would have to learn what makes the capsid protein messenger RNAs so efficient and then how the mRNA for a beneficial protein could be modified so that it would mimic, in efficiency, the viral protein messenger.

One drawback to developing viruses for use in the genetic engineering of more efficient crop varieties is the present gap in our knowledge of the workings of plants and their viruses. At the present time, there is a gross disparity in the number of scientists who study the molecular biology of plants, as contrasted with the much larger number who study this topic in animals or even in microbes. Perhaps, in view of the benefits that might accrue in terms of the more efficient production of sufficient food and other agricultural products, it might be wise to encourage and support the basic study of plants to a considerably greater extent than is now being done.

REFERENCES

1. Matthews, R. E. F. (1970). "Plant Virology." Academic Press. New York.
2. Gibbs, A., and Harrison, B. (1976). "Plant Virology: The Principles." Wiley, New York.
3. Kado, C., and Agrawal, H. O. (1972). "Principles and Techniques in Plant Virology." Van Nostrand-Reinhold, Princeton, New Jersey.
4. Smith, K. M. (1972). "A Textbook of Plant Virus Diseases," 3rd ed. Academic Press, New York.
5. Iwanowski, D. (1892). *Bull. Acad. Imp. Sci. St.-Petersburg* [N.S.] **3**, 65–70.
6. Beijerinck, M. W. (1898). *Verh. Akad. Wet., te Amsterdam* **6**, 3–21.
7. Loeffler, F., and Frosch, P. (1898). *Zentralbl. Bakteriol., Parasitenkd. Infektionskt., Hyg., Orig. Abt. 1:* **23**, 371.
8. Stanley, W. M. (1935). *Science* **81**, 644–645.
9. Best, R. J. (1936). *Aust. J. Exp. Biol. Med. Sci.* **14**, 1–13.
10. Bawden, F. C., Pirie, N. W., Bernal, J. D. M., and Fankuchen, I. (1936). *Nature (London)* **138**, 1051–1052.
11. Vinson, C. G., and Petre, A. W. (1929). *Boyce Thompson Inst. Plant Res., Prof. Pap.* **3**, 131–145.
12. Avery, O., MacLeod, C., and McCarty, M. (1944). *J. Exp. Med.* **79**, 137–158.
13. Hershey, A. D., and Chase, M. (1952). *J. Gen. Physiol.* **36**, 39–56.
14. Gierer, A., and Schramm, G. (1956). *Nature (London)* **177**, 702–703.
15. Fraenkel-Conrat, H. (1956). *J. Am. Chem. Soc.* **78**, 882–883.
16. Garces-Orjuela, G., Jennings, P. R., and Siciles, R. L. (1958). *Plant Dis. Rep.* **42**, 750–751.
17. U.S. Department of Agriculture (1960). *U.S., Dep. Agric., Agric. Res. Serv.* [Rep.] **22–57**.
18. Iida, T. T. (1967). *Virus Dis. Rice Plant, Proc. Symp. Int. Rice Res. Inst., 1967* pp. 3–12.
19. Koehler, B., Bever, W. M., and Bonner, O. T. (1952). *Ill., Agric. Exp. Stn., Bull.* **556**, 567–569.
20. Sill, W. H., and King, C. C. (1958). *Plant Dis. Rep.* **42**, 513–516.
21. Broadbent, L. (1976). *Annu. Rev. Phytopathol.* **14**, 75–96.
22. Klinkowski, M. (1970). *Annu. Rev. Phytopathol.* **8**, 37–60.
23. Thurston, H. D. (1973). *Annu. Rev. Phytopathol.* **11**, 27–52.
24. Phillips, M. P. (1961). *Rep. Cocoa Conf.* Vol. 1, p. 178.
25. Watson, J. D., and Crick, F. H. C. (1953). *Cold Spring Harbor Symp. Quant. Biol.* **18**, 123–134.
26. Baltimore, D. (1971). *Bacteriol. Rev.* **35**, 235–241.
27. Sanger, H. L., Klotz, G., Riesner, D., Gross, H., and Kleinschmidt, A. (1976). *Proc. Natl. Acad. Sci. U.S.A.* **73**, 3852–3856.
28. Diener, T., and Smith, D. (1975). *Virology* **63**, 421–427.
29. Goodman, R. (1977). *Virology* **83**, 171–179.

29a. Harrison, B., and Murant, A. (eds.) (1970–1978). "Descriptions of Plant Viruses." Commonwealth Agricultural Institute, Slough, England.
30. Jaspars, E. M. J. (1974). *Adv. Virus Res.* **19**, 37–149.
31. Caspar, D. L. D., and Klug, A. (1962). *Cold Spring Harbor Symp. Quant. Biol.* **27**, 1–24.
32. Kaper, J. M. (1975). "The Chemical Basis of Virus Structure, Dissociation and Reassembly." Am. Elsevier, New York.
33. Shepherd, R. (1972). *In* "Principles and Techniques in Plant Virology" (C. Kado and H. Agrawal, eds.), pp. 267–294. Van Nostrand-Reinhold, Princeton, New Jersey.
34. Slykhuis, J. T. (1972). *In* "Principles and Techniques in Plant Virology" (C. Kado and H. Agrawal, eds.), pp. 204–221. Van Nostrand-Reinhold, Princeton, New Jersey.
35. Teakle, D. (1972). *In* "Principles and Techniques in Plant Virology" (C. Kado and H. Agrawal, eds.), pp. 248–266. Van Nostrand-Reinhold, Princeton, New Jersey.
36. Taylor, C. E. (1972). *In* "Principles and Techniques in Plant Virology" (C. Kado and H. Agrawal, eds.), pp. 226–247. Van Nostrand-Reinhold, Princeton, New Jersey.
37. Watson, M. A. (1972). *In* "Principles and Techniques in Plant Virology" (C. Kado and H. Agrawal, eds.), pp. 131–166. Van Nostrand-Reinhold, Princeton, New Jersey.
38. Whitcomb, R. (1972). *In* "Principles and Techniques in Plant Virology" (C. Kado and H. Agrawal, eds.), pp. 168–203. Van Nostrand-Reinhold, Princeton, New Jersey.
39. Walters, H. (1969). *Adv. Virus Res.* **15**, 339–364.
40. Gibbs, A. J., and Harrison, B. D. (1968). *Nature (London)* **218**, 927–929.
41. Fenner, F. (1976). *Intervirology* **6**, 1–12.
42. Bennet, C. W. (1967). *Annu. Rev. Phytopathol.* **5**, 87–108.
43. Thresh, J. M. (1974). *Annu. Rev. Phytopathol.* **12**, 111–128.
44. Swanson, K. G. (1968). *Annu. Rev. Phytopathol.* **6**, 351–374.
45. Johnson, C. G. (1960). *Rep. Commonw. Entomol. Conf., 7th, 1960* pp. 140–145.
46. Zink, F. W., Grogan, R. G., and Welch, J. E. (1956). *Phytopathology* **46**, 622–624.
47. Slykhuis, J. T. (1965). *Adv. Virus Res.* **11**, 97–137.
48. Duffus, J. E (1971). *Annu. Rev. Phytopathol.* **9**, 319–340.
49. Severin, H. H. P. (1934). *Hilgardia* **8**, 263–280.
50. Costa, A. S. (1965). *Phytopathol. Z.* **2**, 97–112.
51. Stubbs, I. L., Gray, J. A. D., and Stubbs, K. J. (1963). *Aust. J. Exp. Agric. Anim. Husb.* **3**, 215–218.
52. Watson, M. A. (1938). *Proc. R. Soc. London, Ser. B* **125**, 144–170.
53. Watson, M. A., and Roberts, F. M. (1939). *Proc. R. Soc. London, Ser. B* **127**, 543–576.
54. Kennedy, J. S., Day, M. F., and Eastop, V. F. (1962). "A Conspectus of Aphids as Vectors of Plant Viruses." Commonw. Inst. Entomol., London.
55. Kikimoto, T., and Matsui, C. (1962). *Virology* **16**, 509–510.
56. Hutchinson, P., and Mathews, R. (1963). *Virology* **20**, 169–175.
57. Kassanis, B. (1961). *Virology* **13**, 93–97.
58. Kassanis, B., and Govier, D. (1971). *J. Gen. Virol.* **13**, 221–228.
59. Govier, D., and Kassanis, B. (1974). *Virology* **57**, 285–286.
60. Duffus, J. E. (1963). *Virology* **21**, 194–202.
61. Nault, L., Gyrisco, G., and Rochow, W. (1964). *Phytopathology* **54**, 1269–1272.

62. Sylvester, E. (1969). *Virology* **38**, 440–446.
63. Fukuslie, T. (1940). *J. Fac. Agric., Hokkaido Univ.* **45**, 83–154.
64. Black, L., and Brakke, M. (1952). *Phytopathology* **42**, 269–273.
65. Fukuslie, T. (1933). *Proc. Imp. Acad. (Tokyo)* **8**, 457–460.
66. Black, L. (1953). *Phytopathology* **43**, 9–10.
67. Harrison, B. (1973). *In* "Viruses and Invertebrates" (A. J. Gibbs, ed.), pp. 512–530. Am. Elsevier, New York.
68. Campbell, R. N., and Fry, P. R. (1966). *Virology* **29**, 222–233.
69. Kershaw, W. J. S. (1964). *Plant Pathol.* **13**, 90–91.
70. Hille Ris Lambers, D. (1955). *Ann. Appl. Biol.* **42**, 355–360.
71. Broadbent, L. (1950). *Ann. Appl. Biol.* **37**, 58–65.
72. Slykhuis, J. T. (1955). *Phytopathology* **45**, 116–128.
73. Stubbs, L., and Grogan, R. (1963). *Aust. J. Agric. Res.* **14**, 439–459.
74. Van der Plank, J. E. (1975). "Principles of Plant Infection." Academic Press, New York.
75. Broadbent, L. (1957). "Investigation of Virus Diseases of Brassica Crops." Cambridge Univ. Press, London and New York.
76. Smith, F. F., Johnson, G. V., Kahn, R. P., and Bing, A. (1964). *Phytopathology* **54**, 748.
77. Fraenkel-Conrat, H., Singer, B., and Williams, R. (1957). *Biochim. Biophys. Acta* **25**, 87–95.
78. Wilcockson, J., and Hull, R. (1974). *J. Gen. Virol.* **23**, 107–111.
79. Burdon, R., Billeter, M., Weissmann, C., Warner, R., Ochoa, S., and Knight, C. A. (1964). *Proc. Natl. Acad. Sci. U.S.A.* **52**, 768–775.
80. Ralph, R., Matthews, R. E. F., Matus, A., and Mandel, H. (1965). *J. Mol. Biol.* **11**, 202–212.
81. German, T. L., and de Zoeten, G. (1975). *Virology* **66**, 172–184.
82. Van Griensven, L., and Van Kammen, A. (1969). *J. Gen. Virol.* **4**, 423–428.
83. Lane, L. C., and Kaesberg, P. (1972). *Nature (London), New Biol.* **232**, 40–42.
84. Jackson, A., and Brakke, M. K. (1973). *Virology* **55**, 483–494.
85. Pinck, L., and Hirth, L. (1972). *Virology* **49**, 413–425.
86. Jackson, A., Mitchell, D., and Siegel, A. (1971). *Virology* **45**, 182–191.
87. Nillson-Tilgren, T. (1970). *Mol. Gen. Genet.* **109**, 246–256.
88. Kielland-Brandt, M., and Nillson-Tilgren, T. (1973). *Mol. Gen. Genet.* **121**, 229–238.
89. Jackson, A., Zaitlin, M., Siegel, A., and Francki, R. I. B. (1972). *Virology* **48**, 655–665.
90. Eoyang, L., and August, J. T. (1974). *Compr. Virol.* **2**, 1–59.
91. Ralph, R., Bullivant, S., and Wojcik, S. (1971). *Virology* **44**, 473–479.
92. Bradley, D., and Zaitlin, M. (1971). *Virology* **45**, 192–199.
93. Ralph, R., and Wojcik, S. (1966). *Biochim. Biophys. Acta* **119**, 347–361.
94. Bové, J., Bové, C., and Mocquot, B. (1968). *Biochem. Biophys. Res. Commun.* **32**, 480–486.
95. Semal, J., and Hamilton, R. I. (1968). *Virology* **36**, 293–302.
96. Peden, K., May, J., and Symons, R. (1972). *Virology* **47**, 498–501.
97. May, J., Gilliland, J., and Symons, R. (1970). *Virology* **41**, 653–664.
98. Lafleche, D., Bové, C., DuPont, G., Mouches, C., Astir, T., Garnier, M., and Bové, J. (1972). *In* "RNA Viruses; Ribosomes" (H. Bloemendal *et al.*, eds.), pp. 43–65. North-Holland Publ., Amsterdam.
99. Jacquemin, J. (1972). *Virology* **49**, 379–384.
100. Semal, J., and Kummert, J. (1971). *J. Gen. Virol.* **10**, 79–89.

101. Kummert, J., and Semal, J. (1972). *J. Gen. Virol.* **16**, 11–20.
102. Clark, G. L., Peden, K. W., and Symons, R. H. (1974). *Virology* **62**, 434–443.
103. Mouchès, C., Bové, C., Barreau, C., and Bové, J. (1976). *Ann. Microbiol. (Paris)* **127a**, 75–90.
104. Zaitlin, M., Duda, C. T., and Petti, M. (1973). *Virology* **53**, 300–311.
105. Brishammar, S. (1976). *Ann. Microbiol. (Paris)* **127a**, 25–31.
106. Hadidi, A., and Fraenkel-Conrat, H. (1973). *Virology* **52**, 363–372.
107. Fraenkel-Conrat, H. (1976). *Virology* **72**, 23–32.
108. Hariharasubramanian, V., Hadidi, A., Singer, B., and Fraenkel-Conrat, H. (1973). *Virology* **54**, 190–198.
109. Hadidi, A., Hariharasubramanian, V., and Frankel-Conrat, H. (1973). *Intervirology* **1**, 201–209.
109a. Zabel, P., Jongen-Neven, I., and van Kammen, A. (1979). *J. Virol.* **29**, 21–33.
110. Duda, C., Zaitlin, M., and Siegel, A. (1973). *Biochim. Biophys. Acta* **319**, 62–71.
110a. Ikegami, M., and Fraenkel-Conrat, H. (1978). FEBS Letts. **96**, 197–200.
111. Francki, R. I. B., and Randles, J. W. (1973). *Virology* **54**, 359–368.
112. Reddy, D. V. R., and Black, L. M. (1973). *Virology* **54**, 557–562.
113. Joklik, W. (1974). *Compr. Virol.* **2**, 231–334.
114. Gross, H. J., Domdey, H., Lossow, C., Janki, P., Raba, M., Alberty, H., and Sanger, H. L. (1978). *Nature (London)* **273**, 203–208.
114a. Matthews, R. E. F. (1978). *Nature (London)* **276**, 2728.
115. Mayhew, D., and Ford, R. (1974). *Virology* **57**, 503–509.
116. De Zoeten, G., Assink, A., and Van Kammen, A. (1974). *Virology* **59**, 341–355.
117. De Zoeten, G., Powell, C., Gaard, G., and German, T. (1976). *Virology* **70**, 459–469.
118. Wettstein, D. V., and Zech, H. (1962). *Z. Naturforsch., Teil ?B* **17**, 376–379.
119. Bald, J. (1964). *Virology* **22**, 377–387.
120. Smith, S. H., and Schlegel, D. E. (1965). *Virology* **26**, 180–189.
121. Lodish, H. (1975). In "RNA Phages" (N. Zinder, ed.), pp. 301–318. Cold Spring Harbor Lab., Cold Spring Harbor, New York.
122. Jacobson, M., Asso, J., and Baltimore, D. (1970). *J. Mol. Biol.* **49**, 657–668.
123. Kiehn, E., and Holland, J. (1970). *J. Virol.* **5**, 358–371.
124. Shih, C., and Kaesberg, P. (1976). *J. Mol. Biol.* **103**, 77–88.
125. Shih, D., and Kaesberg, P. (1973). *Proc. Natl. Acad. Sci. U.S.A.* **70**, 1799–1804.
125a. Pelham, H. (1978). *Nature (London)* **272**, 469–471.
126. Siegel, A., Zaitlin, M., and Duda, C. T. (1973). *Virology* **53**, 75–83.
127. Hunter, T., Hunt, T., Knowland, J., and Zimmer, D. (1976). *Nature (London)* **260**, 759–764.
128. Siegel, A., Hari, V., Montgomery, I., and Kolacz, K. (1976). *Virology* **73**, 363–371.
129. Pleij, C. W. A., Neeleman, A., Van Vloten-Doting, L., and Bosch, L. (1976). *Proc. Natl. Acad. Sci. U.S.A.* **73**, 4437–4441.
130. Beachy, R., and Zaitlin, M. (1977). *Virology* **81**, 160–169.
131. Lister, R. M. (1968). *J. Gen. Virol.* **2**, 43–58.
132. Fritsch, C., Mayo, M., and Hirth, L. (1976). *Ann. Microbiol. (Paris)* **127a**, 93–95.
133. Higgins, T., Goodwin, P., and Whitfeld, P. (1976). *Virology* **71**, 486–497.
134. Bruening, G., Beachy, R., Scalla, R., and Zaitlin, M. (1976). *Virology* **71**, 498–517.
135. Hari, V., and Siegel, A., unpublished.
136. Zaitlin, M., and Hariharasubramanian, V. (1972). *Virology* **47**, 296–305.
137. Paterson, R., and Knight, C. A. (1975). *Virology* **64**, 10–22.
138. Sakai, F., and Takebe, I. (1972). *Mol. Gen. Genet.* **118**, 93–96.
139. Knowland, J. (1974). *Genetics* **78**, 383–394.

140. Francki, R., and Matthews, R. (1962). *Virology* **17**, 367–380.
141. Siegel, A., Zaitlin, M., and Sehgal, O. (1962). *Proc. Natl. Acad. Sci. U.S.A.* **48**, 1845–1851.
142. Babos, P., and Kassanis, B. (1962). *Virology* **18**, 206–211.
143. Fraenkel-Conrat, H., and Williams, R. (1955). *Proc. Natl. Acad. Sci. U.S.A.* **41**, 690–698.
144. Bancroft, J. (1970). *Adv. Virus Res.* **16**, 99–135.
145. Klug, A., and Butler, P., eds. (1976). *Philos. Trans. R. Soc. London, Ser. B* **276**, 1–204.
146. Butler, P., Bloomer, A., Bricogne, Champness, J., Graham, J., Guilley, H., Klug, A., and Zimmern, D. (1976). In "Structure-Function Relationships of Proteins" (R. Markham and R. Horne, eds.), pp. 101–111. North-Holland Publ., Amsterdam.
147. Siegel, A. (1971). *Virology* **46**, 50–59.
148. Hatta, T., and Matthews, R. (1976). *Virology* **73**, 1–16.
149. Zaitlin, M., Spencer, D., and Whitfeld, P. (1968). In "Plant Biochemical Regulations in Viral and other Diseases or Injury" (T. Harai, Z. Hidaka, and I. Umitani, eds.), pp. 91–103. Phytopathol. Soc. Jpn., Tokyo.
150. Favali, M., Bassi, M., and Conti, G. (1973). *Virology* **53**, 115–119.
151. Assink, A., Swaans, H., and Van Kammen, A. (1973). *Virology* **53**, 384–393.
152. Shepherd, J., and Claflin, L. (1975). *Annu. Rev. Phytopathol.* **13**, 271–293.
153. Hollings, M. (1965). *Annu. Rev. Phytopathol.* **3**, 367–396.
154. Weathers, L., and Calavan, E. (1959). In "Citrus Virus Diseases" (J. M. Wallace, ed.), pp. 197–202. University of California, Div. Agric. Sci., Berkeley.
155. Kassanis, B. (1959). *Recent Adv. Bot.* **1**, 557–563.
156. Nyland, G., and Goheen, A. (1969). *Annu. Rev. Phytopathol.* **7**, 331–354.
157. Matthews, R., and Smith, J. D. (1955). *Adv. Virus Res.* **3**, 51–148.
158. Shepard, J., and Secor, G. A. (1969). *Phytopathology* **59**, 1838–1844.
159. Todd, J. M. (1961). *Eur. Potato J.* **4**, 316–329.
160. Holmes, F. O. (1965). *Adv. Virus Res.* **11**, 139–162.
161. Taylor, C. (1967). *Ann. Appl. Biol.* **59**, 275–281.
162. Severin, H., and Freitag, H. (1938). *Hilgardia* **11**, 495–558.
163. Murant, A., and Taylor, C. (1965). *Ann. Appl. Biol.* **55**, 227–237.
164. Hull, R., and Heathcote, G. (1967). *Ann. Appl. Biol.* **60**, 469–478.
165. Siegel, A. (1966). In "Viruses in Plants" (A. Beemster and J. Dijkstra, eds.), pp. 3–18. North-Holland Publ., Amsterdam.
166. Smith, K. M. (1965). *Adv. Virus Res.* **11**, 61–96.
167. Takebe, I., and Otsuki, Y. (1969). *Proc. Natl. Acad. Sci. U.S.A.* **64**, 843–851.
168. Bradley, R. (1963). *Can. J. Microbiol.* **9**, 369–380.
169. Loebenstein, G., Alper, M., and Deutsch, M. (1964). *Phytopathology* **54**, 960–962.
170. Siegel, A., Ginoza, W., and Wildman, S. (1957). *Virology* **3**, 554–559.
171. Knowland, J., Hunter, T., Hunt, T., and Zimmern, D. (1975). *Les Colloques de l'Institut National de la Sante et de la Recherche Medicale* **47**, 211–216.
172. Brishammer, S., and Junti, N. (1974). *Virology* **59**, 245–253.
173. Gibbs, A. J. (1973). "Viruses and Invertebrates." Am. Elsevier, New York.
174. Stairs, G. R. (1971). In "Microbial Control of Insects and Mites" (H. G. Burges and N. W. Hussey, eds.), pp. 97–124. Academic Press, New York.
175. Summers, M., Engler, R., Falcon, L., and Vail, P., eds. (1975). "Baculoviruses for Insect Pest Control: Safety Considerations." Am. Soc. Microbiol., Washington, D.C.

176. Bailey, L. (1973). *In* "Viruses and Invertebrates" (A. J. Gibbs, ed.), pp. 533–553. Am. Elsevier, New York.
177. Fenner, F., and Ratcliffe, F. N. (1965). "Myxomatosis." Cambridge Univ. Press, London and New York.
178. Bennett, C. (1969). *Adv. Virus Res.* **14**, 221–261.
179. Diener, T. O. (1972). *Adv. Virus Res.* **17**, 295–313.
180. Van Kammen, A. (1972). *Annu. Rev. Phytopathol.* **10**, 125–149.
181. Siegel, A., and Zaitlin, M. (1965). *Virol.* **4**, 113–125.
182. Robertson, H. D. (1975). *In* "RNA Phages" (N. D. Zinder, ed.), pp. 113–145. Cold Spring Harbor Lab., Cold Spring Harbor, New York.
183. Spiegelman, S. (1971). *Q. Rev. Biophys.* **4**, 213–253.
184. Schneider, I., Hull, R., and Markham, R. (1972). *Virology* **47**, 320–330.
185. Kassanis, B. (1968). *Adv. Virus Res.* **13**, 147–180.
186. Maniatis, T., Kee, S. G., Efstratiadis, A., and Kafatos, F. C. (1976). *Cell* **8**, 163–182.
187. Kacian, D. L., and Myers, J. C. (1976). *Proc. Natl. Acad. Sci. U.S.A.* **7**, 2191–2195.
188. Larkins, B. A., Jones, R. A., and Tsai, C. Y. (1976). *Biochemistry* **15**, 5506–5511.
189. Verma, D. P. S., MacLachlin, G. A., Byrne, H., and Ewings, D. (1975). *J. Biol. Chem.* **250**, 1019–1026.
190. Shepherd, R. J. (1976). *Adv. Virus Res.* **20**, 305–339.
191. Schwinghamer, M., and Symons, R. (1975). *Virology* **63**, 252–262.

Chapter 5

Pathogenic Fungi and Crop Productivity*

Albert H. Ellingboe

Fungi can have both positive and negative effects on plant productivity. Fungi that form mycorrhizal associations with the roots of

*Research supported in part by Grants GB-42124 and PCM 77-05343 from the National Science Foundation.

203

plants are usually considered to be beneficial to their host plants. The mycorrhizal fungi are dealt with in Chapter 6, this volume. This chapter will deal primarily with plant pathogenic fungi and their interaction with plants.

I. EFFECT OF FUNGAL DISEASES ON CROP PRODUCTIVITY

A. Sustained Yield Losses

There is little difficulty in establishing that fungi can cause great losses in plant yield. The experimentally determined estimates of losses in corn production due to the stalk and root rots range from 12 to 28% annually. These estimates of losses have been determined by several different procedures. Probably the best estimates have been obtained by determining the weight of grain on plants with stalk and/or root rot, and on plants without these diseases, in each of a number of fields of single cross hybrids. Such analyses in a large number of fields in Michigan have shown that corn plants with stalk rot yielded 13% less grain than plants without stalk rot. Plants with root rot yielded 17% less grain than plants without root rot. Stalk and root rot can occur together on one plant; they can also occur independently. Plants also can be free of both diseases. If we consider the yield reduction due to each disease, the proportion of plants with both diseases, and the proportion of plants infected in an average field, an average annual loss due to stalk and root rot in corn is about 15% in Michigan, a figure that agrees well with similar studies in other Corn Belt states. But these diseases do more to the plant than cause a reduction in the yield of grain. Plants with stalk or root rot may lodge more severely than healthy plants. The ear from a lodged plant is frequently not recovered by a mechanical harvestor so the grain loss on a lodged plant is frequently 100%. The estimates of loss given above may be very conservative, but they are the annual losses with which we live.

B. Sporadic Yield Losses

Losses in yield with some diseases are more dramatic. Stem rust of wheat may cause a complete loss of harvestable grain 1 year and cause no losses the next year. In 1953 and 1954 there was virtually a 100% loss in durum wheats in Minnesota and North Dakota, and there have been sporadic losses due to stem rust in North American wheat since that time. The sporadic nature of the occurrence and severity of stem rust has made it a disease of which the public is acutely aware. In some parts of the world, control of stem rust is a necessity for wheat production. Without stem rust control in the main wheat growing-areas of the United States, India, and Australia, production of good-quality wheat would be very undependable. Production would follow a boom and bust cycle. Without control measures, the frequency of devastating epidemics would probably increase because of the increase in inoculum carried from 1 year to the next.

C. Limitation of Yield Potential by Fungus Diseases

As a general rule, the incidence and severity of fungus-caused diseases increase as attempts are made to increase acreage and intensify production of a given plant species. Efforts to increase yields per acre have provided particularly good examples of the role of fungus diseases in limiting yields. For example, wheat yields in Michigan generally average 40–45 bu/acre. Farmers who attempt to increase yields by using higher levels of fertilizer, particularly nitrogen, will generally have more severe problems with root diseases, primarily the eyespot disease caused by *Cercosporella herpotrichoides*. Attempts to grow wheat on highly fertile soils frequently result in 100% fungus-infected plants, extensive lodging, and low yields of reduced quality grain. Yields of wheat in Michigan greater than 75 bu/acre are exceedingly (and disappointingly) rare. The eyespot disease and other root diseases limit the maximum yields of wheat obtained in Michigan. The cultivars have the genetic potential for high yields, because they do give high yields in geographic areas where these fungal pathogens do not succeed as well. Fungal pathogens also have their regions of adaptation. A pathogen such as *Cercosporella herpotricoides* may be very limiting to a yield in one geographic area in the world, but not in another. For example, the Green Revolution wheats produced in Mexico by the Rockefeller Foundation will barely produce any seed in Michigan because of their extreme susceptibility to *Septoria nodorum*. Apparently, they were bred in an area in which the species of *Septoria* were not a problem.

D. Establishing Effects of Fungal Diseases on Crop Productivity

Three ways have been previously mentioned in which fungal diseases affect crop productivity. Diseases like the stalk and root rots of corn take a very heavy toll. The percentage loss in yield seems to be somewhat constant with differences in efforts to obtain high yields. To establish the effects of this disease complex on yield is difficult, because we presently do not know how to get a disease-free control in experiments. Basically, the same arguments hold for diseases, such as wheat root rots, that become limiting as efforts are made to obtain higher yields. It is relatively easier to establish the effects of a disease like wheat stem rust on yield. One can make comparisons of yield between years with different amounts of disease, between fields and areas with different amounts of disease in each year, and between highly isogenic lines—some of which are resistant and the others susceptible to the disease—in a year or area where the disease is present on the susceptible line. The effects of different levels of disease, time of appearance, and increase of the disease during the growing season, etc., have been evaluated for diseases such as wheat stem rust.

It is by general agreement that people interested in crop productivity have decided that photosynthesis is a limiting component of the yield potential of a plant species. This is not so for pathologists. They are repeatedly asked for data that substantiate the fact that diseases limit productivity. Almost every plant pathologist in the United States has had to perform experiments demonstrating that the disease investigated by him/her reduces yield—and to what extent—of the crop investigated in that geographic area, under the cultural practices used, etc. These experiments frequently do not give pertinent information as to how these pathogens may affect the maximum yield potential.

II. CONTROL OF FUNGAL DISEASES

Fungal diseases of plants are usually controlled by some combination of cultural practices, use of fungicides, and host plant resistance. Cultural practices are obviously going to change as efforts are made to increase yields. Cultural practices that lead to increased yields—i.e., high fertility, irrigation, and high plant population densities—frequently favor the development of fungal pathogens. Emphasis on uniform quality frequently means low genetic diversity, at least in each geographically or ecologically defined area.

Fungicides will very likely continue to be used in the foreseeable future as efforts are made to increase productivity. However, fungicides in current use are being placed on the rebuttable presumption list by the Environmental Protection Agency. If we get to the situation where only one fungicide is approved for each fungal pathogen, then the possibility of developing a fungicide-resistant pathogen population increases, and the risk of a catastrophe caused by use of ineffective fungicides increases. Diseases for which fungicides are the primary means of control will always be with us, especially if chemical control is temporary, History also tells us that as we move from the more nonspecific fungicides, such as the phenyl mercuries, to the more specific fungicides, such as carboxin, the possibility of obtaining mutants resistant to the fungicide increases.

Most, but not all, fungal diseases of field crops such as wheat, corn, rice, and barley are controlled primarily by breeding for disease resistance. Breeding for disease resistance is usually considered to be an economical, safe method of controlling fungal diseases. An investment in a small number of people, say 1–5, may give disease control and increase in yield of millions of bushels of wheat or corn, or some other crop commodity, per year.

History has also told us that resistance to a pathogen may not last long, since the pathogen genotype changes. Sometimes a host genotype will confer resistance to a fungal pathogen for many years. For example, resistance in cabbage to *Fusarium* has lasted for more than 60 years. On the other hand, breeders have many examples, about which they usually do not wish to speak, where a particular genotype that conferred resistance while the lines were being developed in the breeding program but that was found to be susceptible by the time the line was increased sufficiently and put into commercial production. Why do some host genotypes give resistance for a long period of time and others give resistance lasting only a short period of time? The following discussion will, hopefully, give some clue as to what the answers might be.

I will start with the basic premise that inherent host variability with respect to interactions with fungal pathogens may, in the future, be the most desirable trait to exploit to control diseases caused by fungi. I consider it to be the safest method, because no chemicals of nonbiological origin are involved. The effect on the nontarget organisms should be of a secondary nature. It is economical because a small investment can lead to large increases in total yield to stability in production. The idea that breeding for disease resistance leads to a boom and bust production (boom while resistance lasts, bust when pathogen changes so that the host is no longer resistant) can now be avoided. Epidemic prevention is now a real possibility, and already has been demonstrated with such serious fungal diseases as stem rust of wheat in Australia. There is also the possibility that, by breeding for resistance to fungal diseases, we may introduce or change the composition of chemicals present in the host, and that some of these may be toxic to man. Thus far, the genetic decision for determining whether the pathogen continues to grow and develop in the host does not seem to alter the nutritive value of the host. The effects of that decision may have rather large effects on the host, particularly if the result is death of the host tissue.

III. GENETICS OF HOST–PARASITE INTERACTIONS

The genetics of disease resistance brings to mind the genetics of intelligence in man. The kinds of data available have not changed much in the last 50 years, but the interpretations of those data have changed several times. As more data are collected, we have begun to see and better understand certain basic genetic patterns between host and parasite, the universality of the basic pattern, the perspective of apparent exceptions to the basic pattern, and how an understanding of the genetics (in both host and parasite) of the interactions between host and parasite can be exploited for controlling diseases and increasing crop productivity.

A. Genetics of Host–Parasite Interactions from 1905 to 1940

The first report on the inheritance of disease resistance appeared only a few years after the rediscovery of Mendel's work. Resistance to yellow rust of wheat was shown to segregate in crosses, as if due to a single Mendelian unit (Biffen, 1905). The F_2 generation of a cross of resistant and susceptible cultivars was grown in the field. Early in the season there were three kinds of plants, namely, those that were free of the rust disease, those that were quite heavily diseased, and those that had just a few infections. The ratio of the three types of F_2 plants was 1:1:2, respectively. Later in the season, that is, as the plants approached maturity, there were only two types of plants. One-fourth of the plants were basically free of the rust disease, and three-fourths were heavily diseased. Only the latter data were interpreted, and they were used to conclude that rust resistance in wheat was due to a single recessive gene. It is sufficient to say here that the interpretation would have been different if the data collected early in the season had been used. The first paper published—of which I am aware—which dealt specifically with the inheritance of disease resistance shows the effects of how one does the experiments on the interpretation.

Up until about 1940, there had been a considerable effort to determine whether there was variability in fungal parasite species, and whether fungal parasites followed Mendelian genetics. Early in this period, the existence of physiological races of fungal pathogens was demonstrated. A physiological race is defined as a biotype or group of biotypes that behave similarly when inoculated onto a set of differential host lines. A differential host line helps to distinguish between different physiological races of a pathogen. Physiological races are normally morphologically indistinguishable.

The demonstration of the existence of host plant resistance, and the simple inheritance of that resistance, led to the production of disease-resistant cultivars of crops such as wheat, barley, and corn, crops in which there were intensive breeding programs. After a disease-resistant cultivar was grown for a few years, it was frequently observed to lose its resistance. Breeders frequently called this the "breakdown" of resistance. With the "breakdown" of resistance, pathologists observed changes in the prevalence or the appearance of new physiological races of a pathogen. Most people realized that the host genes did not just disintegrate or disappear from the host population. The pathogen genotype had changed, and the host genes were no longer effective in restricting the development of the pathogen.

It is quite clear that resistance was conceived of as being due to the presence of some toxic compound in the host. The change in the pathogen was conceived as being analogous to mutations to resistance to a toxicant. One need only look at the large number of studies done during this period—selecting mutants resistant to such toxicants (e.g., lead arsenic and mercury compounds)—and to make the analogy with the example of resistance in onions to onion smudge, to see the interpretations given then to host plant resistance and the breakdown of host plant resistance.

B. Development of the Gene-for-Gene Concept

In 1946 and 1947, two papers were published by Flor that dealt with the genetics of the host and parasite. For the first time, the genetics of interaction between the host (*Linum usitatissimum*) and parasite (*Melampsora lini*), and the disease state caused by this interaction, was investigated by studying the genetics of both the host and the pathogen. The importance of this approach and these two papers has just recently begun to be realized.

1. Basic Genetics

Flor had initially begun his research in 1930's with the traditional approach of a plant breeder and pathologist interested in breeding

disease-resistant cultivars. He made a large collection of host lines that
showed promise of having useful genes for resistance to flax rust. He
had collected a large number of strains of the fungus, *Melampsora lini*,
and inoculated a large number of host lines with each collection of the
fungal pathogen. From these experiments, he was able to demonstrate
the existence of a large number of physiological races of the pathogen
(Flor, 1940). From these experiments he was also able to deduce that
the host lines used as differentials differed by a fairly large number of
genes. One host line, a cultivar called Bison, seemed to be susceptible
to all cultures of the fungus *M. lini*—at least all cultures from North and
South America with which he worked. (Bison was later shown to have
resistance to some Australian cultures of *M. lini*.) Each of the differential host lines was crossed with Bison to determine how many gene
differences there were between the two host lines. In most experiments
each parent line and each F_2 plant was inoculated with several different
cultures of the fungus. The first leaves were inoculated with one culture, the second set of leaves was inoculated with a second culture,
the third set of leaves was inoculated with a third culture, and so on.
Though both parents may give the same reactions upon inoculation
with each of three or more cultures (i.e., one host line resistant to each
strain of *M. lini* and the other host line susceptible to all strains) segregation ratios in the F_2 population may suggest that there was only a
one-gene difference between the parents for reaction to one culture of
M. lini, a two-gene difference for reaction to a second culture, a three-
gene difference for a third culture, and so on. Since each F_2 plant was
inoculated separately with each culture of *M. lini*, it was possible to
determine whether the one gene segregating for reaction to culture 1
was one of the two genes segregating for reaction to culture 2. The most
important point derived from these experiments is that the choice of
the culture of *M. lini* determined how many gene differences would be
identified in a cross between two host lines. We can now understand
why there were so many conflicting reports on the inheritance of disease resistance—even between a cross of the same cultivars, but performed in separate institutions—in the two decades preceding Flor's
papers.

Flor also intercrossed the differential host lines to establish the relationship of genes in one differential to the genes in another differential
host line. By inoculating each F_2 plant with individual inoculations of
several cultures of *M. lini*, it was possible to show which genes were
unlinked and which were alleles (or closely linked genes). The data
suggested that there were at least 19 pairs of factors involved in the
conditioning reaction of the 16 differential host lines to *M. lini*. The
genes are now known to be in five "loci" or allelomorphic series.

Flor did more than cross host lines. He also made crosses of cultures of *M. lini* and studied the inheritance of virulence versus avirulence on each of the host differentials. If a host differential was shown to have one gene for reaction to *M. lini*, virulence versus avirulence on that differential was shown to be controlled by one gene. If a host differential was shown to have two genes for reaction to *M. lini*, virulence versus avirulence on that differential was shown to be controlled by two genes. The one-for-one relationship between genes in host and parasite led to the development of the gene-for-gene hypothesis (Flor, 1955). The pattern of inheritance in host and parasite is presented in Table I. If one gene for reaction segregates in the cross of the two host lines, then one gene segregates in a cross of the two strains of the parasite. Note that no segregation in the host was observed with parasite strain 2. Note also that no segregation in the parasite was observed with host line B. In Table I resistance or virulence was not presented, but instead the relationship between host and parasite was given as being compatible or incompatible. Viewed from the standpoint of the host, host line A is resistant to parasite strain 1, host line B is susceptible to parasite strain 1, and the F_2 segregate 3:1 for resistant: susceptible progeny to parasite strain 1. Viewed from the standpoint of the parasite, strain 1 is avirulent on host line A, virulent on host line B, and the F_2 segregate 3:1 avirulent: virulent progeny on host line A. All parasite lines were virulent on host line B. The interdependence of genes in host and parasite can be seen clearly from Table I. The example given is with a diploid host and a functionally diploid parasite, the situation studied by Flor. Most plant pathogenic fungi are haploid. Segregation ratios will be different, but the basic pattern of the interactions of the parent host lines and parent parasite strains remains the same. This

TABLE I
An Example of the Inheritance of Interactions between Host and
Parasite[a]

		Host			
		Parents		Progeny	
Parasite		A	B	F_1	F_2
Parents	1	−	+	−	¾ − : ¼ +
	2	+	+	+	All +
Progeny	F_1	−	+		
	F_2	¾ −	+		
		¼ +	+		

[a] −, Incompatible relationship; +, compatible relationship.

pattern, with designations of gene symbols, is given in Table II. This pattern is now called the quadratic check.

From Tables I and II we can see the interdependence of genes in host and parasite. A host plant can be resistant only if the parasite has the corresponding gene for avirulence. Only the parasite/host genotype, abbreviated P1/R1, can give an incompatible relationship. The other three parasite/host genotypes—P1/r1, p1/R1 and p1/r1—give compatible relationships. The simplest interpretation of this pattern is that there is specific recognition between the products of P1 and R1 to give an incompatible relationship between host and parasite. The other three parasite/host genotypes represent no interaction.

2. Interpretation of the Basic Genetics

It has been frequently argued over the years that one can make an equally valid case for resistance or susceptibility to be an active function. If we have one parasite strain of genotype P1 and two host lines with R1 or r1 (see Table II), one can make an equally valid case for active function for resistance or susceptibility. If we have only one host line R1 and two parasite strains P1 and p1 (see Table II) one can make an equally valid case for active function for virulence or avirulence. However, when consideration is given to the four possible parasite/host genotypes, the simplest interpretation is that only one genotype represents specific interaction between these genes in host and parasite.

Table III provides the basic pattern for two parasite/host gene pairs—two loci in the host, two loci in the parasite, and two alleles at each locus. The pattern is given as a diploid host and a haploid parasite, the most common arrangement with fungal parasites of plants. There are two points to be made in this illustration. One point is specificity, P1 will recognize R1, but not R2, to give an incompatible relationship, while P2 will recognize R2, but not R1, to give an incompatible rela-

TABLE II

The Relationship between Genes in Host and Parasite

	Host	
Parasite	Rl Rl	rl rl
Pl Pl	$-^a$	+
pl pl	+	+

$^a-$, Incompatible relationship; +, Compatible relationship.

TABLE III
The Pattern of Interactions for Two Parasite/Host Gene pairs

Parasite genotypes	Host genotypes			
	R1 R1 R2 R2	R1 R1 r2 r2	r1 r1 R2 R2	r1 r1 r2 r2
P1 P2	$-^a$	−	−	+
P1 p2	−	−	+	+
p1 P2	−	+	−	+
p1 p2	+	+	+	+

^{a} −, Incompatible relationship; +, Compatible relationship.

tionship. Conversely, R1 will recognize P1 but not P2, and R2 will recognize P2 but not P1. The second point is that if one parasite/host gene pair specifies incompatibility, it is epistatic to all gene pairs specifying compatibility. For example, P1/R1 specifies incompatibility and p2/R2 specifies compatibility (Table III). What we see is incompatibility, whereas, we also see that P1 cannot recognize R2 to give an incompatibility relationship.

C. Universality of the Gene-for-Gene Concept

As a graduate student in the middle 1950's, I recall hearing many pathologists and breeders argue that the gene-for-gene relationship was a peculiarity of the rust fungi, basidiomycetes, and obligate parasites. The gene-for-gene relationship has since been shown to hold for fungi belonging to the ascomycetes and phycomycetes. In addition to plants and fungi, the gene-for-gene relationship seems to hold for plants and bacteria, nematodes, possibly viruses, and insects. The same basic pattern seems to hold for the scrapie disease of sheep, and may also be true for other animal pathogens that are not antigenic. Mention is made of these other pathogens to show that the gene-for-gene relationship is not just a peculiarity of a special group of parasites, but seems to be a universal phenomenon in interorganismal genetics.

IV. SELECTION OF RESISTANCE TO A FUNGAL PARASITE

Up to about the 1950's, the principal method for screening plant host lines for resistance to fungal parasites was to inoculate host lines growing either in the greenhouse or in the field. Inoculations in the greenhouse were usually heavy inoculations of seedlings; inoculations in the field were usually heavy inoculations, and may have been repeated in various stages of plant growth. Both procedures are designed to determine which plants can survive when inundated with inoculum of the fungal parasite. Such procedures are very efficient for evaluating large numbers of lines for resistance with a relatively limited effort, but these techniques are not useful in the detection of genes that contribute to the slow development of an epidemic.

In the 1950's and 1960's it became evident that, with the use of standard procedures for the selection of resistance, some host lines that were initially classified as susceptible acquired less disease in the field. They were classified as having field resistance. The genes they possessed contributed to a slow increase in the development of disease.

V. VANDERPLANK'S HYPOTHESIS OF TWO KINDS OF RESISTANCE

In 1963, Vanderplank published a hypothesis that there were actually two types of resistance in plants to parasites—vertical and horizontal (see Table IV). Vertical resistance was postulated to be controlled by genes involved in gene-for-gene relationships between host and parasite, genes where the differences between the presence or absence of alternate alleles were sufficient such that discontinuous segregation was observed in a F_2 population. These genes were also postulated as being effective against only certain races of the parasite. Horizontal resistance was postulated to be controlled by a large number of genes. The number of genes and the small differences between alternate alleles meant that the variability would give continuous variation in an F_2 population, and would have to be handled by the mathematical methods characteristic of quantitatively inherited traits. Resistance would be effective against all strains of a parasite. There may be some differences between host lines and parasite strains, but the ranking of

TABLE IV

Characteristics of Vertical and Horizontal Resistance

Vertical	Horizontal
Few genes	Many genes
Race specific	Species specific

TABLE V
The Type of Variability Expected with Horizontal Resistance

Parasite strains	Host lines				
	A	B	C	D	E
I	1	2	3	4	5
II	2	3	4	5	6
III	3	4	5	6	7
IV	4	5	6	7	8
V	5	6	7	8	9

[a] Based on a scale of 1–9: 1 = low incidence of disease, whereas 9 = high incidence of disease.

resistance or virulence would be constant. Table V presents a simplified version of the variability in host–parasite interactions with horizontal resistance (Robinson, 1976). The type of race specificity that was presented in Table III is missing. Horizontal resistance is defined as being effective against the parasite species and not just a limited number of the parasite genotypes.

A. Basic Assumptions

One assumption of this hypothesis seems to have been that gene-for-gene relationships provide either immunity or very high levels of resistance, even to the extent that no symptoms were obvious on the inoculated host plant. One predicted manifestation of vertical resistance is that it only delays the onset of an epidemic, not the rate of development of the epidemic. Another assumption is that if the host population contains a gene $R1$, the parasite population contains both $P1$ and $p1$. The frequencies of $P1$ and $p1$ in the parasite population determine the delay in the onset of an epidemic. If the initial frequency of $p1$ was low, the initial effective inoculum is low. Another assumption is that parasites with $P1$ cannot multiply at all on host plants with $R1$. Only parasites with $p1$ can multiply on host plants with $R1$. The idea that a P/R interaction can only reduce the ability of the parasite to multiply seems to be missing. Horizontal resistance was predicted to be involved in the rate with which an epidemic develops. Since 1963, the original definitions of vertical and horizontal resistance have become confused with the manifestations predicted with the two types of gene systems.

Horizontal resistance was predicted to be stable, even permanent

(Robinson, 1976). Vertical resistance was unstable, and that conclusion was considered evident in the history of breeding wheat for resistance to stem rust. Vanderplank's hypothesis of two types of resistance was quickly accepted as proven fact. Several breeders told me they were going to discontinue breeding for vertical resistance and breed for horizontal resistance—resistance that would last.

Fourteen years after this hypothesis was presented, it is important to reexamine the evidence for vertical and horizontal resistance. The characteristics studied are basically of four types: (1) stability of resistance, (2) mode of expression of resistance, (3) inheritance of resistance, and (4) race specificity of resistance.

The history of resistance based on a single or a few genes is that it usually did not last long. From the time of introduction of the new cultivar with one or a few genes until the parasite population changed to make that gene ineffective varied from 1 or 2 years to many years. Some simply inherited sources of resistance have lasted for a long time. Resistance to *Fusarium* in cabbage has lasted more than 60 years. The Cebada Capa gene in barley has provided resistance to leaf rust for many years. The Sr26 gene in wheat has given resistance to all known races of stem rust for several years. There are more than two dozen genes that have given resistance for long periods of time. Thus, in some cases, resistance based on one or a small number of genes may give long-term resistance. There have been many observations that what was called horizontal resistance has been eroded. Stability of resistance is, therefore, not a true characteristic of what has been called either vertical or horizontal resistance.

Vertical resistance has frequently been considered to be due to genes that affect infection type (the result of interaction between host and parasite, after a finite number of days, under a given set of environmental conditions). The assumed manifestations of horizontal resistance are not considered to be effects on infection type, but rather characteristics such as number of successful infections, time from inoculation to sporulation of the fungus, degree of sporulation of the fungus, etc.— characteristics that affect the rate with which an epidemic develops in the field.

B. Experimental Analysis

Observations of the manifestations of a particular host and its fungal parasite have frequently been considered sufficient to classify a plant as having vertical or horizontal resistance. The original criteria of inheritance and specificity to race or species have frequently been ignored in deciding between vertical and horizontal resistance. Some of the genes originally studied by Flor gave resistance to all the North American races of M. lini. Had Flor used only North American strains, he would have concluded that these genes were effective against the species M. lini. Resistance in some varieties of flax was simply inherited (one criterion of vertical resistance), but effective against the entire sample of the fungal species (one criterion of horizontal resistance). But Flor also used strains of M. lini from South America, strains that helped to establish that all the genes studied were effective against only certain strains of M. lini. If Flor had been content with a smaller scope of investigation, some of the genes might have been classified as giving vertical resistance and some as giving horizontal resistance.

Some sources of resistance in wheat to Puccinia striiformes are considered to be controlled by many genes. Most of these genes have small effects, and classification of discrete phenotypes in the F_2 is difficult, if not essentially impossible. Some manifestations of these genes are reduced number of successful infections, fewer spores produced per infection, and longer generation time from spore to spore. Resistance is commonly treated as a quantitatively inherited trait in a breeding program. Resistance in wheat to P. striiformes has many of the attributes of horizontal resistance. Are these traits race specific? One experiment measured the number of spores produced on two host lines with two strains of P. striiformes (Johnson and Taylor, 1976). The results are presented in Table VI. Host line A supports the production of many spores of strain 1, but few spores of strain 2. The reciprocal pattern was observed on host line B. This pattern is not consistent with the pattern predicted for variability of horizontal resistance (see Table V). The trait, spore production, is race specific, a characteristic of vertical resistance, which is a pattern consistent with gene-for-gene relations.

TABLE VI

Pattern of Spore Production by Two Strains of *P. striiformes* on Two Host Lines

Parasite strains	Host	
	A	B
1	Many	Few
2	Few	Many

A cultivar of wheat, Genesee, a soft white winter wheat, is generally considered to be susceptible to powdery mildew. Though it is usually classified as being susceptible, it obviously is not as supportive of the development of epidemics of mildew as are other cultivars. An epidemic of powdery mildew just seems to build more slowly on Genesee than on other cultivars. Crosses have been made between Genesee and these other cultivars. F_2 plants from these crosses were inoculated in the greenhouse and evaluated for amount of mildew 5–8 days after inoculation. The frequency of F_2 plants with varying amounts of mildew was consistent with the hypothesis that a large number of genes determined the amount of mildew. The amount of mildew appeared to be a quantitatively inherited trait. When another sample of the F_2 plants was inoculated and held in a controlled-environment chamber, there was a discontinuous distribution of plants. Three-fourths of the plants had less mildew than the other one-fourth. Conclusions from the greenhouse data are that slow mildewing is a quantitatively inherited trait. Conclusions from the controlled environment data are that slow mildewing is controlled by one gene. The precision of the experimental procedure determined the interpretation of the results! Furthermore, an isolate of the fungus, *Erysiphe graminis* f. sp. *tritici*, obtained in Michigan, grew as rapidly on Genesee as on any other host line. Slow mildewing is controlled by one gene and is race specific. Slow development of disease, a trait considered to be characteristic of horizontal resistance, apparently is controlled by gene-for-gene interactions, the pattern illustrated in its simplest form in Table II.

The above discussions are only a small sample of the types of studies undertaken in many laboratories in the past 5–10 years. The results are basically all of the same type. Almost all variability in host–parasite interactions, when analyzed critically, seems to follow the gene-for-gene pattern described by Flor. Resistance that is thought to be controlled by many genes, when analyzed carefully, is found to be controlled by a small number of genes, each of which can be handled independently for experimental purposes.

What is a small number of genes? Wheat has more than 20 loci involved in reaction to *Puccinia graminis* f. sp. *tritici*. All 20 loci are always present. Which of the alternate alleles is present may vary from one host line to the next. By selection of parasite strains of the proper genotype, it is possible to determine which Sr genes are present in a wheat line and which can be observed to segregate individually in a segregating generation. By these techniques, it is possible to observe segregation at one locus at a time. The ability to sort out the variability and handle one locus at a time is contrasted with the situation where the variability cannot be sorted out one locus at a time and has to be dealt with using mathematical analyses assuming large numbers of genes, each with small effects.

Many studies in the past few years have shown that resistance that was thought to be quantitatively inherited was, in fact, qualitatively inherited, and that resistance considered to be species specific was, in fact, race specific. Resistance considered to be horizontal was shown to have the genetic characteristics of vertical resistance. The assumption that manifestations such as numbers of successful infections, numbers of spores produced per infection, length of generation time, etc., were due to genes that do not follow the gene-for-gene relationship is not supported by research. Research in recent years has lent support to the suggestion that horizontal resistance is resistance that has not yet been shown to be vertical. The decision as to whether resistance of a cultivar is vertical or horizontal is, in part, determined by experimental procedure. Cursory investigations tend to conclude in favor of horizontal resistance. Critical, detailed investigations generally lead to the conclusion that resistance is vertical.

How many times is it necessary to show that what was thought to be horizontal resistance is vertical before it is possible to generalize? Where are the critical experiments establishing the fact that there are genes for disease resistance that are not consistent with the gene-for-gene hypothesis? On theoretical grounds I can agree with Vanderplank's hypothesis that there should be genes that do not follow the gene-for-gene relationships. We have attempted to look for host plant resistance which we had reason to suspect as being horizontal resistance (e.g., slow mildewing in wheat, slow leaf rusting in wheat, resistance to yellow leaf blight and eyespot diseases of corn), but careful research has indicated a finite number of genes and/or the existence of race specificity. If it were only my laboratory that was producing data of this type, I would be very suspicious of our procedures, but many other laboratories are coming to the same conclusion. Either horizontal resistance is an artifact of experimental procedure, or it is a phenomenon for which no one seems to be able to find critical supporting evidence. The data collected in the last few years by several laboratories lead me to the tentative conclusion that horizontal resistance is resistance that has not yet been shown to be vertical. I will gladly change my conclusions when I see data different from what has been collected in the past 5 years.

VI. RELATIONSHIP OF HOST–PARASITE GENETICS TO CROP PRODUCTIVITY

What does the discussion on horizontal and vertical resistance have to do with crop productivity? It is considered important that efforts to increase productivity by host plant resistance be based on hypotheses supported by careful experimentation. We should not deceive ourselves by adhering to hypotheses that are not supported by, or are inconsistent with, the experimental evidence. This does not mean we should discard the hypothesis of horizontal resistance, but we should not accept it as proven fact. Essentially all genetic variability in host/parasite interactions follows the pattern given in Table II. Some parasite/host gene pairs give large effects, while some give small effects. The difference between + and − can be small or large. The idea that there is one kind of gene that gives immunity or high levels of resistance, and a different kind of gene that gives low levels of resistance, cannot be substantiated by experimental evidence.

There is growing evidence that the same host genes may give high levels of resistance with one strain of parasite and low levels of resistance with a different strain of the parasite. An example of this is presented in Table VII. Based on infection type, the gene $Pm4$ provides for a very high level of resistance with strain 1. The plant usually shows no macroscopically visible sign of having been inoculated with strain 1. The $Pm4$ gene is also a gene for reduced infection efficiency. The 5% of the parasite units that produce successful primary infections with strain 1 only very rarely continue to develop to the extent of producing a type 4 pustule, i.e., abundant sporulation of the fungus. Our results to date suggest that a large proportion of the parasite units that produce the 19 and 35% successful primary infections by strains 2 and 3, respectively, on host plants with $Pm4$ continue development and eventually produce type 4 pustules and abundant sporulation of the fungus. Based on the growth rate of strain 4 in primary infection, $Pm4$ is a gene for slow growth of the fungus. The $Pm4$ gene does not affect the ability of strain 4 to produce successful primary infections, but it increases the time required to produce them. When plants with $Pm4$ or $pm4$ were inoculated with strain 4 and held in a controlled environment, it was possible to see that the amount of macroscopically visible disease on $Pm4$ plants in 7 days was equivalent to the amount of disease on $pm4$ plants in about 6 1/2 days. The difference is so small that very precise control of environment is necessary to see the effect of the presence of $Pm4$ or $pm4$.

What then is $Pm4$? For strain 1 it is a gene for a high level of resis-

TABLE VII

Observations of Infection Type Seven Days after Inoculation, Infection Efficiencies in Primary Infection, and Growth Rate during Primary Infections of Four Strains of *Erysiphe graminis* f. sp. *tritici* when Inoculated onto Two Highly Isogenic Host Lines, One with *Pm4*, the Other with *pm4* [a]

	Host genotype	
Parasite strain and criterion	Pm4Pm4	pm4pm4
I. Infection Type [b]		
Strain 1	0	4
Strain 2	4	4
Strain 3	4	4
Strain 4	4	4
II. Infection efficiency [c]		
Strain 1	5	80
Strain 2	19	80
Strain 3	35	80
Strain 4	80	80
III. Growth Rate [d]		
Strain 1	Normal	Normal
Strain 2	Normal	Normal
Strain 3	Normal	Normal
Strain 4	Slow	Normal

[a] Modification from Martin, 1974.

[b] 0, no visible symptoms; 4, large pustules 7 days after inoculation.

[c] The percentage of parasite units applied to the leaf that produced elongating secondary hyphae (a criterion used as an indication of a successful primary infection).

[d] The normal time required to each a maximum of elongating secondary hyphae is 26 hr with the environmental conditions used. Strain 4 required 28 hr to reach its maximum percentage of elongating secondary hyphae.

tance. For strains 2 and 3, Pm4 is a gene for a reduced number of successful infections. For strain 4, Pm4 is a gene for longer spore-to-spore generation time of the parasite. We have done enough work with segregating generations of host materials to feel reasonably confident that these results are not due to other gene differences between the highly isogenic host lines.

There seems to be a general feeling, especially among supporters of the horizontal resistance concept, that there are only two levels of disease expression with each parasite–host gene pair in the gene-for-gene relationship—i.e., a host is either susceptible or resistant, a fungus strain is either virulent or avirulent. There have been data from almost all race surveys of plant pathogenic fungi to suggest this is not so. Published data from the last 40 years show that the reaction of a host line may be different to a number of strains of the parasite, even though only one host gene can be demonstrated to effect resistance to all the strains (Flor, 1940, 1946, 1947). An attempt to explain this apparent paradox is presented in Fig. 1. If we assume the initial position in the evolution of corresponding genic systems was in cell 2 (parasite/host genotype $P1/r1$), then we can see why the mutation in the host from $r1$ to $R1$ will give a selective advantage to the host. The mutation in the host does not have to lead to a high level of resistance. It only need be sufficient to confer a selective advantage that outweighs any other disadvantage the mutation may have had. The parasite/host genotype is now $P1/R1$,. Earlier in this chapter I argued that this is the genotype for mutual recognition. Any mutation in the parasite leading to loss of this recognition would give the parasite a selective advantage with its host, unless that mutation from $P1$ to $p1$ carries with it a greater selective disadvantage to the parasite. The mutation from $P1$ to $p1$ does not have to restore the same degree of compatibility to cell 3 found in cell 2 in Fig. 1. The mutation need only increase the selective advantage of the mutant. If $P1$ has a specific interaction with $R1$, then a mutation of $P1$ which reduces the affinity of the $P1$ gene product for the gene product of $R1$ should give a selective advantage. There is no need to postulate a complete loss in affinity of the $P1/R1$ interaction associated with the mutation to increased compatibility. Cell 3 of Fig. 1 need not be identi-

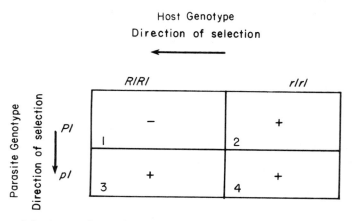

Fig. 1.   Selection in the evolution of the gene-for-gene interactions (modification from Person, 1967, and Ellingboe, 1976). −, Incompatible relationship; +, compatible relationship.

cal in phenotype to cell 2. This is one possible explanation for the observations of strains 2, 3, or 4 summarized in Table VII. Whether strains 2, 3, and 4 represent an allelic series of p4—e.g., p4* and p4**—is not yet known. It is possible that one or more of these strains may be P4 or p4, but with a suppressor or inhibitor of P4 or p4.

VII. EVOLUTION OF HOST–PARASITE INTERACTIONS

The evolutionary scheme presented in Fig. 1 is single-step change in host and parasite. Is there no evolution from cell 3 in Fig. 1? A possible scheme for the evolution of variability in host–parasite interactions is presented in Fig. 2. The arrows labeled 1, 3, and 5 are changes due to mutations in the host. The arrows labeled 2, 4, and 6 are changes due to mutations in the parasite. A sequence such as the changes 1 thru 6 in host–parasite interactions in Fig. 2 may help to explain the variability of strains 2, 3, and 4 presented in Table VII. On the other hand, the strains may be independent mutations from P4. Four of the alleles at the L locus in flax have their corresponding genes in M. lini, either at one locus or as closely linked genes. It is possible they may have the origin of their specificity in a scheme such as presented in Fig. 2.

If the change from r1 to R1 in Fig. 1 is large, e.g., if the reaction goes from susceptible to a very high level of resistance, then the selection pressure on the parasite is very great. If the parasite cannot multiply

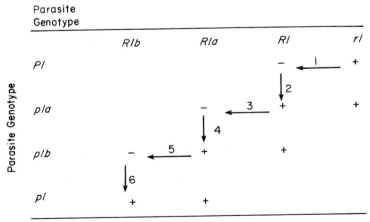

Fig. 2. A possible evolutionary scheme involving one locus in the host and one locus in the parasite. −, Incompatible relationship; +, compatible relationship.

with parasite/host genotype P1/R1 (see cell 1 in Fig. 1), there will be very strong selection pressure for parasite genotype p1. If, on the other hand, the difference between parasite/host genotypes P1/R1 and P1/r1 (see cells 1 and 2 in Fig. 1) is very small—e.g., P1/R1 has a 10% longer generation time or produces 10% fewer spores of the fungus—then the selective advantage in favor of parasite gene p1 over P1 may also be very small.

If a mutation from P1 to p1 gives an allele that has a selective disadvantage for any other function fundamental to the life of the parasite the locus may have, the allele p1 may not increase in frequency. One can conceive of missense mutations that affect host–parasite specificity, but not any other function the locus may have. One can also conceive of missense mutations that would affect host–parasite interactions, as well as any other functions the locus may have. Nonsense mutations would be predicted to be lethal to the parasite, if the locus was crucial to life processes of the parasite. As was mentioned previously, mutation of the host gene from r1 to R1 in the presence of a parasite with P1 should give the host a selective advantage (see Fig. 1). Mutation of the parasite from P1 to p1 should give the parasite a selective advantage. What would happen to the frequency of P1 and p1 if the host genotype were changed back to r1? If the change in the parasite from P1 to p1 had no effect on any other function of the p1 locus—with regard to such traits as viability, growth, and development of the parasite, sensitivity to environment, etc.—then there would be expected to be no change in gene frequency of P1 and p1 with host genotype r1. If, however, the mutation from P1 to p1 gave some intrinsic disadvantage to the parasite's basic life processes, then if the host population were changed to genotype r1, an increase in the frequency of P1 would be expected. Examples can be found in the literature that would support the arguments with both types of missense mutations.

VIII. THE GENOTYPE OF PARASITE AND HOST

Any 42-chromosome wheat plant will always have its more than 20 Sr loci. Some loci will have what we have designated as the dominant allele. Some loci will have what we have designated the recessive allele. The designations given have their origin in particular research results. Any culture of P. graminis f. sp. tritici will have the corresponding P genes for each of the Sr genes in the host. When we write a parasite/host genotype we should write out the genotype for each locus. An example of a parasite/host genotype is shown in Fig. 3.

Parasite	P1	p2	P3	p4	P5	p6	p7	p8
Host	Sr1	Sr2	sr3	sr4	sr5	sr6	Sr7	Sr8

Fig. 3.   An example of a parasite/host genotype.

The genotype given specifies incompatibility based on the P1/Sr1 interaction. All other parasite/host gene pairs specify compatibility, that is, of course, if we assume that the three parasite/host genotypes—Px/srx px/srx, and px/srx—specify the same degree of compability between host and parasite. Examples have been given that suggest that some px/Srx genotypes may not give the same degree of compatibility as genotypes Px/srx and px/srx. There may be a low degree of incompatibility based on the p2/Sr2, p7/Sr7, and p8/Sr8 interactions. The effects of these genes may be additive, but they are still gene-for-gene interactions!

A. The Genetic Perspective

If all strains of P. graminis f. sp. tritici in a researcher's collection contained P5, then any host line containing Sr5 would be classified as being resistant to the species P. graminis f. sp. tritici. If a strain of the fungus is found that contains P5, then Sr5 becomes a race-specific type of resistance. By 1976, Sr26 had been found to be effective against all strains of P. graminis f. sp. Tritici. No one with whom I have talked has evidence of the ineffectiveness of Sr26 in controlling stem rust of wheat. Currently Sr26 is a species-specific gene. A better interpretation is that the corresponding gene p26 has not been recovered in the parasite. It may not be present in the parasite population, or it may be present only as the recessive gene in a heterozygous, functionally diploid parasite.

B. Stability of Resistance

There are many cases of wheat breeding in North America where a p gene (or genes) was known to exist in the parasite population before the new cultivar with its corresponding Sr gene(s) was released. The Sr genes may have been effective against all prevalent races of the parasite, but selfing and crossing studies with the parasite had shown that the corresponding p gene(s) was already present. Resistance that depends on the low frequency of a parasite p gene will last only as long as it takes the parasite to change its gene frequencies. Resistance dependent on recessive p genes in a heterozygous condition will last only as long as it takes a parasite to develop a strain homozygous for p genes through mutation or recombination. Resistance dependent on a combination of R genes will last only as long as it takes the parasite to recombine its corresponding p genes. Resistance dependent on R genes, for which the corresponding p genes are not present in the parasite population, will last only as long as it takes parasite genes to mutate to p and express their p genes. In all of the above cases, we must consider the selective advantages and disadvantages of p genes singly and in combination.

IX. CONTINUOUS CONTROL OF DISEASE

There is nothing mysterious about the genetics of host/parasite relations. Once some of the basic genetics of both host and parasite are known (or only one of the components in some detail), we begin to see certain basic patterns emerging. By monitoring for the presence of p genes in the parasite and for changes in frequency of the p genes, it is possible to get indications as to which R genes should and should not be used in breeding for disease resistance. Flor programmed the use of genes in flax for effecting continual control of flax rust. The plant breeding group at Sydney, Australia, headed by I. A. Watson, has controlled stem rust in wheat successfully. There has not been an epidemic of stem rust in Sydney wheats for more than 20 years. Breeding for stem rust resistance in wheat for Australia has never been in a better position than it is today. More genes than ever before are available for use for future breeding. Stem rust control is a major requirement for wheat production in Australia. So control of diseases through breeding is possible. By careful research and planning one can get continuous control; the boom and bust production can be avoided.

X. RESISTANCE TO HOST-SPECIFIC TOXINS PRODUCED BY FUNGI

There are a number of fungal parasites that produce host-specific toxins. With only a few of these toxin-producing parasites is enough known about the genetics of toxin production and the genetics of response in the host plants to get some idea of the genetic pattern of host/parasite interactions. The pattern of interactions between *Helminthosporium victoriae* and oats, *Avenae byzantina*, is given in Table VIII. The pattern presented is the reciprocal of the pattern presented in Table II. It has been frequently argued that the difference between the

TABLE VIII
Genetic Pattern of Interactions between *Helminthosporium victoriae* and Oats, *Avenae byzantina*

Parasite	Host genotype[a]	
	Vb (=Pc2)	vb (=pc2)
Strain 1 (produces HV toxin)	+	−
Strain 2 (does not produce HV toxin)	−	−

[a] −, Fungus grows and produces disease; −, growth of fungus very restricted.

two patterns could be an artifact of the selection of host lines and parasite strains. It is a possibility that has been seriously considered. Let us look back at the data in Table III. If the second and third host lines and the first two parasite strains were selected, we can see a pattern of interaction between two host lines and two parasite strains that is similar to the pattern presented in Table VIII. If we had selected the third and fourth host lines listed, the pattern would be as presented in Table II. In the latter case, test crosses would verify that the host lines differed by one gene and that the parasite strains differed by one gene. Test crosses between host lines 2 and 3 would have shown that the host lines differed by more than one gene. There has been extensive test crossing of this type (Moseman, 1959), and the data verify that the pattern in Table II is the basic pattern.

Evidence that the pattern presented in Table VIII is not an artifact is not as conclusive. Extensive mutation studies have shown that the Vb gene is necessary for susceptibility. Resistance is recessive. Mutant Vb genes range between the dominant Vb to the recessive vb. A mutant of intermediate resistance is recessive to the dominant Vb and dominant to the recessive vb gene. The Vb locus seems to be the key to reaction to parasite strains which produce the toxin.

Many mutations to loss of production of the toxin have been isolated. All strains that produce the toxin can grow in a host of Vb genotype. All strains that do not produce the toxin cannot grow in host tissue of the Vb genotype. (It must be remembered that the assay for the toxin is based on the response of plants of genotype Vb.) The toxin alone can produce many of the symptoms when applied to the host of Vb genotype. No strains of H. victoriae have been found that can produce disease on plants of genotype vb. Only plants of Vb genotype are susceptible. Though many isolates of H. victoriae of independent origin that do not produce toxin have been obtained, there has never been a study to determine the number of loci involved in toxin production. It would be extremely interesting to know if some of the "nontoxin-producing strains" did produce a toxin specific for mutant Vb alleles.

The simplest interpretation of the pattern presented in Table VIII is that there is specific interaction for a compatible relationship. Only if a fungus produced a toxin and the host had the Vb gene could the parasite develop in the host. Whereas resistance is considered to be a positive function in the pattern in Table II, resistance is considered to be a loss in function in Table VIII. Avirulence is considered a positive function in Table II and a loss of function in Table VIII.

Whether the apparent distinctions between the genetic patterns is real or some artifact of experimental procedures is important in breeding for disease resistance. The pattern presented in Table II is consistent with more than 90% of the naturally occurring genetic variability in host–parasite interactions. Less than one dozen examples of toxins involved in parasitism and pathogenesis have been genetically studied in any detail. All cases with toxins seem to fit the hypothesis of a positive function for parasite development and disease production. Loss of host function (a receptor site?) leads to resistance. Is resistance based on a loss of function going to be more permanent? Resistance to *H. victoriae*, based the vb gene, has lasted more than 25 years. Resistance to *H. carbonum* in corn lasted only till the appearance of race 3. The time that resistance to a toxin will last probably depends on whether the toxin is an absolute requirement for successful parasitism, or whether it is not an absolute requirement but one of the components for the success of a parasite.

Since the fungi producing host-specific toxins appear to follow a different pattern of genetic interactions with their host, we must take these observations into consideration when we try to generalize from the much-studied toxins to other plant pathogenic fungi and their interactions with host plants.

A sound program of breeding for resistance to fungal diseases is dependent upon distinguishing between hypotheses supported by careful research and those that are not, careful and factually based planning, and the basic research necessary to give a program a sound scientific base. It is important to distinguish between what we would like to believe and what the data will support. The hypothesis put forth by Van der Plank (1963,1975) has stimulated a tremendous amount of research, and has challenged many researchers to investigate the genetics of interactions between host and parasite, and the possible manifestations of the genes involved. Whether the hypothesis is found to be true or wanting is not particularly important. It has provided a conceptual basis for experimental analysis, and, therefore, is considered to have been an excellent contribution to plant pathology. Our concern is to distinquish fact from fiction, and Vanderplank's hypothesis has been of great assistance in the design of experiments to do so. When I look at the available evidence, I cannot help but believe that we are deceiving ourselves when we believe that genes that control the slow development of epidemics are part of a different genetic system and/or pattern of genetic interactions from the genes that affect infection type.

The Rockefeller program in Mexico is proof that disease-resistant varieties can be used to increase production. Research programs like the one in Sydney show that the scientific basis of the effective disease control can be determined and used to make breeding for disease resistance in the future a science rather than an art.

REFERENCES

Biffen, R. H. (1905). *J. Agric. Sci.* **1**, 4–48.
Ellingboe, A. H. (1976). *Encycl. Plant Physiol., New Ser.* **4**, 761–778.
Flor, H. H. (1940). *J. Agric. Res.* **60**, 575–591.
Flor, H. H. (1946). *J. Agric. Res.* **73**, 335–357.
Flor, H. H. (1947). *J. Agric. Res.* **74**, 241–262.
Flor, H. H. (1955). *Phytopathology* **45**, 680–685.
Johnson, R., and Taylor, A. J. (1976). *Annu. Rev. Phytopathol.* 14, 97–119.
Martin, T. J. (1974). Ph.D. Thesis, Michigan State University, East Lansing.
Moseman, J. G. (1959). *Phytopathology* **49**, 469–472.
Person, C. O. (1967). *Can. J. Bot.* **45**, 1193–1204.
Robinson, R. A. (1976). "Plant Pathosystems." Springer-Verlag, Berlin and New York.
Van der Plank, J. E. (1963). "Plant Diseases: Epidemics and Control." Academic Press, New York.
Van der Plank, J. E. (1975). "Principles of Plant Infection." Academic Press, New York.

Chapter 6

Vesicular-Arbuscular Mycorrhizae and Crop Productivity*

Gene R. Safir

I. INTRODUCTION

Mycorrhizae are symbiotic associations, between fungi and the roots of higher plants, in which both members normally benefit from the association. These associations are generally divided into two main groups, based primarily on morphology. The first, the ectomycorrhizae, contain a fungal mantle surrounding the host roots, as well as intercellular fungal growth in the first few cell layers of the root cortex. This intercellular growth is referred to as the Hartig net. The second, endomycorrhizae, contain a loose fungal network in the soil and the

*Michigan Agricultural Experiment Stations Article Number 8198.

231

The Biology of Crop Productivity
Copyright © 1980 by Academic Press, Inc.
All rights of reproduction in any form reserved
ISBN 0-12-159850-0

fungus grows both intra- and intercellularly in the root cortex. Two subgroupings occur within the endomycorrhizae, those produced by septate fungi and those produced by nonseptate fungi. The latter are referred to as vesicular-arbuscular (VA) mycorrhizae.

The profound effects of vesicular-arbuscular mycorrhizae (VAM) have only recently begun to be appreciated. This association is obligate for the fungus and symbiotic, in most instances, resulting in improved growth of mycorrhizal plants. The following discussion will be limited to VA mycorrhizae, because this association plays an integral role in the growth and development of nearly all agricultural plants throughout the world. It should be pointed out that, although VA mycorrhizal associations are ubiquitous, there are some sizeable gaps in our knowledge of their biology and physiology. This chapter will include a brief discussion of certain aspects that are particularly relevant to crop productivity. For those who require additional information, there are a number of excellent reviews available on VAM (Gerdemann, 1968, 1975; Khan, 1972a; Mosse, 1973a; Tinker, 1975).

II. MORPHOLOGY

The external structure of a VAM root system is comprised of an extensive network of fungal hyphae, extending from the root surface into the surrounding soil. This network is extremely variable in density and structure, depending on the specific mycorrhizal fungus, the host, and the soil. For example, the fungal network can comprise as little as a few strands of hyphae or as much as 80 cm of hyphae per centimeter of infected root tissue (Sanders and Tinker, 1973). In the soil, the hyphal network consists of irregularly shaped main hyphae, up to 15 μm in diameter, with walls up to 3 μm thick, and smaller side branches 2–3 μm in diameter. Experiments on phosphorus translocation by VAM hyphae to plant roots have indicated that active hyphae may extend up to 7 cm. away from the associated root (Rhodes and Gerdemann, 1975).

As the mycorrhizal association matures, large globose, subglobose, or elliptical to ovoid spores are produced from the hyphal network. These spores may occur singly, in sporocarps, or both, depending on the fungal species involved. These spores are variable in color and size, and can be as large as 500 μm in diameter. The fungal propagules found in the soil include chlamydospores, azygospores, or vesicles, also depending on the fungal species. The fungus penetrates, via an appressoria, into the root hairs or epidermal cells in back of the meristematic region. Mosse (1959b) has reported up to 21 fungal entry points per millimeter length of root tisue. The fungal hyphae may coil in the epidermal cells before moving through and colonizing the cortical cells. Hyphal growth may be either intercellular or intracellular in the cortex, with the development of short-lived haustorial-like structures called arbuscules produced within the cortical cells shortly after the fungus enters the root. These arbuscules are treelike in shape, and are formed by dichotomous branching from a course hyphal base. The fine branches of an arbuscule may be less than 1 μm in diameter. For many years, host digestion of arbuscules was assumed to be the major nutrient transfer mechanism between the fungus and the host. However, a recent study by Cox and Tinker (1976), using an image-analyzing computer to analyze electron micrographs of mycorrhizal onion roots, suggests a mechanism requiring living fungus. They calculated the average life span of an arbuscule to be about 4 days, after which it is digested by the host. They further concluded that digestion of the arbuscules could only account for approximately 1/150 of the published rates of phosphorus inflow to mycorrhizal roots (Sanders and Tinker, 1973). Thus, phosphorus transfer is probably occurring across living membranes of the host and fungus. Arbuscules can fill either a portion of or an entire cortical cell, and heavily infected root segments may have arbuscules in almost all cortical cells. The fungus does not penetrate into the root stele. When the association between the fungus and the root is well established, vesicles may be formed. These vesicles contain oil droplets and are highly variable in shape and size. They may function as thin-walled temporary storage organs, or as thick-walled chlamydospore-like structures, which may be either intracellular or intercellular.

The only macroscopically visible distinction of a VAM root system is the bright yellow color of the unsuberized roots, seen in some but not all plant species. This color, although it disappears rapidly upon exposure to light, is highly correlated with the proportions of the root system infected. Becker and Gerdemann (1977), for example, quantified mycorrhizal infections of onion roots using colorimetric determinations of the amount of yellow pigment present.

III. TAXONOMY AND DISTRIBUTION

Fungi that form VAM with plant roots are members of the family Endogonaceae (Gerdemann and Trappe, 1974). The great diversity in this family may eventually lead to the displacement of some species to other families. Four genera of the family Endogonaceae as defined by Gerdemann and Trappe (1974) are known to form VAM: *Glomus, Gigaspora, Acaulospora,* and *Sclerocystis.* In the past years most of the VAM fungi were assigned to the genus *Endogone,* and most of the literature before 1974 reflects this practice. According to the new classification, most *Endogone* species are probably nonmycorrhizal.

Vesicular-arbuscular mycorrhizal fungi have extremely wide host ranges. According to Gerdemann (1968, 1975), it is easier to list those plant families that do not form VAM than to list those that do. The families not forming VAM include Pinaceae, Betulaceae, Orchidaceae, Fumariaceae, Commelinaceae, Urticaceae, and Ericaceae. Families that rarely form VAM include the Cruciferaea, Chenopodiaceae, Polygonaceae, and the Cyperaceae. Families that form both ectomycorrhizae and VA mycorrhizae include the Juglandaceae, Tiliaceae, Myrtaceae, Salicaceae, Fagaceae, and Caesalpiniaceae. See Gerdemann (1968, 1975) for more complete descriptions of mycorrhizal distribution.

Vesicular-arbuscular mycorrhizal infection has been reported in fields, orchards, sand dune systems (Nicolson, 1955), tropical rain forests (Redhead, 1968), deciduous woodlands (Mosse and Hayman, 1973), semiarid grasslands (Khan, 1974), and marshes (Read *et at.,* 1976). Areas where VAM infection is probably low are aquatic habitats and extremely dense stands of ectomycorrhizal trees (Gerdemann, 1975).

IV. EFFECTS ON PLANT GROWTH

It has been shown in numerous laboratory and field experiments that VAM infection can dramatically improve plant growth (Gerdemann, 1968, 1975; Mosse, 1973a; Tinker, 1975a). The growth-promoting effects of VAM fungi are highly variable (Mosse and Hayman, 1971; Mosse, 1973a, 1975; Bevege and Bowen, 1975; Sanders, *et al.,* 1977). The host ranges of most of these fungi are remarkably large. *Glomus mosseae,* for example, is known to infect at least 20 plant species (Mosse, 1973a), though the actual number is probably well over 1000.

The increased growth of mycorrhizal plants is favored in soils with low to moderate fertility. More specifically, soils favoring mycorrhizal growth stimulation usually have one or more essential nutrients for plant growth in limiting concentrations. Amendment of these soils with sufficient quantities of the limiting nutrient will usually eliminate part or all of the growth advantages associated with mycorrhizal infection. There are instances, however, where a high degree of mycorrhizal dependency exists regardless of soil fertility. Certain citrus varieties (Mehraveran, 1977) and sweetgum seedlings (Kormanik et al., 1976b), may remain stunted if they are nonmycorrhizal, even with the addition of high levels of fertilization. This dependence on mycorrhizal infection may be related to limited root hair development (Baylis, 1970, 1972), although there are instances where plants with well-developed root hair systems still benefited from mycorrhizal infection (Mosse et al., 1973).

In some cases, inoculation with VAM fungi has slightly adverse affects on plant growth. Growth decreases have been associated with mycorrhizal species of Coprosma (Baylis, 1967) and Leptospermum (Baylis, 1971), and at low temperatures with mycorrhizal Allium (Furlan and Fortin, 1973). Mycorrhizal infection adversely affected the growth of Solonum lacinatum at early infection stages. However, after 15 weeks of growth, the mycorrhizal plants were larger than their nonmycorrhizal counterparts (Cooper, 1975). In some cases, the growth depressions have been associated with soil phosphorus concentrations that are either greatly (Baylis, 1971; Mosse, 1973b) or slightly above (Cooper, 1975) concentrations that enable maximum mycorrhizal growth stimulation. Accoring to Cooper (1975), infection may depress plant growth slightly at early stages of infection, when phosphorus is not limiting plant growth. The increases in growth of mycorrhizal plants over nonmycorrhizal plants that occurred later in the growing season were probably associated with increased demand for and utilization of phosphorus, which may have become limiting in the soil at that time. The exact reasons for the reported small mycorrhizal growth depressions are unknown and deserve further study, especially in light of the potential use of mycorrhizal technology in crop production programs.

V. PHYSIOLOGY

A. Role of the Fungus

It is clear that mycorrhizal infections can improve the ability of plant roots to take up nutrients. There have been reports that mycorrhizal infection increases the uptake of potassium, iron, copper, calcium, nitrogen, sulfur, zinc, and phosphorus. The increased uptake of phosphorus by mycorrhizal roots is of particular importance, since improved growth of mycorrhizal plants is most often correlated with improved phosphorus nutrition. Phosphorus is often limiting to plant growth, because it is often in a bound state when added to or present in soil, thus rendering it only partially available to plant roots.

Several models have been proposed for the mechanisms responsible for the improved nutrient uptake capacities of mycorrhizae. One model suggests that the ability of the root surface to absorb particular nutrients is enhanced as a result of VAM infection. Alternatively, a mycorrhizal root system may be capable of utilizing nutrient sources that are unavailable, or less available, to nonmycorrhizal roots (e.g., bound phosphorus). A highly favored model proposes that the hyphal network in the soil may be directly involved in translocating nutrients to roots. This would increase the effective absorptive surface area of the root and extend the roots absorptive range beyond the nutrient depletion zone surrounding it.

Initial work by Gray and Gerdemann (1969) with radioactive phosphorus indicated that infected portions as well as uninfected portions of mycorrhizal roots are more efficient absorbers of phorphorus than are nonmycorrhizal root segments. The infected portions of the root, however, absorbed much greater amounts of phosphorus than the uninfected portions of the root. The above experiments were conducted in sand culture, and it is possible that hyphal position in relation to soil phosphorus influenced the rates of uptake. Uptake of phosphorus (Gray and Gerdemann, 1967) and zinc (Bowen et al., 1974) from aqueous solutions is enhanced by VAM infection. However, the relative absorbing powers of the fungus and the root are not established firmly at this time. Recent work by Bowen et al., (1975) has confirmed that mycorrhizal roots absorb more phosphorus from aqueous solution than nonmycorrhizal roots. However, although mycorrhizal roots from partially mycorrhizal plants absorbed more phosphorus than nonmycorrhizal roots from the same plants, the differences were small and variable. These workers have suggested that, in the case of ions of greater mobility than phorphorus, the increased absorptive efficiency of the mycorrhizal root surfaces is of proportionately greater importance.

Several studies have suggested that mycorrhizal plants utilize different source of soil phosphorus than do nonmycorrhizal plants. In 1966 Holevas demonstrated that mycorrhizal strawberry plants were larger and had a higher phosphorus content than nonmycorrhizal controls, in soils of relatively low phosphorus status. Addition of phosphorus to the soil eliminated the growth increases of mycorrhizal plants. Murdoch et al. (1967) showed that when phosphorus sources of low availability such as rock phosphate were added to soil, mycorrhizal maize plants were larger and had higher phosphorus contents than nonmycorrhizal maize. Mycorrhizal and nonmycorrhizal plants grew equally well when supplied with readily available phosphorus. However, experiments by Sanders and Tinker (1971), Hayman and Mosse (1972), and Tinker (1975b) indicate that mycorrhizal plants and non-mycorrhizal plants are using the same phosphorus sources. The general procedures involved labeling soil containing plants with ^{32}P and then measuring the specific activities (ratios of labeled to unlabeled P) of the soil solutions and the roots with and without mycorrhizal infection. In the above cases, the specific activities of the mycorrhizal and non-mycorrhizal roots, as well as of the surrounding soil, were similar. This indicated that similar phosphorus sources were utilized. Studies with different fungus–host–soil combinations should be undertaken to further confirm this evidence.

Direct involvement of mycorrhizal fungal hyphae in the translocation of nutrients to root systems has recently been unequivacably demonstrated (Hattingh et al., 1973; Rhodes and Gerdemann, 1975; Pearson and Tinker, 1975; Rhodes, 1976). All of these workers used a split plate system, which allowed external hyphae to penetrate areas of soil in which plant growth was excluded. The ^{32}P was added to the soil containing external hyphae and its uptake by roots was measured. When the external hyphae were severed, ^{32}P transport was eliminated.

It has been difficult to characterize infection parameters, which correlate, under a wide variety of conditions, with the increases in nutritional status and growth of mycorrhizal plants versus nonmycorrhizal plants. For example, it has been reported that both the numbers of chlamydospores in the soil (Redhead, 1975) and percent infection levels (Mosse, 1973a) are not always correlated with the increased growth of mycorrhizal plants. Using a mathematical modeling approach, however, Sanders et al. (1977) have calculated that, in later stages of some infections, phosphorus flux into mycorrhizal systems is a function of the length of the root infected by the mycorrhizal fungus. The size of the external mycelial network, as well as the rates of infection spread, were included in this analysis. They also point out that early low levels of infection have a calculated value to the host, in terms of phosphorus inflow, which is far greater than expected. In addition, they suggest that different species of VAM fungi may have different uptake and translocation capacities that are not accounted for in their model.

Gray and Gerdemann (1973) and Rhodes (1976) demonstrated greater sulfur uptake by mycorrhizal plants as compared to nonmycorrhizal plants. Apparently, both hyphal translocation of sulfur to roots, as well as increased absorption by the roots per se, were responsible for the increased sulfur uptake by mycorrhizal plants. The greater sulfur absorption capacity of mycorrhizal roots was correlated with increased phosphorus status of mycorrhizal roots. Addition of phosphorus to nonmycorrhizal roots significantly increased sulfur uptake by these roots.

It has also been shown that zinc uptake is increased by mycorrhizal infection (Gilmore, 1971; LaRue et al., 1975; Rhodes, 1976). Rhodes (1976) demonstrated that zinc is translocated to roots by mycorrhizal hyphae. Also, Rhodes (1976) suggested that extremely high soil phosphorus contents could possibly induce a zinc deficiency in plants, because of reduced mycorrhizal development. Evidence in favor of this hypothesis has recently been obtained by Hirrel (M. C. Hirrel and J. W. Gerdemann, unpublished).

The exact mechanism by which the mycorrhizal fungus translocates phosphorus and other nutrients to root systems is not known. Tinker (1975a) has proposed that bulk flow as well as cyclosis are involved in phosphorus translocation. Cox et al. (1975) have observed what are apparently polyphosphate granules in the vacuoles of hyphae and arbuscules. Callow et al. (1978) have confirmed the presence of polyphosphates in mycorrhizal onion roots, and by calculation have shown that polyphosphate comprises approximately 40% of the total P present in the fungal component of mycorrhizal roots. They conclude that this concentration, coupled with observed rates of protoplasmic streaming, support the hypothesis that phosphate uptake by external hyphae is followed by endergonic synthesis of polyphosphate in granules (vacuolar), which are then transported into the arbuscules by protoplasmic streaming.

Since the transport of ions within the fungal hyphae and their transfer from the fungus to host cells are probably active processes, differences between mycorrhizal and nonmycorrhizal roots in the enzyme systems associated with phosphorus metabolism might be expected. Gianinazzi-Pearson and Gianinazzi (1976; also unpublished results, 1977) have found VAM-specific alkaline phosphatase activity, which is closely correlated with the mycorrhizal growth response of onion. It was suggested that the phosphatase activity may be closely linked to phosphorus assimilation by the mycorrhizal system. Cytochemical evidence led MacDonald and Lewis (1978) to conclude that VAM fungi possess an Embden–Myerhof–Parnes system, a tricarboxylic acid cycle, and a hexose monophosphate shunt.

Thus, the evidence generally favors the hypothesis that, when soil nutrients are in limited supply, the mycorrhizal hyphal network serves to translocate additional nutrients to the root systems. It is possible that there are different fungal uptake mechanisms for different nutrients, and that different fungal strains may have physiological characteristics that confer unto them different uptake capacities. The efficiency of a hyphal network may also depend to a great extent upon its position in relation to available nutrients. In this regard, the size of the nutrient deficiency zone surrounding a given root will directly influence the benefits afforded a plant by mycorrhizal infection. When mobile nutrients are present in the soil in low quantities, the mycorrhizal root system is probably more efficient in nutrient absorption than a nonmycorrhizal root system. It should be kept in mind that the optimal fertility levels will be different for mycorrhizal and nonmycorrhizal plants. For example, most mycorrhizal plants will have lower optimal phosphorus levels than their nonmycorrhizal counterparts.

Mycorrhizal plants have been shown to recover faster than nonmycorrhizal plants from moderate water deficits (Safir et al., 1971, 1972). However, when Hoagland's solution was added to the soil, the differences in recovery rates between mycorrhizal and nonmycorrhizal plants were essentially eliminated. The increased recovery rates of mycorrhizal plants were apparently caused by decreased resistances to water transport of mycorrhizal roots. In these studies, hyphal translocation of water to roots was not demonstrated. Indeed, since the soil was saturated with water at the beginning of the recovery experiments, hyphal translocation may not have been greatly involved in water uptake. Hyphal translocation of water, if it does occur, might be demonstrated if water were made limiting during the experimental uptake procedure.

The importance of phosphorus nutrition in efficient nitrogen fixation has been long recognized. Several studies have linked VAM infection with improved nitrogen fixation by Rhizobium. Asai (1944) first implicated mycorrhizal infection with improved nodulation of legumes. Daft and El-Giahmi (1974) found that VA mycorrhizal Phaseolus in the presence of Rhizobium—when compared with nonmycorrhizal plants in the presence of Rhizobium—had increased growth, nodulation, rates of nitrogen fixation, leghaemoglobin, phosphorus, and total protein content. The application of soluble phosphate to nonmycorrhizal plants duplicated the effects of mycorrhizal infection. Crush (1974) found that mycorrhizal Centrosema, Stylosanthesis, and Trifolium, when grown in phosphorus deficient soils in the presence of Rhizobium, had improved nodulation and nitrogen fixation. These results have been confirmed by Daft and El-Giahmi (1975) and by Mosse et al. (1976). A recent study by Mosse (1977) has shown that the relationship between mycorrhizal infection and nitrogen fixation may be complex. She found that nitrogen fixation was often stimulated more by introduced mycorrhizal fungi than by indigenous species, and that the phosphorus content of plants associated with the introduced strains was the same or lower than those associated with the indigenous strains. Daft and El-Giahmi (1975) have suggested that other synergistic interactions between mycorrhizal infection and *Rhizobium* activity may exist.

B. Role of the Host

The role of the host in the survival and growth of the mycorrhizal fungus is essential but not well understood. It has been demonstrated that the mycorrhizal fungus obtains carbon compounds from the host. The observation that decreased light intensity will under some circumstances inhibit infection indirectly favors this hypothesis. More direct evidence is that $^{14}CO_2$-labeled carbon compounds have been transferred from the host to the mycorrhizal hyphae (Ho and Trappe, 1973; Cox, *et al.*, 1975; Bevege *et al.*, 1975).

In ectomycorrhizas, the concept of the fungus acting as a physiological sink for assimilate is well established (Meyer, 1974; Harley and Lewis, 1969) and involves the one-way transfer of carbohydrate from host to endophyte, where it is converted to the specifically fungal sugars trehalose and mannitol and ultimately to the storage polysaccharide glycogen, none of which can be used by the plant. Since this method of maintaining a concentration gradient is common in many host–parasite interactions (Smith *et al.*, 1969), and since endo- and ectomycorrhizal systems seem at least superficially similar, workers examined the soluble carbohydrate fraction of endomycorrhizal roots, virtually expecting to find evidence of conversion of host assimilates into specifically fungal sugars corresponding to those found in ectomycorrhizae. However, Hayman (1974) found only sucrose, glucose, fructose, and low levels of inositol. He concluded there were probably no special fungal sugars formed. Bevege (1971) examined the insoluble carbohydrate fraction of endomycorrhizal hoop pines and found glucose, xylose, and galactose. In later studies, Bevege *et al.* (1975) investigated the chemical partitioning of assimilate translocated to two species of endomycorrhizal fungi and one ectomycorrhizal type. Comparisons of proportions of ^{14}C assimilates found in various pools showed that while both *Endogone araucareae* and *E. mosseae* (endomycorrhizal species) diverted a high proportion of assimilate in 24 hr into metal-precipitable material (lipid, lipoprotein, and soluble protein), *E. araucareae* had a relatively high label in the ionizable fraction but not in the polysaccharides, while the reverse occurred in *E. mosseae*. Because different host plants were used in these experiments [*E. araucareae* in hoop pine (*Araucaria cunninghamii* Ait.) and *E. mosseae* on subterranean clover (*Trifolium subterraneum*)], the author states that the differences in partitioning may have been due to variations in host physiology rather than to intrinsic differences in fungal metabolism. Since both *Endogone* species form mycorrhizae with clover (Bevege and Bowen, 1975), a comparative study of the carbohydrate physiology of the two species growing in conjunction with a common host would be enlightening.

Interestingly, the extramatrical hyphae in the clover experiment (above) represented only 1% of the total weight of the plant, and diverted a small amount of host assimilate (1.14%), while increasing phosphate uptake enough to produce a 150% increase in plant growth (as measured by total plant weight increase).

Bevege *et al.* (1975) conclude that sucrose and glucose are the principal sugars transferred in endomycorrhizal systems, and that low levels of sucrose in the fungal cytoplasm, maintaining a concentration gradient for further passive movement or facilitated diffusion, are achieved by its conversion into lipid, protein, and amino and organic acids involved in the active growth of the fungus. These conclusions in part echo the suggestions of Cox *et al.* (1975) and Harley (1975) that fungal lipid synthesis could provide an alternative sink, and that the necessary gradient is instead of conversion of carbohydrates into storage products not metabolizable by the host plant.

Cooper and Losel (1978) have provided the first report on the lipid composition of VAM fungi. Comparisons of lipid content and composition of mycorrhizal roots of onion, clover, and ryegrass infected with *Glomus mosseae* with that of uninfected roots show that the mycorrhizal roots contain significantly more lipid than uninfected roots.

It is probable that the host species influences the mycorrhizal fungus (Kruckelmann, 1975). For example, the time for spore germination and infection, the time for development of arbuscules and vesicles, and the amount of external hyphae vary from one host to the next. Conversely, we know that certain strains of mycorrhizal fungi will not develop as well on some plants as they will on others. The exact reasons for these phenomena are unknown.

C. Spore Germination and Infection on Agar Media

Attempts to characterize requirements for spore germination or for the establishment of aseptic infections on agar have met with variable success (Godfrey, 1957; Mosse, 1962; Mosse and Hepper, 1975). Although it is probable that variations in host physiology, rhizosphere invironment, soil fertility, or fungal strain influence germination characteristics, certain generalizations can be made. Generally, spore germination is inhibited by excess nutrients, although spores will not germinate well on leached or Noble agar or in distilled water. Therefore, some external nutrient source is necessary for optimal spore germination. Several reports have indicated positive influences of soil extracts or dialysates (Mosse, 1959a; Daniels and Graham, 1976) on spore germination. Plant extracts do not seem to stimulate germination, nor does the mere presence of a suitable plant host assure germination. Many laboratories do obtain suitable germination rates, however, using carefully selected surface-sterilized spores on plain water agar. Repeated attempts to use pregerminated spores to establish VAM under aseptic conditions have been inconsistent (Hawker et al., 1957; Barrett, 1958; Mosse, 1956; and others). This may indicate that either the requirements for spore germination are different from the requirements for hyphal growth and infection, or that the ability to germinate does not always coincide with the ability to form mycorrhizae. Mosse (1962), using *Glomus mosseae*, established VA mycorrhizas in culture on clover seedlings by adding a *Pseudomonas* sp. to aid root penetration. A commercial pectolytic enzyme preparation produced somewhat the same results, and Mosse concluded that bacterial enzymatic activity may have been responsible for successful root penetration by the fungus. In 1971, Mosse and Phillips obtained mycorrhizal infections with spores not previously germinated and without the *Pseudomonas* sp. by lowering the phosphorus level of the media. It has since been generally found that moderately consistent infection can be obtained by limiting the media concentration of nitrogen and phosphorus to very low levels.

Several additional workers have shown that other microorganisms can influence VAM infection. Bagyaraj and Menge (1978) suggested a synergistic or additive interaction between *Glomus fasciculatus* and *Azotobacter chroococcum*. Azcon et al. (1978) demonstrated that cell-free preparations of *Azotobacter*, *Rhizobium*, and phosphate-solubilizing bacteria (*Pseudomonas* sp.) increased mycorrhizal formation. These increases may have been due to the activity of growth substances known to be produced by the bacteria, since application of pure plant hormones caused similar increases in mycorrhizal formation.

All attempts to obtain a VAM fungus in pure culture have failed. However, at least one species has been obtained in root organ culture (Mosse and Hepper, 1975).

D. Factors Affecting Formation of Mycorrhizae

There are a wide variety of conditions that in some, but not all, situations will favor or inhibit the establishment of VA mycorrhizae. As stated earlier, soils that favor mycorrhizal infection are usually of low to moderate fertility. Conversely, soils of high fertility, particularly those high in phosphorus and nitrogen, generally retard the establishment of mycorrhizae. It has been shown, however, that infection sometimes can be established in soils high in phosphorus, when relatively high inoculum levels are used (Mosse, 1977). Apparently, some mycorrhizal fungi are more tolerant of, and may even by stimulated by, high soil phosphorus levels (Mosse, 1977). It has also been shown that some ectomycorrhizal associations will tolerate rather high levels of soil fertility if the soil microbial populations are high (Meyer, 1974). This observation has not been made in VAM systems. High soil phosphorus may be perceived indirectly by the fungus through the nutritional status of the plant, since foliar feeding of onion leaves with phosphorus can reduce mycorrhizal infection (Sanders, 1975). In support of this hypothesis, Menge et al. (1978) have shown, using a split root system technique, that increased root phosphorus concentration, and not increased soil P concentration, is inversely correlated with rates of infection and spore production.

When plants are heavily shaded, mycorrhizal infection will decrease (Peuss, 1958; Redhead, 1975). However, low levels of shading yield conflicting results (Hayman, 1974; Redhead, 1975). Shading also affects the temperature regimes of the plants involved, and it has been shown that low temperatures can reduce infection (Furlin and Fortin, 1973).

The relationship between soil moisture status and mycorrhizal infection has not been adequately characterized. However, this relationship probably depends on the soil, host, and mycorrhizal fungus involved. Redhead (1975) demonstrated that the optimum water supply for plant growth also favors mycorrhizal infection. High (water logging) levels of moisture, as well as extremely low levels of moisture, reduced infection. It would be interesting to determine the relative effectiveness of various mycorrhizal species under different moisture regimes.

VI. VA MYCORRHIZAE AND PLANT DISEASE

Vescular-arbuscular mycorrhizal infection can promote or inhibit the development of plant diseases in several ways including (1) alternation of the rhizosphere to the benefit or detriment of pathogenic organisms, and (2) alternation of the host plant to benefit or hinder pathogenic development.

It is well documented that subtle changes in the nutrient and/or water status of the soil can affect germination, growth, survival, and/or virulence of many soil microorganisms (Lockwood, 1977). It is also well known that in pathogenic fungi quiescence of spores, lysis of mycelia, and formation of resistant structures can be induced by microbial competition for nutrients (Lockwood, 1977). The exogenous addition of nutrients containing energy sources can reverse the effects of competition. A mycorrhizosphere is different nutritionally, and water status in the surrounding soil and the translocation characteristics of mycorrhizal hyphae as well as hyphal or root exudation may enhance such differences. Propagules of plant pathogens are normally quiescent in the soil apart from the sources of energy-yielding nutrients (such as the nearness of plant roots). Root exudates may stimulate germination and provide the energy required for infection. Mycorrhizal fungi colonizing roots would be expected to compete for such nutrients, thereby reducing the amount available to the pathogens and possibly limiting infection.

Alterations of the host plant by mycorrhizal infection, rendering it more or less susceptible to a given pathogen, could occur by either physical or chemical means. For example, we know that mycorrhizal roots generally have higher concentrations of certain nutrients than do nonmycorrhizal plant roots. Physical alterations, such as the Hartig net of the fungal mantle, which are present in ectomycorrhizal roots, are not present in VAM associations.

Several studies have demonstrated that mycorrhizal root systems are less susceptible to plant disease than nonmycorrhizal systems. Mycorrhizal onion roots have been shown to be less susceptible to pink root disease caused by *Pyrenochaeta terrestris* (Safir, 1968; Becker, 1976). Only the mycorrhizal segments of the root system were more resistant to the pathogen (Becker, 1976). This suggests that greater mycorrhizal infection levels should yield greater levels of resistance to the pathogen.

Fewer Chlamydospores of the root-rotting fungus *Thielaviopsis basicola* (Baltruschat et al., 1973) are produced on mycorrhizal tobacco roots than on nonmycorrhizal roots. Root extracts from mycorrhizal plants inhibited growth of the pathogen in this case. The increased arginine content of mycorrhizal roots may have caused the decreased chlamydospore production.

As mycorrhizal infection levels increase in tomato, the multiplication of tomato aucuba moasic virus also increases (Daft and Okusanya, 1973). In addition, the amount of extractable arabis mosaic virus from petunia and straberry plants was greater from mycorrhizal than from nonmycorrhizal plants. Additions of phosphate to nonmycorrhizal tomato plants increased the virus titer in these plants to levels found in mycorrhizal plants that were not given additional phosphate. We might expect similar results if other nutrients were limiting tomato growth. That is, if mycorrhizal infection were stimulating tomato growth, the more vigorous plants could support increased virus replication. This hypothesis must be investigated, along with other virus–host–mycorrhizal combinations.

Ross (1972) reported that VAM infection on soybean was correlated with increased stem and root discoloration caused by the pathogenic fungus *Phytophthora megasperma* (Drechs var. sojoe Hildeb). This correlation existed only with a soybean variety that was susceptible to the pathogen and not with a resistant variety. There is a problem in interpreting these data in that mycorrhizal infection did not increase the growth of soybean plants in the presence or absence of the pathogen. Also, the mycorrhizal fungus produced large vesicules in the root cortex, which would have mechanically damaged the root and influenced disease development. Woodhead *et al.* (1977) have demonstrated, using pot experiments, that VAM soybean roots suffer less damage from *Phytophthora megasperma* var. *sojoe* Race 1 than nonmycorrhizal plants. They used the mycorrhizal fungus *Glomus caledonius*, which stimulated soybean growth and did not produce extremely large vesicules in the root cortex.

Several nematode–mycorrhizal interaction studies have been reported. Baltruschat *et al.* (1973) have shown that VAM infection inhibits the establishment of the nematode *Meloidogyne incognita* (Kofoid and White) Chitwood on tobacco. Fox and Spasoff (1972) have shown that the nematode *Heterodera solanacearum* (Miller and Gray) will inhibit VAM infection of tobacco. More recently, Schenck and Kinlock (1974) found, in a survey of Florida soybean fields, that high populations of the root-knot nematode (*Meloidogyne hapla*) the cyst nematode (*Heterodera glycines* Ichinohe) were invariably associated with low populations of endomycorrhizal fungi. Schenck *et al.* (1975) have confirmed these field observations in the laboratory. They also confirmed the results of Baltruschat *et al.* (1973) that mycorrhizal infection was antagonistic to nematode infestation when low nematode levels were used. It was also reported that the reaction of resistant and susceptible soybean cultivars to nematode exposure depends upon the species of mycorrhizal fungus present.

The interrelationships between VAM and plant pathogens are obviously extremely complex. The possibility of using mycorrhizal infection as part of a biological pest control program deserves serious study.

VII. VA MYCORRHIZAE AND PESTICIDES

Understanding the effects of agricultural pesticides on the development and efficiency of VA mycorrhizal systems is critical if we wish to utilize mycorrhizal associations effectively in agricultural systems. This is especially true for those crops that rely heavily on the use of chemicals for their production.

There have been entirely too few studies on the effects of agricultural pesticides on mycorrhizal systems. Several nematicides (Bird et al., 1974; Kelinschmidt and Gerdemann, 1972; Backman and Clark, 1977) as well as one insecticide (Kruckelmann, 1973) have been shown to adversely affect VAM development. Nesheim and Linn (1969) observed the effects of eight different soil fungitoxicants on the development of VAM infection of corn. All eight chemicals were detrimental in various degrees to the formation of mycorrhizae. Jalali and Domsch (1975) showed that three systemic fungitoxicants, as seed treatments, were detrimental to the formation of mycorrhizae in wheat. Foliar treatment with these fungitoxicants also reduced mycorrhizal infection, though to a lesser degree than did the seed treatments. Also tested were foliar applications of several nonsystemic fungicides. Several of these compounds also inhibited mycorrhizal infection slightly. The reasons for this latter phenomenon are unkown. More recently, Sutton and Sheppard (1976) tested three systemic fungicides, including benomyl, for activity against mycorrhizal infection. They used an unidentified Glomus species and conducted their experiments in sand. Of the compounds tested, only Vitavax did not inhibit mycorrhizal development. Bailey and Safir (1978) reevaluated the role of the systemic fungitoxicant Benomyl on the establishment of mycorrhizal infection by Glomus fasciculatus on soybean. They confirmed the reports by Sutton and Sheppard (1976), and by Jalali and Domsch (1975), that Benomyl is detrimental to mycorrhizal formation. The inhibitory effects were not as drastic as those reported by Sutton and Sheppard (1976), possibly because Bailey and Safir's experiments were conducted in a sand–soil–peat mixture rather than in sand. In addition, Bailey and Safir (1978) demonstrated that Benomyl reduces but does not eliminate mycorrhizal infection when used at high concentrations in a soil–sand–peat mixture. They also demonstrated that growth increases usu-

ally associated with mycorrhizal infections were completely eliminated when the concentration of benomyl in the soil reduced VAM
infections 50%.

These findings indicate that investigations of the effects of a chemical on mycorrhizal development should consider infection levels as
well as the benefit of such infection levels for the host. It is possible that
agricultural pesticides could permit relatively high mycorrhizal infection levels, while at the same time eliminating mycorrhizal growth
stimulation.

VIII. AGRICULTURAL APPLICATIONS

The incorporation of VAM technology into agricultural production
programs must take into account a great many parameters. We need to
determine the degree to which the host plants are dependent upon
infection and the potential benefits of mycorrhizal inoculation. The
indigenous populations of mycorrhizal fungi must be characterized,
and decisions must subsequently be made as to which species are best
suited to a given host under prevailing environmental and soil conditions. An efficient mycorrhizal system must be fully compatible with
the cultural and pest management conditions prevailing. Finally, the
production and application of mycorrhizal inoculum will have to be
efficient and economical.

Small-scale field trials have demonstrated that, in soils containing
small numbers of indigenous spores of mycorrhizal fungi, the yields of
corn (Khan, 1972b, 1975) and wheat (Khan, 1975) can be improved if
heavily mycorrhizal seedlings are transplanted into nonsterile fields. In
fumigated and then inoculated field plots, the yeilds of soybean (Ross
and Harper, 1970; Schenck and Hinson, 1973) citrus plants
(Kleinschmidt and Gerdemann, 1972), sour orange (Hattingh and Gerdemann, 1975), and peach (LaRue et al., 1975) have shown significant
increases. However, Mosse (1977), has shown, using pot experiments,
that the responses to inoculation in 11 nonsterile soils is smaller and
less predictable than in sterile soils for maize and Stylosanthes
guyanensis. In these experiments, the highest inoculum densities in
soils containing the lowest indigenous mycorrhizal populations favored plant growth. Obviously, the interrelationships, if any, between
mycorrhizal fungi have to be fully characterized.

A classical example of the practical use of VAM technology involves
the growth of citrus seedlings. Some seedlings are commonly stunted
and appear unhealthy in the nurseries. Kleinschmidt and Gerdemann

(1972) determined that a lack of adequate mycorrhizal infection was responsible for this condition. Extensive fumigation for pathogenic fungi and nematodes, a common practice in citrus nurseries, had decimated mycorrhizal fungi in the field. The plants grew normally following inoculation of these stunted plants with a mycorrhizal fungus. In these experiments, heavy phosphorus fertilization only partially overcame the effects of fumigation, indicating that some citrus varieties may be highly mycorrhizal dependent. Mehraveran (1977) determined that the degree of mycorrhizal dependency was inversely related to the efficiency of the citrus cultivars in phosphate uptake and translocation to the leaves. Hattingh and Gerdemann (1975) demonstrated that inoculation of seed of sour orange was one way of inducing infection.

Peaches and sweetgum, grown in fumigated nurseries, also suffer frequently from nutrient deficiencies. To overcome these problems, most peach nurseries apply zinc chelate and phosphoric acid at seedling time. These applications, however, are not 100% effective. LaRue et al. (1975) have shown that inoculation with endomycorrhizal fungi improves zinc nutrition and thus peach tree growth in the nurseries. Brian and Kormanic (1976b) have shown that sweetgum (*Liquidambar styraciflua*) is nearly obligately mycorrhizal. They showed that growth as well as seedling survival benefit greatly from mycorrhizal inoculation.

Newly propagated cuttings of many perennial horticultural plants exhibit physiological dormancy and slow, irregular first-year growth rates. Kormanik et al. (1976a) have demonstrated that vegetatively propagated yellow poplar cuttings can have ninefold growth increases if they are inoculated with endomycorrhizal fungi. Endomycorrhizal cuttings reached plantable size in approximately 4 months, whereas almost all nonmycorrhizal cuttings exhibited first-year dormancy.

One other practical application of mycorrhizal technology deserves mention. D. H. Marx (persmal communication, 1976) has demonstrated the growth-promoting effects of ectomycorrhizal inoculation of several harvest tree species grown in coal spoils. In preliminary experiments, Daft et al. (1975) have shown that endomycorrhizal infection of herbaceous plants may enable faster recolonization of coal spoils by these plants. (Coal spoils are generally highly acidic and low in nitrogen and phosphorus.)

It should be clear from the above examples that if the indigenous populations of VAM fungi are low, plants that are naturally mycorrhizal potentially will benefit from mycorrhizal inoculation (Mosse, 1975). An important research priority, then, must be the development of systems for the production of mycorrhizal inoculum in quantity. Of course, the possibility that certain mycorrhizal fungi may be harmful to plant growth under some conditions must not be overlooked. Inoculum levels might conceivably by built up in fruit and hardwood nurseries, after soil fumigation, by growing heavily mycorrhizal annuals. The mycorrhizal fungus would build up on the roots of the annuals and, when inoculum levels are sufficiently high, the desired crop could be grown. It may also be possible to build up sufficient inoculum on plant roots grown in sterile soil in greenhouses, or on plants grown in border rows surrounding fields to be seeded. Elimination of pathogenic organisms from the inoculum supply would be a concern here.

IX. CONCLUDING REMARKS

I am gratified the role of vesicular-arbuscular mycorrhizae in crop productivity is finally being studied intensively throughout the world.

It should be emphasized that the mycorrhizal condition is normal, and that agricultural pest management, fertilization, and cultural practices have altered this natural relationship in many instances. Thus, when considering the possibility of utilizing VAM systems in crop production programs, we should be attempting to preserve the associations that exist in the field, while at the same time trying to improve their beneficial effects on plant growth. One of the major limitations faced by researchers at this time is our inability to obtain the fungal partner in pure culture. If this were possible, our knowledge of these organisms and of the mycorrhizal association itself would increase rapidly. The number of plant biological processes shown to be affected by these mycorrhizal fungi increases every year, and before long I expect researchers will begin to incorporate mycorrhizal inoculum in many of their experiments in a manner similar to the incorporation of Rhizobia in experiments with legumes.

ACKNOWLEDGMENTS

I would like to thank Ms. S. Claire Coley for her assistance in writing Sections V, B and V, C.

REFERENCES

Asai, T. (1944). *Jpn. J. Bot.* **13**, 463–485.
Azcon, R., Azcon-G de Aguilar, C., and Barea, J. M. (1978). *New Phytol.* **80**, 359–364.

Backman, P. A., and Clark, E. M. (1977). *Nematoropa* **7**, 13–17.
Bagyaraj, D. J., and Menge, J. A. (1978). *New Phytol.* **80**, 567–573.
Bailey, J. E., and Safir, G. R. (1979). *Phytopathology* **68**, 1810–1812.
Baltruschat, H., Sikora, R. A., and Schönbeck, F. (1973). *Proc. Int. Congr. Plant Pathol.,* *2nd, 19* Abstract 0661.
Barrett, J. T. (1958). *Phytopathology*   , 391.
Baylis, G. T. S. (1967). *New Phytol.* **66**, 231–243.
Baylis, G. T. S. (1970). *Plant Soil* **33**, 713–716.
Baylis, G. T. S. (1971). *N.Z. J. Bot.* **9**, 293–296.
Baylis, G. T. S. (1972). *Plant Soil.* **36**, 233–234.
Becker, W. N. (1976). Ph.D. Thesis, University of Illinois, Urbana-Champaign.
Becker, W. N. and Gerdemann, J. W. (1977). *New Phytol.* **78**, 289–295.
Bevege, D. I. (1971). Ph.D. Thesis, University of New England, Armidale, Australia.
Bevege, D. I., and Bowen, G. D. (1975). In "Endomycorrhizas" (F. E. Sanders, B. Mosse, and P. B. Tinker, eds.), pp. 000–000. Academic Press, New York.
Bevege, D. I., Bowen, G. D., and Skinner, M. F. (1975). In "Endomycorrhizas" (F. E. Sanders, B. Mosse, and P. B. Tinker, eds.), pp. 149–174. Academic Press, New York.
Bird, G. W., Rich, J. R., and Glover, S. U. (1974). *Phytopathology* **64**, 48–51.
Bowen, G. D., Skinner, M. F., and Bevege, D. I. (1974). *Soil Biol. & Biochem.* **6**, 141–144.
Bowen, G. D., Bevege, D. I., and Mosse, B. (1975). In "Endomycorrhizas" (F. E. Sanders, G. Mosse, and P. B. Tinker, eds.), pp. 241–260. Academic Press, New York.
Brian, W. C., and Kormanik, P. P. (1977). *South. J. Appl. For.* **1**(1), 21–23.
Callow, J. S., Capaccio, D. M., Parrish, E., and Tinker, P. B. (1978). *New Phytol.* **80**, 125–134.
Cooper, K. M. (1975). In "Endomycorrhizas" (F. E. Sanders, B. Mosse, and P. B. Tinker, eds.), pp. 391–407. Academic Press, New York.
Cooper, K. M., and Losel, D. M. (1978). *New Phytol.* **80**, 143–151.
Cox, G., and Tinker, P. B. (1976). *New Phytol.* **77**, 371–378.
Cox, G., Sanders, F. E., Tinker, P. B., and Wild, J. A. (1975). In "Endomycorrhizas" (F. E. Sanders, B. Mosse, and P. B. Tinker, eds.), pp. 298–312. Academic Press, New York.
Crush, J.R. (1974). *New Phytol.* **73**, 743–749.
Daft, M. J., and El-Giahmi, A. A. (1974). *New Phytol.* **73**, 1139–1147.
Daft, M. J., and El-Giahmi, A. A. (1975). In "Endomycorrhizas" (F. E. Sanders, B. Mosse, and P. B. Tinker, eds.), pp. 581–592. Academic Press, New York.
Daft, M. J., and Okosanya, B. O. (1973). *New Phytol.* **72**, 975–983.
Daft, M. J., Hacskaylo, E., and Nicolson, T. H. (1975). In "Endomycorrhizas" (F. E. Sanders, B. Mosse, and P. B. Tinker, eds.) pp. 516–580. Academic Press, New York.
Daniels, B. A., and Graham, S. O. (1976). *Mycologia* **68**, 101–116.
Fox, J. A., and Spasoff, L. (1972). *J. Nematol.* **4**, 224–225. (abstr.).
Furlan, V., and Fortin, J. A. (1973). *Nat. Can. (Que.)* **100**, 467–477.
Gerdemann, J. W. (1968). *Annu. Rev. Phytopathol.* **6**, 397–418.
Gerdemann, J. W. (1975). In "The Development and Function of Roots" (J. G. Torrey and D. T. Clarkson, eds.), pp. 565–591. Academic Press, New York.
Gerdemann, J. W., and Trappe, J. M. (1974). "The Endogonaceae in the Pacific Northwest," Mycol. Mem. No. 5.
Gianinazzi-Pearson, V., and Gianinazzi, S. (1976). *Physiol. Veg.* **14**, 833–841.
Gilmore, A. E. (1971). *J. Am. Soc. Hortic. Sci.* **96**, 35–38.
Godfrey, R. M. (1957). *Trans. Br. Mycol. Sol.* **40**, 203–210.
Gray, L. E., and Gerdemann, J. W. (1967). *Nature, (London)* **213**, 106–107.
Gray, L. E., and Gerdemann, J. W. (1969). *Plant Soil* **30**, 415–422.

Gray, L. E., and Gerdemann, J. W. (1973). *Plant Soil* **39**, 687–689.

Harley, J. L. (1975). *In* "Endomycorrhizas" (F. E. Sanders, B. Mosse, and P. B. Tinker, eds.), pp. 1–24. Academic Press, New York.

Harley, J. L., and Lewis, D. H. (1969). *Adv. Microb. Physiol.* **3**, 53.

Hattingh, J. J., and Gerdemann, J. W. (1975). *Phytopathology* **65**, 113–116.

Hattingh, J. J., Gray, L. E., and Gerdemann, J. W. (1973). *Soil Sci.* **116**, 383–387.

Hawker, L. E., Harrison, R. W., Nicholls, V. O., and Ham, A. M. (1957). *Trans. Br. Mycol. Soc.* **40**, 375–390.

Hayman, D. S. (1974). *New Phytol.* **73**, 71–80.

Hayman, D. S., and Mosse, B. (1972). *New Phytol.* **71**, 41–47.

Ho, I., and Trappe, J. M. (1973). *Nature (London), New Biol.* **244**, 30–31.

Holevas, C. D. (1966). *J. Hortic. Sci.* **41**, 57–64.

Jalali, B. L., and Domsch, K. H. (1975). *In* "Endomycorrhizas" (F. E. Sanders, B. Mosse, and P. B. Tinker, eds.), pp. 619–626. Academic Press, New York.

Khan, A. G. (1972a). *Biologia, Spec. Suppl.* April, pp. 42–78.

Khan, A. G. (1972b). *New Phytol.* **71**, 613–619.

Khan, A. G. (1974). *J. Gen. Microbiol.* **81**, 7.

Khan, A. B. (1975). *In* "Endomycorrhizas" (F. E. Sanders, B. Mosse, and P. B. Tinker, eds.), pp. 419–436. Academic Press, New York.

Kleinschmidt, G. D., and Gerdemann, J. W. (1972). *Phytopathology* **62**, 1447–1453.

Kormanik, P. P., Brian, W. C., and Schultz, R. C. (1976a). Written communications.

Kormanik, P. P., Brian, W. C., and Schultz, R. C. (1976b). Written communications.

Kruckelmann, H. W. (1973). Diss. Naturwiss. Facultät Tech. Universität. Carolo-Wilhelminas, Brauschweig (Ph.D. Thesis, Brauschweig).

Kruckelmann, H. W. (1975). *In* "Endomycorrhazas" (F. E. Sanders, B. Mosse, and P. B. Tinker, eds.), pp. 511–525. Academic Press, New York.

LaRue, J. H., McClellan, W. D., and Peacock, W. L. (1975). *Calif. Agric.* **29**, 6–7.

Lockwood, J. L. (1977). *Biol. Rev. Cambridge Philos. Soc.* **52**, 1–43.

MacDonald, R. M., Lewis, M. (1978). *New Phytol.* **80**(1), 135–141.

Marx, D. H. (1976). Personal Communication.

Mehraveran, H. (1977). Ph.D. Thesis, University of Illinois, Urbana-Champaign.

Menge, J. A., Steirle, D. Bagyaraj, D. J., Johnson, E. L., and Leonard, R. T. (1978). *New Phytol.* **80**, 575–578.

Meyer, F. H. (1974). *Annu. Rev. Plant Physiol.* **25**, 567–586.

Mosse, B. (1956). *Ann. Bot. (London)* [N.S.] **20**, 349–362.

Mosse, B. (1959). *Trans. Br. Mycol. Soc.* **42**, 439–448.

Mosse, B. (1962). *J. Gen. Microbiol.* **27**, 509–520.

Mosse, B. (1973a). *Annu. Rev. Phytolpathol.* **11**, 171–196.

Mosse, B. (1973b). *New Phytol.* **72**, 127–136.

Mosse, B. (1975). *In* "Endomycorrhizas" (F. E. Sanders, B. Mosse, and P. B. Tinker, eds.), pp. 469–484. Academic Press, New York.

Mosse, B. (1977). *New Phytol.* **78**, 277–288.

Mosse, B., and Hayman, D. S. (1971). *New Phytol.* **70**, 29–34.

Mosse, B., and Hayman, D. S. (1973). *Bull. Br. Ecol. Soc.* **4**, 6.

Mosse, B., and Hepper, C. (1975). *Physiol. Plant Pathol.* **5**, 215–223.

Mosse, B., and Phillips, J. M. (1971). *J. Gen. Microbiol.* **69**, 157.

Mosse, B., Hayman, D. S., and Arnold, D. J. (1973). *New Phytol.* **72**, 809–815.

Mosse, B., Powell, L. C., and Hayman, D. S. (1976). *New Phytol.* **76**, 331–342.

Murdoch, J. A., Jackobs, A. J., and Gerdemann, J. W. (1967). *Plant Soil* **27**, 329–334.

Nesheim, N. O., and Linn, M. B. (1969). *Phytopathology* **59**, 297–300.

Nicolson, T. H. (1955). Ph.D. Thesis, University of Nottingham.

Pearson, V., and Tinker, P. B. (1975). In "Endomycorrhizas" (F. E. Sanders, B. Mosse, and P. B. Tinker, eds.), pp. 277–288. Academic Press, New York.

Peuss, H. (1958). Arch. Mirobiol. **29**, 112–142.

Read, D.J., Koucheki, H. K., and Hodgson, J. (1976). New Phytol. **77**, 641–653.

Redhead, J. F. (1968). Trans. Br. Mycol. Soc. **51**, 377.

Redhead, J. F. (1975). In "Endomycorrhizas" (F. E. Sanders, B. Mosse, and P. B. Tinker, eds.), pp. 469–484. Academic Press, New York.

Rhodes, L. H. (1976). Ph.D. Thesis, University of Illinois, Urbana-Champaign.

Rhodes, L. H., and Gerdemann, J. W. (1975). New Phytol. **75**, 555–561.

Ross, J. B., and Harper, J. A. (1970). Phytopathology **62**, 896–897.

Ross, J. B., and Harper, J. A. (1970). Phytopathology **60**, 1552–1556.

Safir, G. R. (1968). M. S. Thesis, University of Illinois, Urbana-Champaign.

Safir, G.R., Boyer, J.S., and Gerdemann, J.W. (1971). Science **172**, 581–583.

Safir, G.R., Boyer, J.S., and Gerdemann, J. W. (1972). Plant Physiol. **49**, 700–703.

Sanders, F. E. (1975). In "Endomycorrhizas" (F. E. Sanders, B. Mosse, and P. B. Tinker, eds.), pp. 261–276. Academic Press, New York.

Sanders, F. E. and Tinker, P. B. (1971). Nature (London) **233**, 278–279.

Sanders, F. E., and Tinker, P. B. (1973). Pestic. Sci. **41**, 385–395.

Sanders, F. E., Tinker, P. B., Black, R. L. B., and Palmerley, S. M. (1977). New Phytol. **78**, 257–268.

Schenck, N. C., and Hinson, K. (1973). Agron. J. **65**, 849–850.

Schenck, N. C., and Kinlock, R. A. (1974). Plant Dis. Rep. **58**, 169–173.

Schenck, N. C., Kinlock, R. A., and Dickson, D. W. (1975). In "Endomycorrhizas" (F. E. Sanders, B. Mosse, and P. B. Tinker, eds.), pp. 607–618. Academic Press, New York.

Smith, D., Muscatine, L., and Lewis, D. H. (1969). Biol. Rev. Cambridge Philos. Soc. **44**, 17–90.

Sutton, J. C., and Sheppard, B. R. (1976). Can. J. Bot. 54, 326–333.

Tinker, P. B. (1975a). Symp. Soc. Exp. Biol. **29**, 325–349.

Tinker, P. B. (1975b). In "Endomycorrhizas" (F. E. Sanders, B. Mosse, and P. B. Tinker, eds.), pp. 353–371. Academic Press, New York.

Woodhead, S. H., Gerdemann, J. W., and Paxton, J. D. (1977). Data presented at the 3rd North American Conference on Mycorrhizae, Athens, Georgia, August (personal communication).

INTERNAL ORGANIZATION OF PLANTS

Chapter 7

Nitrogen Metabolism and Amino Acid Biosynthesis in Crop Plants

B. J. Miflin

I. INTRODUCTION

The significance of nitrogen metabolism in crop plants can be gauged by the amount of N fertilizer applied to crops and the yield response gained, as well as by the value of the major end product of the process: protein. Any biochemical reaction for which, in 1974, 40 million metric tons of substrate worth 8 billion dollars were made and

255

The Biology of Crop Productivity
Copyright © 1980 by Academic Press, Inc.
All rights of reproduction in any form reserved
ISBN 0-12-159850-0

used must assume major importance. The contribution of nitrogen fertilizer to yield can in part be gauged by the graph shown in Fig. 1, taken from a paper by Hageman *et al.* (1976). This shows the increase in average yield of maize over the last 23 years, which can be attributed to two things: (1) using more N fertilizer, and (2) breeding varieties that are more responsive to fertilizer treatment. The major use of nitrogen fertilizer is on cereal crops which, despite the relatively low protein content of their grain, produce the majority of the plant protein harvested in the world (e.g., see Cooke, 1975b). Under these circumstances, it becomes important that the physiology and biochemistry of the processes involved in nitrogen metabolism are well known and that the steps that limit the efficiency of fertilizer utilization are defined (Miflin, 1975). In this chapter, I shall try to outline the biochemical pathways between nitrate and protein, and to discuss where these pathways are located, how they are controlled and, most importantly,

Fig. 1   Trends in fertilizer use and the yields of corn and soybeans in the state of Illinois over 23 years. (Reproduced with permission from Hageman *et al.*, 1976.)

the energy relationships involved. This last point assumes importance for two reasons: (1) the use of fossil fuel energy to produce N fertilizers at an estimated 1.9 tons of oil per ton of fertilizer, and (2) the competition for the energy sources within the plant between nitrogen metabolism and dry matter (chiefly starch) accumulation.

II. UPTAKE OF NITROGEN

The uptake of nitrate and ammonium ions has been studied in a number of crops, chiefly by using solution culture techniques. Although these methods are of value in obtaining information about the underlying mechanisms involved in uptake, it must be kept in mind that they may not be directly applicable to plants grown in soil. Indeed, there is good evidence that merely transferring roots into solutions or washing them over a period of 2 hr can markedly increase the rate of their uptake of various ions (Leonard and Hanson, 1972). In general, laboratory studies have dealt with ion uptake by young plants. Less information is available on changes that may take place during the whole developmental cycle of plant growth.

Both nitrate and ammonia can be absorbed from solutions at relatively low concentrations. Becking (1956) has shown that there is a hyperbolic relationship between ammonium ion concentration and the rate of its uptake by the roots of intact maize plants, with maximal uptake occurring at around 0.5 mM and a half-maximal value (K_m) of 0.013 mM. Van den Honert and Hooymans (1955) have obtained similar results with nitrate, with maximal uptake rates occurring at about 0.2 mM and a K_m for nitrate of 0.023 mM. When the concentration of nitrate is increased above 1 mM, uptake rates begin to increase again (Fig. 2; Rao and Rains, 1976). Similar results have been obtained for ammonium and many other ions (Epstein, 1976). Various interpretations of these dual adsorption isotherms have been made. However, in an agricultural context it is uptake occurring at low ion concentrations that is important, since this is the region in which roots have to operate in the soil.

The uptake of nitrate is relatively specific and is energy dependent. Factors that increase the energy status of plants, particularly illumination, increase the rates of nitrate uptake. There are some difficulties in interpreting certain of these experiments with nitrate ions because of the rapid, energy-requiring reduction that occurs within the cell. It is possible that the two processes of nitrate uptake and reduction are linked in some way (see Butz and Jackson, 1977, for a discussion of this

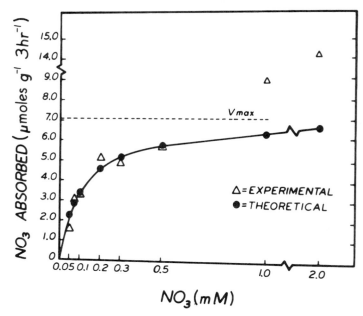

Fig. 2. Absorption of NO₃ by barley seedlings, whose roots were incubated in aerated solutions of NO₃ of different concentrations, showing both experimental and also theoretical values calculated on the basis of single hyperbolic relationship. (Reproduced with permission from Rao and Rains, 1976.)

point), and certain effects on uptake are mediated via effects on reduction. One correlation between the two processes is that they both appear to be induced, that is, the rates are increased by the presence of the substrate. Thus, when roots are exposed to nitrate, there is a lag period before uptake reaches its maximal rate (Jackson et al., 1973). This apparent induction system is sensitive to inhibitors of protein synthesis. When ammonium ions are present, they inhibit nitrate uptake (Lycklama, 1963; Minotti et al., 1969; Rao and Rains, 1976). Again, this could be partly due to an effect on reduction, but the phenomenon also occurs in the absence of measurable reductase activity. These various results suggest that nitrate uptake could be mediated by a permease system synthesized (or activated) in the presence of nitrate, which is dependent on energy to transport the ion across the membrane, and which has a regulatory site that recognizes ammonia.

When nitrate uptake patterns are studied in greenhouse-grown plants over the whole growing season, evidence from xylem analyses (Kirkman and Miflin, 1977, 1979) and total N accumulation (Talibudeen et al., 1976) indicate that roots retain their ability to take up nitrogen even after the plants have entered the reproductive phase. Under field conditions, however, uptake late in the season is likely to be limited by nitrogen availability in the soil, particularly in dry seasons. Thus, in agronomic terms the most important characteristic is the ability of plants to take up nitrate under such conditions, and consideration is being given to breeding for improved uptake characteristics in crops (Hardy et al., 1975). Evidence that suitable variation in these mechanisms can occur comes from comparing the affinity (K_m) for nitrate of barley (0.11 mM, Rao and Rains, 1976), ryegrass (0.033 mM; Lycklama, 1963) and maize (0.021 mM; van den Honert and Hooymans, 1955). All of these are greatly in excess of K_m's for marine diatoms, which are often of less than 1 μM (Eppley et al., 1969).

III. FORMATION OF AMMONIA

It is generally accepted that all commonly available sources of nitrogen are transformed to the level of ammonia before they are assimilated into organic compounds within the plant. The most common sources of N available are dinitrogen from the atmosphere, and nitrate and ammonia from the soil. The reductive fixation of dinitrogen to ammonia is the subject of another chapter. Soil nitrate may be obtained directly, from fertilizer application, or indirectly, from the oxidation of either ammonia fertilizer or soil organic matter.

Nitrate is reduced to ammonium in a two-step process via nitrite.

$$NO_3^- \xrightarrow{2e^-} NO_2^- \xrightarrow{6e^-} NH_3 \tag{1}$$

The first step is a $2e^-$ reduction and is catalyzed by nitrate reductase (Hewitt, 1975). This enzyme is a molybdoflavoprotein of some complexity, which normally accepts the electrons needed for reduction from NADH but can also accept electrons from $FMNH_2$ and reduced cytochromes. The next stage of the reductive process involves a $6e^-$ reduction catalyzed by a single protein, nitrite reductase. All intermediates in nitrite reduction appear to be enzyme bound, and the exact sequence of the events on the enzyme surface is as yet unknown. All higher plant nitrite reductases so far studied, whether derived from roots or leaves, utilize ferredoxin, a nonheme iron protein, as a cofactor and are inactive with pyridine nucleotides (Beevers and Hageman, 1969; Hewitt, 1975). The electron transfer site on the molecule appears to involve a siroheme as well as some nonheme iron and labile sulfur.

The stoichiometry of the reduction process [Eq.(2)] results in the production of the OH^- ions, thus disturbing the pH levels of the cell.

$$NO_2^- + 6H^+ + 6e^- \rightarrow NH_3 + H_2O + OH^- \tag{2}$$

It is generally considered that this production of excess OH^- ions is balanced either by the formation of HCO_3^- production and excretion in the root, or by the formation of organic acid anions and their accumulation in the leaves. This topic is discussed in more detail in recent papers by Kirkby (1974) and by Raven and Smith (1976).

IV. AMMONIA ASSIMILATION

Prior to 1970, it was believed that the great majority of the ammonia produced or present in the plant was assimilated via the reductive amination of 2-oxoglutarate, catalyzed by the enzyme glutamate dehydrogenase (GDH) (E.C.1.4.1.3).

$$\text{2-Oxoglutarate} + NH_3 + NAD(P)H + H^+ \rightleftharpoons \text{glutamate} + NAD(P)^+ + H_2O \tag{3}$$

However, in 1970 Tempest, Meers, and Brown (1970, 1973) described an alternative route of ammonia assimilation, involving glutamine synthetase (GS) (E.C.6.3.1.2.)

$$\text{Glutamate} + NH_3 + ATP \rightarrow \text{glutamine} + ADP + P_i \tag{4}$$

and a hitherto undescribed enzyme, glutamate synthase [alternatively known as GOGAT, the acronym of its original fully classified name (E.C.1.4.1.13).

$$\text{Glutamine} + \text{2-oxoglutarate} + NAD(P)H + H^+ \rightarrow 2\,\text{glutamate} + NAD(P)^+ \tag{5}$$

In this route, glutamate is both the acceptor of ammonia and the product of its assimilation (Fig. 3). Subsequently, GOGAT has been found to be widely distributed in the plant kingdom and to exist in two forms: one utilizing NADH as an electron donor and present in the roots, and other nongreen tissues (Dougall, 1974; Miflin and Lea, 1975); and one inactive with pyridine nucleotides, but capable of accepting electrons from reduced ferredoxin, and present in chloroplasts, leaves, and algae (Lea and Miflin, 1974, 1975a,b; Wallsgrove et al., 1977). There is consider-

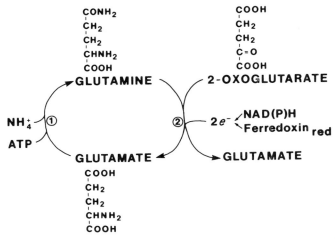

Fig. 3. The formation of glutamate from ammonia via (1) glutamine synthetase and (2) glutamate synthase.

able evidence to suggest that this alternative route is the major pathway for ammonia assimilation in higher plants as well as bacteria (Miflin and Lea, 1976a). The only exception appears to be the yeasts and other fungi; many of these do not have glutamate synthase, and kinetic analysis of $^{15}NH_3$ incorporation (Folkes and Sims, 1974) and specific inhibitor studies (Stewart and Rhodes, 1976) show that glutamate is the predominant primary product of the process.

The evidence in favor of the alternative pathway operating in green plants is based on the use of isotopically labeled nitrogen (^{15}N and ^{13}N), the use of specific inhibitors, and the characteristics of the enzyme involved.

A. Labeled Nitrogen Studies

The best evidence of the kinetics of nitrogen incorporation comes from studies on blue-green algae, using ^{13}N (Wolk et al., 1976). This isotope is radioactive, with an extremely short half-life of 10 min. However, by means of rapid and elegant experiments, Wolk and his colleagues have shown that after only 15 sec of fixation of $^{13}N_2$, the majority of the label is incorporated into the amide group of glutamine; subsequently, the label appears in the α-amino group of glutamate. Studies on higher plants with ^{15}N have involved much longer time periods and are, therefore, more difficult to interpret unequivocally. However, Yoneyama and Fukuzawa (1974, 1975) have shown that feeding both $^{15}NO_3^-$ and $^{15}NH_4^+$ to the roots of rice plants results in the incorporation of ^{15}N, first into glutamine and then into glutamate (more detailed analysis of these experiments is given in Miflin and Lea, 1976a). Recent short-term experiments with ^{13}N substrates have confirmed that the GS/GOGAT route is the major route of ammonia assimilation in tobacco cells in culture (Skokut et al., 1978). Another piece of evidence in favor of the GS/GOGAT pathway is the demonstration by Lewis and Pate (1973) that the N of nitrate, glutamate, and of the amide group of glutamine are all incorporated in the same manner into a wide range of free and protein amino acids in pea leaves. This means that the three nitrogens must be equally available for the formation of α-amino nitrogen, a situation that could only exist if GOGAT were present and operating.

B. Specific Inhibitors

Azaserine and 6-diazo-5-oxo-L-norvaline (DON) are analogs of glutamine, and are known to block all glutamine–amide transfer reactions, including GOGAT. Methionine sulfoximine (MSO) is an analog of the enzyme-bound complex of glutamate with glutamine synthetase. Neither of these compounds has any effect on GDH. Many years ago, van der Meulen and Bassham (1959) showed that azaserine and DON, when fed to green algae, caused $^{14}CO_2$ to accumulate in glutamine and 2-oxoglutarate and prevented incorporation of ^{14}C into glutamate. These experiments have recently been repeated by Stewart and Rhodes (1976) on Lemna with similar results. The conclusion that can be drawn is that carbon reaches glutamate from CO_2 fixation via GOGAT, not via GDH. Methionine sulfoximine has been used chiefly to follow the incorporation of nitrogen. In its presence, incorporation into glutamine and glutamate is blocked and ammonia accumulates; this is true for ammonia derived from nitrate (Stewart and Rhodes, 1976) and dinitrogen (Wolk et al., 1976). These results indicate that GS is the primary assimilatory enzyme for ammonia.

C. Characteristics of the Enzymes

Although it is not always safe to assume that the characteristics of an enzyme measured in a test tube are the same as those it possesses in vivo, it is likely that GDH is not suited to a role in ammonia assimilation, since it has a relatively high K_m for ammonia in the range of 5–100 mM. This would mean that relatively large concentrations of ammonia would have to build up in order for the enzyme to synthesize glutamate at a rapid rate. Large internal concentrations of ammonia in higher plants are rarely observed *in vivo*, and because of the toxic nature of the compound would be deleterious to the plant. Furthermore, GDH is a reversible enzyme and is chiefly located in the mitochondria. However, although isolated mitochondria can be shown to oxidize glutamate, they only synthesize glutamate under nonphysiological conditions (Davies and Teixeira, 1975). In contrast, the affinity of GS for ammonia is high, since the enzyme has a low K_m in the range of 0.02–1 mM and catalyzes an irreversible reaction. These characteristics are common to all of the other major biosynthetic pathways used in biolgical systems. The discovery of GOGAT has provided a mechanism whereby the superior assimilatory characteristics of GS can be linked to α-amino N production.

The energy requirements of this alternative assimilatory pathway are slightly greater than those of GDH in that one extra ATP is utilized. However, the pathway is probably of considerable advantage to the plant, in that it is irreversible and has a high affinity for the initial substrate. But, under conditions of high ammonia concentrations and low energy, GDH could be important, particularly in aquatic plants.

V. UTILIZATION OF ASSIMILATED NITROGEN

A. General Interconversions

In the plant the conversion of ammonia to amino acids via GS and GOGAT may be divided up in space and time. Thus ammonia taken up or produced by the root, including root nodules where present, is assimilated in the root to glutamine, and then transported chiefly as glutamine or asparagine to other parts of the plant. In this case, GOGAT would only need to be operating in the root at a rate sufficient to regenerate the glutamate needed to accept the ammonia. The cycle of events shown in Fig. 4, as proposed by Miflin and Lea (1976a,b) and Scott et al. (1976), is likely to be particularly important in the nodule, where it is known that about 70% of the N_2 fixed is expected from the nodule as asparagine and 12% as glutamine (Pate et al., 1969). Similarly, expanded leaves may reduce incoming nitrate and export it in the form of glutamine to developing seeds (Lewis, 1975). The second stage of the process, the conversion of the amide N to amino acids for protein synthesis, then occurs at the other end of the transport stream, e.g., the apex, young leaves, or the developing seed. The interconversion of glutamine amide N to glutamate and then to other α-amino acids is easily accomplished by GOGAT and transaminases, which are probably

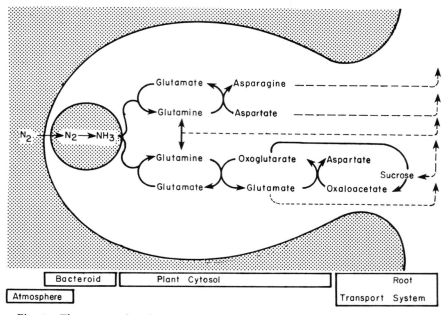

Fig. 4. The proposed pathway of nitrogen from the atmosphere into the transport stream of the plant during N_2 fixation by legume root nodules. Solid lines indicate enzymic reactions; broken lines indicate transport stream. (The length of the dash is a measure of the amount of each compound transported.) (Reproduced with permission from Miflin and Lea, 1976b.)

present in developing seeds of legumes and cereals, as well as in roots and leaves. However, despite suggestions to the contrary, GOGAT is specific for glutamine and does not utilize asparagine. As yet, no asparagine (amide) amino transfer reaction comparable to that for glutamine has been reported. This means that alternative pathways for asparagine utilization may be operating. Two of the possibilities are as follows:

$$\text{Asparagine} \xrightarrow{\text{asparaginase}} \text{aspartate} + NH_3 \qquad (6)$$

$$\text{Asparagine} + \text{2-oxoacid} \xrightarrow{\text{transaminase}} \text{amino acid} + \text{2-oxosuccinamate} \qquad (7a)$$

$$\text{2-Oxosuccinamate} \longrightarrow NH_3 + \text{oxaloacetate} \qquad (7b)$$

The first enzyme [Eq. (6)] has been reported in developing lupin cotyledons (Atkins *et al.*, 1975) from which it has been purified to apparent homogeneity (Lea et al., 1976, 1977). It is very active in these tissues, and has a high K_m for asparagine of approximately 12.5 mM, which is of a similar order of magnitude to the concentration of asparagine in the transport stream (ca. 30 mM: Atkins et al., 1975). A different asparaginase, whose activity is totally dependent on the presence of K^+ ions, has been isolated from developing pea cotyledons (Sodek et al., 1978). Asparagine transaminase [Eq. (7a)] has been found in various tissues. The best-defined system for asparagine breakdown via this route is in the pea leaf, where 2-oxosuccinamic acid is considered to be reduced to homosuccinamate before the second ammonia is lost (Lloyd and Joy, 1978). In all of these pathways of asparagine breakdown, the amide N is liberated as free ammonia, which must be reassimilated.

B. Amino Acid Biosynthesis

The generalized pattern for amino acid synthesis is the provision of a carbon skeleton in the form of a 2-oxoacid that is then transaminated. The transamination is the final reaction in the synthesis of most of the amino acids. A classification of the amino acids can be made, based upon the origin of these carbon skeletons. This division of amino acids into "families" stems largely from work with bacteria. Evidence for the existence of a similar pathway in higher plants is based on carbon

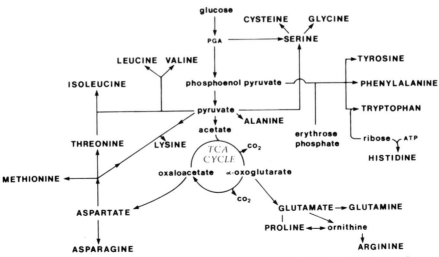

Fig. 5. The origins of the carbon skeletons of amino acids and the familial relationship between various amino acids.

labeling studies, the presence of most of the enzymes in plant tissues, and the presence of certain key intermediates.

In almost every case, the pathways have been shown to be the same as those operating in bacteria. One of the few exceptions is a modification in the synthesis of methionine, which is derived from phosphohomoserine in higher plants (Giovanelli et al., 1974) (see Fig. 10). Detailed references to studies on the individual enzymes in plants can be obtained from recent reviews [Miflin (1973), Bryan (1976), and Miflin and Lea (1977)]. A summary of the origins of the amino acids and their division into families is given in Fig. 5. A key part of this diagram is the relationship of the different amino acid families to the oxoacids of the tricarboxylic acid cycle. Thus the cycle performs two functions in plants: (1) carbon degradation in respiration to release energy, and (2) the provision of skeletons for biosynthetic reactions. The way in which these two functions are independently organized and controlled is one of the more interesting problems of plant biochemistry.

VI. LOCATION OF NITROGEN METABOLISM REACTIONS

A. Within the Plant

Unless foliar fertilizer sprays are used, the nitrogen sources available to crop plants normally enter the plant via the root and are then transported around the plant (Fig. 6). Where ammonia is the source, either from ammonia in the soil or excreted from the bacteroids as a product of nitrogen fixation, it is generally assimilated within the root. It is not usually found as a component of the transport stream.

As a consequence of this assimilation, carbohydrates must be transported down to the roots to provide the energy as well as the acceptor carbon molecules. In contrast, nitrate is readily mobile in the xylem, and may either be reduced to ammonia in the root or passed up the plant and reduced in the leaves. Nitrate may also pass into vacuoles and be stored. This storage pool of nitrate is only slowly released into the metabolic pool, and probably accounts for much of the nitrate found in various plant parts, particularly in fleshy petioles (e.g., spinach and sugar beet) and stem bases. The relative importance of the root and shoot in the reduction process is not well established. Part of the reason for this is that the ratio probably varies a great deal, depending upon environmental conditions and on the plant's own internal rhythm. Wallace and Pate (1965) have made a study of nitrate reduction

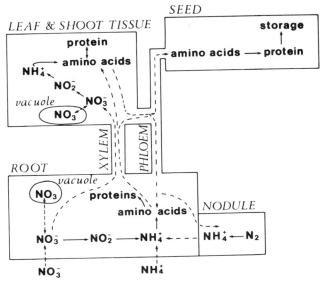

Fig. 6. The movement of nitrogenous compounds around the plant. Solid lines indicate enzymic transformations; broken lines indicate transport of compounds. (Reproduced from Miflin, 1979.)

in the pea plant, and have shown that as the plant receives more nitrate, proportionately more of it is transported to the shoots. Pate (1973) has also studied the ratio of nitrate to reduced amino nitrogen in a range of plants fed 100 ppm of nitrate in a culture solution, and has shown that the amount transported to the shoot varies markedly between different species (Fig. 7). In the plants studied, the variation is from virtually 90% of the incoming nitrate reduced in the root of lupins to no reduction at all in *Xanthium* roots.

Recently, Kirkman and Miflin (1977, 1979) have studied the export of nitrate and amino acids in the bleeding sap of wheat plants over the whole of their developmental cycle. Their results show that a considerable part of the incoming nitrate is reduced in the root (Table I) at all times during the season and under various supplies of nitrate. However, these results, as most others on this topic, have come from plants grown in pots, in which root growth is reduced and root temperature is much higher (particularly in relation to the shoot) than is normal under field conditions. Whether the same ratio of root to shoot reduction would hold in the field remains to be studied.

Another approach to determining the division of nitrate reduction between roots and leaves has been to study the distribution of the

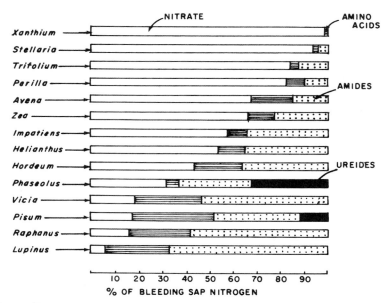

Fig. 7. Percentage composition of the nitrogenous fraction of bleeding sap collected from a range of herbaceous plants. All were continuously supplied with culture solution containing 140 ppm N as nitrate. The species toward the bottom of the figure reduce a large proportion of nitrate in their root system. (Reproduced with permission from Pate, 1973.)

TABLE I

Amount of Nitrogen and the Ratio of that Nitrogen in a Reduced to a Nonreduced Form in the Xylem Sap of Spring Wheat Plants, Grown in Pots, during Their Development[a]

Fertilizer applied: mg N/pot	Harvest at					
	Early stem extension		Caring		Grain filling	
	Total N	NH_2/NO_3	Total N	NH_2/NO_3	Total N	NH_2/NO_3
0	51.9	9.2	32.8	13.9	23.1	14.4
100	96.2	5.3	111.7	5.2	41.8	18.0
200	265.0	3.9	185.9	6.8	70.4	15.0
400	261.9	3.7	197.1	7.8	166.6	21.8

[a] Results from Kirkman and Miflin (1977). Expressed as (1) μg N per day per plant based on the rate of sap exudation from cut shoot bases and the concentration of the N in the sap, and (2) the ratio of animo N (including amides) to nitrate N.

enzymes nitrate and nitrite reductase. Both of these enzymes have long been known to be present in both the roots and leaves of most species (Hewitt, 1975). Wallace and Pate (1967) were able to show that the ratio of shoot to root nitrate reductase in peas increases considerably as the nitrate supply to the plants is increased. Whereas at 10 ppm nitrate almost all of the total nitrate reductase was in the root and the shoot was almost devoid of activity, at 50 ppm and above the reverse was true. Studies of nitrate reductase in *Xanthium* were consistent with the transport results shown in Fig. 7, in that no nitrate reductase was found in the roots. Recently, Brunetti and Hageman (1976), comparing levels of extractable nitrate reductase with an *in vivo* assay of enzyme activity in the leaves and roots of young wheat plants, have shown that whereas there is a much more extractable nitrate reductase in the shoots than roots, the *in vivo* assays indicate approximately equal levels of activity in both tissues. The latter assay was found to be much more closely correlated to the accumulation of reduced nitrogen in the plant and is, therefore, thought to give a more accurate picture than levels of extractable nitrate reductase.

The enzymes of assimilation—GS, GOGAT, and GDH—are also present in both roots and leaves, although GOGAT is ferredoxin dependent in leaves and can use NAD(P)H in extracts from roots and other non-green tissues. In contrast, nitrate reductase is ferredoxin dependent, whether it is isolated from roots or shoots. The two enzymes show remarkable similarities in various properties (Hucklesby *et al.*, 1972; Bourne and Miflin, 1973). This raises the problem of exactly how nitrite is reduced *in vivo*, since ferredoxin does not appear to be present in roots. So far, no alternative electron donor to ferredoxin has been reported.

B. Subcellular Distribution

Most of the available evidence suggests that nitrate reductase is in the soluble fraction of the cell, although sporadic reports have suggested that it may be present in various particulate fractions (see Hewitt, 1975). However, there is at present no convincing evidence that nitrate reductase is located inside any organelle. In contrast, almost all workers have concluded that nitrite reductase is located in the plastids, both in roots and leaves. Suggestions that nitrite reductase might be in the peroxisomes (Lips and Avissar, 1972) appear to be unfounded, when careful density gradient techniques are used that clearly separate peroxisomes from plastids (Miflin, 1974a). Based upon both differential and density gradient centrifugation, GS, GOGAT, and GDH are also found in plastids. [For more detailed evidence in favor of this hypothesis, see Miflin and Lea (1976a, 1977), Lea and Miflin (1979), and Givan and Harwood (1976).] One of the difficulties of these types of distribution study is deciding exactly how much of the total enzyme activity is associated with plastids, since their fragile nature means that much activity is released into the supernatant during isolation. Recently, more gentle techniques of protoplast isolation and rupture have yielded recoveries of greater than 80% of the total chlorophyll in intact chloroplasts Rathnam and Edwards (1976). Using these techniques, all of the nitrite reductase and GOGAT appears in the chloroplast, but only about one-half of the GS (the remainder of which is in the cytoplasm). At least 90% of the nitrate reductase is in the soluble phase of the cell, and only a small proportion (probably not significant) is associated with the chloroplast (Wallsgrove et al., 1979).

The distribution of several of the enzymes involved in the biosynthesis of the carbon skeletons of amino acids has also been studied, and they have been shown to be present in plastids of various sorts. Thus acetolactate synthase is present in root and leaf plastids (Miflin, 1974a), several enzymes of tryptophan synthesis are found in pea etioplasts (Grosse, 1976), homoserine dehydrogenase is located in maize and bean leaf plastids (Bryan et al., 1977, and unpublished results), and enzymes of cysteine (Schmidt and Trebst, 1969) and methionine (Shah and Cossins, 1970) metabolism are also found in chloroplast. Besides this potential capability for amino acid biosynthesis, intact isolated chloroplasts are also capable of synthesizing protein, particularly the large subunit of fraction 1, without supplementation of external amino acids apart from labeled methionine (Blair and Ellis, 1973).

Having shown that chloroplasts have the requisite enzymes, the question then arises as to whether isolated chloroplasts can carry out the overall process of nitrogen assimilation into the organic compounds. Magalhaes et al., (1974) and Miflin (1974b) have shown that isolated, intact chloroplasts reduce nitrite to ammonia and amino acids in a light-dependent, CO_2-independent reaction, without the need for any supplementary additions. More recently, Anderson and Done (1977a,b) have found that isolated chloroplasts can carry out oxygen evolution coupled to the reductive reactions of ammonia assimilation (see Fig. 8). Thus isolated, intact chloroplasts, whose CO_2-dependent evolution is blocked either by lack of CO_2 or by the presence of glyceraldehyde, can evolve oxygen when provided with both 2-oxoglutarate and glutamine. This evolution is light dependent and is inhibited by azaserine. It is presumed to be due to the reoxidation of photoreduced ferredoxin in the GOGAT reaction. Illuminated chloroplasts also evolve

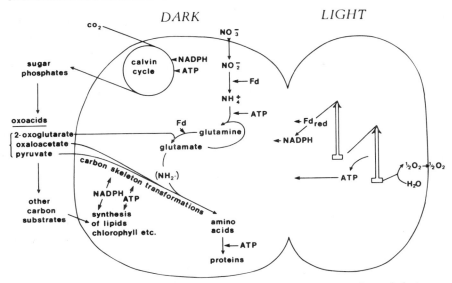

Fig. 8. The location of the light-dependent, energy-producing reactions of photosynthesis and the dark energy-using reactions of carbon and nitrogen metabolism in the chloroplast. (Reproduced from Miflin, 1979.)

oxygen in the presence of ammonia and 2-oxoglutarate when ATP, inorganic pyrophosphate and Mg^{2+} are present. This is interpreted as being due to the coupled activity of GS and GOGAT. The involvement of GDH is excluded, since the reaction is inhibited both by azaserine and methionine sulphoximine. These latter observations confirm the previous work of Mitchell and Stocking (1975), who have shown the ammonia-dependent synthesis of glutamine from glutamate by illuminated chloroplasts. In all of these reactions, it has proved necessary to add carbon acceptors exogenously. There does not appear to be any evidence that chloroplasts themselves can synthesize the carbon skeletons of amino acids directly from CO_2, but rather that carbon must leave the chloroplast at some level—possibly as C_3 or C_6 sugar phosphates—and be metabolized to 2-oxoacid precursors—such as 2-oxoglutarate—in the cytoplasm and/or mitochondria. It has also proved possible to demonstrate that isolated chloroplasts can synthesize the amino acids of the aspartate family from ^{14}C aspartate (Mills and Wilson, 1978, Lea et al., 1979). This reaction is strongly light dependent and the synthesis is inhibited by the end product amino acids in a manner consistent with studies on isolated enzymes (see Section VII,C). Current concepts of the location of nitrogen metabolism in chloroplasts are outlined in Fig. 8. Two consequences flow from this view: (1) that the energy-requiring reactions of nitrogen metabolism, with the probable exception of nitrate reduction, can be powered directly by energy in the form of ATP or reducing power (reduced ferredoxin or NADPH) made available from light-dependent electron transport; and (2) that to consider the dark steps of photosynthesis solely in terms of carbon metabolism (as, for example, the program of recent international conferences might indicate) is inadequate and inaccurate.

VII. REGULATION OF NITROGEN METABOLISM

In the flow of nitrogen to protein it might be expected that any compound that was a substrate for a reaction that was subject to control would accumulate. Similarly, if the rate of protein synthesis is regulated by factors other than the nitrogen supply, then the correspondence between the nitrogen supply and the amount of protein synthesized would not be very great. When these two aspects are investigated in crop plants, there is little evidence to show a great degree of regulation of the gross incorporation of nitrate into protein. The nitrogen compounds that accumulate in plants in significant quantities are (1) nitrate itself, which can be present in very high concentrations under certain situations; (2) the amides glutamine and asparagine; and (3) protein. The accumulation of amides is a special phenomenon concerned with transport; amides only build up outside of the transport stream under extreme conditions, such as senescence and extended periods of darkness or mineral deficiency.

Certain amino acids do accumulate under special conditions, for example, as nitrogen stores in certain legume seeds (Fowden, 1976) and under water stress (Stewart, 1972). In general terms, in healthy plants there is little evidence to show that nitrogen flow is restricted between nitrate and protein.

The effect of nitrogen supply on protein synthesis in crop plants is shown in Fig. 9. In one example, the total above-ground part of the plant is harvested; in the other, only the seeds. However, in both cases there is an almost linear relationship between nitrogen fertilizer applied and protein produced. The limitation in the transfer of nitrogen from the fertilizer bag to plant protein appears to be chiefly in the efficiency of the plant in taking it up from the soil, transporting nitrate to the site of reduction, and in reducing it. In Section VIA the variation in nitrate uptake between species was mentioned. Various attempts have been made to see if there are also differences within cultivars of

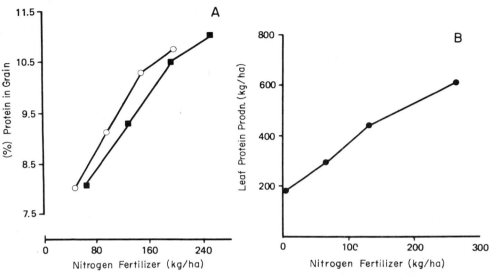

Fig. 9. The relationship between nitrogen fertilization and (A) yield of wheat grain (redrawn from the original data of Cooke, 1975b) and (B) leaf protein production (redrawn from the original data of Arkcoll and Festenstein, 1971).

given crops. Goodman (1974) has shown that considerable variation exists within cultivars of *Lolium* with respect to nitrate uptake, and Huffaker and Rains (1978) report varietal differences in nitrate content between 12 wheat genotypes.

Hageman and many co-workers (Hageman *et al.*, 1976) have carried out a series of experiments with cultivars of wheat and maize grown under controlled and field conditions, in which they have studied the relationship of nitrate reductase activity to the grain yield and protein content of cereals. They have been able to show that there is, in general, a positive correlation between the ability of plants to reduce nitrate and the amount of protein harvested, although there are obviously many complicating factors. One of these is the ability of plants to translocate nitrogen from the vegetative part of the plant to the seed during seed development. Hageman *et al.* (1976) have suggested that the assay of nitrate reductase either *in vivo* or *in vitro* could be used as a selection tool in plant breeding, and they have shown that if it had been applied to a range of 36 hybrid maize lines, then by choosing the 12 best at nitrate reduction, they would have selected three of the four highest yielders and two of the best protein producers. Similar suggestions have been made for the use of nitrate reductase assays to predict crop yield by Johnson *et al.* (1976).

Although the process after nitrate reduction may not be limiting the overall flow of nitrogen into protein, the many reactions involved must nevertheless be properly coordinated. There are many potential mechanisms by which this might occur. In order to make a protein, the plant needs (1) the machinery (enzymes) to carry out the reaction, (2) the energy with which to carry out the reaction, (3) the carbon compounds to join to the assimilated nitrogen, and (4) a correct balance of amino acids. Therefore, it is necessary that all be present in adequate amounts before the process can be completed. Omission of one factor (e.g., one of the 20 amino acids), can completely inhibit the overall process. Within a given cellular compartment, this coordination of control can be achieved by various means, which are basically of two types: (1) those that change the amount of the given enzyme present in the tissue, and (2) those that modify the activity of a given amount of enzyme protein. The first type are relatively gross controls, which operate over longer time periods (minutes to hours), as compared with the second, which are capable of fine tuning activity with a very short response time (seconds to minutes). The types of controls that have been studied with respect to the different stages of nitrogen metabolism will now be discussed.

A. Control of Nitrate Reduction to Ammonia

There is considerable evidence that for a range of green plants the extractable amounts of the enzyme nitrate and nitrite reductase are greater in the presence of nitrate (see Beevers and Hageman, 1969; Hewitt, 1975). Nitrite can also stimulate the levels of activity of both enzymes. Thus these enzymes can be considered to be "induced" by their substrates. However, the word induced must be used with some caution, since it was originally used in an enzymological context, to denote the initiation of the synthesis of an enzyme by its substrate (or some related compound). Most work has been done on nitrate reductase, but so far it has been insufficient to prove that the stimulation of nitrate reductase is solely due to the initiation of synthesis of the enzyme. Although there have been many studies indicating that protein synthesis—including the synthesis of nitrate reductase (Zielke and Filner, 1971)—is necessary for stimulation to occur, there have been none that have shown that there is necessarily a change in the rate of synthesis of the enzyme as distinct from the change in the rate of inactivation or degradation of the enzyme. Indeed, there is considerable evidence to show that inactivation and degradation of the enzyme may be important. Thus, when nitrate is removed from the tissues, or leaves are placed in the dark, there is a rapid loss of activity (Aslam and Oaks, 1975; Travis et al., 1969; Huffaker and Rains, 1978). The rate of loss of activity can be used to calculate a half-life of nitrate reductase of about 4 hr, although this varies slightly for different species and tissues (Huffaker and Petersen, 1974), thus indicating that nitrate reductase is an unstable protein. The loss of activity may be related to the nitrate reductase protease described by Wallace (1975, 1977), which has been isolated from maize roots and found to degrade nitrate reductase, but not a range of other plant proteins. Whether or not this protease is important in the physiological control of nitrate reduction is not yet known. What is certain, however, is that it will drastically reduce the level of enzyme during the extraction of nitrate reductase from the tissue if steps are not taken to inhibit its activity.

As well as being apparently induced by nitrate and nitrite, the level of the enzyme in leaf tissue is also affected by light, CO_2, and other factors (see Hewitt, 1975). Light appears to have multiple effects. There is evidence that light affects the uptake of nitrate into the leaves, and transfer of nitrate from the vacuole to the metabolic pool (Aslam et al., 1976), the level of polysomes in the tissue, and the rate of protein synthesis (Huffaker and Petersen, 1974). Besides these "substrate" effects of light, there is evidence of a phytochrome-mediated stimulation of nitrate reductase (Jones and Sheard, 1973). It has also been shown that the induction of nitrate reductase is considerably reduced in the absence of CO_2 (Kannangara and Woolhouse, 1967), although this CO_2 requirement can be met by acetate or stored carbon compounds, at least in algae (Thacker and Syrett, 1972). Besides these various effects, which generally appear to act synergistically with nitrate, there is evidence that nitrate reductase can be "induced" in the absence of nitrate by a wide variety of compounds—including cytokinins (Parkash, 1972), growth retardants (Knypl, 1974), chloramphenicol (Shen, 1972)—and by incubation of tissues at low pH in the presence of citrate or other compounds (Knypl and Ferguson, 1975).

The ability of N products of nitrate reduction, such as ammonia and amino acids, to repress nitrate reductase has often been studied. In general, positive results have been obtained with studies of plants in aquatic environments. Using green algae, several groups of workers have been able to show that ammonia represses the induction of nitrate and nitrite reductase [i.e., prevents the increases in extractable level of nitrate reductase in the presence of nitrate (see Hewitt, 1975)]. Similar results have also been obtained with the duckweeds Lemna and Spirodela (Orebamjo and Stewart, 1975a, Ferguson, 1969). Repression in these higher plants is generally not absolute, i.e., addition of nitrate in the presence of ammonia usually increases nitrate reductase, but not by as much as in the absence of ammonia. Whether repression is due to ammonia itself, or to a product of its assimilation, is not always clear. Recently, Stewart and Rhodes (1977) have related the amount of repression of *Lemna* nitrate reductase to the internal glutamine concentration and have shown a linear relationship between the two.

Studies with land plants have generally failed to show repressive effects of any eventual products of nitrate reduction on the enzyme from leaf tissue (e.g., Ingle *et al.*, 1966; Schrader and Hageman, 1967), although Smith and Thompson (1971) have shown an effect of ammonium on the nitrate reductase of excised barley roots in nutrient culture. The enzyme from culture tobacco tissue cells also shows repression by amino acids (Filner, 1966), although there is obviously a complex mechanisms involved, since only the enzyme induced by nitrate was repressed, but not that by nitrite (Chroboczek-Kelker and Filner, 1971). More recently, Radin (1975) has shown a differential effect of amino acids on nitrate reductase in roots and shoots of cotton plants. The root enzyme is repressed by the presence of glutamine, glycine, or asparagine, whereas the leaf enzyme is unaffected. Interpretation of some of these experiments is confused, because certain of the amino acids used inhibit the growth of the tissue (Filner, 1966; Radin, 1975). However, there does seem to be sufficient evidence to show that there are controls that decrease the level of nitrate reductase activity in tissue.

Besides the repressive effect of ammonia, several authors have reported that when ammonia is added to nitrate-grown algae, nitrate reductase is rapidly inactivated (Losada, 1976; Solomonson and Spehar, 1977). This effect depends on the presence of light and CO_2. It can be duplicated *in vitro* by NADH, whose effect is markedly and synergistically increased by ADP, but prevented by the presence of nitrate, the substrate for the enzyme (Losada, 1976). Cyanide also acts synergistically with NADH to inhibit the enzyme (Solomonson and Spehar, 1977). Both the *in vivo* and *in vitro* inactivated enzyme can be reactivated by oxidation with ferricyanide. Solomonson and Spehar (1977) have suggested that the *in vivo* inactivation is due to the production of cyanide from hydroxylamine, produced by nitrite reductase, and glyoxylate, a product of CO_2 fixation. The cyanide then binds onto and inhibits the nitrate reductase, and this may be the mechanism that controls the overall flux of nitrate to ammonia, particularly in algae. In support of the role of cyanide in inactivation, it has been shown that nitrate reductase inactivated *in vitro* or *in vivo* releases stoichiometric amounts of cyanide during reactivation (Lorimer *et al.*, 1974). It has also been shown that nitrate reductase can be inactivated in Lemna by the addition of ammonia to the culture (Orebamjo and Stewart, 1975b). However, these authors were unable to find any effect of NADH, ADP, or ammonia, alone or in combination in vitro, although the enzyme could be reactivated by incubation with nitrate and phosphate buffer. They suggest that some different mechanism may occur. Little is known of these inactivation mechanisms in land plants.

In conclusion, it can be fairly stated that control of the amount of nitrate reductase in tissues is complex, with no clear pattern. Undoubtedly, there are species differences, but even within a species (or a tissue of that species) the level of nitrate reductase may change, due to the following reasons:

1. a change in the rate of synthesis;
2. a change in the rate of degradation;
3. chemical or physical modification of the enzyme, causing an alteration in activity;
4. association and disassociation of the enzyme with soluble activators or inactivators.

These possibilities are not mutually exclusive, and any one or more may be affected by some of the factors listed above. Thus, to seek explanation of control solely in terms of simple induction and repression is naive. Further detailed discussion of some of the various strategies of control that might occur is given in a recent paper by Stewart and Rhodes (1977).

B. Control of Ammonia Assimilation

Several workers have shown that ammonia increases the level of GDH in Lemna, root tissues, and leaf disks. This is probably a complex effect, and the studies with leaf tissue of doubtful relevance since ammonia rarely accumulates in leaves.

Little detailed work has been done on factors affecting the level of GS and GOGAT in land plants. However, Rhodes et al. (1975) have recently made a detailed study on GDH, GS, and GOGAT in Lemna, in relation to the nature of the nitrogen supply and the internal concentrations of relevant compounds. Their results suggest that the level of GS is controlled via the internal level of glutamine in a manner similar to that controlling the level of nitrate reductase, which was discussed above. The activity of GS and GDH vary in inverse relationship to one another. Some changes in the level of GOGAT occur independently of the other enzymes, and it is difficult to relate these to the internal pool size of any particular amino acid. Although the changes in levels are severalfold, the absolute levels rarely approach zero, and appreciable levels of all of the enzymes are present under most conditions.

Allosteric controls on GS by various amino acids have often been studied in bacteria, and various complex control patterns elucidated. In higher plants, there is little convincing evidence that any amino acids have a significant regulatory effect on GS, since in most cases the amounts of amino acid required are great and the response small. In leaves and other photosynthetic tissues, nitrite reduction and ammonia assimilation occur in the chloroplast, at the expense of light energy. Evidence, as was reviewed above, is that the whole process from nitrate to amino acids is strongly linked to the supply of that energy. Consequently, it might be expected that the processes would be coordinated with the presence of light. Ways in which this might occur have recently been discussed (Miflin, 1977), and involve the response of glutamine synthetase to Mg^{2+}, pH, and energy charge. Changes in any of these factors can markedly alter the activity of GS.

When the effect of light on the levels of each of these components is measured in the chloroplast stroma, it is found that they change in such a manner as to activate GS. Similar activation mechanisms have been proposed for ribulose diphosphate carboxylase (Walker, 1973). The cessation of CO_2 fixation and ammonia assimilation in the dark is due not only to the lack of substrates, but probably more rapidly to the reverse of the activation reactions. Stewart and Rhodes (1977) have shown that GS is inactivated when *Lemna* is placed in the dark, and the isolated enzyme can be reactivated *in vitro* in the presence of Mg^{2+} and dithiothreitol. Recent work has shown that this reactivation is dependent on the presence of a protein factor (D. Rhodes, personal communication). This again allows an interesting parallel to be drawn with other key enzymes of the Calvin cycle, particularly fructose diphosphatase and sedoheptulose diphosphatase, which are also activated *in vitro* in the presence of a protein factor, Mg^{2+}, and a reducing agent, such as reduced ferredoxin or dithiothreitol (Buchanan et al., 1971; Schurmann and Buchanan, 1975). The effect of these controls means that light not only stimulates nitrogen metabolism and CO_2 fixation by providing the energy required for the processes, but also activates the enzymes involved. The similarity of controls operating on the key reactions for the incorporation of both CO_2 and NH_3 into organic compounds is unlikely to be coincidental, but probably represents an important mechanism whereby the two processes are coordinated.

Much less is known about how the production and assimilation of ammonia is powered in the roots. There is evidence that these processes occur in root plastids (Miflin, 1974a), and it is presumed that the energy is derived from carbohydrates translocated downward in the phloem. However, the reactions involved in channeling this energy into nitrogen metabolism, particularly the transport of electrons to nitrite reduction, are not yet clearly defined; thus it is not surprising that little is known of any regulation. Once ammonia is assimilated into glutamine, it may be utilized for amino acid and protein synthesis or transported to the shoot, as was previously mentioned. The choice of nitrogen transport compounds appears to change with the nitrogen source supplied (Ivanko and Ingversen, 1971) and with the energy status of the plant. It has been suggested that when the carbohydrate status of the plant is high, then glutamine, which has a N:C ratio of 2:5, will predominate, whereas under carbohydrate shortage, such compounds as asparagine (2N:4C) or arginine (4N:6C) are more abundant (Pate, 1973; Lea and Fowden, 1975; Miflin and Lea, 1977). Some evidence for this view has been obtained by *in vivo* studies that show that glucose inhibits asparagine formation in maize root tips (Oaks, 1975), and *in vitro* by studies of glutamine-dependent asparagine synthetase [Eq. (9)], which is inhibited by ATP and 2-oxoglutarate (Lea and Fowden, 1975). In the absence of sufficient carbohydrate, ATP and 2-oxoglutarate will be low and thus unlikely to inhibit asparagine synthetase, whereas the lack of 2-oxoglutarate will limit the GOGAT reaction and may well result in the diversion of the amide-N of glutamine into asparagine.

$$\text{Aspartate + ATP + glutamine} \xrightarrow{\text{Mg}^{2+}} \text{glutamate + asparagine + AMP + PPi} \tag{8}$$

C. Control of Amino Acid Biosynthesis

Many attempts have been made to see if higher plants possess the ability to induce and repress the enzymes of amino acid biosynthesis in a manner similar to that seen in bacteria. So far, none of these have provided any indication that they can (e.g., see Miflin, 1976; Stewart and Rhodes, 1977). In contrast, allosteric mechanisms exist for regulating all the pathways (Miflin, 1976; Miflin and Lea, 1977). This section will deal only with the related amino acids—lysine, methionine, threonine, and with tryptophan—since these are the ones most often found to be nutritionally limiting for nonruminant animals eating plant seed protein.

Although there is no evidence linking the low levels of these amino acids in seed protein to allosteric feedback controls on their synthesis, it remains a possibility. There is also the chance that plants that lack such controls on the production of one or more of these amino acids might accumulate substantial levels of that amino acid in the seed. Consequently, there has been considerable interest in the pathways leading to these amino acids and in selecting feedback-resistant mutants.

Lysine, methionine, and threonine are all derived from aspartate by the pathway outlined in Fig. 10. They are thus all produced via aspartate kinase, the first enzyme in the pathway. The regulation of this enzyme has been studied in several species (Table II). In maize, wheat, barley, and carrot tissue culture, the enzyme is extremely sensitive to

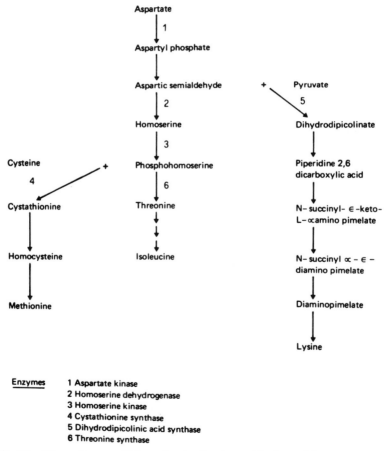

Fig. 10.   The pathways of biosynthesis of amino acids derived from aspartate.

TABLE II
Amino Acids Causing Feedback Inhibition of Aspartate Kinase in Different Organisms[a]

Plant	Amino acid inhibiting aspartate kinase	Concentration (mM)	Inhibition (%)	Reference
Zea mays	Lysine	0.1	46	Bryan et al. (1970)
	Lysine	0.8	90	Cheshire and Miflin (1975)
	Threonine	0.8	86	Aarnes and Rognes (1974)
Pisum sativum	Lysine	8	91	Aarnes (1974)
Helianthus annuus	Threonine	0.8	76	Aarnes (1974)
Sinapsis alba	Lysine	8	69	Aarnes (1974)
Raphanus sativus	Lysine + threonine	8 + 8	94	Aarnes (1974)
Cucumis sativus	Threonine	8	76	Aarnes (1974)
Chlorella pyrenoidosa	Threonine	8	92	Aarnes (1974)
Anacystis nidulans	Lysine	0.3	22	Wong and Dennis (1973)
Triticum aestivum	Lysine + threonine	0.3 + 2	52	Wong and Dennis (1973)
	Lysine	0.25	61	P. R. Shewry and B. J. Miflin (unpublished)
	Lysine + threonine	0.25 + 5	67	
Hordeum vulgare	Lysine	0.5	35	Shewry and Miflin (1977)
	Lysine	5	99	
	Lysine + methionine	0.5 + 0.6	70	
Daucus carota (tissue culture)	Lysine	2	75	Davies and Miflin (1977)
	Threonine	2	22	
	Lysine + threonine	2	97	

[a] The values quoted for the percentage inhibition are given solely as indicators of the levels of effects that have been observed. In cases where it has been studied, it has been shown that the inhibition by lysine (or other amino acids) is at least partially competitive with aspartate.

281

lysine, with 50% inhibition of activity occurring at concentrations less than 1 mM. In contrast, the enzyme from germinating peas appears to be insensitive to lysine but inhibited by threonine (Aarnes and Rognes, 1974). Because aspartate kinase leads to the production of several amino acids, investigators have looked for cooperative effects of more than one amino acid on the enzyme. There is evidence that methionine, which is not inhibitory on its own, can inhibit barley aspartate kinase in the presence of lysine (Shewry and Miflin, 1977), and some preliminary evidence for cooperative effects between threonine and lysine on the enzyme obtained from cucumber (Aarnes, 1974). Recent studies by Davies and Miflin (1977, 1978) with carrot tissue culture enzyme, have shown the presence of two aspartate kinase isoenzymes, one sensitive to threonine and one to lysine. The two isoenzymes can be partially separated by molecular sieve chromatography (Fig. 11A). Although the lysine-sensitive aspartate kinase predominates for most of the growth period of the batch cultures, the threonine-sensitive enzyme is more active in the first few days after subculture (Fig. 11B). Similar aspartate kinases have also been characterized from carrot roots, and the proportions of the two shown to change after slicing of the root (Sakano and Komamine, 1978).

It has also been shown that pea plants have both lysine- and threonine-sensitive aspartate kinase (Lea et al., 1979). Although the enzyme from the germinating seed (chiefly senescing cotyledons) is almost solely threonine-sensitive (Aarnes and Rognes, 1974; Bright et al., 1979) the developing cotyledon and young leaves contain aspartate kinase activity that is more than 50% inhibited by lysine (Lea et al., 1979; Bright et al., 1979).

The second potential control point in lysine biosynthesis occurs after the pathway has branched at the level of dihydrodipicolinic acid synthetase. The enzyme has been studied in both maize (Cheshire and Miflin, 1975) and wheat (Mazelis et al., 1977); the enzyme from the latter source is extremely sensitive to lysine inhibition.

Methionine and threonine are formed by a homoserine dehydrogenase, which is shown to be feedback inhibited by threonine in maize (Bryan, 1969), peas (DiMarco and Grego, 1975, Aarnes and Rognes, 1974), and barley (Aarnes, 1977b). However, no effect of methionine on the enzyme has so far been reported. The only effect of methionine, apart from that on aspartate kinase, mentioned above that has been noted is via S-adenosylmethionine, which Madison and Thompson (1976) have shown to activate threonine synthase 20-fold. Presumably, once the cell has sufficient methionine to satisfy its needs for S-adenosylmethionine, the threonine biosynthetic pathway is acti-

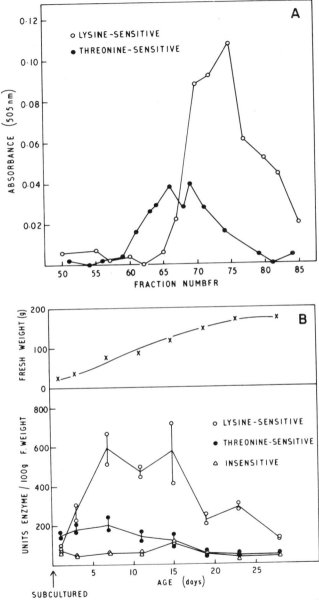

Fig. 11. (A) The separation of lysine-sensitive and threonine-sensitive aspartate kinase by molecular sieve chromatography. (B) The amounts of lysine-sensitive and threonine-sensitive aspartate kinase in carrot tissue culture cells at different times after subculture. (Redrawn from data presented in Davies and Miflin, 1978.)

vated. In contrast, cysteine, which is the sulfur donor for methionine, inhibits threonine synthase.

Tryptophan is formed from shikimic acid via the intermediate chorismic acid (Fig. 12). This intermediate is the last one common to all three amino acids of this pathway (tryptophan, phenylalanine, and tyrosine). Thus, the first enzyme unique to tryptophan biosynthesis is the enzyme anthranilate synthetase, which converts chorismate to anthranilate. This enzyme is subject to feedback inhibition by tryptophan and by the tryptophan analog 5-methyltryptophan.

Several workers have tried to select mutants or variants which lack such feedback controls by isolating individuals resistant to amino acid analogs or to inhibitory concentrations of amino acid. Widholm (1972a,b) has isolated lines of tissue cultures that are resistant to 5-methyltryptophan, which is presumed to inhibit growth by false feedback inhibition of tryptophan synthesis. He found that one of these lines from carrot tissue cultures produces up to 27 times as much tryptophan as the wild type. When the anthranilate synthase from the new line was tested for its feedback sensitivity to tryptophan, it was found that considerably more tryptophan was required to produce 50% inhibition (17 μM as compared with 3.3 μM for the normal enzyme). Widholm (1976) has also isolated an S-3-aminoethylcysteine (an analog of lysine) resistant line of tissue culture that has ten times as much free lysine, but so far its aspartate kinase has not been characterized. Although none of the original isolates were capable of regeneration Widholm (1978) has regenerated plants from a 5-methyltryptophan resistant tobacco line. Surprisingly the regenerated plant

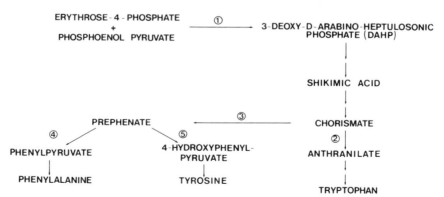

Fig. 12. The biosynthetic pathway for tryptophan, tyrosine, and phenylalanine. Enzymes: (1) deoxyarabinoheptulosonic phosphate synthase; (2) anthranilate synthase; (3) chorismate mutase; (4) prephenate dehydratase; and (5) prephenate dehydrogenase.

does not retain all the characteristics of the cell line. However tissue cultures reisolated from the regenerated plant do show the resistant phenotype of the original selection. This suggests that mutations selected in tissue culture may not always be expressed in the intact plant. However, a methionine sulfoximine-resistant line of tobacco has been regenerated and shown to have approximately four times more methionine in its leaves than the wild plant (Carlson, 1973), although this range of variation may not exceed that found within leaves of normal plants. Hibberd and Green (quoted in Green, 1978) have isolated a line of maize tissue culture resistant to lysine plus threonine and regenerated a plant from it which has not produced further progeny. However the line does contain an aspartate kinase ten times less sensitive to feedback inhibition by lysine. Bourgin (1978) has also isolated a valine resistant line of tobacco using a protoplast technique and this resistance is retained in the regenerated plant and subsequent generations. Little is known of the biochemical basis of this mutation.

An alternative approach has been to use whole mutated barley embryos for selection purposes (Bright et al., 1979a). So far using this technique one mutant line resistant to aminoethylcysteine and four lines resistant to lysine and threonine have been isolated (Bright et al., 1979b) and although insufficient biochemical characterization has been done to establish the nature of the mutations at least one line overproduces threonine and methionine. It will be extremely interesting to see if crop plants that dramatically overproduce certain amino acids can, in fact, be developed.

The controls discussed above have been based on test tube experiments of material which, in the main, has been taken at one stage of growth. There is now much evidence to suggest that this approach is a drastic oversimplification. Control mechanisms in vivo are probably affected by the position of the cells in the tissue, the age of the tissue involved, and the subcellular compartmentation of the enzymes. Thus, Oaks (1965) has made a detailed study of leucine biosynthesis on maize roots, and has shown that when leucine is delivered to the tips in the transport stream, it mixes with the endogenous pool and inhibits endogenous synthesis of leucine. Similar findings indicating an effect of position are (1) that in vivo asparagine synthesis is inhibitied by externally supplied glucose in root tips but not in mature root sections (Oaks, 1975), and (2) changes in the level of nitrate reductase inactivators (proteases) with distance from the tip (Wallace, 1975). In part, these effects of position are probably also due to cell age. Several observations show that this can be a factor in regulation. Matthews et al.

(1975) and DiCamelli and Bryan (1975) have shown that homoserine dehydrogenase extracted from light- and dark-grown maize shoots becomes less sensitive to feedback inhibition as the seedlings age. Similarly, changes occur in the relative proportions of lysine- and threonine-sensitive aspartate kinases during the batch culture of tissue culture cells (see Fig. 11b). The effect of subcellular compartmentation, particularly the movement of regulatory compounds into and out of the compartment, has already been partly discussed in terms of the effect of Mg^{2+} and H^+ concentration on GS. These levels change in the chloroplast stroma, due to ion pumps acting chiefly across the thylakoid membrane. Similar movement of end-product amino acids across the outer chloroplast membranes will undoubtedly affect the activity of the amino acid biosynthetic enzymes within the chloroplast. Further detailed discussion of these problems is given in recent papers by Stewart and Rhodes (1977) and by Miflin (1977).

VIII. THE ENERGETICS OF NITROGEN METABOLISM

After the reduction of CO_2, the reduction of nitrate is the largest energy-requiring process carried out by all crop plants. (N_2 fixation, which also requires reduction to ammonia, has a comparable energy demand.) Consequently, it has considerable importance in the overall energy economy of the plant, and may be expected to affect yield. Various attempts have been made to calculate the carbohydrate cost of producing protein, and the one most frequently quoted is that of Penning de Vries et al. (1974). They have calculated that to produce 1 g of protein will require 1.62 g of glucose if ammonia is used as the nitrogen source, but 2.42 g if nitrate is the starting material. In contrast, 1 g of starch requires only 1.21 g of glucose. Thus if these figures are a correct model of crop growth, they would predict that plants would yield much more on ammonia than on nitrate (which in general they do not), and that there would be a negative relationship between protein content and yield (which is often observed, particularly in comparisons, between different varieties of the same species of crop plant). These values have been used by others to calculate the carbohydrate cost of producing seed protein and lipid (Sinclair and de Wit, 1975) and the possible depression of yield by increasing the protein content of cereals (Bhatia and Rabson, 1976). However, as was clearly stated by Penning de Vries et al. (1974), the calculations are based on dark (heterotrophic) metabolism and thus assume that all the ATP and NAD(P)H required to power the process is derived from glucose. This is unlikely to represent the true situation for crop plants. If current ideas about the role of chloroplast in nitrogen metabolism, as was outlined in Section VI, are correct, then a considerable proportion of the energy from nitrogen metabolism can be derived directly from light-dependent electron transport. Exactly how much is difficult to calculate, but certainly all of the steps from nitrite to glutamate can be directly powered by light energy (Miflin, 1974b; Anderson and Done, 1977a,b), as can the synthesis of the large subunit of fraction 1 (Blair and Ellis, 1973).

It is also probable that "shuttles" exist to transport reducing power and ATP out of the chloroplast and into the cytoplasm, without the necessity for the full synthesis of glucose from CO_2 and its subsequent respiration (Heber, 1974). In fact, most of the proposed shuttles (but not all, e.g., the photorespiratory pathway) have no CO_2 cost at all. Thus, all of this light energy may be available to the leaf without necessarily competing with carbohydrate synthesis. The use of reducing power and ATP for nitrogen metabolism is only likely to detract from yield if yield is limited by the rate of CO_2 fixation and if CO_2 fixation is limited by light energy. These two conditions have not been clearly established, and many authorities (e.g., see Thorne, 1974; Evans, 1976) believe that plants may have surplus fixation capacity and that for most of the day CO_2 fixation is not limited by light energy but by CO_2 concentration (see Bukovac et al., 1975). It is then probable that most, if not all, of nitrate reduction and its further metabolism in leaves could occur at no energy cost to the plant.

Any exact calculation of the competing costs of nitrogen metabolism and carbohydrate synthesis are further complicated by a number of factors. For example, although in short-term experiments with algae under low light intensities (van Niel et al., 1953) the two processes may appear to compete, recent experiments, in which leaf disks have been floated on NO_3^-- or NH_4^+-containing solutions, show that CO_2 fixation is increased in the presence of nitrogen metabolism (Plaut et al., 1976). Also, in the longer term, increased nitrogen nutrition results in increased production of leaf protein (Fig. 9B) (of which about one-half is ribulosediphosphate carboxylase) and chlorophyll, thereby boosting photosynthesis and CO_2 fixation, both on a leaf area and per plant basis. On the other hand, although nitrite reduction may be powered directly by light energy, the resultant charge imbalance may divert carbohydrates from sucrose and starch into organic acids.

Perhaps the best way to calculate how much light energy can contribute to nitrogen metabolism and other processes that are normally powered by respiration in the dark is to compare the carbon balance of plants grown in the light and dark. Raven (1976) has recently assembled such data for a number of plants, and representative values for some of them are given in Table III. Normally, such data are easier to obtain and interpret from unicellular algae than from higher plants, but the values that are available all show that the ratio of respiration (i.e., CO_2 evolved) to growth (measured as C atoms deposited in cell material) is much higher in the light than in the dark. In the unicellular algae the low values for the CO_2/C ratio for growth in the light can be interpreted as showing that light can be used to provide the energy normally provided by respiration in the dark. As Raven has pointed out, part of the lower respiratory energy requirement of plants grown in the light may be a reflection of differences in their composition (i.e., a lower protein and higher carbohydrate content) than dark-grown cells and tissues. This could mean that they had a lower total energy requirement. However, this is unlikely to be the full explanation, and in certain of the quoted cases, the differences in composition between light- and dark-grown plants are likely to be small. The values for algae shown in Table III, grown in light and dark on both ammonia and nitrate, clearly illustrate the points made above regarding these two sources of nitrogen. In the dark, growth on nitrate requires more dark

TABLE III

CO₂/C Ratio for the Growth of Various Organisms in Light and Dark on Different Nutrients[a]

Organism	Energy	Carbon	Nitrogen	CO_2/C Ratio
		Sources of		
Higher plants				
Zea mays (cultured embryos)	Glucose	Glucose	NO_3^-	0.53
Zea mays (whole plant)	Light	CO_2	NO_3^-	0.29
	Light	CO_2	NO_3^-	0.31
Nicotiana tabaccum (callus culture)	Glucose	Glucose	NO_3^-	0.50
Nicotiana tabaccum (whole plant)	Light	CO_2	NO_3^-	0.20
Algae				
Chlorella sp.	Glucose	Glucose	NO_3^-	0.55–1.20
	Light	CO_2	NO_3^-	0.15–0.25
Euglena gracilis	Glucose	Glucose	NH_4^+	0.50
	Light	CO_2	NH_4^+	0.20

[a] The data are taken from Raven (1976), who calculated them from the results of several workers.

respiration than those on ammonia, whereas in the light, there is no difference between the two nitrogen sources.

In view of the above discussion, what may be the relationship between seed protein content and yield, which are often quoted as being negatively correlated? Part of the answer is that intrinsically this is a difficult relationship to analyze, since protein content is a percentage value based on two variables—the nitrogen per grain and the weight of individual grains. Thus, because nonnitrogen compounds make the greatest contribution to grain weight, any decrease in them (independent of nitrogen metabolism) will simultaneously increase nitrogen content and decrease yield. It is, therefore, necessary to exclude from the discussion low-yielding situations, in which carbohydrate malfunction may be occurring, and to examine the relationship at high yields.

The relevant question is "Is it possible to increase protein content, particularly in cereals, without decreasing the total yield per acre, or is there a necessary yield penalty to be paid for increased protein?" This question may be posed in two contexts: (1) by the agronomist applying nitrogen fertilizer, and (2) by the plant breeder interested in selecting improved genotypes.

If there is a necessary cause-and-effect relationship between protein content and yield, then in both instances they should be negatively correlated. However, this is not so. In the first instance, it is almost universally found that cereals respond to nitrogen fertilizer by increasing in yield up to some maximum value; at the same time, the protein content of the seed also tends to increase (Cooke, 1975a). The relationship between yield and percent protein for some experiments at Rothamsted is plotted in Fig. 13, from which it can be seen that the slope is positive, except perhaps at very high fertilizer applications, at which lodging may have occurred.

In the second instance, the results are usually based on plant breeding studies in which varieties have been selected for yield. They tend to produce the type of graph shown in Fig. 14A, in which there is a small negative relationship between the percentage nitrogen in the grain and grain yield (Pushman and Bingham, 1976). However, in many cases these studies are carried out at one fixed nitrogen fertilizer level (often unstated in the papers) thus one explanation of these results is that the nitrogen content of the grain is limited by the amount of available soil nitrogen. It is often not realized how much extra nitrogen is required to raise protein content. Bhatia and Rabson (1976) have calculated that to increase rice protein content from 8 to 10% at constant yield would require a 22% increase in the amount of nitrogen fertilizer applied. In

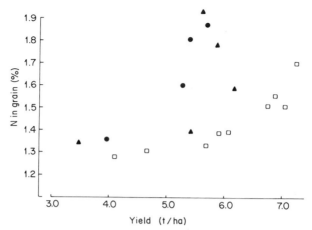

Fig. 13. The relationship of percentage of N in grain and yield as affected by different nitrogen fertilizer treatments. The points are derived from different experiments at Rothamsted, reported by Benzian (1975). Filled circle: continuous winter wheat; filled triangle: wheat after beans grown on Broadbalk, 1969–1972; open square: winter wheat grown after three types of leys at Rothamsted, 1962.

the absence of sufficient fertilizer it might be expected that all the varieties would produce the same amount of nitrogen per unit area (i.e., conditions are such that there is no possibility of any genetic effect on nitrogen metabolism being observed), and the negative correlation is produced by the enhanced ability of some varieties to accumulate carbohydrate. This is clearly the case in the quoted example, since it can be seen from Fig. 14B that protein content is increased by increasing

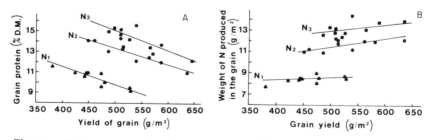

Fig. 14. (A) Regression of grain protein on yield for ten varieties of winter wheat grown at three levels of fertilizer. Filled triangle: different varieties given 38 kg N/ha; filled circle: same varieties given 98 and 34 kg N/ha as split dressing; filled square: same varieties given 98 and 34 kg N/ha as a split dressing, plus 45 kg N/ha as urea spray. (B) Regression of weight of nitrogen produced in the grain on yield of grain for the same experiment as (A). (Reproduced with permission from Pushman and Bingham, 1976.)

nitrogen application, and that protein production per hectare is unaffected by genotype.

The true relationship between protein content and yield, as affected by genotype, can only be examined where it can be clearly shown that both are a function of genotype and not of environment. Even if such a correlation were to be established on the basis of existing varieties, which have chiefly been bred for yield, it is by no means certain that such a correlation could not be broken when selection is made for both yield and protein content. In fact, there are now a number of examples in which breeders have appeared to successfully select lines that satisfy both criteria (e.g., see review by Rhodes and Jenkins, 1977).

IX. CONCLUSIONS

The practical value of understanding the biochemistry of nitrogen metabolism in crop plants is to identify the processes that limit total yield and protein production per acre, so that they may be attacked by the plant breeder and/or the agronomist. On the basis of the material reviewed here and elsewhere in the literature, I would like to stress the following points:

1. The ability of plants to assimilate ammonia via the highly efficient GS/GOGAT system removes a potential block (due to the poor characteristics of GDH) on the flow of nitrogen into proteins. Thus, the steps after nitrate reduction up to and including protein synthesis are unlikely to be limiting.

2. Studies have shown that correlation exists between nitrate reductase and final protein content and yield. Of all the enzymes involved in the process, this would appear to be the most important one in selection procedures. Since the level of this enzyme and the amount of protein produced by the plant are dependent on the amount of nitrate entering the plant, those steps involved in the removal of nitrate from the soil and the transport of it to the site of metabolism are of major importance.

3. Many of the key processes in nitrogen metabolism can take place at the expense of light energy in the chloroplast. For this and other reasons, the energy demand on the plant for carrying out nitrogen metabolism may easily be overestimated, and there is no good evidence that there is a necessary yield penalty to be paid for increased nitrogen metabolism.

4. The quality of plant products, particularly seed proteins, is lim-

ited by the levels of certain amino acids. Controls on the production of these amino acids are understood (at least in part), but not the controls on their incorporation into storage proteins. Ways now exist to select plants that have relaxed controls on amino acid biosynthesis, and in the future it should be possible to test whether or not such plants have an improved amino acid composition in the seed.

REFERENCES

Aarnes, H. (1974). *Physiol. Plant.* **32**, 400–402.

Aarnes, H. (1976). *Plant Sci. Lett.* **7**, 187–191.

Aarnes, H., and Rognes, S. E. (1974). *Phytochemistry* **13**, 2717–2724.

Anderson, J. W., and Done, J. (1977a). *Plant Physiol.* **60**, 354–359.

Anderson, J. W., and Done, J. (1977b). *Plant Physiol.* **60**, 504–508.

Arkcoll, D. B., and Festenstein, G. N. (1971). *J. Sci. Food Agric.* **32**, 49–56.

Aslam, M., and Oaks, A. (1975). *Plant Physiol.* **56**, 634–639.

Aslam, M., Oaks, A., and Huffaker, R. C. (1976). *Plant Physiol.* **58**, 588–591.

Atkins, C. A., Pate, J. S., and Sharkey, P. J. (1975). *Plant Physiol.* **56**, 807–812.

Becking, J. H. (1956). *Acta Bot. Neerl.* **5**, 1–79.

Beevers, L., and Hageman, R. H. (1969). *Annu. Rev. Plant Physiol.* **20**, 495–522.

Benzian, B. (1975). *Annu. Rep., Rothamsted Exp. St.* Part I, pp. 80–83.

Bhatia, C. R., and Rabson, R. (1976). *Science* **194**, 1418–1421.

Blair, G. I., and Ellis, R. J. (1973). *Biochim. Biophys. Acta* **319**, 222–234.

Bourgin, J-P. (1978). *Mol. Gen. Genet.* **161**, 225–230.

Bourne, W. F., and Miflin, B. J. (1973). *Planta* **111**, 47–56.

Bright, S. W. J., Norbury, P. B., and Miflin, B. J. (1979a). *Theor. Appl. Genet.* **55**, 1–4.

Bright, S. W. J., Lea, P. J., and Miflin, B. J. (1979b). In "Biology of Sulphur," CIBA Foundation Symp., April 1979. Elsevier, Amsterdam.

Brunetti, N., and Hageman, R. H. (1976). *Plant Physiol.* **58**, 583–587.

Bryan, J. K. (1969). *Biochim. Biophys. Acta* **171**, 205–216.

Bryan, J. K. (1976). In "Plant Biochemistry" (J. Bonner and J. E. Varner, eds), 3rd ed., pp. 525–560. Academic Press, New York.

Bryan, J. K., Lissik, E. A., and Matthews, B. F. (1977). *Plant Physiol.* **59**, 673–679.

Bryan, P. A., Cawley, R. D., Brunner, C. E., and Bryan, J. K. (1970). *Biochem. Biophys. Res. Commun.* **41**, 1211–1217.

Buchanan, B. B., Schurmann, P., and Kalberer, P. P. (1971). *J. Biol. Chem.* **246**, 5952–5959.

Bukovac, M. J., Moss, D. N. and Zelitch, I. (1975). In "Crop Productivity—Research Imperatives" (A. W. A. Brown et al., eds.), pp. 177–200. MSU-Kettering Found., Michigan.

Butz, R. G., and Jackson, W. A. (1977). *Phytochemistry* **16**, 409–418.

Carlson, P. S. (1973). *Science* **180**, 1366–1368.

Cheshire, R. M., and Miflin, B. J. (1975). *Phytochemistry* **14**, 695–698.

Chroboczek-Kelker, H., and Filner, P. (1971). *Biochim. Biophys. Acta* **252**, 69–82.

Cooke, G. W. (1975a). In Bread: Social, Nutritional and Agricultural Aspects of Wheat and Bread" (A. Spicer, ed.), Appl. Sci., London.

Cooke, G. W. (1975b). *In* "Fertilizer Use and Protein Production," I.P.I. Conf., pp. 29–52. Potash Inst., Berne, Switzerland.

Davies, D. D., and Teixeira, A. R. N. (1975). *Phytochemistry* **14**, 647–650.

Davies, H. M., and Miflin, B. J. (1977). *Plant Sci. Lett.* **9**, 323–332.

Davies, H. M., and Miflin, B. J. (1978). *Plant Physiol.* **62**, 536–541.

DiCamelli, C. A., and Bryan, J. K. (1975). *Plant Physiol.* **55**, 999–1005.

DiMarco, G., and Grego, S. (1975). *Phytochemistry* **14**, 943–947.

Dougall, D. K. (1974). *Biochem. Biophys. Res. Commun.* **58**, 639–646.

Eppley, R. W., Rogers, J. N., and McCarthy, J. J. (1969). *Limnol. Oceanog.* **14**, 912–920.

Epstein, E. (1976). *In* "Transport in Plants" (A. Pirson and M. H.Zimmermann, eds.), Vol. II, Part B. Springer-Verlag, Berlin and New York.

Evans, L. T. (1976). *In* "Photosynthesis and Productivity in Different Environments" IBP (J. P. Cooper, ed.), pp. 501–507. Cambridge Univ. Press, London and New York.

Ferguson, A. R. (1969). *Planta* **88**, 353–363.

Filner, P. (1966). *Biochim. Biophys. Acta* **118**, 299–310.

Folkes, B. F., and Sims, A. P. (1974). *J. Gen. Microbiol.* **82**, 77–95.

Fowden, L. (1976). *In* "Perspectives in Experimental Biology" (N. Sunderland, ed.), Vol. 2, pp. 263–272. Pergamon, Oxford.

Giovanelli, J., Mudd, S. H., and Datko, A. H. (1974). *Plant Physiol.* **54**, 725–736.

Givan, C. V., and Harwood, J. L. (1976). *Biol. Rev.* **51**, 365–406.

Goodman, P. J. (1974). *Proc. Int. Grass. Congr., 12th, 1974* pp. 178–182.

Green, C. E. (1978). *In* "Frontiers of Plant Tissue Culture 1978" T. A. Thorpe, ed.), pp. 411–418. IAPTC, Calgary.

Grosse, W. (1976).*Z. Pflanzenphysiol.* **80**, 463–468.

Hageman, R. H., Lambert, R. J., Loussaert, D., Dalling, M., and Klepper, L. A. (1976). *In* "Genetic Improvement of Seed Proteins," Proc. Int. Workshop, pp. 103–131. Natl. Res. Counc., Washington, D.C.

Hardy, R. W. F., Filner, P., and Hageman, R. H. (1975). *In* "Crop Productivity—Research Imperatives" (A.W.A. Brown *et al.*, eds.), pp. 133–176. MSU-Kettering Found., Michigan.

Heber, U. (1974). *Annu. Rev. Plant Physiol.* **25**, 393–421.

Hewitt, E. J. (1975). *Annu. Rev. Plant Physiol.* **26**, 73–100.

Hucklesby, D. P., Dalling, M. J., and Hageman, R. H. (1972). *Planta* **104**, 220–233.

Huffaker, R. C., and Petersen, L. W. 1974). *Annu. Rev. Plant Physiol.* **25**, 363–392.

Huffaker, R. C., and Rains, D. W. (1978). *In* "Nitrogen in the Environment" (D. R. Nielsen and J. G. Macdonald, eds.), Vol. 2, pp. 1–43. Academic Press, New York.

Ingle, J., Joy, K. W., and Hageman, R. H. (1966). *Biochem. J.* **100**, 577–588.

Ivanko, S. and Ingversen, J. (1971). *Physiol. Plant* **24**, 355–362.

Jackson, W. A., Fletcher, D., and Hageman, R. H. (1973). *Plant Physiol.* **51**, 120–127.

Johnson, C. B., Whittington, W. J., and Blackwood, G. C. (1976). *Nature (London)* **262**, 133–134.

Jones, R. W., and Sheard, R. W. (1973). *Can. J. Bot.* **51**, 27–35.

Kannangara, C. G., and Woolhouse, H. W. (1967). *New Phytol.* **66**, 554–554.

Kirkby, E. A. (1974). *In* "Plant Analysis and Fertilizer Problems" (J. Wehrmann, ed.), p. 557–568. Publ. Ger. Soc. Plant Nutr., Hanover.

Kirkman. M. A. and Miflin, B. J. (1977). *In* "Progress Reports on Research and Development 1975–1976," pp. 47–51. Home-Grown Cereals Authority, London.

Kirkman, M. A., and Miflin B. J. (1979). *J. Sci. Food Agric.* (in press).

Knypl, J. S. (1974). *R. Soc. N. Z., Bull.* **12**, 71.

Knypl, J. S., and Ferguson, A. R. (1975). *Z. Pflanzenphysiol.* **74**, 434–438.

Lea, P. J., and Fowden, L. (1975). *Biochem. Physiol. Pflanz.* **168**, 3–14.
Lea, P. J., and Miflin, B. J. (1974). *Nature (London)* **251**, 614–616.
Lea, P. J., and Miflin, B. J. (1975a). *Biochem. Soc. Trans.* **3**, 381–384.
Lea, P. J., and Miflin, B. J. (1975b). *Biochem. Biophys. Res. Commun.* **64**, 856–862.
Lea, P. J., and Miflin, B. J. (1979). *In* "Photosynthesis" (M. Gibbs and E. Latzko, eds.), Vol. II, pp. 445–456. Springer-Verlag, Berlin and New York.
Lea, P. J., Fowden, L., and Miflin, B. J. (1976). *Plant Physiol.* **57**, Suppl., 213.
Lea, P. J., Fowden, L., and Miflin, B. J. (1977). *Phytochemistry* **17**, 217–222.
Lea, P. J., Mills, W. R., and Miflin, B. J. (1979). *FEBS Lett.* **98**, 165–168.
Leonard, R. T., and Hanson, J. B. (1972). *Plant Physiol.* **49**, 430–435.
Lewis, O. A. M. (1975). *J. Exp. Bot.* **23**, 440–449.
Lewis, O. A. M., and Pate, J. S. (1973). *J. Exp. Bot.* **24**, 596–606.
Lips, S. H., and Avissar, Y. (1972). *Eur. J. Biochem.* **29**, 20–24.
Lloyd, N. D. H., and Joy, K. W., (1978). *Biochem. Biophys. Res. Commun.* **86**, 181–192.
Lorimer. G. H., Gewitz, H. S., Volker, W., Solomonson, L. P., and Vennesland, B. (1974). *J. Biol. Chem.* **249**, 6074–6079.
Losada, M. (1976). *J. Mol. Catal.* **1**, 245–264.
Lycklama, J. C. (1963). *Acta Bot. Neerl.* **12**, 361–423.
Madison, J. T., and Thompson, J. F. (1976). *Biochem. Biophys. Res. Commun.* **71**, 684–691.
Magalhaes, A. C., Neyra, C. A., and Hageman, R. H. (1974). *Plant Physiol.* **53**, 411–415.
Matthews, B. F., Gurman, A. W., and Bryan, J. K. (1975). *Plant Physiol.* **55**, 991–998.
Mazelis, M., Whatley, F. R., and Whatley, J. (1977). *FEBS Lett.* **84**, 236–240.
Miflin, B. J. (1973). *In* "Biosynthesis and Its Control in Plants" (B. V. Milborrow, ed.), pp. 49–68. Academic Press, New York.
Miflin, B. J. (1974a). *Plant Physiol.* **54**, 550–555.
Miflin, B. J. (1974b). *Planta* **116**, 187–196.
Miflin, B. J. (1975). *In* "Fertilizer Use and Protein Production," pp. 53–74. Int. Potash Inst., Berne, Switzerland.
Miflin, B. J. (1976). *In* "Genetic Improvement of Seed Protein," Proc. Workshop, pp. 135–158. Natl. Res. Counc. Washington, D.C.
Miflin, B.J. (1977). *In* "Regulation of Enzyme Synthesis and Activity in Higher Plants" (H. Smith, ed.), pp. 23–40. Academic Press, New York.
Miflin, B. J. (1979). *In* "Carbohydrate and Protein Synthesis" (B. J. Miflin and M. Zoschke, eds.), pp. 13–31. Commission of the European Community, Luxembourg.
Miflin, B. J., and Lea, P. J. (1975). *Biochem. J.* **149**, 403–409.
Miflin, B. J., and Lea, P. J. (1976a). *Phytochemistry* **15**, 873–885.
Miflin, B. J., and Lea, P. J. (1976b). *Trends Biochem. Sci.* **1**, 103–106.
Miflin, B. J., and Lea, P. J. (1977). *Annu. Rev. Plant Physiol.* **28**, 299–329.
Mills, W. R., and Wilson, K. G. (1978). *FEBS Lett.* **92**, 129–132.
Minotti, R. L., Williams, D. C., and Jackson, W. A. (1969). *Planta* **86**, 267–271.
Mitchell, C. A., and Stocking, C. R. (1975). *Plant Physiol.* **55**, 59–63.
Oaks, A. (1965). *Plant Physiol.* **40**, 149–155.
Oaks, A. (1975). *Biochem. Physiol. Pflanz.* **168**, 371–374.
Orebamjo, T. O., and Stewart, G. R. (1975a). *Planta* **122**, 27–36.
Orebamjo, T. O., and Stewart, G. R. (1975b). *Planta* **122**, 37–44.
Parkash, V. (1972). *Planta* **102**, 372–373.
Pate, J. S. (1973). *Soil Biol. & Biochem.* **5**, 109–119.
Pate, J. S., Gunning, B.E.S., and Briarty, L. G. (1969). *Planta* **85**, 11–34.

Penning de Vries, F. W. T., Brunsting, A. H. M., and van Laar, H. H. (1974). *J. Theor. Biol.* **45**, 339–377.
Plaut, Z., Platt, S., and Bassham, J. A. (1976). *Plant Physiol.* **57**, Suppl., 58.
Pushman, F. M., and Bingham, J. (1976). *J. Agric. Sci.* **87**, 281–292.
Radin, J. W. (1975). *Plant Physiol.* **55**, 178–182.
Rao, K. P., and Rains, D. W. (1976). *Plant Physiol.* **57**, 57–58.
Rathnam, C. K. M., and Edwards, G. F. (1976). *Plant Physiol.* **57**, 881–885.
Raven, J. A. (1976). *Ann. Bot. (London)* [N.S.] **40**, 587–602.
Raven, J. A., and Smith, F. A. (1976). *New Phytol.* **76**, 415–431.
Rhodes, A. P., and Jenkins, G. (1977). *In* "Plant Proteins" (G. Norton, ed.), pp. 207–226. Butterworth, London.
Rhodes, D., Rendon, G. A., and Stewart, G. R. (1975). *Planta* **129**, 203–210.
Sakano, K., and Komamine, A. (1978). *Plant Physiol.* **61**, 115–118.
Schmidt, A., and Trebst, A. (1969). *Biochim. Biophys. Acta* **180**, 529–535.
Schrader, L. E., and Hageman, R. H. (1967). *Plant Physiol.* **42**, 1750–1756.
Schurmann, P., and Buchanan, B. B. (1975). *Biochim. Biophys. Acta* **376**, 189–192.
Scott, D. B., Robertson, J., and Farnden, K. J. F. (1976). *Nature (London)* **262**, 703–705.
Shah, S. P. J., and Cossins, E. A. (1970). *Phytochemistry* **9**, 1545–1551.
Shen, T. C. (1972). *Plant Physiol.* **49**, 546–549.
Shewry, P. R., and Miflin, B. J. (1977). *Plant Physiol.* **59**, 69–73.
Sinclair, T. R., and de Wit, C. T. (1975). *Science* **189**, 565–567.
Skokut, T. A., Wolk, C. P., Thomas, J., Meeks, J. C., and Shaffer, P. W. (1978). *Plant Physiol.* **62**, 299–304.
Smith, F. W., and Thomspon, J. F. (1971). *Plant Physiol.* **48**, 219–223.
Sodek, L., Lea, P. J., and Miflin, B. J. (1978). *Plant Physiol.* **61**, Suppl., 68.
Solomonson, L. P., and Spehar, A. M. (1977). *Nature (London)* **265**, 373–375.
Stewart, G. R. (1972). *Plant Physiol.* **50**, 679–681.
Stewart, G. R., and Rhodes, D. (1976). *FEBS Lett.* **46**, 340–342.
Stewart, G. R., and Rhodes, D. (1977). *In* "Regulation of Enzyme Synthesis and Activity in Higher Plants" (H. Smith, ed.), pp. 1–22. Academic Press, New York.
Talibudeen, O., Page, M. B., and Ramachandran Nair, P. K. (1976). *J. Sci. Food Agric.* **27**, 1179–1189.
Tempest, D. W., Meers, J. L., and Brown, C. M. (1970). *Biochem. J.* **117**, 405–407.
Tempest, D. W., Meers, J. L., and Brown, C. M. (1973). *In* "The Enzymes of Glutamine Metabolism" (S. Prusiner and E. R. Stadtman, eds.), pp. 167–182. Academic Press, New York.
Thacker, A., and Syrett, P. J. (1972). *New Phytol.* **71**, 435–441.
Thorne, G. N. (1974). *Annu. Rep., Rothamsted Exp. St. for (1973)* Part II, pp. 5–21.
Travis, R. L., Jordan, W. R., and Huffaker, R. C. (1969). *Plant Physiol.* **44**, 1150–1156.
van den Honert, T. H., and Hooymans, J. J. M. (1955). *Acta Bot. Neerl.* **4**, 376–384.
van der Meulen, P. Y. F. and Bassham, J. A. (1959). *J. Am. Chem. Soc.* **81**, 2233–2239.
van Niel, C. B., Allen, M. B., and Wright, B. E. (1953). *Biochim. Biophys. Acta* **12**, 67–74.
Walker, D. A. (1973). *New Phytol.* **72**, 209–235.
Wallace, W. (1975). *Plant Physiol.* **55**, 774–777.
Wallace, W. (1977). *In* "Regulation of Enzyme Synthesis and Activity in Higher Plants" (H. Smith, ed.), pp. 177–197. Academic Press, New York.
Wallace, W., and Pate, J. S. (1965). *Ann. Bot. (London)* [N.S.] **29**, 655–671.
Wallace, W., and Pate, J. S. (1967). *Ann. Bot. (London)* [N.S.] **31**, 213–228.
Wallsgrove, R. M., Harel, E., Lea, P. J., and Miflin, B. J. (1977). *J. Exp. Bot.* **28**, 588–596.

Wallsgrove, R. M., Lea, P. J., and Miflin B. J. (1979). *Plant Physiol* **63**, 232–236.

Widholm, J. M. (1972a). *Biochim. Biophys. Acta* **261**, 52–58.

Widholm, J. M. (1972b). *Biochim Biophys. Acta* **279**, 48–57.

Widholm, J. M. (1976). *Can. J. Bot.* **54**, 1523–1529.

Widholm, J. M. (1978). *In* "Frontiers of Plant Tissue Culture 1978" (T. A. Thorpe, ed.), p. 491. IAPTC, Calgary.

Wolk, C. P., Thomas, J., Shaffer, P. W., Austin, S. M., and Galonsky, A. (1976). *J. Biol. Chem.* **251**, 5027–5034.

Wong, K. F., and Dennis, D. T. (1973). *Plant Physiol.* **51**, 322–325.

Yoneyama, T., and Kumazawa, K. (1974). *Plant Cell Physiol.* **15**, 574–578.

Yoneyama, T., and Fukuzawa, K. (1975). *Plant Cell Physiol.* **16**, 21–26.

Zielke, H. R., and Filner, P. (1971). *J. Biol. Chem.* **246**, 1772–1779.

Chapter 8

Translocation and Source–Sink Relationships

Ian F. Wardlaw

I. INTRODUCTION

A key question in crop physiology is whether harvestable yield can be increased through more efficient use of photosynthate already available to the plant, or whether more can be gained by improving the net

297

The Biology of Crop Productivity
Copyright © 1980 by Academic Press, Inc.

photosynthetic input of the plant to fulfill an already established, but unsatisfied, demand. In several crops, there is in fact evidence to suggest that the improvement in yield with the change from ancient to modern cultivars, or species, has been associated with an improved "harvest index," rather than an increase in total biomass (Evans and Dunstone, 1970; Donald and Hamblin, 1976). However, there is no obvious reason why considerable advances should not be achieved through improved photosynthetic rates at the leaf or canopy level (cf. Evans and Wardlaw, 1976), particularly in those crops where improvement has already occurred in the direction of an increased harvest index. However, as Gifford (1974) has pointed out, a superior photosynthetic rate at the leaf level is not necessarily reflected in dry matter production at the crop level.

Clearly, growth and photosynthesis are two processes that cannot be examined in isolation; their operation is interdependent throughout the life of a plant. With this in mind, an attempt has been made in this chapter to synthesize our knowledge of the formation, or uptake, and transport of metabolites and nutrients within and between sources and sinks, and to examine how these factors might regulate the partitioning of dry matter in plants.

II. LEAVES AS COLLECTING AND DISTRIBUTING AGENTS OF ASSIMILATES AND NUTRIENTS

There are inherent differences in the rate of CO_2 fixation per unit leaf area between species (see Evans and Wardlaw, 1976). However, although differences within a species are not always so evident, these are often of more concern to the plant breeder. Wilson and Cooper (1969) concluded that varietal differences in the photosynthetic rate of *Lolium perenne* were inversely related to mesophyll cell size of the leaf, while Khan and Tsunoda (1971) found that high photosynthetic rates in wheat were associated with a compact panicoidlike leaf structure. The latter authors also noted an inverse relation between net photosynthesis and the spacing of the vascular bundles. This sort of information led Hanson and Rasmusson (1975) to examine interveinal distances of 210 cultivars of barley and to establish that there are varietal differences in this characteristic.

The subtropical C_4 species, such as maize and sugar cane, and the more temperate C_3 species, such as wheat and sugar beet, present two contrasting groups of plants that are of particular interest in relation to variations in photosynthetic rates. The C_4 species will, for example, show an increase in photosynthesis up to full sunlight, with much higher maximum rates than those obtained for C_3 species, and photosynthesis in the latter will be saturated at about one-third of full sunlight (Black, 1973).

There are distinctive anatomical, as well as biochemical, differences between the leaves of C_3 and C_4 species (Laetsch, 1974). It has been postulated that the higher photosynthetic rates, which are also accompanied by high translocation rates, must necessarily be associated with a more efficient vascular network for the collection of sugars. Some of these differences can be seen in a comparison between the leaves of two grasses, darnel (*Lolium temulentum*), a C_3 species, and Sudan grass (*Sorghum sudanense*), a C_4 species, which are compared in Fig. 1. The distance between the veins is much smaller in the thinner Sudan grass leaf than in darnel, and the bundle sheath arrangement of Sudan grass is such that photosynthate will only have to traverse a few cells to move from the site of fixation to the phloem. In a recent survey, Crookston and Moss (1974) found that photosynthetic carbon was required, on the average, to move through four to seven mesophyll cells to reach the veins in C_3 grasses, but only one mesophyll cell in C_4 grasses. The rate of photosynthate export from the leaf of darnel (24 mg dry wt. dm^{-2}

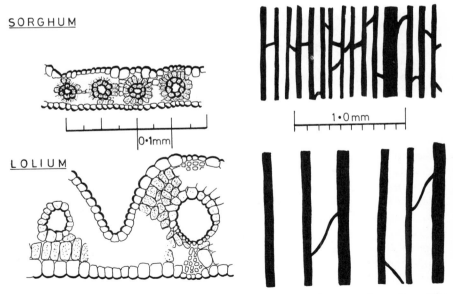

SORGHUM

0·1mm

1·0mm

LOLIUM

Fig. 1. The vascular arrangement in transverse section and pattern of venation of the leaves of *Sorghum sudanense* (a C_4 grass) and *Lolium temulentum* (a C_3 grass).

hr^{-1}) was shown (Wardlaw, 1976a) to be less than that found in Sudan grass (32 mg dry wt. dm^{-2} hr^{-1}). These rates are probably representative of other C_3 and C_4 species under moderate light conditions (cf. Terry and Mortimer, 1972; Sovonick et al., 1974; Lush and Evans, 1974). However, when Lush and Evans (1974) examined the vascular tissue at the base of the blade of several grasses, they found that the phloem cross section per unit area of the blade was very similar for both the C_3 and C_4 species. Thus the specific mass transfer of dry matter through the phloem of the C_4 species was higher than that through the phloem of the C_3 species examined. Work with labeled carbon (^{14}C and ^{11}C) suggests that this difference in specific mass transfer is probably associated with a difference in the speed of movement of photosynthate through the phloem (Lush and Evans, 1974; Troughton, 1975; Wardlaw and Marshall, 1976), and therefore may not necessarily involve large concentration differences.

A. Vein Loading

The pathway for movement of photosynthetic metabolites from the chloroplast to the sieve element is complex (Fig. 2), and detailed reviews of vein loading in C_3 species have recently been presented by Geiger (1975a,b, 1976a). One of the features of this short-distance transfer within a leaf is the continuous exchange of photosynthate between a small, mobile pool of sucrose in the cytoplasm and a larger, stationary pool, presmuably in the vacuoles (Kursanov and Brovchenko, 1970; Outlaw et al., 1975; Ho, 1976), and also with starch in the chloroplasts (Porter and Bird, 1962). A second feature is that the mobile carbohydrate (generally sucrose) is moved against a concentration gradient from the mesophyll cells to the sieve elements, an energy-requiring step (Geiger, 1976a). Cataldo (1974) found that isolated mesophyll cells from tobacco exhibited K_m values of 30 mM for sucrose uptake, but values of only 16 mM for the minor veins, whereas glucose showed the reverse.

Servaites and Geiger (1974) and Ho (1976) have noted a proportional relation between CO_2 fixation and export of dry matter from a leaf, which suggests a relation between substrate level and export. However, although Habeshaw (1969) found a similar relationship, this did not appear to be associated with the overall concentration of sucrose in sugar beet leaves. The rates of dry matter export are lower in the dark than in the light, but in the dark (Terry and Mortimer, 1972) there does appear to be a good relation between export and leaf sugar concentration, an association also observed by Pakianathan (1968). The lower

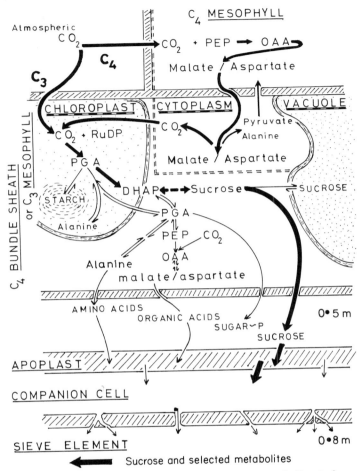

Fig. 2. The formation and movement of photosynthetic metabolites in leaves. This is a composite diagram, incorporating the general features and barriers to movement from the sites of fixation to the sieve elements of both C_3 and C_4 species.

rate in the dark suggests that the "transport pool" is more directly maintained by current photosynthate than by storage corbohydrate, and this would result in a change in the relation between total leaf sucrose and carbohydrate export in the light and dark.

It has been suggested by Geiger (1976a), following an earlier proposal of Kursanov and Brovchenko (1970), that sucrose enters the free space of the leaf prior to uptake into the vascular tissue. This pathway would appear to have an advantage over the direct transfer of sugars through

plasmodesmatal connections, if large differences in osmotic potential
and turgor are to be maintained between these tissues. However, there
is still inadequate information about the control of solute movement
through plasmodesmata (see Gunning and Robards, 1976). Schneider
(1965) has pointed out that within 24 hr of mechanical inoculation of a
leaf with virus, it may spread from one epidermis to the other, yet it
takes much longer to move into the vascular system. There is evidence
to suggest that virus particles spread via the plasmodesmata, and part
of the delay observed before the virus becomes systemic may be related
to the poor plasmodesmatal connections between the conducting elements and the adjacent tissue. This could also explain why enforced
penetration of tobacco mosaic virus by jet injection into tissue close to
the vascular system of *Nicotiana glutinosa*, does not improve the rate at
which this virus becomes systemic (Helms and Wardlaw, 1976).

An important feature of vein loading is, of course, the selective
transport of leaf metabolites, a selection that may occur at several
points along the transfer pathway, starting with the chloroplast membrane (Heber, 1974). Discrimination does appear to occur in the uptake
of metabolites at the point of phloem loading. Thus Brovchenko (1963)
observed differential uptake of amino acids by isolated vascular traces
of stems and leaves, and Chopowick and Forward (1974) found that
alanine applied to the surface of a sunflower leaf, and presumably the
free space in contact with the phloem, was translocated not as alanine
but as sucrose. Although uptake into the phloem is also a likely point
for discrimination between glucose and sucrose (Cataldo, 1974), it is
apparently not a barrier for discrimination between sucrose and stachyose (Hendrix, 1973).

Nutrients also show considerable differences in transport out of a leaf
through the phloem, with, for example, the well-documented contrast
between mobility of phosphorus and calcium, the latter being almost
totally excluded (Ziegler, 1975). However, little work has been undertaken on the mechanics of uptake and recycling of nutrients entering
the leaf. Thus it is unclear whether nutrients are taken up through the
plasmalema of the cells adjacent to the xylem and then transported
symplastically from cell to cell to the sites of utilization, or storage, or
whether this transport occurs largely in the cell wall free space. Also, it
has yet to be established whether nutrients that are recycled from the
leaf move directly from the xylem to the phloem, or first move into the
mesophyll and then back to the phloem for export. In their work on the
nature of the mestome sheath and plasmodesmatal connections to the
enclosed vascular system, Kuo *et al.* (1974) proposed that there were
two distinct patterns of flow into the phloem and out from the xylem of

the veins of the wheat leaf. Mellor and Tregunna (1971) concluded that nitrate reduction occurred mainly in the mesophyll of sorghum, but that ammonium incorporation into organic compounds by glutamate dehydrogenase was localized in bundle sheath cells. Also sharkey and Pate (1975) have shown that in lupin certain amino acids, such as valine and asparagine are readily transferred from the xylem to the phloem, while others such as glycine and aspartic acid show very little exchange and consequently very little movement into growing organs such as fruits.

Vein loading in C_4 species provides an interesting contrast to the pathway suggested for C_3 species (see Fig. 2). The organic acids (malate and aspartate) formed in the mesophyll cells must be transferred through the plasmodesmatal connections to the bundle sheath cells (Osmond and Smith, 1976). In the bundle sheath cells the organic acids are decarboxylated and the CO_2 reassimilated through the normal C_3 pathway. Lush and Evans (1974) have suggested that the concentration of sucrose in the bundle sheath may be high enough to provide a concentration gradient to the phloem, without the necessity for a further step up in concentration similar to that observed in C_3 species. However, the plasmodesmatal connections between the mesophyll and bundle sheath cells, which allow the ready passage of organic acids, make it difficult ot envisage how a sucrose concentration gradient could be maintained between these cells.

There is little information available at present on whether the respective barriers to movement (which also act as safeguards for the system) significantly restrict the outflow of metabolites, or whether leaf venation is adequate to transfer the available photosynthate out of the blade. Even this basic question is complicated by the possibility that the most efficient supply system is one that regulates the outflow of assimilates during the day, so that some material is available for growth during darkness, when temperature and plant water relations may be more suitable. Many C_3 species are known to export carbon at a rate of about 3 to 5 mg. dm^{-2} (leaf surface) hr^{-1} (Terry and Mortimer, 1972; Sovonick et al., 1974; Wardlaw, 1972). Gunning et al. (1974) calculated a sucrose vein loading flux for legumes at about 14 pmole sec^{-1} cm^{-2} of plasma membrane, which is close to the general range for other plant cells. A similar calculation for sugar beet (Sovonick et al., 1974), with an export rate of 2.5 mg C dm^{-2} hr^{-1}, indicated a vein loading flux across the plasma membrane of 53 pmole sec^{-1} cm^{-2}. At present there are inadequate data available to draw a conclusion on the limits to vein loading, or the carrying capacity of the sieve elements servicing a leaf. However it does appear, from some observations of Pakianathan (1968)

showing a parallel increase in phloem area with an increase in leaf size
of both sunflower and cotton, that the transport system adjusts to some
degree in relation to the demands likely to be placed on it.

Only a brief mention will be made here of the influence of environmental factors on the movement of metabolites through the leaf. Low
temperature has been shown to slow the rate of export of ^{14}C photosynthate from the leaves of several species (Hofstra and Nelson, 1969;
Webb, 1970; Wardlaw, 1974a), as well as being associated with reduced
starch mobilization (Buttrose and Hale, 1971; Garrard and West, 1972).
In addition to a reduction in photosynthetic rates and decreased starch
levels (Hsiao, 1973), water stress would also appear to slow down the
rate of ^{14}C photosynthate export from a leaf (Wardlaw, 1967,1969).

B. Source–Sink Interactions

Several workers have suggested that high rates of translocation are an
important factor in maintaining high photosynthetic rates in many
plants, particularly the subtropical C_4 species (Hofstra and Nelson,
1969; Liu et al., 1973; Lush and Evans, 1974; Rathnam and Das, 1975;
Stephenson et al., 1976). The corollary to this has also been suggested,
that inadequate utilization of photosynthate and low translocation rates
will result in a reduction of photosynthesis (Neales and Incoll, 1968).
The latter interaction between source and sink is an important factor to
be considered when comparing photosynthetic rates of different cultivars, or species, particularly if photosynthetic rate is a factor included
in a plant breeding program.

There are many reports of an apparent association between growth
activity and photosynthetic rates. For example, Thorne and Evans
(1964) found that the net assimilation rate of spinach beet leaves was
enhanced when the shoot was grafted on to the more actively growing
sugar beet roots, while Hackett (1973) calculated that the potential
photosynthetic rate of tobacco exceeded that of growth by 70 to 170%.
Also, photosynthetic rates have been found to be positively correlated
with fruit growth rates of peas (Flinn, 1974) and peach (Crews et al.,
1975). In the grass, Digitaria decumbens, starch will accumulate in the
chloroplasts of slow-growing, nontillering plants when night temperatures are low, but not in the chloroplasts of actively tillering plants. The
latter, more rapidly growing plants also show higher net CO_2 exchange
rates.

The basis of sink-limited photosynthesis has been suggested as some
kind of end-product inhibition due to the accumulation of metabolites.
These metabolites may act directly on the photosynthetic mechanism,

or indirectly through, for example, stomatal closure, disruption of the chloroplasts due to starch accumulation, or even the formation and action of growth regulators in the leaf (Hartt, 1963; Satoh and Ohyama, 1971; Chatterton et al., 1972; Habeshaw, 1973; Moore et al., 1974; Milford and Pearman, 1975; Chalmers et al., 1975).

Strong arguments have also been made for an alternative association between growth and photosynthesis through long-distance hormone action rather than carbohydrate accumulation (Kriedemann et al., 1976; Geiger, 1976b). However, the two points of view are not necessarily mutually exclusive, and either one or both mechanisms of control may operate in plants. It would appear that there is a strong possibility that any effect on root growth could be transmitted to the shoot through an effect on the level of cytokins moving to the leaves in the transpiration stream (Itai and Vaadia, 1965; McDavid et al., 1973; Torrey, 1976). This could also be an important component of the photosynthetic increases obtained with the initiation of root growth on leafy cuttings (Humphries, 1963). There are also many situations where reduced photosynthesis is associated with high levels of carbohydrate (cf. Habeshaw, 1973; Chalmers et al., 1975), and the response is rapid enough (King et al., 1967) to make it unlikely that a sink-operated hormonal control system is involved (cf. Geiger, 1976b). The main difficulty in assessing the possible assocation between carbohydrate accumulation and photosynthesis arises from the point made earlier in dealing with vein loading, i.e., a considerable part of the carbohydrate of a leaf will be in storage pools and only indirectly will influence the smaller transport pool. Also, there may be a threshold level of carbohydrate below which photosynthesis does not respond to concentration.

A continued low demand for photosynthate and high carbohydrate levels in the leaf are often associated with premature senesence (Allison and Weinmann, 1970; King et al., 1967). A related phenomenon has been observed in carrot tissue culture experiments, when sucrose was shown to suppress chlorophyll synthesis (Edelman and Hanson, 1972). In contrast, it has also been found that the senesence of photosynthetic tissue may be delayed following the removal of developing fruits (Kriedemann et al., 1976), or the failure to set grain in the florets of cereals or grasses. In the cereals, the absisic acid level of the grain has been shown to increase toward maturity (King, 1977), and it is possible than an inhibitor such as ABA produced in a seed or fruit as these mature could be involved in the induction of senesence of the adjacent photosynthetic tissue.

The source–sink association is clearly very complex, but still important when considering the photosynthetic superiority of one cultivar over another. In practical terms, it is not always clear whether an interaction observed in single plants under artificial conditions will be relevant to the field situation. This issue was raised by Neales and Incoll (1968), and more recently by Milford and Pearman (1975), and it is a problem that needs careful scrutiny.

III. VASCULAR REGULATION

There is little evidence to suggest that the sieve tubes do not have the capacity to carry all the photosynthate required for growth (Milthorpe and Mooby, 1969; Wardlaw, 1976b), yet there are still many ways in which the phloem may influence plant growth and development. It is not the purpose of this chapter to discuss in any detail the structure of the phloem, or the mechanism of translocation, although these are clearly linked to the control of movement. Detailed discussion of these points can be seen in three recent publications (Aronoff et al., 1975; Zimmermann and Milburn, 1975; Wardlaw and Passioura, 1976).

A. Mobility Characteristics

One of the features of vein loading in leaves is the selective nature of the process, but there are as yet inadequate guidelines on the importance of specific chemical and structural characteristics of metabolites, nutrients, and applied substances that make them phloem mobile (see Ziegler, 1975; Pate, 1976a).

1. Endogenous Materials

Neutral, nonreducing sugars—such as sucrose and stachyose—and in some species the sugar alcohols—such as sorbitol—are the main forms of translocate. Arnold (1968) considered sucrose as a protected form of the hexoses, while Ziegler (1975) suggested that the di- or oligosaccharides were energetically more economic to transport than the free hexoses, because monoses bound to the terminal fructose can be transglycosylated and have no need for ATP-dependent activation to join the metabolic pathways. It was pointed out in Section II, A that the phloem shows a preferential accumulation of sucrose in comparison with glucose, but there is no evidence to indicate that glucose, if it could enter the conducting system, cannot be translocated.

Phosphorus as PO_4^{3-} is extremely phloem mobile, but other anions, such as SO_4^{2-} and Cl^- are much less so, and some not at all, as in the case of NO_3^- (Hall and Baker, 1972; Läuchli, 1972). Sulfur and chlorine can be redistributed from older leaves to other parts of the plant (Bukovac and Wittwer, 1957; Rinne and Langston, 1960), although this does not always occur, as was shown by Taniyama and Sawanaka (1973) for high concentrations of sulfur in rice. Loneragan *et al.* (1976) have recently pointed out that the mobility of several elements may depend on their availability and concentration in the leaf, a fact that may explain some of the differences in results and conclusions drawn from earlier work.

The monovalent cations K^+ and Mg^+ are far more mobile than the divalent cations Ca^{2+} and Mn^{2+} (VanGoor and Wiersma, 1974). Tammes and Van Die (1966) estimated that K^+ was just as mobile as PO_4^{3-} in the phloem of *Yucca*, if differences in concentration in the source leaf were taken into account. The general failure of the divalent cations to enter the phloem has one advantage in that it will prevent possible complications due to the precipitation of salts such as calcium phosphate, a reaction that is likely to occur at the high pH values generally found in sieve tubes (cf. Pate, 1976a).

Mobility is dependent on availability, preferential uptake, and retention during translocation. Potassium transport probably differs from transport of sucrose and PO_4^{3-}, at least in part, because it is readily exchanged between cells. Thus a limited retention in the conduting tissue would explain why K^+, although readily mobile, is less efficiently redistributed than PO_4^{3-} to the grain of cereals from the vegetative organs (Hanway, 1962; Kido and Yanatori, 1963; Roy and Wright, 1974).

The transport of organic nitrogen in the phloem is an integral part of plant nutrition, and chemically it is of interest that the amino acids and amides concerned are zwitterions varying from predominately basic to acidic in nature. Again, selective uptake is found to operate between the various amino acids, and Pate (1976b) has observed that several amino acids (aspartic, glutamic, glycine, and γ-aminobutyric acid), although present in the xylem of lupin, were ineffectively transferred to the phloem. However, aspartic acid and glutamic acid have been identified as some of the main amino acids occurring in the phloem sap of willow (Mittler, 1953; Leckstein and Llewellyn, 1975). Asparagine would appear to be common in the phloem of willow (Leckstein and Llewellyn, 1975) and several legumes, where its slow rate of metabolism may be a feature favoring its long-distance transport (Lewis and Pate, 1973; Schiller and Martin, 1975). Pate (1976a) has suggested that there is species specificity in the major forms of nitrogen translocated, also it does appear that the more basic amino acids such as lysine are not readily phloem mobile. However, there is insufficient data available at present from which any conclusions can be drawn concerning the relation between mobility and the chemical structure of amino acids. The patterns of uptake and redistribution of nitrogen would suggest that the amino acids are just as phloem mobile as phosphorus and potassium.

2. *Exogenous Materials*

The movement of applied substances and disease organisms through the phloem also provides some further information on the characteristics necessary for phloem mobility.

a. Viruses. Viruses, probably as complete particles, are known to move through the phloem in the sieve tubes (Schneider, 1965); in some instances this movement may be quite rapid. Tobacco mosaic virus (TMV) has been shown to move at a minimum of 3.5 cm/hr over long distances in *Nicotiana glutinosa* (Helms and Wardlaw, 1976) and at 17.5 cm/hr in tomato (Kunkel, 1939). Tobacco mosaic virus is a rod-shaped virus, 15 nm in diameter and 300 nm long, which gives some indication of the size of particle that may be actively moved down a sieve element. The most rapid speed that has been recorded for virus through the phloem is 150 cm/hr for sugar beet curly top virus (Bennett, 1934).

The sieve element is not, however, the only phloem cell type involved in long-distance transport of viruses in plants. Worley (1965) has shown that Southern bean mosaic virus will move considerable distances through phloem fibres, although at much slower speeds (0.08 to 0.5 mm/hr) than metabolites moving in sieve tubes. This movement appears to be associated with the streaming activity of the fibre cell cytoplasm (Worley, 1968).

The mycoplasma associated with diseases such as witches broom, or aster yellows, have sizes ranging from 80 to 800 nm across, and some of these have been identified in sieve tubes, penetrating across sieve plates (Doi *et al.*, 1967; Jacoli, 1974). However, it is not clear how rapidly these large bodies move in a longitudinal direction through the phloem.

b. Hormones and Herbicides. Of the naturally occurring plant hormones, the available data suggest that the floral stimulus—gibberellins and absisic acid—are likely to be transported through the phloem (McCombe, 1964; Chin and Lockhart, 1965; Hocking *et al.*, 1972; Couillerot and Bonnemain, 1975; King, 1976). However, probably none of the hormones, including the cytokinins and auxins, are entirely excluded from the phloem (D. A. Phillips and Cleland, 1972; Field and Peel, 1972; Hall and Medlow, 1974; Vonk, 1974). Many of our assumptions relating to the movement of naturally occurring hormones are, however, based on observations following exogenous applications.

The phloem mobility of several of the growth regulators commonly used as herbicides often depends on the concentration at which these are applied (Van Overbeek, 1956) and this is particularly evident in the case of auxins such as 2,4-dichlorophenoxyacetic acid (2,4-D.)

Perhaps the only common feature of the phloem-mobile hormones and herbicides is their general anionic nature. Mitchell (1961) quoted an early observation by Hamner, Lucas, and Sell that acid solutions of some regulators are more effectively translocated than the same ones in an alkaline form. It is disappointing, however, that more information is not available on the relation between chemical structure and the trans-location of herbicides. Mitchell and Linder (1962) noted that the movement of methyl 3-indoleacetate could be enhanced if a methoxy group was added to form methyl α-methoxy-3-indoleacetate (Fig. 3). It was suggested that the methoxy group could enhance uptake or trans-location, or reduce degradation, but unfortunately no attempt was made to distinguish between these aspects. Field and Peel (1972) have more recently suggested, from their work with willow, that lateral transfer rather than longitudinal movement as such limited the phloem mobility of many growth regulators. Jacob (Ziegler, 1975) commented on the lack of any relation between the solubility of growth regulators in water and transport, but did stress the importance of carboxyl groups (Fig. 3), although there were exceptions to the rule.

B. Associated Transport and Bidirectional Movement

Inherent in a mechanism of mass flow, such as the pressure flow described by Münch, is that movement of all the metabolites in a single sieve tube will be uniderectional. However, whether or not two sub-stances will move at the same speed, or appear to do so, will depend on their relative exchange rates between the sieve elements and adjacent cells, and on their relative absorption to the structural components of the sieve tube (the chromatographic effect). In a lamina flow system, molecular size will only influence movement when it is extremely large, and even a virus such as TMV, (15 nm in diameter), may move readily if the particles are not too numerous and the flow orientates the 300 nm-long rods parallel to the sieve tube walls.

Sucrose, as the main metabolite, is the standard that is generally used for comparison with other materials moving in the phloem. Probably

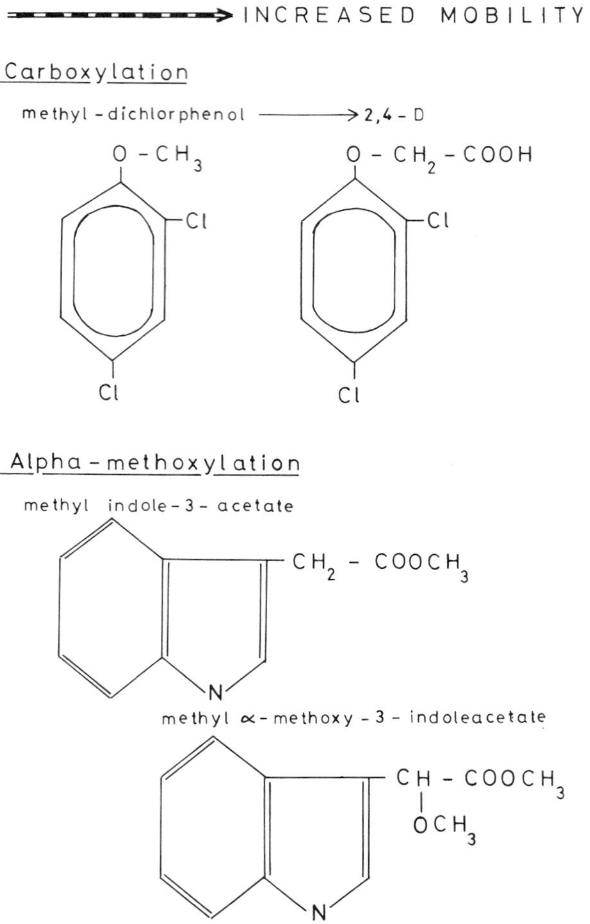

━━━━━━━━━➤ INCREASED MOBILITY

1. Carboxylation

methyl - dichlorphenol ─────➤ 2,4 - D

O – CH₃ → $O-CH_3$

O – CH₂ – COOH → $O-CH_2-COOH$

2. Alpha – methoxylation

methyl indole – 3 – acetate

CH₂ – COOCH₃ → $CH_2-COOCH_3$

methyl α - methoxy - 3 - indoleacetate

CH – COOCH₃ → $CH-COOCH_3$
OCH₃ → OCH_3

Fig. 3. Two examples of changes in chemical structure that have been associated with increased phloem mobility of exogenous materials. 1: Carboxylation (see Ziegler, 1975). 2: α-Methoxylation (see Mitchell and Linder, 1962).

the closest association that has been observed is that between sucrose and phosphorus (as PO_4^{3-}), which show a parallel distribution pattern from source leaves to sinks and similar speeds of movement through the phloem (Wanner and Bachofen, 1961; Marshall and Wardlaw, 1973). Also, many other substances (see Crafts and Crisp, 1971)— including other nutrients, virus particles (Bennett, 1940; Schneider, 1965), growth substances (Mitchell and Brown, 1946; Hay and Thimann, 1956; Crafts, 1966), and other metabolites—have patterns of distribution from a leaf similar to that of sucrose. This apparent association between the movement of unrelated materials is, of course, one of the arguments used in favor of a mass flow mechanism of translocation.

The movement of the floral stimulus is also closely associated with the movement of carbohydrate in several plants, with similarities in the patterns of distribution and speed of movement (King, 1976), although in one species (*Lolium temulentum*) the speed of movement of the floral stimulus appears to be much slower than that of carbohydrate (Evans and Wardlaw, 1966). The variation found with *Lolium* may not necessarily mean that there are large differences in the nature of the floral stimulus between species, but could, for example, be the result of a change from an anionic to a cationic form, with a resulting change in retention along the pathway.

Evidence indicating that bidirectional movement may occur in a single sieve tube within the phloem has been obtained by several workers. However there are no instances where the observations cannot be explained in other ways, such as, for example, lateral transfer between adjacent sieve elements (see Eschrich, 1975). There are, of course, instances where it has been clearly shown that movement of metabolites may occur in opposite directions through different parts of the phloem in a stem, such as the internal and external phloem of the tomato (Bonnemain, 1968) or the leaf and stem traces of bean (Peterson and Currier, 1969).

C. Carrying Capacity

Canny (1975), in reviewing the literature on the specific mass transfer of dry matter through phloem, drew attention to the fact that for "fast" translocating systems, specific mass transfer was about 4.5 g cm^{-2} phloem hr^{-1}. It was mentioned in Section II,A that the bigger the leaf the greater the vascular system, and a similar association has been found between sink size and the vascular system in wheat (Evans et al., 1970). This kind of vascular adaptation, and the apparently uniform maximum rates of translocation observed in the early translocation work, did seem to indicate that there might be some sort of limit to the carrying capacity of the phloem. However, there are probably too many exceptions to the rule to make this completely acceptable. In wheat, Patrick (1972) estimated a specific mass transfer through the phloem of 35 g cm^{-2} hr^{-1}, while Passioura and Ashford (1974) obtained rates of 180 g cm^{-2} hr^{-1} for movement of dry matter into a specially adapted root system. Lush and Evans (1974) calculated that the specific mass transfer of dry matter through the phloem of a leaf of *Chloris gayana* could reach 14.9 g dry wt cm^{-2} hr^{-1}.

Another approach used to determine the limits to growth imposed directly by the transport system itself has been to artifically restrict the path of movement. Mason and Maskell (1928b) found that when the cross-sectional area of phloem available for transport through the stem of cotton was reduced, the reduction in mass transfer was less than expected. There was an adaptation in transport that was found to be associated with an increase in the concentration gradient across the restricted zone. Also, in two cereals—sorghum (Fischer and Wilson, 1975) and wheat (Wardlaw and Moncur, 1976)—it has been shown that cutting one-half the vascular system entering the head through the peduncle did not appear to alter the total transport of carbohydrate from the leaves to the grain. In wheat, the analysis of ^{14}C photosynthate profiles suggested that there was an increase in both the speed of movement and the concentration of carbohydrate moving through the restricted part of the peduncle.

The evidence available to date suggests that the resistance to longitudinal flow through the sieve tubes is unlikely to be a major factor limiting the translocation of metabolites from source to sink under nonstress conditions of growth. An association has been obtained between reduced translocation and callose formation across the seive plates of several species under stress conditions (McNairn and Currier, 1968; McNairn, 1972; King and Zeevart, 1974; Van Die, 1975). However, it has also been shown that considerable sieve plate blockage with callose can occur without any effect on transport (Ullrich, 1963; Currier and Webster, 1976; Eschrich et al., 1965; Eschrich, 1975). Thus, a quantitative assessment of the relation between callose blockage and translocation rates could provide valuable information on the control of transport in sieve tubes.

A special situation occurs in the intercalary meristem of the Gramineae. Forde (1965), studying the developing leaf of Lolium perenne, concluded that crushing of the phloem elements in the intercalary meristem would prevent translocation past the region of growth and favor the accumulation of metabolites. Also, Patrick (1972) noted continued destruction and differentiation of sieve elements in the intercalary meristem of the wheat culm during growth, and suggested that internode elongation could possibly produce "bottlenecks" in the transport system.

D. Phyllotaxis and Vascular Connections

One of the characteristics of phloem movement already described is the active retention of many metabolites within the conducting tissue, with relatively little lateral loss as they move along the path of transport (Zimmermann, 1961). Thus, although the resistance to longitudinal movement of solutes may be low, it does appear that vascular connections, as well as source and sink location, are important in determining the pattern of dry matter partitioning in plants.

The distribution of ^{14}C photosynthate and $^{32}PO_4^{3-}$ along phyllotaxic pathways has been reported for several plant species (see Wardlaw, 1968). In addition, the movement of metabolites between vascular bundles, or for that matter between individual sieve elements, is a complex process. Bonnemain (1968) observed that ^{14}C photosynthate entering the stem of tomato from a mature leaf, first moved down toward the roots in the external phloem and subsequently up the stem to the shoot apex, or a fruit, in the internal phloem. Also, Crafts (1967) noticed that the herbicide 2,4-D, applied to the primary leaf of a soybean plant, descended to 1 cm above the cotyledon node, before it ascended to the upper part of the shoot. Thus the major exchange of metabolites between vascular traces may not occur until these anastomose some distance below the point of insertion of the leaf (cf. Wardlaw, 1968).

Limited lateral exchange between vascular traces, or discontinuities in the vascular system, may have certain advantages for a plant under disease or stress situations. Thus Worley (1965) showed that the transmission of Southern bean mosaic virus was inhibited by a discontinuity in the phloem fibers of *Phaseolus vulgaris*, and it has been suggested that the freedom of the shoot apex from virus in many infected plants is related to the lack of any direct phloem connections (Schneider, 1965). Discontinuity has also been observed in the xylem strands entering developing wheat grains (Zee and O'Brien, 1970) and this, in association with transfer cells, may act as a filter of material entering the seed through the transpiration stream.

E. Lateral Transfer and Storage

A feature of many plants is their ability to temporarily store photosynthetic metabolites and nutrients in tissues, along the transport pathway between the source and sink. This stored material is subsequently available for remobilization and use later in development, when either the demand is increased or the availability of current photosynthate inadequate. Storage associated with the transport system would appear to be important over the long term, as well as showing some of the short-term diurnal responses observed with leaves (Mason and Maskell, 1928a; Peel and Weatherley, 1962; Lush and Evans, 1974).

There has been considerable discussion of the importance of temporary storage for grain growth in cereals. In wheat, probably 90% of the grain requirement for carbohydrate is derived from current photosynthesis (Wardlaw and Porter, 1967), unless the plant is subject to stress (Rawson and Evans, 1971). However, rice, with low glume photosynthetic rates and considerable starch storage in the stem, would appear to be more dependent on stored material for growth of the grain than wheat (Cock and Yoshida, 1972). Sugarcane might be considered an extreme case of temporary storage in the culm of gramineae, with the cane being harvested before the stored sucrose can be remobilized to the inflorescence. Stored carbohydrate is also an important factor in the seasonal pattern of tree growth, with considerable storage in the wood when vegetative growth is minimal. In this last case, there is the added complication of lateral transport of both carbohydrate and nutrients through the ray parenchymatous tissue (Kozlowski and Winget, 1964; Höll, 1975).

Unfortunately, little is known about the mechanisms controlling photosynthate and nutrient storage along the path of movement, how it is regulated, or what it costs in terms of additional respiratory losses or permanent retention of nutrients and carbohydrates. Evidence obtained with yucca (VanDie, 1975) and willow (Peel and Weatherley, 1962) indicate that there is a very rapid change from current photosynthate as a source of carbohydrate moving through the phloem to stored material as a source, if the direct photosynthetic supply is removed. Rawson and Evans (1971) also noted that the mobilization of carbohydrates from the lower internodes of wheat during grain development is enhanced if photosynthesis is reduced. The control of transfer between the storage and transport systems is a complex one, but it appears that the concentration of metabolites both inside and outside the conducting elements are factors in this exchange (Ho and Peel, 1969; Wardlaw and Moncur, 1976). The effect of cooling the transport pathway provides an indication of the two-way control operating between the transport and stoarge cells. Thus Ford and Peel (1966) in willow, and Tammes et al. (1969) in yucca have shown that cooling increases the length of the transport tissue contributing to exudation, i.e., the availability of stored material is reduced. Cooling has also been shown to reduce the retention of ^{14}C photosynthate as it moves through the vascular system (see Wardlaw, 1972). Interpretation of data relating to phloem exudates is not always straightforward. However, the earlier work of Peel and Weatherley (1963), in which they examined the effects of a xylem pressure gradient and the inhibitors dinitrophenol (DNP) and potassium cyanide (KCN) on exudation through applied stylets, suggests that solute concentration in the sieve elements adjusts to a constant level.

Although concentration gradients would appear to be important in lateral exchange, Milburn (1974) suggested that turgor pressure may also be involved, when he observed an increase in concentration with time of exudates obtained from *Ricinus*. VanDie (1975) also suggested that turgor may play a role in controlling lateral exchange between the conducting tissue and adjacent nonconducting cells in yucca. If turgor does influence exchange, alterations in plant water potentials, induced by soil moisture stress, or transpiration, may also effect storage patterns as well as altering growth and phosynthesis. The importance of ions in this balance is difficult to assess, since normally sucrose would be the dominant solute. However, Hoad and Peel (1965) found evidence for an inverse relation between sugar and potassium levels in the sieve elements of willow, which suggests that this ion may play some role in the water relations and carbohydrate balance of the phloem.

This discussion has largely centered on the storage of carbohydrates about which there is the most information. Presumably nutrients such as PO_4^{3-} and K^+ may accumulate in the vacuoles of cells in stems and petioles, as is found in the roots of many plants (Pitman, 1976). There is no clear evidence for specific storage proteins in stems or leaves comparable to those found in seeds, in which nitrogen can accumulate and then be remobilized for later use, although Tromp and Ovaa (1973) have suggested that there could be an argenine-rich storage protein in the bark of apple trees. Also, it is not impossible that the P protein, which is found in large amounts in the sieve elements of many cucurbits (Cronshaw, 1975), may provide a source of nitrogen late in plant development. Presumably, much of the additional nitrogen is accumulated in the structural and functional protein of a cell, although some high nitrogen amino acids such as argenine and asparagine, and the proline formed under water stress, may partially serve in this role (Tromp and Ovaa, 1973; Hsiao, 1973; Lea and Fowden, 1975; Zeigler, 1975).

The most detailed study of the pathway of movement of metabolites from the vascular system to the storage cells of stems has been made for carbohydrates in sugarcane (Hawker, 1965; Glasziou and Gayler, 1972), in which it appears that sucrose moves from the vascular system into the cell wall free space, where it is hydrolyzed to glucose and fructose. The hexoses are, in turn, phosphorylated prior to uptake into the cytoplasm of the storage parenchyma and sucrose formed again. However, whether this process is common to other stem tissue or is a special feature of sugarcane still needs to be established.

F. Transport Controls

Ringing trees has been used extensively in agriculture for many years as an aid in clearing land. The removal of a ring of bark, with a cut deep into the wood below the cambium, adequate to prevent phloem regeneration, will prevent phloem transport and eventually result in the death of the tree. There are, however, less direct ways in which the movement of metabolites through the phloem may be controlled.

1. Hormonal Control

Patrick (1976) has recently reviewed some of the literature relating to the hormonal control of phloem transport. The central issue that still needs to be resolved is whether specific hormones, particularly the auxins, can act directly or only indirectly on phloem transport. In practical terms, it may not matter whether an auxin application decreases the leakiness of the sieve tubes or speeds up the transport mechanism, but it is an important physiological issue. The interpretation of many auxin experiments are complicated by the ability of IAA to move both through the sieve elements with photosynthate (see King, 1976), or in a strictly polar direction through parenchymatous tissue, and the picture is further complicated by the ability of auxins to influence cellular transfer of sugars and vein loading (Lepp and Peel, 1970, 1971).

Cytokinins and gibberellins would appear to have only indirect effects on assimilate transport through their role in regulating growth and leaf function (Halevy et al., 1964; Müller and Leopold, 1966), although there is some evidence that they could interact with auxin transport in stems (see Patrick, 1976).

2. Metabolic Inhibitors

The mechanism of action of metabolic inhibitors on translocation will not be discussed in detail here, but it should be pointed out that it is often difficult to confine inhibitors close to the point of application, so that the site of their action is clear, or to ensure that the less mobile inhibitors actually penetrate as far as the phloem. Also, the effectiveness of an inhibitor in preventing transport does not necessarily imply a mechanism of transport directly associated with pathway metabolism (Wardlaw, 1974b; Geiger and Sovonick, 1975).

Cyanide appears to inhibit sugar transport through the phloem of several species (e.g., Ho and Mortimer, 1971; Qureshi and Spanner, 1973), an effect that can be reversed when cyanide is removed (Willenbrink, 1966). Also, dinetrophenol (DNP) and (NaF) have been found to stop the movement of $^{32}PO_4^{3-}$ through the petiole of a bean leaf (Kendall, 1955), but some confirmation of this, with the assurance that the inhibitors have not reached the source leaf (Harel and Reinhold, 1966), is needed. One treatment that is not likely to spread far from the site of application is low oxygen (anoxia), and Sij and Swanson (1973) found that although this initially prevented the movement of ^{14}C photosynthate through the petiole of a squash leaf, the effect was only temporary.

3. *Environmental Controls*

Temperature changes along the path of transport can alter translocation rates, although these effects have often been shown to disappear with time (Geiger and Sovonick, 1975). One observation that is of interest in terms of possible controls has been made by Bauer (Geiger, 1969). He showed that the recovery of translocation at low temperature varied between northern and southern ecotypes of Canada thistle, and suggested that in some species transport may be an important limit to growth and development at low temperature. However, in these experiments on Canada thistle, no parallel experiments were undertaken to establish whether growth and photosynthesis were more or less sensitive to temperature than was translocation.

Giaquinta and Geiger (1973) reported that the inhibition of transport at low temperature in bean was associated with a displacement of P protein and blockage of the sieve plates. This plug was later dispersed as transport returned to normal at low temperature, suggesting that the temperature effect on transport was causally related to physical plugging of the transport system. It may, therefore, be significant that transport in the grasses has so far been found to be insensitive to a wide range of temperatures (Wardlaw, 1972, 1974a) and that to date there is no evidence for P protein occurring in the grasses (Evert *et al.*, 1971; Singh and Srivastava, 1972).

The importance of solute concentration and turgor gradients in generating pressure flow of solute suggests that plant water relations might directly influence translocation. It does appear, however, that photosynthesis, vein loading, and growth are more responsive to stress than translocation, and that any changes in the transport system are associated indirectly with other plant functions (Wardlaw, 1974b), although there is not complete agreement on this interpretation (Reinhold, 1975). When stress is great enough to cause stomatal closure, the decrease in plant water potential is probably transmitted uniformly throughout the plant, without necessarily altering the pressure gradient in the phloem between the source and sink. However, water potential gradients have been reported to occur down the length of the plant (cf. Begg and Turner, 1970), and these gradients may be altered by variation in transpiration rates, which may be reflected to some extent in turgor pressure gradients and translocation rates (see Wardlaw, 1974b).

IV. ATTRIBUTES OF SINKS

In this necessarily brief section, an analysis has been made of the factors regulating the partitioning of metabolites to specific centers of growth in the plant, with particular emphasis on the nature of the sink itself.

A. Competition

Sashara and Tsunoda (1971) found a positive correlation in *Brassica* species between relative growth rates and the ratio of cell surface area to cytoplasmic volume of a tissue. High growth rates were associated with both small, nonvacuolated cells in the meristem and large, highly vacuolated cells in the leaves. Although this implies a causal relationship, it is at the same time a description of growth when there is rapid cell division and the formation of large cells. Williams (1975) has suggested that the relative growth rate of shoots in some crop plants is likely to be regulated by the physical space available for development of each succeeding leaf, with a certain degree of hindrance imposed at critical stages by the outermost leaf on the next younger leaf enclosed by it. These two examples illustrate the problem of isolating those factors that are limiting growth. In addition, it must be emphasized that any analysis of this problem should consider any indirect control system such as hormonal stimulation or inhibition of growth and nutritional or other environmental factors.

Absolute size may not necessarily be a factor influencing the dominance of one organ over another, and Starck and Ubysz (1974) have porposed that the organ with the higher relative growth rate (stem in sunflower, apical shoot in bean) is the dominant acceptor of metabolites, even under conditions of limited supply. This suggests that an apex may compete effectively against a growing leaf or stem.

In relation to transport, some of the main attributes presumed to be important in the dominance of one sink over another include: (1) the dimensions of the unloading zone (i.e., sieve tube surface area) associated with the growing tissue; (2) the potential rate of transfer of metabolites out of the sieve elements; and (3) the ability of the vascular traces to channel material to the growing organ. In effect, this is a reflection of the ability of the sink to establish a favorable concentration gradient for the movement of metabolites in the direction of the sink.

In an informative experiment using willow aphids, Peel and Ho (1970) noted that when two aphid colonies were in competition for current photosynthate from a leafy shoot, the larger colony predominated, while the smaller colony relied to a much greater extent on contiguous resources. The use of aphids may be considered atypical where normal sinks are concerned. However, Cook and Evans (1976) noted a similar effect when comparing the competition for current photosynthate between the ears (with differing grain numbers) of two tillers on a wheat plant. The ear with the larger number of grains received a disproportionately greater part of the current photosynthate. However, when the supply of reserves was reduced and current photosynthesis limited to a single supply leaf, the dominance of the larger sink was less pronounced.

An analysis of apical dominance has not been included in detail in this chapter, but it is clearly a factor influencing the dominance of one sink over another. Although the exact mechanism has yet to be fully elucidated, there is little doubt that the main shoot apex can, for example, dominate and prevent competitive lateral bud growth. The more conventional explanation is that presented by Thimann, Sachs, and Mathur (1971) for *Coleus*, who suggest that bud growth is inhibited by auxin moving down the stem from the apex, and that buds have a greater sensitivity to auxin under low light and nutrient conditions. High light and nutrition would be expected to stimulate the production of cytokinins, which are known to stimulate bud growth in isolated sections. This general concept is perhaps more acceptable than one involving the diversion of nutrients away from inhibited buds, in view of Phillips (1968) observation that inhibition is not related to N, P, or K levels in the bud, or to a control related to vascular development between the stem and the bud (Wardlaw and Mortimer, 1970; Hall and Hillman, 1975).

B. Vascular Control of Growth

Mention has already been made of the controls that might be exerted by the vascular system on growth and development (see Section III). Two important features are the proximity between source and sink and the nature of the vascular connections between the two (cf. Wardlaw, 1968). However, futher control may arise within the growing organ itself, for example, at the shoot apex when penetration of the vascular system is incomplete. The *Gramineae* have a very different pattern of growth to other species, and Forde (1965) noted that in the intercalary meristem of the leaf of *Lolium perenne* there was an acute constriction in the active meristematic region and a crushing of the phloem. Based on these observations, Forde suggested that there would be a tendency to divert assimilates into the meristematic tissue. Patrick (1972) also envisaged a greater resistance to flow of photosynthate in an acropetal direction through the rather mutilated vascular system in the meristematic tissue of the developing wheat stem. In this case, the failure of the vascular system appeared to impose a constraint on open competition between developing organs. This is in line with an earlier suggestion by Kawahara, Chonan, and Wada (1968) that the regulation of development of the leaf, panicle, and internode of rice was associated with the constriction and development of vascular bundles in the culm.

Of particular interest, in relation to control, is the development of the vascular system servicing the shoot apex, and this association is illustrated for *Coleus* in Fig. 4, with data taken from Jacobs and Morrow (1958). The first sieve tubes of *Coleus* are formed in the second pair of leaves below the apex. Leaves shorter than 400 μm contained no sieve tubes, and it was suggested that beyond this length, normal diffusion—which was assumed to operate in the absence of a conducting system—would be inadequate for growth.

Cormack and Lemay (1963), using microautoradiographic techniques, observed that when [^{14}C]glucose was applied to the cut surface of a white mustard cotyledon, radioactivity could later be detected in the intercellular spaces and to a lesser extent in the cell walls of the root tip. From this observation, they suggested that free space provided the channels of transport of soluble nutrients from the ends of differentiat-

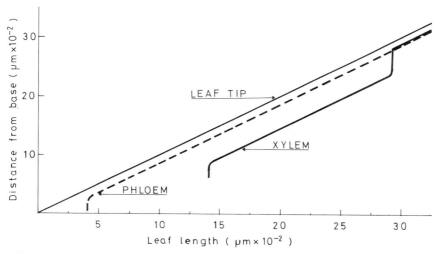

Fig. 4. The relation between the length of young *Coleus* leaves and the formation of the first xylem elements and sieve tubes in those leaves (adapted from Jacobs and Morrow, 1958).

ing vascular strands to dividing cells in the root meristem. There is some similarity between this and the suggested manner of sugar movement in the stems of sugar cane (Hawker, 1965).

However, diffusion may not be the only mechanism involved in the entry of materials into a developing apex, and Bruström (1975a,b), following experiments on etiolated pea seedlings, suggested that growth-induced water flux into the apex would account for a lot of this movement. Burström envisaged what he termed an autocatalytic system for each internode, with a growth-induced water flux followed by more nutrients, more growth, more water, etc., until cell differentiation began. The sequence would then be repeated at the next internode. This would presumably allow for the transport of both xylem nutrients and metabolites entering the free space from the phloem. With shoot apex development, it is probably not necessary to envisage a recycling of water or the return of nutrients to the rest of the plant to account for the level of nutrients and metabolites in the growing tissue. However, observations following the application of $^{32}PO_4^{3-}$ to the leaf of *Lolium temulentum* (Rijven and Evans, 1967) suggest that there may be some entry and retranslocation of phosphorus from apical tissue.

Mason and Maskell (1931) calculated from the ratios of N, P, and K to carbohydate in the bark of cotton that these nutrients were in excess of the requirements for growth of the lower parts of the plant, and that the excess must be liberated into the tracheal sap and returned to the tops in the transpiration stream. Root morphology and function is quite distinct from that of the shoots, and carbon, as well as being required for respiration and growth, also provides the framework for reduced nitrogen to be transported through the xylem, as amides and amino acids, to the shoot (Pate, 1975).

The fruit and seed provide another distinctive type of growth, where a long period of dry matter accumulation follows the initial phase of cell division and expansion. This is of particular interest in terms of the effectiveness of a sink, as fruits and seeds tend to dominate the vegetative growth of plants (cf. Wardlaw, 1968). Unfortunately, few studies have been concerned with the actual mechanics and control of assimilate movement into fruits, although Jenner (1976) has recently described a possible mechanism for the transfer of photosynthate into the grain of wheat (Fig. 5).

Grain development is temperature sensitive (Wardlaw, 1974a). Metabolic processes could be important in unloading the sieve element and transfer of sucrose across the pigment strand, but would also be expected to affect the enzymatic conversion of sucrose to starch in amyloplasts. Unlike the vegetative apex, much of the accumulation of

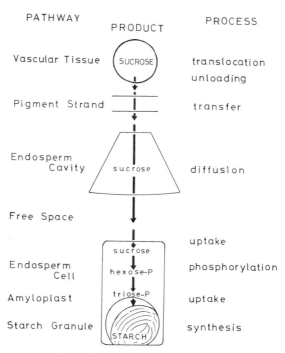

Fig. 5. The pathway and metabolism of photosynthate as it moves from the vascular trace of the wheat grain to the starch in the endosperm (adapted from Jenner, 1976).

dry matter by the grain occurs without a net change in the water content of the cells (Sofield *et al.*, 1977), and there is not likely to be any mass flow of solution to transfer metabolites to the center of the grain, in the way Burström (1975a) described for the vegetative shoot apex. Jenner (1976) has suggested that the synthesis of starch in the amyloplasts, rather than being responsible for the flow of sucrose into the grain, is activated by the concentration of sucrose that has entered the grain, and this in turn may be controlled by the rate of transfer out of the vascular system. However, this descriptive analysis does not go far enough to allow us to draw any firm conclusions as to the mechanism whereby one sink dominates another.

As it develops, the leaf changes from an active sink to a source of carbohydrate supply (Turgeon and Webb, 1973, 1975; Fellows and Geiger, 1974), with no further import of carbohydrate, except under extreme conditions (Thrower, 1974). Any associated changes in the vascular tissue of the leaf as it develops might provide useful information on the nature of the controls operating in a sink, and O'Brien (see Wardlaw and Passioura, 1976, p. 369) recently suggested that the protophloem of young leaves, in which sieve elements are not associated with companion cells, is only of use in unloading. In contrast, the companion cells of the minor veins of mature leaves of several species have been shown to be very large relative to the sieve elements (Geiger, 1975b). Protophloem, presumably containing sieve elements without associated companion cells, is a feature of most rapidly growing organs, including roots and shoot apices.

C. Utilization of Exudates

One area that needs further comment is the harvesting of phloem exudates. This provides a special kind of "sink," and VanDie (1975) has pointed out that in the palm, withdrawal of assimilates by tapping the infloresence stalk is several times higher than the rate of assimilate flow into the stalk during fruit formation. Also, this flow occurs without the normal metabolic controls. The tapping of a coconut infloresence may yield 1.5 liters per day of exudate over 12 months, which, for a 17% solution, represents a yield of 93 kg dry wt/year. This compares with 55 to 93 dry fruits per tree per year (VanDie, 1975).

Many aphids and leaf hoppers utilize the phloem contents, and recently Tammes and VanDie (1976) calculated that a yucca leaf could support 4 g dry wt. of aphid growth per day, or 30 μg cm^{-2} leaf day^{-1}. This calculation is based on the assumption that 1 g dry wt of aphid requires 10 g dry wt (55 ml) of sieve tube sap.

Clearly, it could be of considerable advantage to collect exudates from plants not normally of use in other ways to man. However, the main problem appears to be the efficient protective blockage of the sieve elements that rapidly follows phloem damage in many species. Although blockage may be prevented by the addition of a chelating agent such as EDTA to the solution into which exudation takes place (King and Zeevaart, 1974), there is a need for much more work in this area before a practical solution will be obtained.

The rapid flow of exudates in some species does suggest that the greater the pressure drop the greater the flow of assimilates. Also, the metabolic activity of the sink and the production of hormonal stimulants is not necessary for movement along the pathway to the sink, although Dixon (1975) has warned that it would be unwise to regard the aphid entirely as a simple sink.

D. Metabolism and Sink Activity

The response of growing organs to low temperatures and anoxia confirm that metabolic processes are associated with sink activity.

Thus Geiger (1966) showed that cooling both the beet crown and actively growing leaf to 0°C severely retarded the import of photosynthate to these organs, and, as was reported in Section IV,C, temperature was found to regulate the flow of assimilates into the cereal grain (Wardlaw, 1974a). Nagao and Wada (1970) observed a decrease in the movement of ^{14}C photosynthate to the roots of tobacco when they were placed under anaerobic conditions, while Geiger and Christy (1971) demonstrated that anaerobic conditions inhibited the growth of a young sugar beet leaf. In the latter example, the reduced growth was found to be associated with a decline in ATP and the output of respiratory CO_2.

Unfortunately, it is not possible to decide from the data presently available at what level metabolic processes are regulating growth—for example, whether this primary control lies, as suggested by Jenner (1976), in the transfer of metabolites out of the conducting system, or more directly in the synthetic processes associated with cell growth and storage.

V. INTERACTIONS

Although some of the interactions that occur among source, sink, and the transport system in regulating growth and development have been discussed previously, it is worthwhile to consider a few aspects in more detail.

A. Integration in Plant Systems

1. Partitioning and Root: Shoot Ratios

A simple model is presented in Fig. 6 to indicate the patterns of metabolite movement in plants. The overall partitioning of dry matter is influenced by many factors, including light, soil moisture, and nutrition (see Evans and Wardlaw, 1976). The movement of carbon from a particular leaf will also be influenced by the pattern of vascular connections, as well as by the proximity of sinks and alternative sources. The storage component adds a further complication, with the importance of redistribution of dry matter to growth depending on both environmental conditions and species (cf. VanDie, 1975). Another factor that must be considered is the variation in respiratory losses between plant organs, where the total loss can be as much as 50% of the photosynthetic input into the plant (see Evans and Wardlaw, 1976).

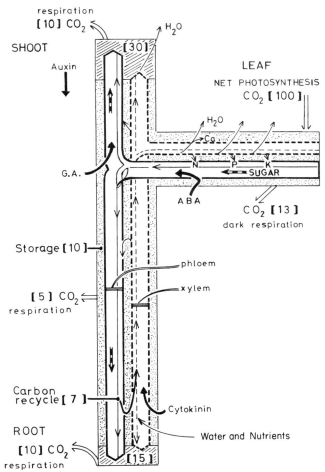

Fig. 6. Flow diagram of the pattern of movement of nutrients and metabolites between leaves, roots, and growing shoots. Carbon from net photosynthesis of the leaves in the light is represented by a value of 100 units, which has been balanced by respiratory losses, storage, root and shoot growth, and a factor for recycling carbon as amino acids from the roots back to the shoot.

There is a strong interaction between the function of roots and shoots. Nutrient uptake is associated with root respiration and the movement of carbohydrate from the shoot (Starck, 1973; Sarkissian and Fowler, 1974). Thus Bowling (1968) was able to demonstrate a marked reduction in the uptake of potassium by the roots of sunflower following ringing of the stem, and several workers have shown an association between light and the uptake of nutrients by the roots (Nichiporovich and Chen, 1959; Starck and Ubysz, 1974; Felippe et al., 1975). Reduced light will drastically reduce the relative growth rate of roots (cf. Murata et al., 1965), and roots often appear to be at a competitive disadvantage with the shoots (cf. Wardlaw, 1968). In terms of transport, two factors might possibly be involved—the distance between the root tip and the source of carbohydrates, and the relatively small zone of growth at the root apex.

The function of the shoot is in turn dependent on root function. Murata et al. (1965) found that damage to rice roots slowed down leaf photosynthesis, an effect that was correlated with reduced protein nitrogen in the leaves. It was suggested by Murata et al. (1965) that there was a direct relation between root function and protein metabolism of the leaf, without involving an inhibition due to sugar accumulation. One effect of water stress is a reduction in cytokinin production by the roots, and this is known to influence leaf protein synthesis and photosynthesis (Itai and Vaadia, 1965, 1971; see also Torrey, 1976). The enhancement of apical dominance under low light and nutrition may reflect poor root development and a reduction in the supply of cytokinins, which may stimulate release from apical dominance.

2. Hormonal Controls

Perhaps one of the greatest gaps in our knowledge of the control of dry matter distribution and growth is exactly how growth substances are involved in this control. In the model (Fig. 6), auxin is shown to move away from the shoot apex (Scott and Briggs, 1960; Bellandi and Doerffling, 1974; Cutter and Chiu, 1975), but this deliberately ignores the possibility of auxin movement through the sieve elements from more mature tissue, the significance of which is still unknown (King, 1976). Although cytokininlike activity has been identified in phloem sap (Phillips and Cleland, 1972; Vonk, 1974), the possible movement of cytokinins through the phloem has also been ignored. The cytokinins are presumed to originate in the root system, traveling throughout the plant in the xylem (Torrey, 1976). Absisic acid can migrate from a mature leaf, and may act to stimulate senesence in other parts of the plant or modify developmental processes, such as flowering, under stress conditions (Rasmussen, 1976; King and Evans, 1977). Gibberellins, the only other group to be included, are shown here to move from mature to actively growing tissue, as was suggested by McCombe (1964). However, the most detailed studies of this group of hormones have been concerned with movement from the embryo to the aleurone layer of cereal grains during germination. One of the main complexities in dealing with the action of endogenous plant hormones, in addition to problems of extraction and analysis, is the additional and often overriding regulation that can be imposed by other metabolites (inhibitors) that may prevent hormone production, transport, or function at the site of action (see Kefeli and Kadyrov, 1971).

3. Nutrient Recycling

Another area of integrated function is the uptake and recycling of nutrients, and some of the most intensive studies of this problem have been made by Pate and his co-workers in relation to the uptake and movement of nitrogen in legumes (see Pate 1975, 1976b). A flow pattern, similar to that shown here, has recently been presented by Pate (1976b) for nitrogen in *Lupin*. Ninety percent of the nitrogen fixed by the root nodules of *Lupin* moved to the shoot in the transpiration stream as amides and amino acids (mainly asparagine), recycling back with it 13.7% of the carbon that had moved down from the leaves to the roots. Lupins and peas both require about 4 mg of carbon from the shoots to fix 1 mg of nitrogen from the atmosphere. Nitrogen reaching the leaves is in turn retranslocated through the phloem to the main centers of growth. Pate (1976b) estimated that the fruit of *Lupin* would obtain 40% of its water, 86% of its nitrogen, and 96% of its carbon through the phloem. Some of the retranslocated nitrogen is also used in root growth, and Pate (1976b) has suggested that nitrogen fixed from the atmosphere by a legume nodule is not itself used directly for root growth.

The movement of nutrients (and also many endogenously applied substances) into and through the phloem appears to be dependent on the supply and movement of carbohydrates out of the leaf (see Crafts and Crisp, 1971), as was shown with $^{32}PO_4^{3-}$ and ^{14}C photosynthate in wheat (Marshall and Wardlaw, 1973). This data, together with the strong evidence in support of a mechanism of transport involving the mass flow of solution (see Zimmermann and Milburn, 1975; Wardlaw and Passioura, 1976), suggest there is a need to revise the concept of separate sink controls for the movement of individual nutrients. It seems more realistic to propose that the direction of movement of any individual component in the phloem—with some adjustments for retention along the pathway, lateral exchange, and recycling in the xylem—will be controlled by the concentration gradient and movement of the main osmotic component (generally sucrose).

One implication of this view is that, when growth of the shoot is reduced due to a nutrient deficiency, the flow of nutrients from the leaves to the growing tissue, as well as the movement of carbohydrate, will be reduced, thus magnifying the deficiency effect. In contrast to the shoot, there are several reasons why root growth should be less affected by a nutrient deficiency. First the roots are better placed to receive the limited nutrient supply (cf. Bieleski, 1973) and, second, the roots, as the less competitive growing organs, are likely to be limited by the availability of carbohydrate while the shoot is actively growing (Wardlaw, 1968) and less sensitive to nutrient changes. Any change that favors the movement of carbohydrate to the roots will also reinforce the redistribution of nutrients from the leaves to the roots, further enhancing the differential in root to shoot growth.

The greater mobilization of nutrients from leaves of plants under nutrient difficiency conditions need not necessarily imply that this is the direct result of an increased nutrient demand. For example, a nitrogen difficiency, resulting in reduced growth, will result in the accumulation of carbohydrate in the mature tissue (see Wardlaw, 1968), and carbohydrate accummulation may in turn induce or hasten leaf senesence (cf. King et al., 1967). Also, a high nitrogen requirement for growth of soybean seeds, as was suggested by Sinclair and de Witt (1976) could, if not satisfied, result in faster leaf senescence due not directly to enhanced withdrawl of nitrogen from the leaves, but in the first instance to carbohydrate accumulation.

B. Response to Environmental Stress

It is necessary that with an analysis of net assimilation and growth in relation to the transport system of plants, an environmental impact statement should be included. Some aspects of this have already been dealt with, for example, in Section V,A,3, but some further brief comments on the mode of action and sequence of events following the induction of temperature and water stress are included here.

1. Temperature

It seems unlikely, from the evidence available, that temperature will regulate plant growth indirectly through effects on translocation. Where this has been suggested, for example, in Ladino clover (Hoshino et al., 1972), whole plant temperatures have been varied, and reduced translocation could equally well result from reduced growth and not the reverse.

Whether temperature regulates growth directly or through the supply of photosynthate may depend on the species and the temperature range being considered. There is a range over which photosynthesis is fairly insensitive to temperature, possibly because CO_2 is limiting (see Wardlaw, 1974a), and where any growth response is likely to be direct. In this range, a fall in temperature will result in an increased storage of carbohydrate along the path of movement between the source and sink. Further lowering of the temperature (possibly below 15°C in temperate species) will result in reduced photosynthetic rates and vein loading, and if this is more severe than the direct effects of temperature on growth, there will be a reduction in storage along the pathway. Finally, as temperatures are lowered further (< 1°C for some temperate species, but < 15°C for some subtropical species), a critical temperature will be reached at which many plant functions cease to operate effectively. Levitt (1972) has summarized many of the changes that are likely to be important at these critical temperatures.

Variations in temperature can vary the proportion of different metabolites being utilized in growth. For example, wheat, if grown through the period of grain development at high temperature, will produce small grains with a high percentage nitrogen (Sofield et al., 1977). This could result from an enhanced demand for photosynthate at higher temperatures where there is a greater reliance on the lower parts of the plant for photosynthate and the relative supply of nitrogen to carbohydrate is greater. However, increasing temperature will also increase the rate of mobilization of nitrogen from the upper parts of the plant, and the relative importance of these two factors would be difficult to separate. This sequence of events, together with the shorter duration of growth at high temperatures, will result in a small grain with a relatively high nitrogen content. These necessarily brief comments can only serve to indicate the variety of interactions that are likely to occur with a change in temperature.

2. Water

There is evidence that leaf and root expansion are more sensitive to water stress than photosynthesis (Wardlaw, 1969; Boyer, 1970), and that the long-distance movement of sugar through the phloem is resistant to stress (Wardlaw, 1967, 1969; Moorby et al., 1975), although the latter conclusion has been challenged by Reinhold (1975). This sequence of events does, however, help to explain the build up of carbohydrates in the stems of plants, such as cotton (Eaton and Ergle, 1948), under drought conditions (see Iljin, 1957), and it provides an explanation for the practice of stressing sugarcane just prior to harvest. Continued translocation under stress conditions can be seen as an adaptive advantage, as it will allow for the redistribution of nutrients, such as nitrogen (Mothes, 1931; Gates, 1957), from the mature to the younger, less susceptible tissue. Continued transport of carbohydrate under stress may also provide some additional osmotic protection against excessive water loss from the young explanding tissue of shoots and roots. Stability of the transport system under stress conditions will also allow the establishment of more favorable growth patterns. For example, as soil moisture supplies are depleted, some roots will stop growing as they enter dry soil. However, the fewer remaining roots will be stimulated by an increasing availability of carbohydrate and consequently will provide a greater exploration of the deeper, moister areas of soil (see Evans and Wardlaw, 1976).

It is worth considering again the effect of water stress on nutrient distribution in cereals. Grain growth and translocation are both relatively insensitive to stress. Thus, as photosynthesis is reduced under stress, there is a greater utilization of stored material and current photosynthate from the lower parts of the plant (Wardlaw, 1967). The high percentage of nitrogen of grains from droughted plants would arise both because of the greater rate of mobilization of nitrogen from stressed leaves in association with a shorter duration of growth, and because of the greater utilization of nitrogen from the lower parts of the plant, where the supply of carbohydrate is proportionately less.

C. Disease

Insects, and fungal and viral diseases of plants not only inhibit growth directly through physical damage, or by the introduction of toxins, but also result in modification and adaptation of the physiology of the plant for their own benefit, often to the detriment of the host. Some of these responses are related to the interactions between source and sink, and also to the integrity of the transport system. Several aspects of this are discussed below.

1. Photosynthesis and Vein Loading

Leaf function is altered by several plant pathogens, and any simple reduction in net assimilation, or inhibition of the export of photosynthate from the leaves, would be expected to alter the pattern of distribution in a predictable manner.

Cereal rusts have been shown to reduce photosynthesis and vein loading with enhanced dry matter accumulation at the site of infection, and this reduced supply is reflected in relatively poorer growth of the root system (Shaw, 1963; Manners and Meyers, 1973). Rust-infected leaves initially show a net gain in protein, ^{32}P accumulation, and green islands typical of cytokin activity (cf. Shaw, 1963). Powdery mildew appears to have much the same effect as the rusts, with a marked retention of photosynthate in the infected leaves (Edwards, 1971; Fric, 1975).

Reduced photosynthesis in the leaves of sugar beet infected with beet yellows virus was related to stomatal closure (greater leaf resistance to water loss), a reduction in Ribulose diphosphate (RuDP) carboxylase, and an accumulation of soluble carbohydrate (Hall and Loomis, 1972). However, although beet yellows virus is phloem mobile and has been found in large numbers in the sieve elements of the minor veins (Esau et al., 1967), there was no evidence from the work of Hall ahd Loomis (1972) to suggest that reduced photosynthesis was directly associated with carbohydrate accumulation due to phloem blockage.

The bacterial disease, halo blight, of beans also results in a greater retention of photosynthate in infected leaves, although photosynthetic rates are not necessarily reduced (Hale and Whitbread, 1973). Infection of the developing trifoliate leaf of bean with halo blight results in its continuing as a sink for carbohydrate for a prolonged period, at the expense of the root system. This response is similar to an earlier one observed by Thrower and Thrower (1966), which showed that an infection of *Uromyces fabae* (rust) on the developing fourth leaf of broad bean increased and prolonged its activity as a sink, although in this case at the expense of the leaves above it.

2. *Root and Xylem Function*

Take-all (*Ophiobulus graminis*) in wheat has an effect very similar to mild water stress, with a slowing of ^{14}C assimilate export from the leaves, a decreased movement to the infected roots, but with some compensating movement of ^{14}C to uninfected crown roots (Asher, 1972). Infection of bean plants with *Xanthomonas phaseoli* (Whitbread and Bhatti, 1976) and Dutch elm disease (Roberts and Stevens, 1968) also result in wilting of the leaves and are associated with vascular damage.

3. *Alternative Sinks*

There are several parasitic diseases where the main damage to the host, other than a localized tissue response at the site of infection, may well result from competition for a limited supply of metabolites.

Some of the work described earlier on the effects of rust and mildew on leaves could come under this category. Also, like the fungal infections, there is an accumulation of photosynthate from all parts of the leaf into the fleshy tissue and enclosed larvae of the oak leaf gall (Jankiewicz et al., 1969), which presumably reduces the availability of dry matter for growth in other parts of the plant. The translocation of ^{14}C photosynthate into the hypocotyl of cabbage is stimulated by an infection of clubroot, and the movement of photosynthate past the site of infection is reduced, presumably starving the roots (Keen and Williams, 1969). Also, when a root-knot nematode, such as *Meloidogyne arenaria*, invades the tip of a root, it induces the formation of giant cells that develop marked wall ingrowths and appear to act as transfer cells for the transfer of metabolites from the root to the nematode (Jones and Northcote, 1972; Jones, 1976).

Dodder is another parasite that can deprive its host of photosynthate, with little chance of the direction of flow being reversed (Allred, 1966; Littlefield et al., 1966). Dodder has been shown to completely inhibit the setting and growth of fruits of Vicia faba L., an effect that Wolswinkel (1974a) associated with the tapping of the phloem system of the bean by the parasite. Even the flowering of the dodder, Cuscuta campestris, appears to be dependent on material (apparently an inhibitor) translocated from its host (Fratianne, 1965). One of the features of this host–parasite relationship would appear to be an enhanced release of photosynthate and nutrients from the vascular tissue into the free space of the host, with the absorptive hyphae of the dodder acting as transfer cells for the efficient uptake of these metabolites (Wolswinkel, 1974b, 1975).

Mistletoe provides another interesting host–parasite association, but, unlike dodder, there does appear to be evidence for a two-way exchange of metabolites (Rediske and Shea, 1961; Gill and Hawksworth, 1961). While the dwarf mistletoe acts as a strong competitive sink for host photosynthate, the green mistletoe appears appears to be independent (Leonard and Hull, 1966).

As was mentioned earlier, aphids and leaf hoppers are closely associated with the transport system in plants and may compete directly for the available metabolites. Dixon (1975) has pointed out that aphids tend to congregate where food is of high quality, and Hassib and Rasmy (1974) have shown that aphids accumulate on cotton plants under water stress, when nitrogen levels are high. Rapid removal of large volumes of phloem sap by insects might be expected to result in phloem blockage, and it is interesting to note that only the smaller, immature sycamore aphid will feed on the small minor veins of the leaf, while the mature aphid feeds on the larger veins (Dixon, 1975).

VI. CONCLUDING REMARKS

A description is now emerging of the way in which assimilates and nutrients are partititioned in plants and of the factors likely to affect this partitioning, but probably no single aspect can be said to be fully understood. Particularly lacking, with a few isolated exceptions, are quantitative analyses of the source, sink, and transport processes as they interact in the whole plant. In terms of improved productivity, disease control, efficient use of nutrients, and adaptation to environmental stress, a fuller understanding of the mechanisms and factors influencing and controlling the uptake of carbon and intake of nutrients and their partitioning and utilization in growth would be invaluable.

ACKNOWLEDGMENTS

I would like to thank Dr. B. T. Watson for his helpful comments on this review, and Mrs. M. Allardyce for her help in the preparation of this manuscript.

REFERENCES

Allison, J. C. S., and Weinmann, H. (1970). *Plant Physiol.* **46,** 435–436.
Allred, K. R. (1966). *Adv. Front. Plant Sci.* **16,** 1–9.
Arnold, W. N. (1968). *J. Theor. Biol.* **21,** 13–20.
Aronoff, S., Dainty, J., Gorham, P. R., Srivastava, V. A., and Swanson, C. A., eds. (1975). "Phloem Transport." Plenum, New York.
Asher, M. J. C. (1972). *Ann. Appl. Biol.* **72,** 161–167.
Begg, J. E., and Turner, N. C. (1970). *Plant Physiol.* **46,** 343–346.
Bellandi, D. M., and Doerffling, K. (1974). *Physiol. Plant.* **32,** 365–368.
Bennett, C. W. (1934). *J. Agric. Res.* **48,** 665–701.
Bennett, C. W. (1940). *J. Agric. Res.* **60,** 361–390.
Bieleski, R. L. (1973). *Annu. Rev. Plant Physiol.* **24,** 225–252.
Black, C. R., Jr. (1973). *Annu. Rev. Plant Physiol.* **24,** 253–286.
Bonnemain, J. L. (1968). *Rev. Gen. Bot.* **75,** 579–610.
Bowling, D. J. F. (1968). *J. Exp. Bot.* **19,** 381–388.
Boyer, J. S. (1970). *Plant Physiol.* **46,** 233–235.
Brovchenko, M. I. (1963). *Fiziol Rast.* **10,** 416–425.
Bukovac, M. J., and Wittwer, S. H. (1957). *Plant Physiol.* **32,** 428–435.
Burström, H. G. (1975a). *Z. Pflanzenphysiol.* **75,** 53–66.
Burström, H. G. (1975b). *Z. Pfanzenphysiol.* **76,** 339–352.
Buttrose, M. S., and Hale, C. R. (1971). *Planta* **101,** 166–170.
Canny, M. J. (1975). *In* "Transport in Plants" (M. H. Zimmermann and J. A. Milburn, eds.) Vol. I, pp. 139–153. Springer-Verlag, Berlin and New York.
Cataldo, D. A. (1974). *Plant Physiol.* **53,** 912–917.
Chalmers, D. J., Canterford, R. L., Jerie, P. H., Jones, T. R., and Ugalde, T. D. (1975). *Aust. J. Plant Physiol.* **2,** 635–645.
Chatterton, N. J., Carlson, G. E., Hungerford, W. E., and Lee, D. R. (1972). *Crop Sci.* **12,** 206–208.

Chin, T. Y., and Lockhart, J. A. (1965). *Am. J. Bot.* **52**, 828–833.

Chopowick, R. E., and Forward, D. F. (1974). *Plant Physiol.* **53**, 21–27.

Cock, J. H., and Yoshida, S. (1972). *Proc. Crop Sci. Soc. Jpn.* **41**, 226–234.

Cook, M. G., and Evans, L. T. (1976). *In* "Transport and Transfer Processes in Plants" (I. F. Wardlaw and J. B. Passioura, eds.), pp. 393–400. Academic Press, New York.

Cormack, R. G. H., and Lemay, P. (1963). *J. Exp. Bot.* **14**, 232–236.

Couillerot, J-P., and Bonnemain, J-L. (1975). *C. R. Acad. Sci., Ser. D* **280**, 1453–1456.

Crafts, A. S. (1966). *In* "Isotopes in Weed Research," pp. 3–7. IAEA, Vienna.

Crafts, A. S. (1967). *Hilgardia* **37**, 625–638.

Crafts, A. S., and Crisp, C. E. (1971). "Phloem Transport in Plants." Freeman, San Francisco, California.

Crews, C. E., Williams, S. L., and Vines, H. M. (1975). *Planta* **126**, 97–104.

Cronshaw, J. (1975). *In* "Phloem Transport" (S. Aronoff *et al.*, eds.), pp. 79–115. Plenum, New York.

Crookston, R. K., and Moss, D. N. (1974). *Crop Sci.* **14**, 123–125.

Currier, H. B., and Webster, D. H. (1964). *Plant Physiol.* **39**, 843–847.

Cutter, E. G., and Chiu, H-W. (1975). *J. Exp. Bot.* **26**, 828–839.

Dixon, A. F. G. (1975). *In* "Transport in Plants" (M. H. Zimmermann and J. A. Milburn, eds.), Vol. I. pp. 154–170. Springer-Verlag, Berlin and New York.

Doi, Y., Teranaka, M., Yora, K., and Asuyama, H. (1967). *Ann. Phytopathol. Soc. Jpn.* **33**, 259–266.

Donald, C. M., and Hamblin, J. (1976). *Adv. Agron.* **28**, 361–405.

Eaton, F. J., and Ergle, D. R. (1948). *Plant Physiol.* **23**, 169–187.

Edelman, J., and Hanson, A. D. (1972). *J. Exp. Bot.* **23**, 469–478.

Edwards, H. H. (1971). *Plant Physiol.* **47**, 324–328.

Esau, K., Cronshaw, J., and Hoefert, L. L. (1967). *J. Cell Biol.* **32**, 71–87.

Eschrich, W. (1975). *In* "Transport in Plants" (M. H. Zimmermann and J. A. Milburn, eds.), Vol, I, pp. 39–56. Springer-Verlag, Berlin and New York.

Eschrich, W., Currier, H. B., Yamaguchi, S., and McNairn, R. B. (1965). *Planta* **65**, 49–64.

Evans, L. T., and Dunstone, R. L. (1970). *Aust. J. Biol. Sci.* **23**, 725–741.

Evans, L. T., and Wardlaw, I. F. (1966). *Planta* **68**, 310–326.

Evans, L. T., and Wardlaw, I. F. (1976). *Adv. Agron.* **28**, 301–359.

Evans, L. T., Dunstone, R. L., Rawson, H. M., and Williams R. F. (1970). *Aust. J. Biol. Sci.* **23**, 743–752.

Evert, R. F., Eschrich, W., and Eichhorn, S. E. (1971). *Planta* **100**, 262–267.

Felippe, G. M., Dale, J. E., and Marriott, C. (1975). *Ann. Bot. (London)* [N.S.] **39**, 43–55.

Fellows, R. J., and Geiger, D. R. (1974). *Plant Physiol.* **54**, 877–885.

Field, R. J., and Peel, A. J. (1972). *New Phytol.* **71**, 249–254.

Fischer, K. S., and Wilson, G. L. (1975). *Aust. J. Agric. Res.* **26**, 11–23.

Flinn, A. M. (1974). *Physiol. Plant.* **31**, 275–278.

Ford, J., and Peel, A. J. (1966). *J. Exp. Bot.* **17**, 522–533.

Forde, B. J. (1965). *Am. J. Bot.* **52**, 953–961.

Fratianne, D. G. (1965). *Am. J. Bot.* **52**, 556–562.

Fric, F. (1975). *Phytopathol. Z.* **84**, 88–95.

Garrard, L. A., and West, S. H. (1972). *Crop Sci.* **12**, 621–623.

Gates, C. T. (1957). *Aust. J. Biol. Sci.* **10**, 125–146.

Geiger, D. R. (1966). *Plant Physiol.* **41**, 1667–1672.

Geiger, D. R. (1969). *Ohio J. Sci.* **69**, 356–366.

Geiger, D. R. (1975a). *In* "Phloem Transport" (S. Aronoff *et al.*, eds.), pp. 251–281. Plenum, New York.

Geiger, D. R. (1975b). In "Transport in Plants" (M. H. Zimmermann and J. A. Milburn, eds.), Vol. I, pp. 395–431. Springer-Verlag, Berlin and New York.

Geiger, D. R. (1976a). In "Transport and Transfer Processes in Plants" (I. F. Wardlaw and J. B. Passioura, eds.), pp. 167–183. Academic Press, New York.

Geiger, D. R. (1976b). Can. J. Bot. **54**, 2337–2345.

Geiger, D. R., and Christy, A. L. (1971). Plant Physiol. **47**, 172–174.

Geiger, D. R., and Sovonick, S. A. (1975). In "Transport in Plants" (M. H. Zimmermann and J. A. Milburn, eds.), Vol. I, pp. 256–286. Springer-Verlag, Berlin and New York.

Giaquinta, R. T., and Geiger, D. R. (1973). Plant Physiol. **51**, 372–377.

Gifford, R. M. (1974). Aust. J. Plant Physiol. **1**, 107–117.

Gill, S., and Hawksworth, F. G. (1961). U.S., Dep. Agric., Tech. Bull. **1242**.

Glasziou, K. T., and Gayler, K. (1972). Bot. Rev. **38**, 471–490.

Gunning, B. E. S., and Robards, A. W. (1976). In "Transport and Transfer Processes in Plants" (I. F. Wardlaw and J. B. Passioura, eds.), pp. 15–41. Academic Press, New York.

Gunning, B. E. S., Pate, J. S., Minchin, F. R., and Marks, I. (1974). Symp. Soc. Exp. Biol. **28**, 87–126.

Habeshaw, D. (1969). J. Exp. Bot. **20**, 64–71.

Habeshaw, D. (1973). Planta **110**, 213–226.

Hackett, C. (1973). Aust. J. Biol. Sci. **26**, 1057–1071.

Hale, C. N., and Whitbread, R. (1973). Ann. Bot. (London) [N.S.] **37**, 473–480.

Halevy, A. H., Monselise, S. P., and Plaut, Z. (1964). Physiol. Plant. **17**, 49–62.

Hall, A. F., and Loomis, R. S. (1972). Plant Physiol. **50**, 576–580.

Hall, S. M., and Baker, D. A. (1972). Planta **106**, 131–140.

Hall, S. M., and Hillman, J. R. (1975). Planta **123**, 137–143.

Hall, S.M., and Medlow, G. C. (1974). Planta **119**, 257–261.

Hanson, J. C., and Rasmussen, D. C. (1975). Crop Sci. **15**, 248–251.

Hanway, J. J. (1962). Agron. J. **54**, 217–224.

Harel, S., and Reinhold, L. (1966). Physiol. Plant. **19**, 634–643.

Hartt, C. E. (1973). Naturwissenschaften **21**, 666–667.

Hassib, M., and Rasmy, A. H. (1974). Appl. Entomol. Zool. **9**, 191–192.

Hawker, J. S. (1965). Aust. J. Biol. Sci. **18**, 959–969.

Hay, J. R., and Thimann, K. V. (1956). Plant Physiol. **31**, 446–451.

Heber, V. (1974). Annu. Rev. Plant Physiol. **25**, 393–421.

Helms, K., and Wardlaw, I. F. (1976). In "Transport and Transfer Processes in Plants" (I. F. Wardlaw and J. B. Passioura, eds.), pp. 283–293. Academic Press, New York.

Hendrix, J. E. (1973). Plant Physiol. **52**, 688–689.

Ho, L. C. (1976). Ann. Bot. (London) [N.S.] **40**, 1153–1162.

Ho, L. C., and Mortimer, D. C. (1971). Can. J. Bot. **49**, 1769–1785.

Ho, L. C., and Peel, A. J. (1969). Physiol. Plant. **22**, 379–385.

Hoad, G. V., and Peel, A. J. (1965). J. Exp. Bot. **16**, 433–451.

Hocking, T. J., Hillman, J. R., and Wilkins, M. B. (1972). Nature (London), New Biol. **235**, 124–125.

Hofstra, G., and Nelson, C. D. (1969). Planta **88**, 103–112.

Höll, W. (1975). In "Transport in Plants" (M. H. Zimmermann and J. A. Milburn, eds.), Vol, I, pp. 432–450. Springer-Verlag, Berlin and New York.

Hoshino, M., Oizumi, H., and Okubo, T. (1972). Proc. Crop Sci. Soc. Jpn. **41**, 509–513.

Hsiao, T. C. (1973). Annu. Rev. Plant Physiol. **24**, 519–570.

Humphries, E. C. (1963). Ann. Bot. (London) [N.S.] **27**, 175–184.

Iljin, W. S. (1957). Annu. Rev. Plant Physiol. **8**, 257–274.

Itai, C., and Vaadia, Y. (1965). *Physiol. Plant.* **18**, 941–944.
Itai, C., and Vaadia, Y. (1971). *Plant Physiol.* **47**, 87–90.
Jacobs, W. P., and Morrow, I. B. (1958). *Science* **128**, 1084.
Jacoli, G. G. (1974). *Can. J. Bot.* **52**, 2085–2088.
Jankiewicz, L. S., Plich, H., and Antoszewski, R. (1969). *In* "The Mechanism of Fruiting, Translocation and Accumulation of Nutrients in Plant Organisms," pp. 1–2. Warszawa-Skiermiewice.
Jenner, C. F. (1976). *In* "Transport and Transfer Processes in Plants" (I. F. Wardlaw and J. B. Passioura, eds.), pp. 73–83. Academic Press, New York.
Jones, M. G. K. (1976). *In* "Transport and Transfer Processes in Plants" (I. F. Wardlaw and J. B. Passioura, eds.), pp. 65–71. Academic Press, New York.
Jones, M. G. K., and Northcote, D. H. (1972). *Protoplasma* **75**, 381–395.
Kawahara, H., Chonan, N., and Wada, K. (1968). *Proc. Crop Sci. Soc. Jpn.* **37**, 372–382.
Keen, N. T., and Williams P. H. (1969). *Plant Physiol.* **44**, 748–754.
Kefeli, V. I., and Kadyrov, C. S. (1971). *Annu. Rev. Plant Physiol.* **22**, 185–196.
Kendall, W. A. (1955). *Plant Physiol.* **30**, 347–350.
Khan, M. A., and Tsunoda, S. (1971). *Jpn. J. Breed.* **21**, 143–150.
Kido, M., and Yanatori, S. (1963). *Proc. Crop Sci. Soc. Jpn.* **31**, 241–244.
King, R. W. (1976). *In* "Transport and Transfer Processes in Plants" (I. F. Wardlaw and J. B. Passioura, eds.), pp. 415–431. Academic Press, New York.
King, R. W. (1977). *Planta* **132**, 43–51.
King, R. W., and Evans, L. T. (1977). *Aust. J. Plant Physiol.* **4**, 225–233.
King, R. W., and Zeevart, J. A. D. (1974). *Plant Physiol.* **53**, 96–103.
King, R. W., Wardlaw, I. F., and Evans, L. T. (1967). *Planta* **77**, 261–276.
Kozlowski, T. T., and Winget, C. H. (1964). *Am. J. Bot.* **51**, 522–529.
Kriedemann, P. E., Loveys, B. R., Possingham, J. V., and Satoh, M. (1976). *In* "Transport and Transfer Processes in Plants" (I. F. Wardlaw and J. B. Passioura, eds.), pp. 401–414. Academic Press, New York.
Kunkel, L. O. (1939). *Phytopathology* **29**, 684–700.
Kuo, J., O'Brien, T. P., and Canny, M. J. (1974). *Planta* **121**, 97–118.
Kursanov, A. L., and Brovchenko, M. I. (1970). *Can. J. Bot.* **48**, 1243–1250.
Laetsch, W. M. (1974). *Annu. Rev. Plant Physiol.* **25**, 27–52.
Läuchli, A. (1972). *Annu. Rev. Plant Physiol.* **23**, 197–218.
Lea, P. T., and Fowden, L. (1975). *Biochem. Physiol. Pflanz.* **168**, 3–14.
Leckstein, P. M., and Llewellyn, M. (1975). *Planta* **124**, 89–91.
Leonard, O. A., and Hull, R. J. (1966). *In* "Isotopes in Weed Research," pp. 31–46. IAEA, Vienna.
Lepp, N. W., and Peel, A. J. (1970). *Planta* **90**, 230–235.
Lepp, N. W., and Peel, A. J. (1971). *Planta* **97**, 50–61.
Levitt, J. (1972). "Responses of Plants to Environmental Stresses." Academic Press, New York.
Lewis, O. A. M., and Pate, J. S. (1973). *J. Exp. Bot.* **24**, 596–606.
Littlefield, N. A., Pattee, H. E., and Allred, K. R. (1966). *Weeds* **14**, 52–54.
Liu, P., Wallace, D. H., and Ozbun, J. L. (1973). *Plant Physiol.* **52**, 412–415.
Loneragan, J. F., Snowball, K., and Robson, A. D. (1976). *In* "Transport and Transfer Processes in Plants" (I. F. Wardlaw and J. B. Passioura, eds.), pp. 463–473. Academic Press, New York.
Lush, M. W., and Evans, L. T. (1974). *Aust. J. Plant Physiol.* **1**, 417–431.
McCombe, A. J. (1964). *Ann. Bot. (London)* [N.S.] **28**, 669–687.
McDavid, C. R., Sagar, G. R., and Marshall, C. (1973). *New Phytol.* **72**, 465–470.

McNairn, R. B. (1972). *Plant Physiol.* **50**, 366–370.

McNairn, R. B., and Currier, H. B. (1968). *Planta* **82**, 369–380.

Manners, J. G., and Myers, A. (1973). In "Fungal Pathogenicity and the Plants' Response" (R. J. W. Byrde and C. V. Cutting, eds.), pp. 319–330. Academic Press, New York.

Marshall, C., and Wardlaw, I. F. (1973). *Aust. J. Biol. Sci.* **26**, 1–13.

Mason, T. G., and Maskell, E. J. (1928a) *Ann. Bot. (London)* **42**, 189–253.

Mason, T. G., and Maskell, E. J. (1928b). *Ann. Bot. (London)* **42**, 571–636.

Mason, T. G., and Maskell, E. J. (1931). *Ann. Bot. (London)* **45**, 125–173.

Mellor, G. E., and Tregunna, E. B. (1971). *Can. J. Bot.* **49**, 137–142.

Milburn, J. A. (1974). *Planta* **117**, 303–319.

Milford, G. F. J., and Pearman, I. (1975). *Photosynthetica* **9**, 78–83.

Milthorpe, F. L., and Moorby, J. (1969). *Annu. Rev. Plant Physiol.* **20**, 117–138.

Mitchell, J. W. (1961). *Bull. Torrey Bot. Club* **88**, 299–312.

Mitchell, J. W., and Brown, J. W. (1946). *Bot. Gaz. (Chicago)* **107**, 393–407.

Mitchell, J. W., and Linder, P. J. (1962). *Agric. Food Chem.* **10**, 82–83.

Mittler, T. E. (1953). *Nature (London)* **172**, 207.

Moorby, J., Munns, R., and Walcott, J. (1975). *Aust. J. Plant Physiol.* **2**, 323–333.

Moore, K. G., Illsley, A., and Lovell, P. H. (1974). *J. Exp. Bot.* **25**, 887–898.

Mothes, K. (1931). *Planta* **12**, 686–731.

Müller, K., and Leopold, A. C. (1966). *Planta* **68**, 167–185.

Murata, Y., Iyama, J., and Honma, T. (1965). *Proc. Crop Sci. Soc. Jpn.* **34**, 148–153.

Nagao, T., and Wada, Y. (1970). *Proc. Crop Sci. Soc. Jpn.* **39**, 21–25.

Neales, T.F., and Incoll, L. D. (1968). *Bot. Rev.* **34**, 107–125.

Nichiporovich, A. A., and Chen, I. N. (1959). *Fiziol. Rast.* **6**, 513–522.

Osmond, C. B., and Smith, F. A. (1976). In "Intercellular Communication in Plants: Studies on Plasmodesmata" (B. E. S. Gunning and A. W. Robards, eds.), pp. 229–241. Springer-Verlag, Berlin and New York.

Outlaw, W. H., Jr., Fisher, D. B., and Christy, A. L. (1975). *Plant Physiol.* **55**, 704–711.

Pakianathan, S. W. (1968). M.Sc. Thesis, Dept. of Bontany, University of Aberdeen.

Passioura, J. B., and Ashford, A. E. (1974). *Aust. J. Plant Physiol.* **1**, 521–527.

Pate, J. S. (1975) In "Transport in Plants" (M. H. Zimmermann and J. A. Milburn, eds.), Vol, I. pp. 451–473. Springer-Verlag, Berlin and New York.

Pate, J. S. (1976a). In "Transport and Transfer Processes in Plants" (I. F. Wardlaw and J. B. Passioura, eds.), pp. 253–281. Academic Press, New York.

Pate, J. S. (1976b). In "Transport and Transfer Processes in Plants" (I. F. Wardlaw and J. B. Passioura, eds.), pp. 447–462. Academic Press, New York.

Patrick, J.W. (1972). *Aust. J. Biol. Sci.* **25**, 455–467.

Patrick, J. W. (1976). In "Transport and Transfer Processes in Plants" (I. F. Wardlaw and J. B. Passioura, eds.), pp. 433–446. Academic Press, New York.

Peel, A. J., and Ho, L. C. (1970). *Physiol. Plant.* **23**, 1033–1038.

Peel, A. J., and Weatherley, P. E. (1962). *Ann. Bot. (London)* [N.S.] **26**, 633–646.

Peel, A. J., and Weatherley, P. E. (1963). *Ann. Bot. (London)* [N.S.] **27**, 197–211.

Peterson, C. A., and Currier, H. B. (1969). *Physiol. Plant.* **22**, 1238–1250.

Phillips, D. A., and Cleland, C. F. (1972). *Planta* **102**, 173–178.

Phillips, I. D. J. (1968). *J. Exp. Bot.* **19**, 617–627.

Pitman, M. G. (1976). In "Transport and Transfer Processes in Plants" (I. F. Wardlaw and J. B. Passioura, eds.), pp. 85–99. Academic Press, New York.

Porter, H. K., and Bird, I. F. (1962). *Indian J. Plant Physiol.* **5**, 5–32.

Qureshi, F. A., and Spanner, D. C. (1973). *J. Exp. Bot.* **24**, 751–762.

Rasmussen, O. S. (1976). *Physiol. Plant.* **36**, 208–212.

Rathnam, C. K. M., and Das, V. S. R. (1975). *Biochem. Physiol. Pflanz.* **167**, 565–576.
Rawson, H. M., and Evans, L. T. (1971). *Aust. J. Agric. Res.* **22**, 851–863.
Rediske, J. H., and Shea, K. R. (1961). *Am. J. Bot.* **48**, 447–452.
Reinhold, L. (1975). *In* "Phloem Transport" (S. Aronoff *et al.*, eds.), pp. 367–388. Plenum, New York.
Rijven, A. H. G. C., and Evans, L. T. (1967). *Aust. J. Biol. Sci.* **20**, 13–24.
Rinne, R. W., and Langston, R. (1960). *Plant Physiol.* **35**, 210–215.
Roberts, B. R., and Stevens, J. M. (1968). *Adv. Front. Plant Sci.* **21**, 127–134.
Roy, R. N., and Wright, B. C. (1974). *Agron. J.* **66**, 5–10.
Sarkissian, G. S., and Fowler, M. W. (1974). *Planta* **119**, 335–350.
Sashara, T., and Tsunoda, S. (1971). *Jpn. J. Breed.* **21**, 1–8.
Satoh, M., and Ohyama, K. (1971). *Proc. Crop Sci. Soc. Jpn.* **40**, 525–529.
Schiller, R., and Martin, P. (1975). *Biochem. Physiol. Pflanz.* **167**, 427–438.
Schneider, I. R. (1965). *Adv. Virus Res.* **11**, 163–221.
Scott, T. K., and Briggs, W. R. (1960). *Am. J. Bot.* **47**, 492–499.
Servaites, J. C., and Geiger, D. R. (1974). *Plant Physiol.* **54**, 575–578.
Sharkey, P. J., and Pate, J. S. (1975). *Planta* **127**, 251–262.
Shaw, M. (1963). *Annu. Rev. Phytopathol.* **1**, 259–294.
Sij, J., and Swanson, C. A. (1973). *Plant Physiol.* **51**, 368–371.
Sinclair, T. R., and de Wit, C. T. (1976). *Agron. J.* **68**, 319–324.
Singh, A. P., and Srivastava, L. M. (1972). *Can. J. Bot.* **50**, 839–846.
Sofield, I., Wardlaw, I. F., Evans, L. T., and Zee, S. Y. (1977). *Aust. J. Plant Physiol.* **4**, 799–810.
Sovonick, S. A., Geiger, D. R., and Fellows, R. J. (1974). *Plant Physiol.* **54**, 886–891.
Starck, Z. (1973). *Acta Soc. Bot. Pol.* **42**, 143–162.
Starck, Z., and Ubysz, L. (1974). *Acta Soc. Bot. Pol.* **43**, 427–445.
Stephenson, R. A., Brown, R. H., and Ashley, D. A. (1976). *Crop Sci.* **16**, 285–288.
Tammes, P. M. L., and vanDie, J. (1966). *Proc. K. Ned. Akad. Wet.*, Ser. C **69**, 655–659.
Tammes, P. M. L., and vanDie, J. (1976). *Neth. J. Plant Pathol.* **82**, 9–12.
Tammes, P. M. L., Vonk, G. R., and vanDie, J. (1969). *Acta Bot. Neerl.* **18**, 224–229.
Taniyama, T., and Sawanaka, K. (1973). *Proc. Crop Sci. Soc. Jpn.* **42**, 143–147.
Terry, N., and Mortimer, D. C. (1972). *Can. J. Bot.* **50**, 1049–1054.
Thimann, K. V., Sachs, T., and Mathur, K. N. (1971). *Physiol. Plant.* **24**, 68–72.
Thorne, G. N., and Evans, A. F. (1964). *Ann. Bot. (London)* [N.S.] **28**, 499–508.
Thrower, L. B., and Thrower, S. L. (1966). *Phytopathol. Z.* **57**, 267–276.
Thrower, S. L. (1974). *New Phytol.* **73**, 685–687.
Torrey, J. G. (1976). *Annu. Rev. Plant Physiol.* **27**, 435–459.
Tromp, J., and Ovaa, J. C. (1973). *Physiol. Plant.* **29**, 1–5.
Troughton, J. H. (1975). *In* "Environmental and Biological Control of Photosynthesis" (R. Marcelle, ed.), pp. 373–385. Junk, The Hague.
Turgeon, R., and Webb, J. A. (1973). *Planta* **113**, 179–191.
Turgeon, R., and Webb, J. A. (1975). *Planta* **123**, 53–62.
Ullrich, W. (1963). *Planta* **59**, 387–390.
vanDie, J. (1975). *In* "Phloem Transport" (S. Aronoff *et al.*, eds.), pp. 427–446. Plenum, New York.
vanGoor, B. J., and Wiersma, D. (1974). *Physiol. Plant.* **31**, 163–168.
vanOverbeek, J. (1956). *Annu. Rev. Plant Physiol.* **7**, 355–372.
Vonk, C. R. (1974). *Acta Bot. Neerl.* **23**, 541–548.
Wanner, H., and Bachofen, R. (1961). *Planta* **57**, 531–542.
Wardlaw, I. F. (1967). *Aust. J. Biol. Sci.* **20**, 25–39.

Wardlaw, I. F. (1968). *Bot. Rev.* **34**, 79–105.
Wardlaw, I. F. (1969). *Aust. J. Biol. Sci.* **22**, 1–16.
Wardlaw, I. F. (1972). *Planta* **104**, 18–34.
Wardlaw, I. F. (1974a). *R. Soc. N.Z., Bull.* **12**, 533–538.
Wardlaw, I. F. (1974b). *Annu. Rev. Plant Physiol.* **25**, 515–539.
Wardlaw, I. F. (1976a). *Aust. J. Plant Physiol.* **3**, 377–387.
Wardlaw, I. F. (1976b). *In* "Transport and Transfer Processes in Plants" (I. F. Wardlaw and J. B. Passioura, eds.), pp. 381–391. Academic Press, New York.
Wardlaw, I. F., and Marshall, C. (1976). *Aust. J. Plant Physiol.* **3**, 389–400.
Wardlaw, I. F., and Moncur, L. (1976). *Planta* **128**, 93–100.
Wardlaw, I. F., and Mortimer, D. C. (1970). *Can. J. Bot.* **48**, 229–237.
Wardlaw, I. F., and Passioura, J. B., eds. (1976). "Transport and Transfer Processes in Plants." Academic Press, New York.
Wardlaw, I. F., and Porter, H. K. (1967). *Aust. J. Biol. Sci.* **20**, 309–318.
Webb, J. A. (1970). *Can. J. Bot.* **48**, 935–942.
Whitbread, R., and Bhatti, M. A. R. (1976). *Ann. Bot. (London)* [N.S.] **40**, 499–509.
Willenbrink, J. (1966). *Z. Pflanzenphysiol.* **55**, 119–130.
Williams, R. F. (1975). *J. Aust. Inst. Agric. Sci.* **41**, 18–26.
Wilson, D., and Cooper, J. P. (1969). *New Phytol.* **68**, 627–644.
Wolswinkel, P. (1974a). *Acta Bot. Neerl.* **23**, 48–60.
Wolswinkel, P. (1974b). *Acta Bot. Neerl.* **23**, 177–188.
Wolswinkel, P. (1975). *Acta Bot. Neerl.* **24**, 211–224.
Worley, J. F. (1965). *Phytopathology* **55**, 1299–1302.
Worley, J. F. (1968). *Plant Physiol.* **43**, 1648–1655.
Zee, S. Y., and O'Brien, T. P. (1970). *Aust. J. Biol. Sci.* **23**, 783–791.
Ziegler, H. (1975). *In* "Transport in Plants" (M. H. Zimmermann and J. A. Milburn, eds.), Vol. I, pp. 59–100. Springer-Verlag, Berlin and New York.
Zimmermann, M. H. (1961). *Science* **133**, 73–79.
Zimmermann, M. H., and Milburn, J. A., eds. (1975). "Transport in Plants," Vol. I. Springer-Verlag, Berlin and New York.

GENETIC MANIPULATIONS

Chapter 9

Molecular Biology of Higher Plants

Virginia Walbot

I. WHAT IS MOLECULAR BIOLOGY?

Molecular biology is that branch of the biological sciences which attempts to provide an explanation for biological phenomena in terms of the interaction of molecules and their polymers. The basic tools of this discipline are genetics, biochemistry, and physical chemistry. Clearly, molecular biology provides elegant, albeit not necessarily useful, answers to specific questions regarding the chemical nature and behavior of biological molecules. In this chapter, some questions of fundamental importance to improving crop productivity, which are amenable to investigation by molecular biologists and which, furthermore, seem likely to provide areas of common ground between plant breeding and molecular biology, are outlined. I would hope that enumeration of these potential common interests would persuade more scientists in each discipline to cooperate in the description and experimental manipulation of processes fundamental to plant life.

343

The Biology of Crop Productivity
Copyright © 1980 by Academic Press, Inc.
All rights of reproduction in any form reserved
ISBN 0-12-159850-0

Of course, the goals of each group may not be identical. Division of the scientific enterprise between applied and basic research or short-term and long-term efforts has obscured to some extent the spectrum of goals of various disciplines. However, within this spectrum, molecular biologists view themselves as primarily investigating problems of intrinsic scientific interest; agricultural scientists have emphasized the improvement of particular crops or processes. To the extent that particular questions in the agricultural sciences require more than operational answers, molecular biology can provide a complete explanation. This is not to say that all questions require this kind of explication. However, elucidation of the molecular bases for various physiological phenomena, and enumeration, mapping, and manipulation of the genes impinging on important phenotypic traits should provide the basis for more successful plant breeding and crop improvement.

II. IS MOLECULAR BIOLOGY DEAD?

The noted molecular biologist Gunther Stent once proclaimed, "Molecular biology is dead!" He expressed the sense of disappointment many bacterial geneticists felt at having no new worlds to conquer after solving the fundamental problems of heredity and the genetic code in the 1960's. What challenging problems remained? This lament was voiced when scientists believed that the genetic material was static and that only regular, predictable mutational and recombinational events occurred. Recently, this view of genetics has undergone a rapid transformation. The discovery of plasmids and transposons has revitalized bacterial and eukaryotic genetics by providing a set of tools with which genomes may be manipulated and constructed (Cohen, 1976). The utility of plasmids as vectors for introducing new genetic material into cells was recognized when the restriction DNA endonucleases were discovered. By specifically cleaving a plasmid and the "foreign" DNA with a restriction nuclease, complementary overlapping ends can be created; these ends allow the ligation of the foreign DNA into a plasmid. The recombinant DNA molecule will now be replicated as a single unit, and the inserted DNA will be transferred with the plasmid. Plasmid technology provides a means for introducing new genetic material into a variety of hosts, including higher plants and their organelles.

Extremely rapid DNA sequencing methods have also prompted renewed interest in bacterial genetics. Direct examination of the informational content of the genetic material is now possible: the approximately 5300 bases of ϕX174 have now been completely sequenced (Sanger et al., 1977). The sequence revealed unpredicted properties of the genome, such as the inclusion of two small genes within larger genes; the gene sets do not share amino acid sequences, since the reading frame of each small gene is shifted from the triplet frame of the surrounding larger gene. This economy of base usage is further illustrated by the overlap of termination and initiation signals of contiguous genes. Discoveries such as this immediately raise the question of whether such phenomena exist in bacteria and eukaryotes. Corn and other higher plants, with well-studied classical genetics, will provide good systems in which to investigate these aspects of eukaryotic gene organization, sequence, and usage.

Although Stent may have been premature in his pronouncement on the death of molecular biology, it is clear that many notable microbial geneticists have initiated projects on more complex organisms. Recombinant DNA techniques allow the selective study of small portions of eukaryotic genomes, using microbiological procedures and growth rates; DNA sequencing makes it possible now to examine at the most exact level the actual composition of genes, even in eukaryotes lacking formal genetics. Unfortunately, the agricultural sciences have captured the imagination of too few molecular biologists seeking new problems. This situation is due, in part, to the largely separate, insular environments of the land grant colleges and of the major research centers in molecular biology. The lack of training in basic plant biology in most biological curricula must also be cited as a reason for the unfamiliarity of molecular biologists with the unsolved problems of plant biology. The funding situation in the agricultural sciences, however, remains a major barrier to the recruitment of new scientific talent; if fundamental problems of plant biology are to be solved at the molecular level, the vast reserve of talent employed outside the land grant institutions must be recruited.

It behooves everyone committed to increasing crop productivity to attempt to recruit new talent. The recruitment task falls to those who know the problems and can convince molecular biologists that these problems are significant and challenging. The problems outlined in Section IV are amenable to molecular explication, and should serve as bait to attract a new generation of scientists.

III. AN EXAMPLE OF A MOLECULAR EXPLANATION

A successful crop plant has a suitable genetic background; adequate responses to environmental stress; a structure suitable for harvesting; a high final yield of usable product; and a minimum of undesirable traits such as toxicity, allergenicity, or nonpalatability. The molecular aspects of these characteristics are not always obvious, but the basis for all phenomena lies in the molecular constituents of the cells. The difficulty in acquiring useful knowledge about these phenomena is due in part to a lack of clear definition of the real unsolved problems in each area. For example, increasing the balanced protein content of corn is an undefined goal, for this statement conveys none of the reasons why such an obvious goal has not been met with traditional breeding practices. To discuss a simple example first, consider the problem of food allergy in molecular terms. The agronomic goal is to decrease the allergenicity of a crop plant without adversely affecting yield. At the molecular level, this problem can be broken down into the following questions and procedures.

1. Develop a rapid and sensitive assay for the allergen.
2. Determine where the allergen is located.
   a. Fractionate plant parts.
   b. Purify allergenic components.
   c. Determine when allergen appears during development.
3. What is the composition of the allergenic component(s)?
   a. Characterize the composition.
   b. Postulate a role for the component, i.e., enzymatic or structural protein, wall carbohydrate.
4. Does the component serve an important function in the plant?
   a. Select strains lacking or with an altered component, and test plant viability.
   b. Find an inhibitor of component synthesis or activity, and test plant viability after inhibitor application.
5. What is the regulation of the synthesis and activity of the component?
   a. Determine half-life.
   b. Determine pathway of synthesis and degradation.
   c. Isolate strains with altered regulation of synthesis and/or degradation.
6. Can favorable combinations of altered component and regulatory mutant strains be constructed in which high yield and acceptable levels of allergenicity are found?
   a. Using somatic or standard genetics, construct lines.
   b. Test hybrid lines for allergenicity and yield.

The information generated by this investigation is far in excess of that required by an agronomist. Plant breeders are most interested in the last item, since this is the strategy employed in traditional breeding programs. However, a molecular biologist approaches the big problem by defining a set of unknowns. What is the compound? Where and how is it metabolized? How stable is it? What is the phenotype of a cell or organism lacking the component? What is the function of the substance? It is significant that the first goal of this analysis is to develop a simple and sensitive assay with which all of the work will be standardized. This assay, which may be only indirectly related to the phenomenon of allergenicity, can be used immediately by physiologists and agronomists to screen large quantities of material successfully, so long as there is a general correlation between the assay and allergenicity.

The principle I hope to have illustrated here is that the questions posed by a molecular biologist are very specific and amenable to a direct experimental analysis. Many years of effort must be devoted to a complete analysis. One danger of this approach is that problems trivial to agriculture will be examined, due to a lack of foresight or knowledge. A second problem for molecular biologists switching to plant materials is a naive appreciation of whole-plant physiology. With the advent of recombinant DNA technology and the experimental introduction of novel genetic material into eukaryotic cells, many molecular biologists have become interested in using plant materials to create new organisms and solve intractable problems. For example, introduction of nitrogen fixation capacity via the *nif* gene cluster into plants or their symbionts, elucidation of the mechanism of cancerous transformation in plants infected by plasmid DNA from *Agrobacterium tumefaciens*, and introduction of heavy-metal resistance genes into plants to be grown on mine tailings are but a few of the seemingly fantastic possibilities suggested for genetically engineered plants. However, these possibilities must be tempered by the reality of plant metabolism; for example, where in a plant is an anaerobic compartment for oxygen-sensitive nitrogenase?

Successful cooperation between molecular biologists and agronomists will involve the education of each group with the basic knowledge of the other, in order to avoid producing molecular masterpieces irrelevent to the everyday life of the plant. Selective use of the techniques of both the molecular and agronmic fields should be used to advance crop plants toward desirable traits. Crop breeding, in particular, may benefit shortly from novel approaches developed by molecular biologists.

IV. NEW APPROACHES TO PLANT BREEDING USING MOLECULAR BIOLOGY

Traditional plant breeding has been successful due both to art and science. Genetics and statistical analysis have been the two primary scientific disciplines that have contributed to the success of long-term plant breeding programs. To reach a specific goal, such as increased yield, from a group of starting test lines has required the examination of enormous numbers of individuals in large-scale plantings; if crosses are made, the number of biotypes rapidly increases from a manageable number of starting lines to potentially millions of biotypes. Limitations of space and time have forced successful breeders to adopt strategies involving both random mating and the considered selection of certain biotypes for more intensive scrutiny. The ability of the breeder to judge the potential of a line for further development is not a defined process, and hence remains somewhat of an art form.

The genetics of plant breeding rests on the basic principles of Mendelian and classical genetics. These principles include

1. Inheritance of many characters is unitary rather than a blending.
2. Characters are usually dominant or recessive.
3. Since many plants are polyploid, heterozygosity at many loci can be obtained.
4. The genes are in a fixed, linear order on the individual chromosomes.
5. The blocks of gene of a particular chromosome are assorted together.
6. The linkage between contiguous genes can be broken by crossing over.
7. Nonlinked genes assort randomly at meiosis.

Plant breeding using these principles then becomes a process of testing enough individuals to recover rare natural phenomena, and of applying screens to eliminate individuals of marginal value. The analysis of important plant characteristics, such as water stress resistance and photosynthetic efficiency, is complicated by the many genes involved in determining such traits. Polygeny, a termed coined by Mather, has been used to describe the multigenic, and hence quantitative, nature of many such macro traits. The variability of polygenic traits can often be shown, in practice and in theory, to actually be determined by a small number of genes (Thompson, 1977). The major genes contributing to the trait are modulated by many of the "housekeeping" genes, that large gene group contributing to viability. Important physiological traits, such as photosynthetic efficiency, will be set primarily by a few genes at rate-limiting steps. These genes are complemented by interaction with numerous other genes contributing to the general metabolic state of the cell and plant. Consequently, only rarely by chance will an especially fortuitous association of the requisite genes occur in the absence of strong selection pressure for each individual (desirable) allele.

Novel approaches to plant breeding using molecular biology and non-Mendelian genetics would circumvent the limitations of time, space, and expense associated with traditional breeding practices. The most crucial factor in designing a more efficient selection scheme is the development of positive or negative selective pressures strong enough to greatly favor the desirable genotype. The other major approach is to take existing genetic systems containing favorable traits but located in different organisms and recombine these traits through direct manipulation of the nucleic acids or organelles.

At least five types of non-Mendelian genetics are currently being examined in higher plants to exploit or create new genetic combinations

1. Transformation of nucleic acids directly into a recipient plant or cell.

2. Manipulation of gene regulation, using controlling elements, paramutation, and other intracellular regulatory phenomena.

3. Somatic cell genetics, such as cell fusion of nonhybridizable species.

4. Transplantation of nuclei or other organelles into recipient cells.

5. Construction and introduction into recipient cells of artificial genetic systems such as new organelles or plasmids.

These approaches are discussed in detail below.

A. Transformational Events

Transformation of novel genetic traits into higher plants or plant cells has been reported by several laboratories (Gresshof, 1974); Doy et al., 1973; Ledoux et al., 1974; Ledoux, 1974). Although there is considerable precedent in bacterial systems for transformation, the experiments reported thus far are not completely convincing as described. Furthermore, few other laboratories have reported positive results using transformation, which indicates that the present reports of gene transfer are difficult to repeat due to methodological or theoretical problems. One such problem is that DNA prepared for transformation has been subjected to such unfavorable conditions that the molecules were likely degraded. This is a significant problem, since cytokinins are a byproduct of DNA degradation, and application of a plant hormone may be responsible for the appearance of new phenotypes. Proof that a new phenotype is correlated with a heritable genetic trait rather than a consequence of an epigenetic change should be demonstrated as the criterion for the success of transformation. Transformation may be an easy method for the "shotgun" transfer of genes, and therefore deserves a most rigorous and complete characterization. Such a characterization would include a description of the DNA, an analysis of the metabolic fate of exogenous DNA in the plant or culture, as well as within the affected cells, and a definitive proof of gene expression by the new genetic material. This analysis should also provide an estimate of the efficiency of gene transfer and of limitations of DNA size or composition. Now that a variety of plants can be propagated via a cycle of somatic cell culture–plant regeneration–sexual cycle, the genetic proof of transformation should also be presented. In organisms with strong formal genetics, the location of the new genetic material, if integrated into the chromosomes, should be mapped as well.

To be permanently maintained, DNA transformed into plant cells may be integrated into the nuclear or cytoplasmic genomes or maintained as a self-replicating entity. The properties of DNA that allow it to integrate into a bacterial or eukaryotic chromosome, and the effects of DNA insertion on gene structure and regulation, have recently received much attention in the literature. Some bacteriophages, i.e., lambda, have a high degree of insertion specificity in that there are preferred sites in the bacterial genome for lambda entry. Other phages, i.e., Mu, insert randomly in the host genome (see reviews by Kleckner, 1977; Lewin, 1977). A more recently discovered class of translocatable elements in bacteria, transposons, carries only a few genes, such as antibiotic resistance markers, flanked by direct or inverted repetitious DNA termini; these termini have in some cases been indentified as insertion sequences (IS sequences), which are the smallest segments of DNA capable of independent translocation. The transposons and IS sequences can apparently insert at any position in the bacterial chromosome. Mobile sequences of DNA such as phage and the transposons may control important aspects of gene evolution and regulation as well as providing a means for gene movement in bacteria; currently, microbial geneticists are attempting to understand the means by which the frequency of gene movement and mode of insertion are regulated. Unfortunately, there is far less information on the mechanisms of DNA insertion and movement in eukaryotic cells, and no basis for understanding how the reported successful transformation events in plant cells worked at the molecular level.

There are a number of pressing technical problems to be solved in the area of exogenously applied DNA metabolism in target cells. As evidenced in a recent study of the metabolism of viral DNA sequences in animal cells, many problems can be encountered in the interpretation of the fate of exogenous DNA in eukaryotic cells. Botchan *et al.* (1976) have recently demonstrated that the small, double-stranded DNA virus SV40 can integrate at a variety of chromosomal locations in transformed rat cells. The junction between cellular DNA and the integrated SV40 genomes was localized in a different region of the viral genome in each cell line tested. It has not yet been determined whether the cellular DNAs flanking integrated SV40 genomes share a common sequence or topography. Within a single clonal cell line, there is a stable and specific location of the SV40 genome, but each clone contains SV40 at a different chromosomal site. The implications of this promiscuity of insertion for genetic regulation, and the movement of other segments of DNA within or between chromosomes and organisms, are only now being explored.

Since the original rat cell lines chosen for this study expressed a SV40-specific transformed state, an additional question remains concerning the phenotypic expressions of SV40 integrated at different locations. For example, can cell lines be obtained in which SV40 is integrated but never expressed? Such a cryptic viral genome could remain unexpressed due to (1) the mode of insertion—an essential region may be lost; (2) the site of insertion—insertion may occur within an essential region and hence disrupt it; (3) the negative control of flanking cellular DNA sequences; and (4) other modes of negative cellular control.

Those interested in the transformation of DNA sequences into higher plants must recognize the complexity of the modes of DNA replication, insertion, and expression. Most shotgun experiments will introduce DNA lacking a means of self-replication, and those elements will be lost unless they are replicated after insertion or maintained extrachromosomally by host gene products. The extent to which transforming DNA produces a stable genetic type and suitable phenotype will depend on the interaction of the new DNA with the existing genome. The stability of transformed segments should be examined carefully, in order to exclude the possibility of a "jumping gene" with a deleterious or revertant phenotype. Whether the novel DNA is inserted or extra chromosal, a careful characterization of its rate of replication relative to cell division will be required to ensure that a desirable phenotypic trait will persist in the somatic tissue of the crop plant.

This discussion of transformation has required some comment on insertion sequences and plasmids, two topics to be considered in greater detail below, to demonstrate the extent of our lack of knowledge concerning the fate of exogenous DNA in eukaryotic cells. Although spectacular successes in transforming higher plant cells with DNA have been claimed, many fundamental molecular problems concerning the mechanism of transformation and the expression of the exogenous DNA remain unsolved. Clearly, prior to the release of a new crop plant containing a novel property introduced by transduction, a thorough molecular characterization of the resultant recombinants should be provided. The major concern is with the safety and stability of the novel combination. In other words, does the new segment move within the genome or between chromosomes and an extrachromosomal location, and does this movement cause undesirable phenotypic or genetic changes in the whole plant properties originally sought? For example, it is not unlikely that some DNA sequences introduced by transformation would contain strong promoters for transcription. Such elements might have very profound consequences on cellular gene expression, depending on where the new promoter were inserted. Instability of promoter or repressor insertion would further complicate the characterization of the phenotype of the cell and plant.

B. Controlling Elements, Paramutation, and Other Intracellular Events Governing Gene Expression

Modification of plant phenotype might be accomplished by the introduction of new genetic material, or perhaps more readily by modulating the expression of existing genes. Traditional breeding programs have modified plant height, fruit size and color, seed set and size, and have made dioecious plants monoecious and annual plants perennials. Directed selection and specific control of desirable genes might be possible if the basis for gene regulation were understood or were experimentally accessible. For example, it might be desirable to precociously turn on storage protein synthesis in legumes, to accumulate an existing cereal protein of balanced amino acid content as a storage protein, or to increase the apparent gene dosage of a desirable gene. Our knowledge of gene regulation in eukaryotes is limited. However, several phenomena best known in plants—paramutation and the controlling elements—demonstrate that it is possible to experimentally modify the timing, intensity, and frequency of specific gene action.

1. Controlling Elements

Plant geneticists, notably Barbara McClintock, were among the first to note that the arrangement of the genetic material within the chromosomes was not necessarily stable. In fact, the transposable elements in corn described by McClintock (reviewed, 1956) have elicited much excitement recently among molecular geneticists who have only just

discovered translocatable genes in bacteria. The transposable controlling elements of maize include three well-characterized classes: *Ac*
equivalent to *Mp*, *Spm* equivalent to *En*, and *Dt* (see reviews by Fincham and Sastry, 1974; Nevers and Saedler, 1977; the dual terminology
reflects the multiple discovery of the same element). The controlling
elements may be either one- or two-element systems. The one-element
or complete systems named above contain DNA sequences that confer
on the element the ability to transpose, receive (receptor function), and
send (regulator function) regulatory signals. Two-element systems can
be derived from each class of one-element system, when the
transposition-regulator functions are separated from the receptor function. The regulator, a trans-acting element, is postulated to make a gene
product affecting the receptor; the receptor, a cis-acting element,
modulates the activity of a gene near which it has been inserted. A
single regulator can control the activity of receptors of its class inserted
in many parts of the genome. The controlling elements modulate the
timing and frequency of gene action, as is often illustrated by the ap-
pearnce of anthocyanin spots on seeds: pigmented regions appear on
an otherwise colorless background each time a controlling element
changes from "on" to "off" or vice versa.

**a.Controlling Elements of Maize Share Genetic Properties with
Bacterial DNA Elements.** As was mentioned before, bacteria contain
translocatable genetic elements. For example, the translocatable elements TnA and TnS of the pSC50 plasmid of *E. coli* have been recently
studied by Kopecko *et al.* (1976). Each of these elements contains antibiotic resistance coding segments that facilitates genetic scoring. Both
elements are structurally defined DNA segments containing an approximately 104-nucleotide, inverted repeat DNA sequence at each end of
the element. The elements move between plasmids of the bacterium
and the chromosome as discrete units. These observations suggest that
the transposable segments' ends may be involved in site-specific recognition, insertion, and excision. In addition, the termini of the transposable segments render contiguous sequences recombinational hot
spots subject to deletion. This effect parallels the behavior of the controlling element *Ds* of corn (*Ds* is part of *Ac*), which when inserted in
chromosome 9 conditions a cycle of chromosome loss (Fincham and
Sastry, 1974). Kopecko *et al.* (1976) describe one case in which the
Km–Nm gene, lying between translocatable element TnS and an insertion sequence IS1, can be spontaneously deleted, making TnS and IS1
contiguous.

Another interesting example of gene movement is Mu1, a bacteriophage of *E. coli* that can integrate at random into the bacterial chromosome (Bukhari and Zipser, 1972). Recently, two laboratories have demonstrated that Mu can mediate the transposition of other genes into the bacterial chromosome (Faelen and Toussaint, 1976; Casadaban, 1976). Mu consists of a small, discrete genome plus two variable regions at the termini; these variable regions contain bacterial DNA and are lost during integration. Mu promotes insertion of a circular DNA, such as a plasmid or phage, into a host DNA. The final orientation of these inserted DNAs is Mu–circular DNA–Mu; this structure may be found at any site in the bacterial chromosome, and the breakage site in the (circular) DNA also appears to be random. After Mu induction, Mu–DNA circles are formed in which Mu is carrying a portion of a contiguous DNA. Controlling elements in higher plants may also facilitate the transposition of normally stable genetic elements to new sites.

Discussion of the impact of IS sequence insertion on contiguous gene expression will illustrate the influence even the smallest class of translocatable elements can exert. The IS sequences are normal components of the bacterial chromosome; speculation assigns such diverse roles as control of the spontaneous mutation rate, generation of sites of homology for chromosome–episome interaction, and on–off control of gene expression to these insertion elements. Insertion elements exhibit polarity; transcription of genes following IS is usually repressed. Insertion elements may interfere with normal promoter activity, or they may contain terminator signals that stop transcription in progress. In addition to negative control, IS2, when inserted in reverse orientation, results in constitutive expression at 3 times the normal level of the genes under its control. Inversion of control regions in genes may be a simple on–off or more complex switching mechanism; DNA inversion is hypothesized to result in the alternate production, from the same DNA region, of the two flagellar types of *Salmonella*. (Zieg, et. al, 1978) In addition to the immediate impact of IS insertion, affected genes may also be changed during IS excision. If excision is exact, the gene is returned to its precise previous state. However, inexact excision will result in either deletion or addition of DNA sequences to the gene region, with a permanent change in gene expression possible.

b. Controlling Elements of Maize and Gene Structure. The structure of the controlling elements of maize is, at present, unknown. Some properties of the elements suggest that they may be analogous to certain kinds of translocatable or extrachromosomal elements in bacteria. Insertion sequences, transposable elements, and Mu, a promiscuous insertion phage, all share some apparent properties with the controlling elements. These properties include movement, effects on gene expression (cis-acting), and induction of deletions or recombinational hot spots. Another shared aspect of the translocatable elements of bacteria and eukaryotes is that these elements are all presumed to be normal constituents of the chromosome and not invasive sequences.

i.Insertion and excision. The translocatable elements of bacteria fall into three classes with regard to insertion site specificity; they may have (1) no preferred sites and show random insertion such as Mu; (2) some preferred sites, but retain the capacity of insertion at most, if not all, sites, such as most transposons; or, (3) a specific insertion site(s), such as many bacteriophage.

Each of the controlling elements of corn has been mapped to several locations, either as a one-element or a two-element system. Isolates of some genes have been brought under the control of different controlling elements, indicating that the DNA sequence near the affected gene is not specific for one controlling element class.

The sites available for controlling element insertion in corn have not been characterized as to sequence or special structures or properties. Within eukaryotic genomes several kinds of DNA sequences exist; the three major categories of sequence type are the unique sequences (Mendelian gene regions), repetitive sequences, and palindromic* sequences. Recent evidence indicates that the corn genome is approximately one-half repetitive and one-half unique copy DNA, and that this genome is particularly rich in palindromic DNA (S. Hake and V. Walbot, unpublished data). If specificity of insertion exists in the chromosomal DNA, palindromic regions seem especially attractive as chromosomal insertion sites. This is due to their special topography, which allows recognition from either direction as well as to the potential nonde-

---

*Palindromes are DNA sequences that are tandem, inverted, repeat sequences of the

sort 5′ $\frac{\text{ATAT}}{\text{TATA}}$ / $\frac{\text{ATAT}}{\text{TATA}}$ 5′, with a center of symmetry as indicated by the / mark. Each 5′ strand reads the same. Such sequences can exist in two configurations: linear or cruciform. The first case is the usual conformation of double-stranded DNA, the second configuration is possible with palindromic sequences, due to intrastrand base pairing around the center of symmetry.

TA
AT
TA
AT
TA
AT
TA
AT

structive crossing-over required for insertion and excision of an inserted element. The palindromes of maize are clustered and complex; this complexity is manifested as several centers of symmetry around which double-stranded regions form in a given piece of DNA. Such clusters of palindromes might form hot spots for the insertion and excision of DNA.

Palindromic regions have been found in all eukaryotic genomes so far examined, including plants, animals, and yeast (Wilson and Thomas, 1974). Several plant genomes have been analyzed. Walbot and Dure (1976) reported that the *Gossypium hirsutum* genome contains about 1% palindromic regions; these regions were found in clusters of two to three contiguous palindromic sequences, but the clusters were randomly distributed in the genome. Zimmerman and Goldberg (1977) report that approximately 2% of the genome of *Nicotiana tabacum* consists of palindromic regions. Goldberg (personal communication) has also found palindromic DNA in pea and soybean nuclear DNA in a roughly similar proportion of the total genome.

Excision of DNA from palindromic regions could result in the formation of either single- or double-stranded elements. Excision from chromosome palindromes could be exact or inexact, depending on the topography of the exit. Excision of DNA from a stem and loop (the inserted sequence) element palindrome would result in the formation of a single-stranded, linear element held together by a double-stranded stem. A portion of the chromosome would also be removed, but repair synthesis from the remaining strand would be possible. A double-stranded structure could be formed, if the inserted region were excised from linear DNA to create free ends, which might circularize, or by excision of opposite loops, which reformed a double stranded structure. Excision of chromosomal DNA without the possibility of opposite strand repair synthesis is possible. The formation of double-stranded structures, possibly circles, as the stable controlling element free state seems more likely for several reasons.

1. Transposons and IS are double stranded, and they may represent structures analogous to controlling elements.

2. Double-stranded DNA is more resistant to nucleases.

3. Circularization of double-stranded DNA is possible even in the absence of ligation if overlapping ends are present, while single-stranded circles would be maintained only if a double-stranded stem persisted.

4. Removal of a single-stranded loop would create a single-stranded "gap" in the chromosomal DNA in which intramolecular base pairing might persist, thus preventing synthesis of the complementary strand.

5. Insertion of a double-stranded structure at a new site would not require extensive DNA synthesis, as would insertion of a single stranded loop.

An underlying assumption in discussion of translocatable DNA sequences is that chromosomal DNA sequences play some role in the insertion and excision process. Enzymatic activities coded for by chromosomal genes could also be required for excision, ligation, repair synthesis, and other functions. It is also possible that the controlling elements contain all of the information required for their own insertion and excision; either the structure of the element itself would be sufficient to catalyze these processes or the element would carry its own enzymatic functions required for insertion and excision. Nonspecificity of insertion site does not imply autonomous insertion and excision. Mu, a promiscuous insertion phage, requires host activities. Excision of Mu is controlled by the X locus of the E. coli host chromosome (Bukhari, 1975). Promiscuous insertion of controlling elements may involve a parallel role in the nuclear chromosome in the regulation of excision.

The controlling elements might parallel the class of translocatable bacterial elements that show preference for some sites on the host chromosome. For example, controlling elements might share homology with a repetitive DNA family of corn nuclear DNA, in which case each member of the family would be a potential insertion site, via recombination. The repetitive sequences of higher eukaryotes, including corn, are dispersed throughout the genome and are contiguous to structural genes, as will be discussed in more detail below. The insertion of the controlling element into a repetitive DNA region would allow for multiple and preferred insertion sites, without excluding rare insertion into other locations.

Excision from a random chromosomal site or from a repetitive DNA element might involve structures discussed initially as possibilities involving palindromic chromosomal DNA. However, in those cases in which the controlling element carries the information required for transposition, no chromosomal DNA would be expected to be involved in unusual topographical structures. If this is a valid assumption, i.e., that no chromosomal DNA would be intimately involved in an excision structure, it might be presumed that excision would be precise. Specialized DNA sequence in the controlling element itself would, perhaps in response to a specific host enzymatic function, mediate the excision. However, the bacterial transposons that are capable of transposition, and that contain endogenous excision-mediating sequences, often condition deletion when excised. Consequently, a specialized excision sequence(s) in the controlling element does not preclude the possibility of inexact excision resulting in addition or deletion of DNA in the gene region.

At present, there is insufficient information to describe the mechanics or regulation of insertion and excision behavior of the controlling elements. The separability of the transposition function from the receptor function implies the existence of specialized excision DNA sequences, an enzymatic function, and/or a topographical feature such as the ability to form snap-back structures within the complete one element system. The controlling element carries some, but not necessarily all, of the information required for its movement. The role of the nuclear genome in providing either specific topographical sites, specific recognition sequences, or an enzymatic function(s) remains to be determined.

ii. Regulation of gene expression. Controlling elements may have either positive or negative effects on loci in which an appropriate receptor has been inserted. The most common case is for insertion of a controlling element to repress the synthesis of a particular protein— negative control of gene expression—which is commonly found with IS elements exerting polarity on genes under their control. However, Dooner and Nelson (1977) have reported an interesting case of Ds positive regulation. In this case, the genotype BzBzBz produced a bronze pigment color in the triploid aleurone, while the genotype bzbzbz is colorless. The Bz gene is the structural gene for UDPG-quercitin 3'-glycosyltransferase, which is responsible for the conversion of flavanol to 3'-glucosylquercitin. The Bz mutable lines, in which Ds has caused a "mutation" in this gene by the insertion of Ds into the gene region, typically contain no quercitin transferase activity at maturity and are CRM* minus for transferase protein. Two observations suggested that Ds insertion does not completely destroy the appearance of color in all cases. One bz-mutable stock (bz-M4) shows 0.6% of normal enzyme levels in an in vitro transferase assay; also, some bz genotypes contain faint aleurone pigment at maturity, indicating a leaky mutant. The appearance of transferase activity has been measured during development in bz-mutable stocks. Thirty days after pollination, bz-M4 contained 50% of normal enzyme level. However, enzyme activity rapidly disappeared from bz-M4 during development, while wild-type enzyme activity progressively increased. An examination of the kinetics of heat inactivation of the isolated enzyme showed that the bz-M4

---

*CRM, cross-reacting material to an antibody prepared against authentic antigen, in this case 3'-glucosyltransferase.

enzyme was very labile. In Bz-weak mutable genotypes, in which some pigment is produced, Ds insertion suppresses the leaky character of this allele such that the tissue is usually CRM negative but does contain about 20% of the normal pigment; the enzyme produced may be very unstable. It is likely that the affect of Ds is, therefore, highly position dependent, in that bz genotypes can be caused to produce enzyme and some pigment, while Bz genotype pigment production can be repressed.

The variability in effect on gene expression is expected as a function of position and orientation of IS insertion in bacteria. The activity of the more complex controlling elements of corn may also be a function of the interrelationship of the component parts of the element. Nevers and Saedler (1977) have proposed that the controlling element Spm may be differentiated into six or more separable functions, several of which are capable of independent inversion. Reversible segments result in on–off switching of the various functions of the element: transposition, receptivity, and regulatory activities. Since controlling elements are observed to undergo changes of state—changes in the ability to modulate gene expression as a result of changes in the frequency and timing of on–off switches—rearrangement of DNA within the element seems likely.

When controlling elements excise from a gene region, the gene may become a null allele, novel allele, an allele responsive to the controlling element (receptor function remains) but otherwise normal, or a mutable allele. Peterson and his colleagues have examined the controlling element En (enhancer analagous to Ac) in maize. The En element induces new allelic forms at specific loci, and such new alleles will continue to arise when under En control. Some new alleles are not responsive (nr) to En, and consequently remain fixed. At a particular locus affected by En, a wide variety of new phenotypes can be recovered, e.g., grades of anthocyanin production from null to fully pigmented. Quantitative changes in mutable alleles derived from controlling element affected lines are not always found. For example, Sager (1951), working on mutable wx (waxy) alleles, could detect no difference in the amylose content or the amylose–amylopectin ratio among wild-type Wx and 40 wx-mutable stocks. The En mutable alleles in a2 (a2-m), a gene involved in anthocyanin expression, do show a graded series in pigment content (Fowler and Peterson, 1974). Using four a2-m lines derived from the same A2 allele, Reddy and Peterson (1976) demonstrated that different pigment levels of a2-m can arise from the same parent allele.

If we accept the presence of these controlling elements, what role can they be assigned in gene structure? The model of chromosome and gene organization proposed by Davidson and Britten (1973) has provided a framework for understanding the organization of the reassociation kinetic classes of eukaryotic DNA. Basically, this model states that unique copy DNA, present once per haploid genome, contains most of the structural genes. Unique copy DNA is defined as that fraction of the genome that reassociates at a rate expected for a sequence of moderate length present only once per haploid genome. However, if long fragments of DNA are reassociated, the unique copy component of eukaryotic genomes reassociates at a much faster rate. Britten and Davidson proposed that the unique copy DNA is, therefore, interspersed with repetitive DNA (Davidson and Britten, 1973). Repetitive DNA is the component of the genome that reassociates more quickly, at a lower $C_0 t^*$ value, than unique sequences. The reiteration frequency of a class of repetitive DNA may vary from 10 to 10^6 copies of a (nearly) identical sequence per genome. The basic repeating pattern, now described in a number of animal genomes (reviewed in Davidson *et al.*, 1975) and plants (reviewed in Walbot and Goldberg, 1979), is a short-period interspersion of repetitive copy DNA of 300–1000 nucleotides, alternating with unique copy DNA of 600–2400 nucleotides. This arrangement, if the assumption that most structural genes are in the unique copy class is correct, implies that most genes are flanked at both the 3′- and 5′-terminus by repetitive copy DNA. Repetitive DNA in the Britten–Davidson model is responsible for gene regulation. They have proposed that the temporal coordination among coordinately regulated genes is accomplished by the following mechanism. Each gene of such a group has a similar regulatory repetitive sequence preceding the gene, and the genes are coordinated by signals received by the similar regulators. This model has the virtue of explaining several puzzles of eukaryotic genome organization not encountered in prokaryotes, including the following:

1. There is a large amount of DNA in many eukaryotic genomes (the "C" paradox); most of the DNA of large genomes is repetitive DNA, which is not likely to code for protein. This DNA may be involved in both the regulation and maintenance of chromatin superstructure. Hence, eukaryotic organisms would not differ in the number of genes as much as in the amount of repetitive DNA.

---

*$C_0 t$ = product of DNA concentration (moles nucleotide/1) × time (sec). $C_0 t$ values are used to measure the reiteration frequency of a particular DNA sequence element. Interstrand duplex formation occurs from $C_0 t$ 10^{-4} to 10^{-5} in corn, with unique (gene?) sequences reassociating between $C_0 t$ 10^3 to 10^5. Intrastrand formation due to palindromic sequences occurs at $C_0 t$ 10^{-5} before any interstrand duplexes form. The reassociation kinetics of DNA are thoroughly discussed by Britten *et al.* (1974).

2. Unlike prokaryotes, in which genes of a biochemical pathway are physically linked and share regulatory properties (e.g., a single promoter for genes of a biochemical pathway), the eukaryotic genes of a single pathway are typically unlinked and are often found on different chromosomes. The Britten–Davidson proposal—that each gene of the pathway or developmental program shares a common repetitive regulatory element—provides a mechanism for coordinate regulation of the genes.

3. The initial RNA transcripts—heterogeneous nucular RNA* produced in many eukaryotes—are considerably larger than the actual mRNAs, indicating that transcription begins and probably ends far from the translational initiation and termination codons of the mRNA. The interspersed repetitive and unique copy sequence unit may indicate the actual transcriptional unit size.

With the exceptions of certain insects, e.g., *Drosophila* (Manning et al., 1975) and *Chironomus* (Wells et al., 1976), the genomes analyzed so far seem to fit the basic interspersion pattern, despite the evolutionary divergence of the species. It seems likely, therefore, that the repetitive sequences and their physical arrangement play an important role in gene expression. The length of the repetitive DNA class of eukaryotes is large: 300–1000 nucleotides. This length is sufficient to contain numerous regulatory sites and promoters. The fine structure within repetitive DNA is just now being examined, so that we do not yet know the amount of organization within repetitive components, i.e., whether they are composed of many mini-subrepeats, palindromic regions, a single repeat, and so on.

The insertion of a controlling element may be possible at many sites within a region for which it has homology. The diversity of possible insertion sites within a repetitive component might contribute to the graded responses of genes caused by controlling element insertion, from null to partial expression to full expression at certain developmental stages (Reddy and Peterson, 1976). The position of element insertion may be as important as the autonomous properties of the element in controlling gene expression. Controlling element action within gene regulatory regions would not affect the coding portion of the repetitive/unique DNA unit, but only the regulation of transcription. The change in regulatory properties would be heritable until the

---

*Heterogeneous nuclear RNA is believed to be the initial transcription product from genes. These transcripts often include transcription from repetitive sequences near the gene itself. Subsequent endonucleolytic processing reduces the length of the HnRNA and releases the mRNA for transport to the cytoplasm.

controlling element moved out of the cistron; if excision were precise, so that neither insertion into or deletion from the original DNA sequence by controlling element occurred, the gene should revert to its original regulatory properties.

This view of controlling elements forces the deduction that insertion should occur at a limited number of chromosomal sites, i.e., insertion through recombination with a homologous sequence in a repetitive family of fixed reiteration frequency. This is a testable prediction, requiring a description of the corn genome and isolation of controlling element DNA. The repetitive kinetic classes can be isolated and tested for homology with the controlling element DNA. Isolation of controlling element DNA is the major technical block for such a study, but with the procedures of gene isolation and DNA cloning it is theoretically possible to obtain a homogeneous sample of any eukaryotic DNA sequence.

The alternative view of the controlling elements as promiscuous insertion elements such as Mu, which requires no homology with the insertion site, predicts there are an unlimited number of insertion sites. Insertion could be both within a gene and in regulatory sequences. Insertion within a gene could result in production of a completely non-functional or (partially) functional protein; consequently, the expected phenotypes are identical to those expected from insertion into regulatory regions.

In lieu of precise genetic mapping or DNA sequencing, the only criterion for distinguishing between controlling element insertion near or in the coding region would be discovery of an altered gene product. An altered gene product, such as the heat-labile glycosyltransferase of bz-m4, presumably arises if the controlling element disrupts the gene. Insertion into regulatory sequence may affect the amount or timing of gene product synthesis, but the product should be unaltered. To prove this, the two forms of the enzyme must be purified and characterized. If the controlling element insertion is within the normal gene region, its position might be deduced from the change in amino acid sequence within the affected protein.

iii.Future prospects.   The obvious parallels between bacterial translocatable elements and maize controlling elements should provide sufficient inducement for molecular biologists to begin characterizing the maize genome and its regulation. An important first step would be for an investigator familiar with the genetic properties and phenotypes of alleles at each mutable locus to write a descriptive account of that locus, tabulating properties qualitatively and quantitatively. Although a considerable data base exists, it is not available in a useful form to novices in the genetics of crop species. The long life cycle and complex genetics of crop plants makes it likely that geneticists and molecular biologists will work cooperatively, rather than by establishing a single laboratory engaged in genetic as well as molecular research. Consequently, the geneticists must describe their materials carefully in order to ensure their appropriate use. This dual approach to solving genetic and molecular problems was not required for work with bacteria, since the genetic manipulations are considerably simpler. A single laboratory could generate and analyze mutants, as well as characterize the molecular basis of the mutation. With higher plants, mutant generation and analysis is a full-time occupation. But this devotion to a particular species should not be so specialized that it precludes useful interaction and communication with nongeneticists. Hence, it is necessary for geneticists of each major crop plant to explain the kinds of mutants available, so that molecular biologists will know how much has already been accomplished.

The controlling elements, perhaps somewhat bizarre at first acquaintance, provide valuable clues to the basis for control of gene expression during development or physiological change. The normal, temporal pattern of gene expression of higher cells eludes direct experimental description or control at the molecular level, due to the complexity of dealing with a whole system to maintain normal regulatory control. The introduction of a controlling element into the regulatory apparatus of a gene changes the temporal expression of the gene so that gene expression can be analyzed. The controlling element system may provide a mechanism for introducing specific receptors of regulatory signals next to particular genes. The basis for receptor activation or repression of gene expression as a function of the activity of the regulator of its controlling element would be amenable to molecular description, provided the receptor and gene could be isolated. The base sequence of an isolated gene and its regulatory region could be determined, and the consequences of controlling element insertion assessed directly in terms of gene structure. That the control of gene expression through modulation of the timing, frequency, and intensity of gene expression is important in the orderly development of organisms is obvious. An understanding of how timing and frequency changes in genes under the regulation of controlling elements would be an exciting first step in understanding the control of gene expression in higher eukaryotes.

2. Paramutation

Paramutation can be defined as directed genetic change involving unstable or metastable chromosome components. Paramutations are not random, however, but show predictable behavior in a given genetic condition. Brink et al. (1968) and, more recently, Coe and Neuffer (1977), have reviewed the evidence for this phenomenon; paramutation was first noted as character instability in *Malva* by Lilienfeld (1929). The best-studied case of paramutation involves the R gene of maize; this locus governs anthocyanin expression in the plant and is, therefore, easy to observe.

The basic observation of paramutation is that certain genes change their behavior, usually by association with particular alleles of the same locus. A typical case is illustrated in Table I; test crosses 1 and 2 give aleurone pigment color, as expected for their endosperm genotype. Test cross 3, involving a F_1 pollen parent heterozygous $R^r R^{st}$ produces an unexpected result: 50% of the progeny resemble $R^{st} r^g r^{g.}$ as expected, but the $R^r r^g r^g$ genotype is much paler than expected. The R^r allele, a paramutable allele, has been changed by association with R^{st}, a paramutagenic allele of R. Various lines of evidence suggest that R^{st} and R^r do not recombine (Brink et al., 1968), but rather that an inherent instability of R^r is enhanced in the presence of $R^{st.}$

There are two views of the structure of the R region and of the basis for paramutation. Gavazzi (1977) has proposed that the R locus may be composed of up to nine dissociable, color-enhancing elements, believed to be individual genes; R is, therefore, a region of gene duplication. These genes can be transferred between R alleles, resulting in greater or lesser expression of R during development, as a function of gene dosage.

Sastry et al. (1965) proposed that there is only a single structural gene in R, in combination with a variable amount of heterochromatin. The heterochromatin, composed of a variable number of repetitive elements consisting of a common unit, the metamere, represses R function

TABLE I

Paramutation in the R Locus of Maize[a]

Test cross[b]	Endosperm genotype	Color
1. $r^g r^g \times R^r R^r$	$R^r r^g r^g$	Standard mottled
2. $r^g r^g \times R^{st} R^{st}$	$R^{st} r^g r^g$	Stippled
3. $r^g r^g \times F_1 R^r R^{st}$	50% $R^r r^g r^g$	Pale mottled
	50% $R^{st} r^g r^g$	Stippled

[a] Adapted from Brink et al. (1968).

[b] r^g = colorless. R^r = standard R; one dose gives a mottled aleurone color; paramutable allele. R^{st} = stippled R; paramutagenic allele.

as a function of dosage. Paramutation would result from unequal crossing over within a gene duplication region, changing the amount of repressive regulatory DNA preceding the R gene. Alternatively, paramutation could result from over- or underreplication of the regulatory (metamere) region preceding the R locus. Sastry et al. (1965) proposed that each gene with multiple regulatory sites is capable of paramutation, since R can change function in hemizygous plants in which interallelic crossing over or interaction is not possible. Paramutation occurs in the somatic tissues of plants, so that it is not involved exclusively with meiotic crossing over.

Paramutation in R and other loci is sometimes considered an esoteric phenomenon, and yet these mutable loci represent fortunate instances of obvious changes in gene structure or regulation. In order to study paramutation, a more detailed genetic map of a paramutable–paramutagenic region is required. At present, the gene duplication and multiple metamere models of R can both be accomodated within the gene region R; the recombinational map of corn is not a measure of the actual distance in base pairs between markers. However, nine gene duplications implies a stretch of DNA that may exceed 10^4 base pairs, allowing 10^3 base pairs for each gene and a minimum of 10^3 base pairs for regulatory regions. The multiple regulatory regions and a single gene could be accommodated in 2×10^3 base pairs or less. Such a large difference in minimal size of the two models might be used to exclude the gene duplication model if R could be shown to be small. If R could be isolated, i.e., transferred to a fragment or B chromosome and the chromosome isolated, the DNA of the region could be analyzed in much greater detail. If the R region is composed of repetitive units, the length of genes or short tandem repeats of such sequences can be described by their reassociation kinetics. It is possible that these repetitive regions, either genes or regulatory regions, would be arranged in a way that suggested their origin: tandem repeats or duplication–inversion. Paramutable and paramutagenic alleles could be correlated with specific structural features postulated to govern paramutation.

If the multiple regulatory element model is correct, there is an additional interesting aspect of the fine structure of R. The Britten–Davidson model of gene regulation postulates that various regulatory regions must precede genes, with each regulator specific to a particular developmental or physiological state. Although repetitive sequence DNA, presumed to contain these regulatory sites, has been isolated and characterized as a class, individual repetitive regions contiguous to known genes have not yet been studied. The phenotypic and genotypic consequences of the regulatory regions of R and other paramutable alleles in higher plants are known, so that an examination of the DNA sequence arrangement of these regulatory regions might be especially informative in elucidating how the length or topography of multiple regulatory regions influences gene expression.

One consideration of gene regulation relevant to this discussion concerns the increase in target size for regulatory molecules afforded by a repetitive regulatory region. If, for example, interaction of repressors or activators with any one of a group of regulatory regions preceding a gene modulates gene expression, then it follows that the quality of activation and repression should vary with the number of interaction sites, provided that the number of regulatory molecules remains fixed. Thus far we have little information on either the length or the internal reiteration of control regions preceding genes in eukaryotic organisms. Lacking means until recently to isolate genes and flanking sequences, averaging techniques such as reassociation kinetics have been used to study repetitive DNA. With the advent of DNA cloning and sequencing technologies, it is likely that repetitive sequences near easily isolated genes—e.g., globin, ovalbumin, and other genes for which isolated mRNAs can be obtained—will be examined in detail. However, the average length of 300 base pairs of repetitive sequences in animal genomes is considerably shorter than the up to 1200 average repeat length that has been found in several plant genomes (reviewed by Walbot and Goldberg, 1979). Consequently, examination of individual gene control regions in plants may reveal a higher order of redundancy or complexity.

Many plants have exceedingly large genomes, in which gene regulation becomes correspondingly more difficult due to the low "concentration" of individual genes and their regulators. As was mentioned previously, one method for enchancing the likelihood of specific regulatory molecule–regulatory DNA sequence interaction is to increase the number of possible target sites, so that a regulatory molecule will be more effective in modulating gene expression. It is possible that favored alleles (those alleles more often expressed) arising during genome evolution are those that have enchanced their visibility by amplification of gene control regions. Alternatively, alleles may cease expression if control regions are modified. A great number of the angiosperms are allo- or autotetraploids in which initial gene redundancy may have evolved toward new expression as well as toward new gene function. Ferris and Whitt (1977) recently found less than one-half of the expected isozyme heterozygosity in a group of tetraploid fish evolved 50×10^6 years ago. Their explanation for this observation derived primarily from consideration of nucleotide change within the gene region, leading to one functional allele and one new potential gene. However, it is equally possible that evolution of the regulatory regions precludes expression of the allele prior to significant change in the gene. The paramutable alleles in which gene regulation is rapidly modified may provide an excellent test system for examining the diversity of regulatory regions and their evolution, duplication, and possible movement.

3. *Other Intracellular Events Governing Gene Expression*

In addition to a set of unique structural genes, each complex eukaryote genome contains the regulatory information with which to use the genes in a developmentally and physiologically significant way. This field has recently been reviewed by Davidson (1976), and only highlights of his conclusions will be presented here. So far, almost all of the available evidence on gene regulation is drawn from animal studies. Current evidence favors the concept of transcriptional control as the primary site of regulation of gene usage. Each differentiated cell type contains a common set of "housekeeping gene products" and a unique combination of specific gene products that allow that cell to carry out its differentiated functions. The means by which these cell type-specific genes, or any higher plant genes, are regulated has not been elucidated. Recent evidence suggests that, in sea urchin embryos, each cell type or embryo developmental stage contains a different set of mRNAs; the complexity of these mRNAs may be very high in some tissues, with as many as 30,000 different mRNA types present. These mRNAs are transcribed preferentially from unique copy DNA contiguous to repetitive DNA, as was postulated by Britten and Davidson's model of gene regulation. Another postulate of this model that has been demonstrated is that the repetitive DNA types represented in heterogeneous nuclear RNA in a specific tissue type are a subset of the total population of repetitive sequences. Therefore, the repetitive sequences are correlated with specific transcription, although it has yet to be proved whether specific repetitive sequence classes are the sole means of regulating the transcription of neighboring structural genes.

For pathways such as chlorophyll or anthocyanin biosynthesis, in which the structural and regulatory genes have been mapped in several higher plants, it would be possible to determine whether such gene groups share common regulatory properties, i.e., the same repetitive sequence next to each gene. This may be proved first for a pathway of *Drosophila* or mouse, but it is critical to extend the study to plant systems with strong formal genetics. The implications of shared regulation are exceedingly important. For example, rather than enchancing a pathway by gradually selecting improvements at each step, it might be possible to define a single change in a regulatory gene product that enhanced all genes of the pathway by means of altered interaction with repetitive regulatory sequences contiguous to the structural genes.

Infection by viruses or viroids often leads to altered gene expression in specific tissues or in the whole plant. Plant biologists have yet to determine the molecular basis for these alterations, or even whether changes occur primarily at the transcriptional or translational level. Despite this lag behind "cancer biology" in animal studies, plant molecular biologists have a considerable advantage in the use of plant tissue cultures in which redifferentiation and regeneration are possible. As a consequence, the activity of infectious agents can be readily examined in different tissues and as a function of development. Recent work on crown gall (reviewed by Schell, 1979) indicates that it is possible to examine, at a molecular level, aspects of bacterial activity as well as plant response during and after infection.

The study of gene regulation may seem far removed from the concerns of agronomists, but ultimately what they seek are changes in gene expression that result in higher yield. The ability to modulate gene expression will increase in parallel with our understanding of model systems for studying gene expression, i.e., after viral infection or in culture. Such studies are means of examining the fundamental problem of molecular biology—how are genes turned on and off.

C. Somatic Cell Culture

Somatic cell culture and the expression of totipotency by plant cells under appropriate conditions have provided a fantastic opportunity for plant biologists. Since this topic has been widely discussed, I will confine my remarks to a few points of special molecular interest.

One aspect of cell culture not often given attention is that the time of the cell cycle can be varied over several orders of magnitude. Most investigators have simply tried to shorten doubling time as much as possible in order to obtain more cells. However, in the plant many important differentiation events occur in cells that do not divide at all or that divide only slowly. In a culture of rapidly growing cells, cytoplasmic events and the appearance of specific metabolites can be correlated with nuclear DNA synthesis; consequently, such events are thought to occur at a specific time in the cell cycle. However, in vivo the coordination between the appearance of a specific function and the cell cycle may not exist. For example, organellar DNA synthesis and organelle replication are presumed to occur coordinately with cell division to maintain a stable number of mitochondria and proplastids per meristematic cell. When the dividing cell population begins to differentiate to form a leaf, there is a large increase in the number of plastids and in their DNA content (Possingham and Rose, 1976). The organelles in situ replicate their DNA and the compartment more quickly than the cell cycle, and perhaps in the absence of further cell division.

Rather than attempting to optimize cell division rate in culture, perhaps some attention should be devoted to changing the length of the cell cycle in order to study the control of cell differentiation in vitro. If photosynthetic efficiency is correlated with the number and size of the chloroplasts, then it is exceedingly important to understand how chloroplast number per cell and individual plant plastid ploidy is regulated. The regulation of differentiated protein synthesis could also be examined in vitro, but perhaps not in a rapidly growing cell population.

The control of cell cycle length and of the synchrony of cell division between cells is in itself an interesting problem. Cleavage-stage embryos of many higher plants have an extremely rapid cell cycle and also may divide synchronously. As the embryo increases in size, the proportion of cells dividing rapidly, or at all, decreases, and divisions are no longer synchronous. If a goal of agriculture is to provide large quantities of usable biomass, an increase in the rapid cell division phase of the embryo would have a dramatic effect. If the rate of cell division of once every 24 hr of early cotyledon stage, day 12 bean embryos was maintained throughout the remaining 24 days of development, the bean would contain 16,000 times more cells! (Walbot, 1978). It is a matter of conjecture whether the plant would ever provide sufficient nutrients to fill the additional cells with food reserves; however, a small increment in cell division rate might yield a large edible crop more quickly. The molecular and genetic bases for control of cell cycle length and of synchronous division in a cell population are not understood in higher eukaryotes. However, these problems have been examined in yeast and true slime molds with success, and it should be possible to extend many of the techniques to plant cell cultures.

The ability to regenerate whole plants from single cells or clones provides plant biologists with a means of distinguishing epigenetic and genetic events. Many metastable cell states may exist in culture, and their susceptibility or resistance to treatments or ability to express a specific phenotype may be studied. However, these states, although useful for study and of possible economic value in the production of single cell products, are not heritable through a sexual cycle. Consequently, plant cell cultures exhibiting interesting properties must be tested genetically, if at all possible, to determine whether an epigenetic stable state or a new genetic character has been found. The existence and persistence of epigenetic events in culture suggests that major changes in gene expression are possible, while preserving the fundamental abilities of the cell to divide and regenerate normal tissues. Such changes in whole plants—e.g., tolerance to salt or herbicides—might be useful agronomic traits cryptic in the normal phenotype of the plant. Once again, if we knew the basis of gene expression, we could contemplate eliciting novel expression in the plants as well as in culture.

D. Transplantation of Nuclei and Organelles

The organelles of higher plants contain genomes of sufficient size to code for approximately 200 chloroplast proteins and 100 mitochondrial proteins (Avers, 1976). Some critical proteins are organelle gene products; for example, the large subunit and presumed catalytic unit of ribulosebisphosphate carboxylase—the ultimate site of all CO_2 fixation in green plants—is the product of a chloroplast gene (reviewed by Kung, 1977). In most plants the organelles are maternally inherited (Grun, 1976), precluding mixed organelle populations in somatic tissues and, therefore, preventing recombination. Even if paternal organelles are transferred to the zygote, there is no evidence of genetic recombination between higher plant organelles prior to segregation in species with biparental organelle inheritance, or of destruction or dilution of the paternal organellar genomes in species with maternal inheritance. In fact, organelle DNA recombination in the green alga *Chlamydomonas* in which + and − mating types contribute a single chloroplast to the zygote is exceedingly rare (Gillham, 1974). In plants with biparental chloroplast inheritance, no recombination has been observed (Grun, 1976), although mixtures of plastids persist in some tissues; this inability to find recombination may be due to a lack of recognizable markers. *In vitro* fusion of two species of tobacco protoplasts containing chloroplasts with electrophoretically distinct carboxylase proteins has also been used to test for recombination. Subsequent regeneration of plants and analysis of chloroplast proteins indicated that primarily homoplastidic plants are recovered and that no evidence for chloroplast recombination could be found (reviewed by Kung, 1977).

If chloroplasts and mitochondria become genetically fixed, due to maternal inheritance and barriers against recombination, it is likely that considerable intraspecific, as well as interspecific, differences may exist among organelles. In maize, at least four mitochondrial DNA types can be distinguished on the basis of restriction endonuclease patterns (Pring and Levings, 1976). Chloroplast DNAs of maize also vary (Bedbrook and Bogorad, 1976; V. Walbot, unpublished data), and there is considerable variation within genera and families as well (Atchison et al., 1976; Vedel et al., 1976). In a sense, the organelles have coevolved with the nuclear genome, a genome in which considerable heterozygosity exists. The optimal combination of organellar and nuclear genotypes may be only rarely produced in nature, and may be quickly lost, due to uniparental inheritance of the organelle and assortment of nuclear factors. Since the organelles are primarily responsible for the energy metabolism of the plant, it would be worthwhile to investigate the "quality" of organelle types in a variety of nuclear backgrounds.

Although the organelles contain genomes, they are not autonomous for a variety of nuclear gene products are required for organelle maintenance; consequently, nuclear variation in the quality of nucleo–cytoplasmic interaction is expected. One way to test for organelle diversity and variation in nuclear interaction with the organelle is to use transplantation combined with plant regeneration. For example, albino protoplasts could be fed chloroplasts of a defined type, and the success of the whole plant evaluated.

Transplantation or protoplast fusion studies might also provide a greater opportunity for organelle DNA recombination if cells are maintained nondividing to prevent assortment of organelles into homoplastidic lines. This approach might be the only way to recover recombinant organellar DNAs. If no recombinants are ever found, the impact on plant breeding should be considerable. A lack of recombination would suggest that modification of crop plant organellar properties will only arise by spontaneous mutation or by selection for specific nuclear factors modulating organellar phenotype. Furthermore, if the cytoplasmic base on which crop plants are built is so fixed, each organelle of each species should be characterized as quickly as possible in a variety of nuclear backgrounds in order to find optimal combinations. In addition, a rapid assay for each organelle type, perhaps using restriction endonucleases to cleave the DNA into a fixed set of fragments, should be developed so that organellar mutations in breeding lines can be readily identified.

Another aspect of organelle biology was brought to light by the discovery of the C_4 pathway of photosynthesis. One characteristic of plants utilizing C_4 photosynthesis is the dimorphism of the bundle sheath and mesophyll chloroplasts (Black, 1973). The chloroplasts of C_4 plants also differ in their biochemical capabilities, and it is possible that the chloroplasts differ genetically, as a result of the specific assortment of two populations of proplastids or as a result of somatic mutation. Although C_4 and C_3 plants can be found within the same genus, it is also possible that the chloroplasts of C_4 plants differ extensively in their genetic potential from C_3 plants. All of these "ifs" came together in a variety of recent suggestions that transplantation of C_4 chloroplasts from corn to C_3 plants such a soybean would create a new C_4 super-soybean. However, it is now clear that not only are the mesophyll and bundle sheath chloroplast genomes of at least one C_4 plant identical, but that these genomes differ very little from the chloroplast DNA of a C_3 plant in the same genus (Walbot, 1977). Therefore, there probably is not a specific C_4 chloroplast genome, and transplantation experiments are unlikely to introduce novel information via the chloroplast.

The identity of the genomes should not obscure the very real differences in function in the two C_4 and C_3 chloroplasts. These differences are a consequence of differential gene expression. The most dramatic difference is the absence of ribulose bisphosphate carboxylase activity and protein from mesophyll chloroplasts (Huber et al., 1976); the major gene product of chloroplasts is not expressed. Most of the enzymes of the C_4 pathway are cytoplasmically located (Hatch et al., 1975) and are likely products of the nuclear genome; each of these must be turned on to make a C_4 plant. A more realistic test of the capabilities of chloroplasts than trying to transform a C_3 plant with a C_4 chloroplast would be to transplant a C_3 chloroplast into a C_4 cell. If the primary control of C_4 pathway expression and anatomical development resides in the nuclear genome, and the transplanted C_3 plastid contains most, if not all, the genes required to be either a C_3 or a C_4 chloroplast, the cell should regenerate to a functional C_4 plant. If this experiment failed to produce a functional C_4 plant, then some input from the chloroplast to the regulation of genes in the pathway is possible. This experiment could also fail to produce a functional C_4 plant if the nucleus and chloroplast were incompatible; for example, the nucleus might supply gene products that failed to interact normally with the chloroplast structure.

The C_4-to-C_3 transplantation experiments might provide an interesting clue to another aspect of nucleocytoplasmic relations. If a C_4 plant with a high temperature optimum for photosynthesis were used as the recipient of C_3 chloroplast from a cool-temperature plant, considerable incompatibility between organelle and nuclear gene products might be expected. For example, the nuclear genome might specify particular lipid components for chloroplast membranes appropriate for high temperature, while the chloroplast proteins were selected to mesh with a set of lipids fluid at a lower temperature. Experiments deliberately designed to produce such incompatibilities might provide an excellent system in which to elucidate the contribution of the nuclear and chloroplast genomes to organelle structure and function. If the contribution of the two genomes to plastid fitness were known, a more concentrated and specific selection program would be feasible.

E. Construction of Artificial Genetic Systems

Despite the remarkable success with which plant breeders have been able to change basic plant properties, many recent suggestions for plant improvement have emphasized the introduction of completely new genetic material into plants. The concern for the genetic vulnerability, the lack of genetic variability, in major crop species has been heightened by economic disasters such as the Southern corn leaf blight of corn and the presumed susceptibility of other major crops to similar disasters. Although there is an enormous reservoir of untapped genetic diversity in crop plants and their wild relatives, some problems associated with crop productivity may be solved more quickly by the introduction of engineered genomes. As was pointed out in Section IV,D, there are barriers to recombination in the organelle genomes and also, of course, among various plant nuclear genomes as well. Consequently, if problems can be carefully defined and the relevant desirable genes isolated, it may be possible to artificially introduce these genes into the crop plant. Before discussing genetic engineering per se, the levels at which gene product accumulation can be rate limiting, and some of the solutions to these problems that have been achieved in microbial systems, will be reviewed.

1. Means for Amplifying a Gene Product

The concentration of a particular gene product such as a storage protein is determined by four factors: (1) the maximum rate of transcription of that gene, a function controlled by the gene promoter region; (2) the number of copies of the gene per cell; (3) the rate of translation and stability of the mRNA coding for the protein; and (4) the stability of the protein product. For a metabolite, concentration is determined by the relative activity of the enzymes involved in synthesis versus degradation, and by the regulatory properties of these two sets of enzymes. In bacteria and fungi, thousandfold or greater increases in the concentration of a particular metabolite have been achieved by selection (1) for derepressed synthesis of the anabolic enzymes of a pathway and (2) for low feedback inhibition by the product on synthesis.

Selection of plant lines carrying abnormally high levels of vitamins, amino acids, or other desirable metabolites will be possible if sufficient selective pressure can be exerted to recover cells or plants with the desirable properties. If the gene product is itself the desired product, then more modest levels of enhancement of production are likely, since few cell types produce exclusively one or a few proteins. Mutations increasing the rate of gene expression through alteration of the promoter have resulted in 10- to 20-fold enhancement of certain bacterial enzyme concentrations—nicotinamide deamidase (Pardee et al., 1971), glucose 6-phosphate dehydrogenase (Fraenkel and Parola, 1972), and lac operon (Bruenn and Hollingsworth, 1973). Promoter mutations share the following properties (Scaife and Beckwith, 1966):

1. cis-Specificity: only genes in the cis arrangement will be affected; the rate of gene expression of a nonmutant copy of the gene and promoter in the trans position will be unaffected.

2. Pleiotropy: all genes in the transcriptional unit or operon under the control of the promoter will be affected.

3. Normal regulation: regulation of promoter use and of enzyme activity will operate normally in the mutant strain.

Promoter mutations are, therefore, advantageous in that only a single set of genes is affected and the normal regulatory mechanisms are still operative. As a result, the protein would appear at the normal developmental stage. In eukaryotes, promoter mutations would probably not result in pleiotropic effects, since the genes for enzymes of major pathways are not contiguous in the genome. Genes sharing coordinate control are often on different chromosomes, as was discussed previously in considering the Britten–Davidson model of eukaryotic genome organization. Crop plants are also at least diploid, if not highly polyploid, so that a promoter mutation would affect only one of multiple copies of a particular gene.

Since the positive promoter mutations discovered thus far result in only a 10- to 20-fold enhancement in the rate of gene expression, it is likely that major increases in the level of an enzyme in the cell will be due to changes in gene copy number. Most structural genes in eukaryotes are present only once or a few times per haploid genome; the rapid and massive synthesis of such proteins as ovalbumin and hemoglobin by particular differentiated cells is a result of maximal transcription from a few genes and maximal translation of the resultant mRNAs. Endosperm and cotyledonary cells of major seed crop plants also produce a few proteins in massive amounts utilizing the existing endowment of genetic material and regulatory mechanisms. The production of these proteins is unlikely to be greatly enhanced by promoter mutation or by changes in gene copy number, since they are already major cell constituents. Many of the seed storage proteins are, however, deficient or unbalanced in their content of amino acids essential in human nutrition. Hence, overproduction of an alternative or additional protein of more balanced amino acid content might improve the food quality of the seed. The increase in such a protein could be accomplished by several means, each with a different set of possible unfavorable side effects.

1. Derepression of a gene not normally expressed during seed maturation: This might result in vivipary or other developmental abnormalities.
2. Promoter mutation in a gene normally expressed during seed maturation: Normal regulatory mechanisms might be upset if this gene product is involved in the regulation of other developmentally significant genes, either directly or by metabolite production.
3. Increase in the copy number of a gene coding for a protein with a balanced amino acid content: This might result in either of the two deleterious situations described in (1) and (2) above. If a gene could be identified in which the protein produced had no deleterious side effects on the normal ontogeny of the seed, the maximum rate of production would be achieved by combining the two approaches of altered promoter and an increase in the copy number per cell. That is, to increase the concentration of a protein from 0.01% of the total cell protein to 1% would require both an altered rate of transcription in the original genes and an increased number of genes per cell.

There are two basic means for increasing the number of gene copies per cell: higher chromosomal dosage or extra chromosomal elements. The phenomenon of gene dosage is well known; organisms triploid for a particular allele often contain 150% of the enzyme activity found in normal diploid stocks. There is a limit to the number of copies of a particular allele that can be conveniently added to a particular genome, however, since increased dosage is usually achieved using trisomics for an entire chromosome or arm. Not just the gene itself but the entire chromosomal region in which the gene is located is introduced. Such individuals carrying an unbalanced chromosome set are not always as vigorous as the original parental stocks, nor do all enzymes show an increase in activity when the gene dosage level per cell is increased. J. Birchler (personal communication) has reported that introduction of

an extra long arm of chromosome 1 of corn increases the level of alcohol dehydrogenase as expected, but that several other enzymes show
a decrease in activity. His results suggest that extra copies of particular
chromosomes or arms may result in deleterious decreases in some
required enzymatic functions. These results are not unexpected, however, given the large amounts of genetic material transferred by translocation or other means used for the production of three and four gene
copy numbers per cell. In addition to the desirable genes, perhaps 5 to
10% of the entire genome is transferred, and this results in a wide range
of pleiotropic effects.

A more precise method for increasing the copy number per cell is to
introduce a self-replicating plasmid into the cell. In bacteria, each
plasmid type maintains a nearly constant plasmid copy number per cell
during each cell generation. The copy number is, therefore, one of the
characteristics used to identify the plasmid type. Plasmids carry far less
genetic information than chromosome arms, and they can be engineered to contain a relatively precise gene complement, including
specific promoters contiguous to desirable genes. An ideal plasmid in a
higher plant cell would remain at a copy number of one per cell until
the developmental stage at which the gene product was required, e.g.,
during seed development. If plasmid amplification occurred at this
stage, hundreds of copies of a particular gene per cell would be made; if
each of these genes had a superpromoter, a several thousandfold increase in protein product might result. If the regulatory properties of
the gene product and of gene expression were well understood, genes
that had no adverse effects on normal development or normal metabolite concentration could be chosen for the plasmid.

2. Recombinant DNA Technology

Few biological discoveries have elicited as much excitement and
furor as those that have provided us with the capability of joining DNA
segments from different species into plasmids and of transferring these
plasmids to bacteria, where the foreign DNA is replicated. The requirements for cloning DNA in this way are relatively simple: a plasmid or viral vector with a specific cut or free end; a foreign DNA
segment with free ends capable of reannealing to the free ends of the
vector; and DNA ligase, an enzyme capable of sealing the joints between the vector and foreign DNA to form a continuous double helix.
When introduced into an appropriate bacterial host, the hybrid plasmid
or virus will be replicated to a copy number per cell characteristic of
that vector. In this way, the original DNA segment can be amplified
many times in the bacterium. In some cases, the foreign DNA may be

transcribed and the mRNA translated into protein. In shotgun experiments, an entire eukaryotic genome may be reduced to DNA fragments of approximately gene size and cloned. Bacteria carrying particular DNA segments of interest may be recognized by *in situ* hybridization of isolated probe mRNAs to individual clones of lysed bacteria; when a positive hybrid is found, the bacterial cell is carrying the gene for that mRNA.

Federal safeguards to prevent the amplification and escape of DNA sequences of harmful genes and the genes for harmful products have been written with viral and animal genomes in mind. Little attention has been paid to the benefits and risks of cloning plant or plant pathogen DNA. In many ways, plants are more susceptible to disease than animals because so little attention has been paid to curing plant diseases, except through breeding a better plant. In research on animals, a considerable amount of research effort is devoted to the diagnosis and cure or amelioration of disease symptoms in the affected animal. If a cloned, dangerous DNA escaped and created a danger to animals, at least some remedies would be available. However, few curative treatments are available for crop plants.

Cloning DNA will allow a more thorough examination of the properties of the genes, including their expression and regulatory properties. However, it is a long way from isolated gene to new crop variety. Genetic engineering may be able to circumvent barriers to interspecific crosses and organelle recombination, and may quickly direct the evolution of a plant with new traits. The plant must still be able to produce a crop that is abundant, nontoxic, nonallergenic, and profitable. Cloning technology is considerably ahead of our understanding of the genetic components of yield or photosynthetic efficiency. Until a trait can be screened *in vitro* in bacterial culture, cloning cannot aid the search for useful genes. An example of molecular biology outracing plant biology is found in the nitrogen fixation field. The nif genes, the nitrogen fixation gene cluster, of *Klebsiella* have been isolated and cloned by several laboratories. The nif genes have been introduced into *E. coli*, and the transformed bacteria will fix nitrogen in an anaerobic environment, indicating successful translation of the nif group mRNAs (F. Ausubel, personal communication). This result lends hope to those who would transfer the nif gene cluster to all higher plants, until the following questions are considered:

1. Nitrogenase requires an oxygen-free atmosphere: where in the plant is there an anaerobic compartment?

2. The nif genes are replicated in *E. coli* because they are on a normal

plasmid of this bacterium: what vector(s) will be replicated by plant replication enzymes?

3. *E. coli* is only a single cell: will vectors continue to be replicated during cell differentiation and be expressed in a physiologically significant way in higher plants? Will vectors persist in gametes or will it be necessary to introduce the vector in each generation?

Recombinant DNA technology will be extremely useful in characterizing genes such as the nif complex, but it is unlikely that new properties will be conferred on higher plants within the next few years. The major unsolved problems hindering the introduction of new genes via genetic engineering are the construction of a suitable vector and an understanding of the regulation of gene expression in eukaryotic cells. The foreign DNA must be taken up by the cells and replicated at (least) the same rate as cell division in order to be maintained. The DNA of plant cells is found as chromatin in the nucleus and as protein-free DNA in the organelles. Except for viral DNAs, no free DNA is known to exist initially in the cytoplasm. A vector given to cells would presumably exist initially in the cytoplasm; how would such a vector be replicated if DNA polymerase exists in the nucleus and organelles? Even if the vector is replicated successfully, the novel genetic information must be expressed in a physiologically significant way; the new genes must, therefore, interact with positive and negative regulators as well as with the RNA polymerase and other enzymes involved in nucleic acid metabolism.

V. LIMITATIONS AND PROSPECTS FOR THE MOLECULAR EXAMINATION OF HIGHER PLANTS

In this brief chapter, only an overview of current research in molecular biology as it relates to higher plants has been possible. The major focus has been on the genetic aspects of molecular biology, primarily because the intriguing genetic problems posed by some higher plants are of considerable interest to molecular biologists. Such phenomena as the controlling elements are parallel to recently discovered bacterial transposable and insertion elements. The opportunity to grow plants as individual cells and to regenerate an entire plant from a single cell in some species holds great promise for the elucidation of the genetic basis for a number of plant properties. And, to the extent that plant cells behave as organisms in culture, selection can be biased to favor the reproduction of cells with peculiar properties. Some such selected cells may have undergone genetic rather than epigenetic changes in their capabilities, and, consequently, a new plant property can be selected and proven to exist by traditional genetic crosses on regenerated individual plants.

A more basic approach to altering the capabilities of cells and plants is to manipulate the genetic material directly. Transformation by DNA or construction of artificial, specific vectors for the introduction of genes seem likely to succeed with plant materials, although the experiments to date have not been rigorously quantified. Much work is required to understand the fate of exogenously supplied DNA in plant cells. An alternative method for introducing novel genetic material into plant cells is via the organelles. Although the genetic potential of the mitochondria and chloroplasts is limited, there is undoubtedly some variability in organelle populations. Since the organellar genomes of many species may be fixed by maternal inheritance and barriers to recombination, it seems likely that some changes in plant properties could be achieved by organelle transplantation within or between species. Also, the organelles contain naked circular DNAs similar to plasmids or other likely vectors of novel genetic information; the organelles may provide an appropriate environment for the maintenance of artificial genetic systems, which would then be introduced by organelle transplantation.

These direct approaches for the introduction of genetic material into cells may be supplemented by an increased understanding of the normal mechanisms for gene regulation in plant cells. For example, if we knew how the controlling elements or paramutable alleles exercised their positive and negative regulation of gene expression, it might be possible to modulate genetic expression without introducing foreign DNA. If we understood gene regulation, it could be controlled in a specific manner by genetic manipulation.

It is clear that a substantial amount of basic research is required to elucidate the mechanism of gene regulation in eukaryotes; hopefully, plant material favorable for such analysis will be utilized as much as possible. Our understanding of the organization of eukaryotic genomes is increasing at an exponential rate, now that recombinant DNA technology has provided the means for the examination of eukaryotic DNA sequences in the plasmids of bacteria. In fact, eukaryotic DNA sequences can be expressed in bacteria. However useful these studies of eukaryotic genes in bacteria may prove to be, they still do not provide information on how to introduce novel genes into eukaryotic cells and to insure the appropriate expression of such genetic material. The major challenge of molecular biology is to elucidate the regulatory controls of gene expression in eukaryotic organisms.

To provide answers to these problems in gene regulation in higher plants will require the cooperation of all geneticists working with plant materials, from agronomists to the most sophisticated molecular geneticists. As mentioned in Section I, these two groups of scientists have lived in largely separate environments and training programs for a number of years. We should remember, however, the work at the turn of the century in plant genetics that provided the foundation for so much of modern genetics. Studies as diverse as the confirmation of Mendel's experiments to the discovery and description of tobacco mosaic virus were completed by people trained in traditional plant biology who sought the most sophisticated answers to their questions. Perhaps it is impossible to return to these seemingly more halcyon days, in which all scientists professed some knowledge of the natural world with which they worked. But molecular biologists will have to familiarize themselves with the properties of plants that both make them useful and sometimes difficult experimental materials in order to successfully attack problems of plant gene expression. Agricultural scientists will also have to change, to modernize their thinking to include the possibility that new discoveries will render obsolete some time-honored practices of breeding, selection, and testing. The tenacity with which the land grant colleges and experimental stations have retained control of the programs on the genetics of higher plants must be loosened if molecular biologists not associated with such institutions are to be recruited to work on the fundamental problems of plant gene regulation.

Two important facts make me optimistic that a successful partnership of agricultural scientists and molecular biologists is possible. First, the goals of successful plant breeding are so important to the health of individuals as well as of the world that factional disputes should be put aside. Second, the unsolved problems in plant gene expression are so exciting that many new scientists should be attracted to this field to invigorate the present programs and to design new programs of their own.

REFERENCES*

Atchison, B. A., Whitfeld, P. R., and Bottomley, W. (1976). *Mol. Gen. Genet.* **148**, 263–269.

*Literature review completed in March, 1977.

Avers, C. J. (1976). "Cell Biology." Van Nostrand-Reinhold, Princeton, New Jersey.
Bedbrook, J., and Bogorad, L. (1976). Proc. Natl. Acad. Sci. U.S.A. **73**, 4309–4313.
Black, C. C. (1973). Annu. Rev. Plant Physiol. **24**, 253–286.
Botchan, M., Topp, W., and Sambrook, J. (1976). Cell **9**, 269–287.
Brink, R. A., Styles, E. D., and Axtell, J. D. (1968). Science **159**, 161–164.
Britten, R. J., Graham, D. E., and Neufeld, B. R. (1974). In "Methods in Enzymology" (L. Grossman and K. Moldave, eds), Vol. 29, Part E, pp. 363–418. Academic Press, New York.
Bruenn, J., and Hollingsworth, H. (1973). Proc. Natl. Acad. Sci. U.S.A. **70**, 3693–3697.
Bukhari, A. I. (1975). J. Mol. Biol. **96**, 87–99.
Bukhari, A. I., and Zipser, D. (1972). Nature (London), New Biol. **236**, 240–243.
Casadaban, J. M. (1976). J. Mol. Biol. **104**, 525–539.
Coe, E. H., Jr., and Neuffer, M. G. (1977). In "Corn and Corn Improvement" (G. F. Sprague, ed.), 2nd ed., pp. 111–223. Am. Soc. Agron., Madison, Wisc.
Cohen, S. (1976). Nature (London) **263**, 731–738.
Davidson, E. H. (1976). "Gene Activity in Early Development," 2nd ed. Academic Press, New York.
Davidson, E.H., and Britten, R. (1973). Q. Rev. Biol. **48**, 555–613.
Davidson, E.H., Galau, G. A., Angerer, R. C., and Britten, R. J. (1975). Chromosoma **51**, 253–259.
Dooner, H. K. and Nelson, O. E. (1977). Proc. Natl. Acad. Sci. U.S.A. **74**, 5623–5627.
Doy, C. H., Gresshoff, P. M., and Rolfe, G. G. (1973). Proc. Natl. Acad. Sci. U.S.A. **70**, 723–726.
Faelen, M., and Toussaint, A. (1976). J. Mol. Biol. **104**, 525–539.
Ferris, S. D., and Whitt, G. S. (1977). Nature (London) **265**, 258–260.
Finchman, J. R. S., and Sastry, G. R. K. (1974). Annu. Rev. Genet. **8**, 15–20.
Fowler, R. G., and Peterson, P. A. (1974). Genetics **76**, 433–440.
Fraenkel, G. G., and Parola, A. (1972). J. Mol. Biol. **71**, 107–111.
Gavazzi, G. (1977). Stadler Genet. Symp. **9**, 37–62.
Gillham, N. W. (1974). Annu. Rev. Genet. **8**, 347–391.
Gresshof, P. M. (1974). In "Genetic Manipulations with Plant Material" (L. Ledoux, ed.), pp. 539–549. Plenum, New York.
Grun, P. (1976). "Cytoplasmic Genetics and Evolution." Columbia Univ. Press, New York.
Hatch, M. D., Kagawa, T., and Craig, S. (1975). Aust. J. Plant Physiol. **2**, 111–128.
Huber, S. C., Hall, T. C., and Edwards, G. E. (1976). Plant Physiol. **57**, 730–733.
Kleckner, N. (1977). Cell **11**, 11–23.
Kopecko, D. J., Breet, J., and Cohen, S. N. (1976). J. Mol. Biol. **108**, 333–360.
Kung, S. D. (1977). Annu. Rev. Plant Physiol. **28**, 401–437.
Ledoux, L. (1974). In "Genetic Manipulations with Plant Material" (L. Ledoux, ed.), pp. 479–498. Plenum, New York.
Ledoux, L., Huart, R., Mergeay, M., and Charles, P. (1974). In "Genetic Manipulations with Plant Materials" (L. Ledoux, ed.), pp. 499–517. Plenum, New York.
Lewin, B. (1977). "Gene Expression-3." Wiley, New York.
Lilienfeld, F. A. (1929). Bibl. Genet., Leipzig **13**, 1–48.
McClintock, B. (1956). Cold Spring Harbor Symp. Quant. Biol. **21**, 197–216.
Manning, J. E., Schmid, C. W., and Davidson, N. (1975). Cell **4**, 141–155.
Nevers, P., and Saedler, H. (1977). Nature (London) **268**, 109–115.
Pardee, A. B., Benz, E. J., St. Peter, D. A., Krieger, J. N., Meuth, M., and Trieshmann, U. W., Jr. (1971). J. Biol. Chem. **246**, 6792–6796.

Possingham, J. V., and Rose, R. J. (1976). *Proc. R. Soc. London, Ser. B* **193**, 295–305.
Pring, D. R., and Levings, C. S., III (1976). *Science* **193**, 158–160.
Reddy, A. R. and Peterson, P. A. (1976). *Theor. Appl. Genet.* **48**, 269–278.
Sager, R. (1951). *Genetics* **36**, 510–540.
Sanger, F., Air, G. M., Barrell, B. G., Brown, N. L., Coulson, A. R., Fiddes, J. C., Hutchinson, C. V., III, Slocombe, P. M., and Smith, M. (1977). *Nature (London)* **265**, 687–695.
Sastry, G. R. K., Cooper, H. B., Jr., and Brink, R. A. (1965). *Genetics* **52**, 407–424.
Scaife, J., and Beckwith, J. R. (1966). *Cold Spring Harbor Symp. Quant. Biol.* **31**, 403–408.
Schell, J. (1979). *In* "Nucleic Acids of Plants" (T. C. Hall and J. Davies, eds.), CRC Press, West Plam Beach, Florida.
Thompson, J. N. (1977). *Stadler Gene. Symp.* **9**, 63–82.
Vedel, F., Quétier, F., and Bayen, M. (1976). *Nature (London)* **263**, 440–442.
Walbot, V. (1977). *Cell* **11**, 729–737.
Walbot, V. (1978). *In* "Dormancy and Developmental Arrest" (M. E. Clutter, ed.), pp. 113–166. Academic Press, New York.
Walbot, V., and Dure, L. S. (1976). *J. Mol. Biol.* **101**, 503–536.
Walbot, V., and Goldberg, R. E. (1979). *In* "Nucleic Acids of Plants" (T. C. Hall, and J. Davies, eds.), CRC Press, West Palm Beach, Florida.
Wells, R., Roger, H. D., and Hollenberg, C. P. (1976). *Mol. Gen. Genet.* **141**, 45–51.
Wilson, D. A. and Thomas, C. A. (1974). *J. Mol. Biol.* **84**, 115–144.
Zieg, J., Silverman, M., Hilmen, M., and Simon, M. (1978). *Stadler Genet. Symp.* **10**, 65–76.
Zimmerman, J. L., and Goldberg, R. E. (1977). *Chromosoma* **59**, 227–252.

Chapter 10

Mutagenesis and Crop Improvement

R. D. Brock

I. INTRODUCTION

The role of induced mutations in plant breeding has been a controversial subject for several decades. The first report of induced mutagenesis (Muller, 1927) mentioned the potential use of this technique for the improvement of crop plants. In the succeeding decades, there have been some extravagant claims for its potential and some severe criticisms of its use. However, a relatively small group of workers has investigated the scientific basis for the technique, and have encouraged the use of mutagenesis as an adjunct to plant breeding,

383

The Biology of Crop Productivity
Copyright © 1980 by Academic Press, Inc.

where it has had some notable success (Sigurbjörnsson and Micke, 1974). As a result of this work, a much clearer appreciation of the theoretical basis for its use and of the prospects and potential for its application to plant breeding situations now exist.

II. GENETIC AND BIOLOGICAL BASIS

Mutations are induced in single cells, and mutants are observed in the progeny of the mutated cell. In haploid, single-cell organisms such as bacteria, the genetic basis for expression and selection procedures are simple and striaghtforward, but crop plants are neither haploid nor single-cell organisms. Diploidy and higher levels of polyploidy influence the frequency and the stage at which mutations will be expressed and can be selected. The simplest situation in which induced mutations can be induced and observed in higher plants follows the treatment of haploid pollen grains and self-fertilization (Table I). Dominant mutations are expressed in the first generation after mutagenic treatment (M-1 generation), although the mutant plant will be heterozygous and will segregate mutant and nonmutant phenotypes in the subsequent M-2 generation. Recessive mutations will occur in the M-1 generation as heterozygotes and will not normally be expressed. Self-fertilization of the M-1 plants will permit expression of the homozygous recessive mutants in the M-2 generation. In cross-fertilizing species, homozygous mutants will only be produced by enforced selfing of heterozygotes. Where self-fertilization is not possible, as in self-incompatible species, homozygous mutants cannot be expressed before the M-3 generation, and then only following sib-mating of sister M-2 plants.

When mutagenic treatment is applied to multicellular organs—such as seeds, buds, or growing plants—the same genetic principles apply, with the added complexity of cellular heterogeneity (chimera) in the M-1 plants. Seed is the most convenient organ for treatment, and, as the embryo is multicellular, the resultant M-1 plant will be chimerical. Throughout the growth of the M-1 plant, the opportunity for competition between the mutant and wild-type cells exists, and the results of this diplontic selection influences the frequency of mutants observed in the M-2 generation. Dominant mutations can express in the M-1 plant, but only in the chimerical sector that results from the original mutated cell. Such mutated sectors are often visible as chlorophyll-deficient stripes or patches on M-1 plants, where the effect of diplontic

TABLE I
Mutant Expression after Mutagenic Treatment of Different Tissue

Tissue treated	Parent genotype	Mutation	M-1 generation		M-2 Generation			
					Self-fertilized		Cross-fertilized[a]	
			Genotype	Phenotype	Genotype	Phenotype	Genotype	Phenotype
Pollen	AA	A → a	Aa	Parental	AA	Parental	AA	Parental
					Aa	Parental	aA	Parental
					aa	Mutant		
	aa	a → A	aA	Mutant	aa	Parental	aa	Parental
					aA	Mutant	Aa	Mutant
					AA	Mutant		
Seed	AA	A → a	AA/ Aa	Parental	AA/			
					AA	Parental	AA	Parental
					Aa	Parental	aA	Parental
					aa	Mutant		
	aa	a → A	aa/ aA	Mutant chimera	aa/			
					aa	Parental	aa	Parental
					aA	Mutant	Aa	Mutant
					AA	Mutant		
Vegetative tissue	AA	A → a	AA/ Aa	Parental	Sexual reproduction same as for seed			
	Aa	A → a	Aa/ aa	Mutant chimera	Vegetative propagation of mutant sector			
	aa	a → A	aa/ aA	Mutant chimera				

[a] Cross-fertilization implies fertilization with a nonmutant gamete.

selection can sometimes be observed as a progressive change in the size of the mutated sector as the plant develops.

The observed frequency of mutants in the M-2 generation will be influenced by the mutation freuqency and by the number of cells in the treated seed that contribute to the M-2 generation (genetically effective cells). As we have already seen (Table I), treatment of a single haploid cell (e.g., pollen grain) of a diploid organism, followed by self-fertilization, will result in simple Mendelian segregation ratios for the mutants in the M-2 generation: dominant mutant 3:1, recessive mutant 1:3. Treatment of a multicellular organ of a diploid plant followed by self-pollination will result in the same segregation ratios in the progeny from the mutated cell, but the frequency of mutants will be reduced by the contribution of wild-type progeny from the nonmutated cells that contribute to the M-2 progeny. Observed segregation ratios of readily detectable mutants indicate that a small number of embryo cells, generally from two to five, contribute to the M-2 progeny (see Beard, 1970, for references). Polyploidy introduces a further complication, for recessive mutations can only express phenotypically when all alleles at a locus are present in the homozygous recessive condition.

In species that are propagated vegetatively by cuttings, buds, tubers, corms, etc., or by apomictic seeds, the absence of sexual recombination precludes the opportunity for the segregation of homozygous recessive mutations. Such species are often heterozygous at many loci, and induced recessive mutations at these loci will express immediately in the chimerical sectors resulting from the mutated cell. There remains the problem of devising suitable propagation systems to permit the expression of these chimerical sectors as organs that can be subjected to selection and further propagation.

III. NATURE OF INDUCED MUTATIONS

Mutations are detectable and heritable changes in the genetic material and can involve changes at the level of the chromosome, the gene, or the extrachromosomal hereditary determinants. In organisms well suited for genetic analysis, the level of the mutational change and its nature can be precisely determined. However, most crop plants are not well suited for precise genetic, cytogenetic, or molecular genetic studies. While changes of chromosome number, large chromosomal deletions, and structural rearrangements are readily detectable, as are extranuclear mutations, detailed studies at the genic and intragenic level are often not possible.

A. Nuclear Mutations

Haploid prokaryotic species (bacteria and viruses) are most favorable for molecular genetic analysis and, in such species, the different types of genic and intragenic changes induced by mutagenic agents have been characterized as deletions, duplications, rearrangements, and substitutions of nucleotide bases. Such species, because they are haploid and do not have large amounts of repeated-sequence DNA, do not readily tolerate large deletions of genetic material. However, higher plants (eukaryotes)—particularly the polyploid species—and those species with large amounts of repeated-sequence DNA in their complement, will tolerate more gross changes in the form of chromosomal deletions and structural changes.

There is still uncertainty as to the extent to which chromosomal changes, as opposed to genic changes, contribute to the yield of induced mutations in higher plants. Major structural changes, such as cytologically observable deletions or chromosome rearrangements, are induced with high frequency by ionizing radiation and many chemical mutagens. Most gross changes are highly deleterious and rarely persist beyond a few cell generations. Smaller changes, however, have less drastic effects and may persist through the haploid gametophytic phase and be transmitted to succeeding sexual generations as mutations. Conventional cytological examination is not capable of detecting small structural changes that would simultaneously affect a group of adjacent genes, or of distinguishing these from intragenic changes. Precise genetic tests can be applied to detect simultaneous mutations of closely linked loci in those species having adequate marker genes, e.g., peas, maize, barley, tomatoes and *Arabidopsis*. Such tests have revealed a high frequency of mutations affecting groups of adjacent genes (Stadler and Roman, 1948; Gottschalk, 1968, 1976; Amano, 1968; Mottinger, 1970). However, some cases of mutation of individual loci without any change to closely linked marker genes have been observed (Amano, 1968; Lifschyts and Falk, 1969), particularly after chemical mutagen treatment.

Another method of distinguishing between genic and chromosomal changes as the cause of mutation is to attempt to back-mutate the mutant to its original form. Phenotypic revertants can be categorized as being due to suppressor mutations occurring at different loci or possible back-mutations, where the secondary mutation occurs at the same locus as the original mutation. This latter category can include intragenic suppressors, which are known to occur, but the test provides an estimate of the proportion of the original forward mutations that can be reverted by a second change at the same locus. It is reasonable to assume that these are not the result of a substantial deletion. Such tests have been conducted with barley and with *Arabidopsis*. Forty-one of 44 revertants of a yellow virescent mutant of barley were shown to be the result of suppressor mutations that occurred at a number of different loci. Three revertants were due to mutations at, or closely linked to, the site of the original mutation (Tuleen *et al.*, 1968). Eight leaf color mutants of *Arabidopsis* were shown to revert at rates which were characteristic of the original mutant and the mutagen used to induce the revertants. Many of the revertants were sterile, indicating gross chromosomal change. Among the fertile revertants of all of the mutants, more than 90% were due to suppressor mutations (Röbbelen, 1969).

These studies indicate that, while true intragenic mutations occur in higher plants and contribute to induced genetic variability, their frequency is low compared with the frequency of small chromosomal changes.

B. Cytoplasmic Mutations

Extranuclear genetic determinants are important in crop plants, for example, in the determination of male sterility and disease resistance (Harvey *et al.*, 1972). Relatively few attempts have been made to induce and detect cytoplasmic mutations in higher plants, although there are some reported incidences (von Wettstein, 1961; Hagemann and Scholz, 1962; Favret and Ryan, 1966; Levy and Ashri, 1978).

C. Increasing the Specificity of Mutation

The early dreams of chemical mutagens that would recognize and specifically mutate particular genes have been dashed by our present understanding of the organization of the genes as linear sequences of the same four bases. The chance of obtaining a chemical mutagen that will recognize the sequence of a structural gene appears very remote. However, there are other possibilities.

While induced mutations are generally regarded as occurring at random throughout the genome, there are reports that indicate that this is not always so. Detailed analyses of a large number of mutants at the erectoides (*ert*) and the eceriferum loci of barley reveal locus specificity in response to different physical and chemical mutagens. Mutants occur much more frequently at the *ert a* locus after treatment with sparsely ionizing radiations (X and γ rays) and with certain chemicals than after treatment with densely ionizing radiations (neutrons). In contrast, the ert c locus is more frequently mutated by neutrons (Persson and Hagberg, 1969). Similar differential responses to different mutagens occur at certain eceriferum loci (Lundqvist et al., 1968). Differences occur in the relative frequencies of different types of chlorophyll mutations, and in the ratio of viable to lethal mutations, after treatment with different mutagens (see Nilan, 1972, for review). Certain chemical mutagens induce chromosome breakage at specific regions of the chromosomes, e.g., maleic hydrazide specifically breaks at heterochromatic regions (Kihlman, 1966). Widely varying ratios of chromosome aberrations to mutations are induced by different mutagenic agents. Compared with ionizing radiations, certain chemical mutagens—such as ethyl methane sulphonate, diethyl sulfate, and, notably, sodium azide—induce a high ratio of mutations to chromosome aberrations (Nilan, 1972). Interpretation of these results is restricted by our incomplete understanding of the mutational processes, and application of the findings to mutation plant breeding is hampered by our lack of knowledge of the mutational change required to produce a particular mutant phenotype.

Auerbach (1967) favors control of the mutational process by manipulation of the physical, cellular, or genetic environments, in order to influence the type and frequency of mutations that are recovered. I am completely in agreement with this approach, for it implies specific selection objectives, large populations, and manipulation of the environment to select the required mutant.

Some suggestions for more direct control of the mutation process have also come from genetic studies with microorganisms.

Cerdá-Olmedo et al. (1968) have reported that nitrosoguanadine treatment of Escherichia coli, in which DNA replication was synchronized, resulted in sequential mutation of a linear array of genes. This work suggests that nitrosoguanadine mutates by direct action at the DNA replication fork, and opens the possibility for some control of the mutation spectrum by applying pulsed mutagenic treatments to tissue in which mitoses can be synchronized. Data are available from plants, demonstrating that when seeds are treated with alkylating agents during the S phase of DNA synthesis the mutation frequency is significantly increased (Mikaelsen et al., 1968; Natarajan and Shivasankar, 1965; Savin et al., 1968). Furthermore, pulsed EMS treatments applied to germinating barley seeds have resulted in suggestions of altered chlorophyll mutation spectrum (Swaminathan, 1969; Swaminathan and Sarma, 1968).

I have earlier (Brock, 1969) referred to other experiments with microorganisms that offer prospects for a more direct control of the mutational process via the controlling elements rather than the structural genes.

The first is the prospect of differential sensitivity to mutation of active as compared with inactive genes. Alkylating agents have been shown to induce a higher frequency of mutations at the β-galactosidase gene of *Escherichia coli* when the mutagen was applied to the gene in the active state (induced) than when applied to the inactive (uninduced) gene. Other types of mutagens, ionizing radiation, and base analogs did not show this differential action (Brock, 1971a). This finding has not yet been confirmed in higher plants, but if a similar differential action can be demonstrated, some control of the mutation process should be possible by applying such mutagens when particular genes or sets of genes are active during development and differentiation.

A second is the prospect of utilizing the DNA-recognizing property of a regulator protein of an operator–regulator controlling system to carry a mutagen to a specific locus in the genome. If these control systems operate in higher plants, it should be possible to produce operator constitutive mutants by making a regulator protein mutagenic by incorporating ^{3}H-labeled amino acids.

IV. INDUCED MUTATIONS AS A SOURCE OF GERM PLASM

Plant breeding is genetic advance achieved by applying selection to genetic variability existing or generated in the population. Selection can be applied to naturally variable populations and progress achieved toward a particular selection objective. However, with most crop plants in modern agricultural systems, this has already been done and little useful variability remains. Consequently, additional variability has to be generated. The conventional method of generating this variability is by sexual hybridization between naturally occurring genotypes.

Plant breeders are well aware of the need for large and diverse sources of germ plasm to generate this variability. These needs have been supplied from the reservoirs of the natural gene pools existing in current and obsolete cultivars, special genetic stocks, primitive varieties, and the wild and weed relatives of the cultivated species. However, in recent times there has been increasing concern about the erosion of these natural gene pools (Frankel and Bennett, 1970). The threat comes partly from the narrowing of the genetic basis in the transition from primitive to modern cultivars, and partly from the spread of highly productive cultivars, such as the CIMMYT wheats and the International Rice Research Institute rice varieties, into areas that have been the reservoirs of primitive cultivars and land races.

In view of the advances in our knowledge of the nature of genes and genetic variation, and our ability to create variation by the induction of mutations, is there any need to preserve natural gene pools?

Natural variation is simply the product of spontaneous mutation, molded by recombination and natural selection. We can induce any mutation that has occurred naturally, and probably many that have either never occurred spontaneously or have been lost from the natural populations. We can, by applying the appropriate selection techniques, retain those mutants suitable for modern agricultural systems rather than be dependent upon those that have survived natural and primitive selection. Thus, at the level of the individual gene, there seems little doubt that we can induce the full range of genetic variation that exists in the natural gene pools. The choice of the most appropriate system to be used then becomes largely a question of the efficiency of selection that can be applied for the mutant gene compared with the ease of transfer of the mutant character to other genotypes. As we shall see later, these are largely questions of working economics and are determined by the genetic nature of the character under study and the breeding system of the species. For characters determined by the action of single genes, there is no theoretical need for the preservation of natural germ plasm, but it may be more economical to transfer rather than to induce mutations. While this is undoubtedly true at the level of the individual gene, does it apply for quantitatively inherited characters that are determined by the action of many genes?

Induced mutations can be used to generate useful variation in quantitatively inherited characters and, where appropriate selection has been applied, improvements in yield, adaptability, maturity time, and numerous other traits have been obtained (Bogyo *et al.*, 1969; Gregory, 1968; Gustafsson, 1965; Sigurbjörnsson and Micke, 1974). The extent to which induced mutations provide a useful alternative to natural variation as a source of germ plasm for the improvement of such traits is largely determined by the importance of linked groups of genes, and by the degree to which natural selection has built up linked gene complexes of adaptive significance in naturally occurring genotypes. Where such linked sets of genes occur, they can be transferred to other genotypes, but they are unlikely to be produced as the result of random mutations.

There is good genetic evidence for the existence of coadapted complexes of genes, and it is generally believed that they are important in the adaptation of populations of natural races and species (Dobzhansky, 1970; Allard et al., 1972a). While it is also generally assumed that similar complexes of genes are important for plant improvement, there is surprisingly little evidence to support this assumption. Allard and co-workers (Allard 1975; Allard et al., 1972b; Clegg et al., 1972; Kahler and Allard, 1970; Weir et al., 1972, 1974) conducted an extensive study of the frequency of four esterase loci in two experimental populations of barley, synthesized from 30 barley varieties and propagated in large plots over many generations. In each population, natural selection and restricted recombination resulted in nonrandom associations of alleles at the four esterase loci. Three of the loci were closely linked; the fourth segregated independently. While this study shows very convincingly the importance of the two chromosomal regions marked by the esterase loci in responding to selection, it does not demonstrate what loci actually respond to selection and whether they are few or many.

Similarly, in the case of the most recent, striking example of plant improvement, the semi-dwarf wheats, opinions differ as to the genetic nature of the contribution made by the exotic parent. The Japanese Norin dwarf wheats contributed high straw strength, high tillering, and a large number of seeds per head. However, the semidwarf character was tightly linked to shrunken, poor-quality grain type, and disease resistance and adaptation to high fertility conditions were lacking (Krull and Borlaug, 1970). Was the success that followed the use of the Norin wheats as parents due to the transfer of balanced gene combinations, or to the astute plant breeding efforts of Vogel and Borlaug in assembling relatively simple, but most desirable, combinations of simply inherited traits?

Until these questions can be answered unequivocally and the role of linked-gene complexes in plant breeding situations is established, the importance of induced mutations as an alternative to natural germ plasm for quantitatively inherited traits must remain uncertain. Thus, for safety, we must continue to regard linked complexes as potentially important and consider induced mutations as a supplement rather than as an alternative to the conservation of genetic resources.

V. INDUCED MUTATIONS IN PLANT BREEDING

Any proposal to use induced mutations in plant breeding must consider the likelihood of success when compared with conventional techniques and the effort required to obtain the desired genotype. The likelihood of success can be considered in relation to the genetic control of the character to be improved and the breeding system of the species.

For simplicity, the alternative breeding systems and types of genetic control are considered as discrete systems. This is, however, not strictly correct. While most species are predominantly self- or cross-fertilizing and predominantly sexually or asexually reproducing, many intermediate situations occur. Similarly, while some traits are simply inherited, the phenotypic expression of genes of large effect can be modified by genetic background, and mutations of large effect sometimes occur in traits normally inherited in a quantitative fashion.

A. Simply Inherited Traits

The choice between induced mutations and gene transfer in the case of simply inherited traits is largely determined by the ease with which the gene can be mutated, compared with the ease with which it can be incorporated from another genotype.

The induction of a recessive mutation is a much more likely event than the induction of a dominant mutant. This fact, plus the ease of intraspecific transfer of a dominant gene by conventional genetic methods, favors hybridization breeding where the desired characteristic is known, or is presumed to be conditioned by a dominant gene.

In the case of recessive genes, the induction of mutations is more worthy of consideration. If the gene is available in a genotype closely related to the agricultural cultivar, transfer of the gene by back-crossing would normally be favored as the method more likely to prove successful. However, there are examples of rapid adjustment of single undesirable characteristics by means of mutation. If close linkage with undesirable characters or undesirable pleiotropic effects is found to be involved in a gene-transfer program, or if transfer of the desired gene involves interspecific of intergeneric crossing, induced mutations may be the preferable technique. If there is no known source from which the gene can be transferred, induced mutations are, of course, the only possibility. The decision to initiate a program based on induced mutations then depends largely upon economic considerations such as the importance of the objective and the cost of screening for the desired mutation.

Mutations are particularly efficient aids to the domestication of wild species. Evolution under natural conditions results in the accumulation of genes advantageous to the survival of the wild plant. Many of these genes are disadvantageous in agricultural situations. Where they occur as dominant alleles in the wild plant, their activity can be destroyed by deletion, or mutation to recessive alleles, or suppressed by modification of other genes. Removal or suppression of undesirable features such as a toxin, spines, or thorns is the first step in the adaptation of a plant to man's use. With all of our older agricultural species, this has already been accomplished, but it remains of importance for the introduction of new species into agriculture. For example, many of the potentially valuable high-protein grain and pasture legumes have undesirable antinutritional factors and toxins limiting their use.

B. Quantitatively Inherited Traits

These characters are controlled by the interaction of many genes each of small effect. In these situations, the efficiency of selecting the desired mutant is generally lower than for specific characters controlled by a single gene, but this is largely offset by the increased frequency of mutants resulting from the greater number of genes involved. Alternative sources of variability, and the price to be paid in terms of alteration to the background genotype are the most important considerations in deciding whether to use induced mutations to improve characters, such as yield, maturity time, adaptability, etc. (Brock, 1965).

In situations where the species under consideration has not been closely adapted to the environment by intensive plant breeding, substantial variation is likely to be generated by either mutation or intervarietal hybridization. Consequently, the choice between the alternative methods of inducing variability will be largely determined by the extent to which the background genotype will be changed by the different methods. Where mutant identification is highly efficient (e.g., early flowering), induced mutations appear to be an attractive proposition, for many mutants can be obtained and selection for other characters can be practised. On the other hand, if selection is difficult and expensive (e.g., yield), hybridization would be favored because the high-yielding segregants would be less likely to be deficient for some other character.

In situations where the species has been closely adapted to the environment by intensive plant breeding, further intervarietal hybridization of high-yielding, well-adapted genotypes generates very limited variability. In these situations, substantial variability can only be generated by wide hybridization or by mutation. Both methods will upset adaptation, and, where the effect of inducing mutations is likely to be less drastic, it would be the preferable method.

C. Self- and Cross-Fertilizing Species

In general, induced mutations offer less prospect for the improvement of cross-fertilizing species than for self-fertilizing species. This is partly because of the difficulty of selecting, incorporating, and maintaining recessive mutations in such populations, and partly because the plant breeding problems in cross-fertilizing species are more often problems of handling the existing variability than lack of variability per se. However, several successful plant improvement ventures have utilized variability induced by mutagenic agents (Gupta and Swaminathan, 1967; Sigurbjörnsson and Micke, 1974).

Where the lack of variability exists for specific, simply inherited traits, the basis for choosing between induced mutations and hybridization is essentially the same in self- and cross-fertilizing species. However, the genetic consequences of the failure of recessive mutations to express in cross-fertilizing systems without forced selfing or sibmating must be taken into account in assessing the cost of such ventures.

Compared with the situation with self-fertilizing species, relatively few experimental studies involving mutation and selection for quantitatively inherited characters are available with cross-fertilizing species. Experiments with maize (Gardner, 1969) and poultry (Abplanalp *et al.*, 1964) show that mutagenic treatment results in a sharp depression of the mean of the character under study. An enhanced selection response can be achieved in the mutated population, but the selections from the mutated populations have not exceeded those from the unmutated controls. In view of the fact that lack of genetic variability is rarely the factor limiting improvement of quantitatively inherited characters in cross-fertilizing species, the use of induced mutations in these situations cannot be generally recommended, unless it has been clearly established that naturally occurring variability has been fully utilized.

D. Vegetatively Propagated Species

Vegetatively propagated species fall into two main categories. First, there are those that are capable of sexual reproduction but are commercially propagated vegetatively, e.g., many horticultural and floricultural species. These species are generally highly heterozygous and are often polyploid or aneuploid. The variability generated by crossing is so great that there is little chance of selecting for improved types among seedling progeny and at the same time retaining the general characteristics of the variety. Plant improvement has depended largely on the selection of naturally occurring mutants (sports). Consequently, techniques that increase the frequency of mutations should be of great value, particularly where they can be combined with adventitious bud, formation to avoid the production of chimeras. This is already proving to be the case, and many new floricultural varieties, produced as the result of the induction of mutations, have been released (Broertjes and van Harten, 1978). Restrictions imposed by the preponderance of recessive mutations, and by the failure of such mutations to express unless homozygous, are largely offset by the heterozygosity of the cultivars. The largely deleterious nature of mutations and the detrimental effects of mutations occurring in the background genotype are offset to a considerable degree in floricultural species, where novelty is of value in itself and "yield" is not as important as it is in agricultural species. However, these factors remain important in most of the horticultural species.

The second category of vegetatively propagated species are the apomicts and sterile forms. In obligate apomicts, hybridization fails to generate any variability. In such situations, induced mutations are the only available method for generating variability, but it should not be assumed that obligate apomicts occur frequently. An exhaustive search for sexual forms or facultative apomicts should be made before assuming that a species is an obligate apomict.

VI. THE COST OF MUTATION BREEDING

The cost of mutation breeding must be assessed both in terms of alterations to the background genotype of the parental variety and in terms of the effort that will have to be expended to obtain the desired mutant.

A. Plant Genotype

A common misconception about induced mutations is that they occur without any alteration to the background genotype. Consideration of the effect of mutagenic treatments on quantitatively inherited characters shows that this is not so. All of the mutagenic treatments at our command induce essentially random changes in the genotype, and at the treatment levels used to give an appreciable amount of visible mutations, considerable variation in quantitatively inherited characters is also induced (Brock, 1965; Gaul, 1965; Gregory, 1968; Scossiroli,

1970). Hence, if selection is applied only for a specific mutant phenotype, the selected mutant is very likely to be changed in a number of other subtle but nevertheless important ways. Random mutation increases the variance for all quantitatively inherited characters, and, in the absence of any selection or correlated response, the mean of the character will shift away from the direction of the previous selection (Brock, 1965, 1967, 1976). As most agricultural species have already been selected for high performance and adaptability, random mutation will, on the average, be deleterious and will reduce overall performance. This trend can, of course, be reversed by applying selection for all important characters or by incorporating the selected mutant into a breeding program where the desired mutant gene can be separated from the undesirable mutations.

B. Effort

An assessment of the comparative effort—in terms of plant material, labor and time—of producing a new and useful genotype by mutation breeding or by conventional breeding is, unfortunately, not often possible. However, before a mutation breeding program is initiated, some assessment should be made of the plant population that will have to be examined to obtain the desired mutation.

For single gene mutations, if we assume a mutation rate (μ) and set a level of probability for the occurrence of at least one mutation (p_1), then the number of treated cells that have to be examined (n) can be calculated from the formula

$$n = \frac{\log (1-p_1)}{\log (1-\mu)}$$

Induced mutation rates for specific loci vary greatly, depending upon the locus studied, the nature of the mutational event and the mutagenic treatment. Rates are best known for ionizing radiations, but there are numerous reports of higher rates for chemical mutagens (Kawai, 1969).

Mutation rates for specific recessive loci, excluding deletions, fall within the range 7×10^{-10} to 3×10^{-7} rad^{-1} locus^{-1} haploid genome^{-1} or from 6×10^{-6} to 5×10^{-4} locus^{-1} cell^{-1} (Brock, 1979). Where mutation is the result of a deletion, higher rates are obtained.

However, many mutant phenotypes can be produced by mutation at a number of different loci. For example, in barley the erectoides are known to occur by mutation at 26 loci (Persson and Hagberg, 1969), and the eceriferum mutants at 59 loci (Lundqvist 1975.,); male sterile mutants in tomato occur at 24 loci (Rick and Butler, 1956; Rick, 1966), and in maize at an even larger number of loci.

Lyons *et al.* (1964) reported induced mutation rates per gamete in mice varying from 3×10^{-1} for recessive lethals to 5.5×10^{-4} for dominant visibles. Gustafsson (1965) estimated the expected frequency of various classes of potentially useful mutations in barley ranging from 8×10^{-2} for chromosomal rearrangements to 1.3×10^{-3} for conspicuous mutants. Brock (1979) proposed the following mutation frequencies as a basis for assessing the number of treated cell progeny in mutation breeding experiments (Table II).

As recessive mutations are not detected until at least the M-2 generation, the values of n given in Table II represent the number of M-2 families that have to be examined. Assuming the mutagenic treatment to have a 50% lethal effect (LD_{50} dose), the number of first generation (M-1) plants required to provide these M-2 families is represented by the value 2n.

The number of plants that have to be examined per M-2 family (m) is determined by the segregation ratio (a) and the probability of occurrence of at least one homozygous mutant (p_2). For a single recessive gene, the segregation ratio after self-fertilization (a) is ¼ following treatment of a haploid gamete (pollen treatment). The segregation ratios after self-fertilization, where several embryo cells contribute to the next generation in the absence of any cell selection, are given in Table III. The M-2 family size (m) for various values of a and p_2 can be calculated from the formula

$$m = \frac{\log (1-p_2)}{\log (1-a)}$$

and is also given in Table III.

TABLE II

Number of Cell Progenies to be Examined for Various Mutation Rates (μ) and Probabilities of Occurence

Mutation rate (μ)	Number of cell progenies (n)		Type of mutation
	p = 0.90	p = 0.99	
1×10^{-2}	230	460	Chromosome changes and quantitatively inherited variation
1×10^{-3}	2300	4600	Several recessive genes
1×10^{-4}	23,000	46,000	Single recessive gene
1×10^{-5}	230,000	460,000	
1×10^{-6}	2,300,000	4,600,000	Single dominant gene

[a] From Brock, 1979.

TABLE III

M-2 Family Sizes of Different Segregation Ratios and Levels of Probability of Occurrence of the Homozygous Mutant[a]

Number of genetically effective cells	Segregation ratio (a)	M-2 family size (m)	
		$p_2 = 0.90$	$p_2 = 0.99$
1	1/4	8.0	16.0
2	1/8	17.2	34.5
3	1/12	26.3	52.6
4	1/16	35.7	71.4
5	1/20	45.5	91.0

[a] From Brock, 1971b.

For plants that cannot be completely self-fertilized in the M-1 generation, further increases in M-2 family size are necessary. Reduction in the proportion of self-fertilization to 50% after gametic treatment reduces the segregation ratio from ¼ to ⅛, and reduction to 25% selfing reduces the segregation ratio to 1/16. If no selfing is possible, recessive mutations will not express until the M-3 generation, and then only after sib mating.

When the size of the M-2 population is limiting, a compromise will be necessary between the probability of mutation (n) and the probability of detection (m). Rédei (1974) has reviewed the numerous considerations influencing the optimal size of M-2 families, and concludes, in conformity with most other authors, that the greatest efficiency is achieved by large populations of treated cells (M-1 population) and small M-2 families.

From a practical point of view, it is rarely possible to predict mutation frequencies accurately, and these calculations are useful only as guidelines. However, they do serve to emphasize the large populations required even in the simplest cases and the importance of utilizing highly efficient, low-cost methods of detecting mutants.

VII. MUTATION AND SELECTION

In conventional plant breeding, once a pool of genotypes has been assembled, it is sometimes possible to select directly a particular genotype that is superior to the existing cultivars. Similarly, after the induction of mutations it is sometimes possible to select directly a mutant genotype that is superior to the parental cultivar. Indeed, 127 of the 195 crop varieties that have resulted from induced mutations to date were direct selections (Sigurbjörnsson and Micke, 1974; Mutation Breeding Newsletters, 1974–1979).

These successful selections have been largely the result of selection for readily detectable plant characteristics. Much effort is currently being directed at the utilization of new screening techniques, such as chemical tests for the detection of recombinant and mutant genotypes with altered chemical and nutritional characteristics. The development of mass screening techniques for fatty acids, proteins, and amino acids is permitting large plant breeding populations to be screened for these characteristics. Considerable natural variation exists in the cross-fertilizing *Brassica* species, so the induction of mutation has not been necessary in the development of new genotypes with zero erusic acid and altered fatty acid composition. However, in efforts to improve the nutritional characteristics of the self-fertilizing cereals by altering the protein composition and content, relatively little natural variation is available, and induced mutants are being sought.

The discovery that the opaque-2 mutant of maize had a high lysine content (Mertz *et al.*, 1964) stimulated attempts to locate similar mutants in other species. One comparable, naturally occurring mutant was located by screening the world barley collection (Hagberg and Karlsson, 1969). Subsequently, Doll *et al.* (1974) selected a number of high-lysine induced mutants of barley. These mutants are single recessive mutations; they occur with a frequency of approximately 1×10^{-3} per treated cell, and are estimated to occur at about ten loci (H. Doll, personal communication). Similarly, in sorghum, Axtell (1976) has isolated both naturally occurring and induced mutant genotypes with high lysine levels in the grain. Similar attempts to detect either naturally occurring or induced mutants in wheat and rice have not been successful, despite massive efforts. Whether this failure is due to the different seed protein composition of these species or to their polyploid nature has not been positively determined as yet.

Mutants with altered protein contents have been detected in the cereal species where mutation breeding programs have been established. However, these efforts are being complicated by the need to maintain high yield levels, and many of the "high-protein" mutants are associated with reduced starch synthesis and reduced yield. To date, only one high-protein cereal genotype, resulting from mutationally induced genetic variability, has been recommended for release (Parodi and Nebreda, 1979). One new wheat variety, Lancota, with high yield and increased protein content has been bred by conventional methods (Johnson *et al.*, 1978). However, this breeding program was commenced in 1954, whereas the mutation breeding programs have been operating for less than 10 years.

The new techniques of plant cell culture offer great potential for mutant selection, and two facets are important for mutation breeding. The first is the ability to regenerate complete plants from single cells grown in culture. This is now established for tobacco, rice, carrot, sugar cane, and orchids, and there are recent reports of complete regeneration of rape, wheat, rye, coffee, barley, *Stylosanthes hamata,* and *Petunia hybrida.* This wide range of species suggests that appropriate conditions will be found for the regeneration of complete plants from any species. The second important point is that haploid cells can be cultured. These cells provide the opportunity for the direct selection of recessive mutations, and after chromosome doubling, homozygous mutant plants become available. The use of plant cell culture thus offers the prospect of applying to crop plants many of the highly sophisticated techniques developed in prokaryote genetics. These techniques offer obvious prospects for selecting mutants in the biosynthetic pathways with changes in the amount or composition of an end or intermediate product. This is of potential importance, for example, in the domestication of wild species by the removal of toxins and other compounds deleterious to man or his domestic animals, in the adaptation of plants to special environmental conditions such as high salt concentration, and in the modification of products from crop plants grown for nutritional, industrial or medicinal purposes.

Attempts have been made to select for salt-resistant clones in cultures (Dix and Street, 1975), and some progress has already been reported in the combination of mutagenesis and biochemical selection techniques applied to plant cell cultures. Heimer and Filner (1970) selected mutant tobacco cells capable of growing in concentrations of threonine inhibitory to nonmutant cells. These resistant cells had increased ability to assimilate nitrate in the presence of threonine, indicating that the mutation had occurred in the nitrate uptake system which, in wild-type cells, is sensitive to the level of free amino acids. Mutants of this type could increase seed protein levels in seed protein crops, for the rate of protein synthesis is likely to be limited by the supply of organic nitrogen.

Knowledge of biochemical pathways and control systems enables selection to be applied, with the object of influencing the concentration of intermediate or alternative end products where branched biosynthetic pathways are involved. This has already been utilized in the microorganism, *Micrococcus glutamicus,* to greatly increase its capacity to produce lysine in industrial fermentation processes. In this case, a mutant blocking threonine formation resulted in large quantities of lysine being excreted in industrial fermentation (Nakayama et al., 1966). This was possible in M. *glutamicus* because only the aspartate kinase and not the dihydropicolinic acid synthetase is sensitive to feedback inhibition (Fig. 1). There are suggestions that rice has the same minimal control of lysine formation (D. H. Halsall, personal communication), which might make it particularly suitable for deregulating lysine biosynthesis.

A more direct method of decontrolling amino acid biosynthesis is to inactivate the feedback receptor site by mutation. The required mutant can be isolated by selection for resistance to an analog of the appropriate amino acid. This has frequently been done with bacteria to give overproduction of amino acids. The same technique has now been used to deregulate amino acid synthesis in plant cell cultures.

Widholm (1972a,b) selected tobacco and carrot cells in culture for resistance to a tryptophan analog, 5-methyltryptophan, and obtained resistant cells with markedly increased levels of free tryptophan. In each case, it was shown that the anthranilate synthetase from the mutant cells had reduced sensitivity to inhibition by tryptophan or 5-methyltryptophan (Fig. 2). In later experiments (Widholm, 1974), further resistant cells were isolated in which the resistance was due to a decreased uptake of the analog and not to alteration in the anthranilate synthetase. This cell line had only a relatively small increase in the level of free tryptophan compared with the cell lines in which the anthranilate synthetase was mutated.

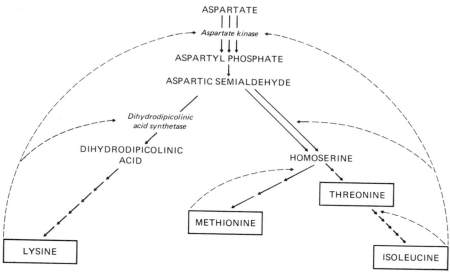

Fig. 1. Feedback control of biosynthesis of lysine, methionine, isoleucine, and threonine in *Escherichia coli*.

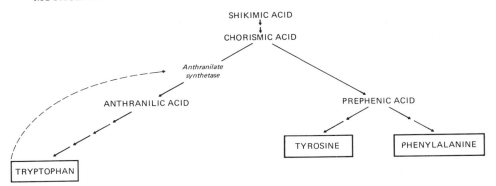

Fig. 2. Feedback inhibition of tryptophan.

Carlson (1973) used a similar technique to select tobacco cells resistant to a methionine analog, methionine sulphoximine. Haploid cells in culture were treated with ethylmethane sulphonate and three resistant calluses were obtained. Diploid progeny were regenerated from these resistant calluses, and in two of them the free methionine concentration in leaves, stems, and roots was substantially increased.

Chaleff and Carlson (1975) selected diploid rice cells in culture for resistance to the lysine analog, S-(β-aminoethyl)-cystine. Three resistant cell lines were obtained, and these had alterations of the free and total levels of a number of amino acids, including those derived from aspartate (Fig. 1). No enzyme studies were made, so it is not clear whether these were mutations affecting amino acid biosynthesis pathways. It was not possible to regenerate plants from these cell lines, so no information is available about the possible effects of these mutants on seed storage proteins.

Palmer and Widholm (1975) also selected carrot and tobacco cells in culture for resistance to an analog of phenylalanine, p-fluorophenylalanine. They isolated resistant cells in both species, but in this case their results suggested that the mutation had altered a general uptake mechanism rather than a specific enzyme concerned with phenylalnine biosynthesis. The resistant carrot cells had a six-fold increase in the level of free phenylalanine, but the resistant tobacco cells showed showed no such increase. Gathercole and Street (1976) also selected a cell line of sycamore resistant to p-fluorophenylalanine. This line had reduced uptake of both the analog and phenylalanine, and did not exhibit any increase in the pool level of phenylalanine.

An important feature in the success of these experiments has been the ability to apply an extremely efficient selection sieve to large numbers of cells. Although mutants resistant to 5-methyltryptophan and to methionine sulfoximine occurred at frequencies of 1 in 3×10^5 to 9×10^5 cells, the resistant lines were detected and selected.

While plant cell culture is undoubtedly of value in handling such large numbers of mutagen-treated cells, it is not essential. Where cell cultures are not available, whole plants can be used. James and Jacobs (1976) selected from 14,500 M-2 *Arabidopsis thaliana* plants a recessive mutant resistant to p-fluorophenylalanine. The mutant does not overproduce phenylalanine or tyrosine, nor is its uptake system impaired. Resistance appears to be due to the ability of the mutant plant to discriminate between phenylalanine and p-fluorophenylalanine for incorporation into proteins. In our laboratory, 120,000 cell progenies of barley have been screened for resistance to the lysine analog, S-(β-aminoethyl)-cysteine in search of mutants which overproduce lysine (Brock *et al.*, 1973). Progenies from resistant seedlings are now being assayed for free lysine levels.

Efficiency of selection is an obvious requirement for the successful detection of induced genetic variation. This can be improved by modifying the genetic as well as the physical environment. While it is obviously sensible to choose a high-yielding, well-adapted genotype as the starting material for a mutation breeding program designed for the direct selection of useful mutant cultivars, this does not necessarily apply if the object is to provide sources of new variability that will be used in subsequent hybridization programs. In such cases, it may be most appropriate to start with a genotype in which improvement in the desired characteristic can be most readily expressed. For example, mutant alleles contributing to earliness may be most easily selected in a late-flowering genotype or dwarfing alleles in a tall variety.

Before moving to the role of mutations as sources of variation in hybridization programs, brief mention must be made of the use of mutations in those species in which hybridization is not possible (obligate apomicts), or not conventionally practiced because of the long commercial life of individual plants and the highly heterozygous and sometimes chierical nature of the species (e.g., fruit trees). The application of mutagenic treatment that increases variability is of obvious use in providing material for selection. It is surprising that of the 195 mutant-derived cultivars of crop plants released to date, only 13 were vegetatively propagated species. Seven were fruit trees, and one of these involved a self-fertile cherry mutant seedling that was used in crossing to produce a self-fertile sweet cherry. The others were two potato, two sugarcane and two peppermint varieties. This relatively low number of successful mutants induced in vegetatively propagated crop plants is supplemented by 140 reported variants in ornamentals. This number is probably an underestimate, for the technique is used by commercial breeders who rarely report their methods.

A highly successful mutation breeding program produced *Verticillium* wilt-resistant mutants of the vegetatively reproduced sterile, polyploid peppermint (*Mentha piperita*) (Murray, 1969). Over 100,000 irradiated cuttings were grown in heavily infected soil, and repeated selection for disease resistance, vigor, yield and quality of oil produced improved commercial strains.

Numerous other vegetatively propagated field plants and tree crops are under investigation, and selected mutants of sugar cane, cassava, and Bermuda grass, as well as temperate and tropical tree crops, are under test (Anonymous, 1976).

There are excellent prospects for greater use of induced mutations in these vegetatively reproduced species. The heterozygosity of many horticultural species, which permits the ready expression of recessive mutations, and the value of novelty in floricultural species are special features not often present in agricultural plants.

VIII. MUTATION AND RECOMBINATION

It is difficult to assess the extent to which induced mutants are currently being used in cross-breeding programs. Because the development and testing of a commercial cultivar of a crop plant takes from 10 to 15 years, statistics on current releases do not reflect the current situation. It is nevertheless surprising that only 13 of the 98 varieties of crop plants emanating from mutations up to 1973 were the result of mutants being utilized in cross-breeding programs, the remainder being direct selections of mutants (Sigurbjörnsson and Micke, 1974). However, there are indications that this situation has changed, since 55 of the 97 varieties of mutational origin released since 1973 have utilized mutants as parents in hybridization programs. Only 42 were direct selections, and five of these were in cross-breeding species where some recombination was likely to have occurred.

These figures indicate that the technique is being incorporated into regular plant breeding programs and is no longer the exclusive province of a few specialists or those who have access to radiation facilities.

This is further indicated by the repeated occurrence of particular genotypes as parents in the pedigree of a number of successful cultivars, something that is a well-known occurrence in many successful conventional breeding programs. Gustafsson (1976) and Gustafsson and Lundqvist (1976) have described the use of the mutant barley varieties Pallas and Mari in recombination breeding programs. These two varieties have contributed to the pedigree of an additional nine varieties. Similar instances are reported in durum wheats (Scarascia-Mugnozza et al., 1972) and oats (Sigurbjörnsson and Micke, 1974).

A further surprising feature is the predominance of ionizing radiation as the mutagenic agent used to induce the mutations in the successful genotypes. In view of the many reports of greater efficiency and effectiveness of certain chemical mutagens, particularly ethylmethane sulphonate, one can only assume that this also is a reflection of the time required for the development and release of a commercial variety.

Little reference has been made in this review to the detailed methods of mutagenic treatment, but these are readily available in the Manual on Mutation Breeding (1977).

IX. CHROMOSOME MANIPULATION AND INCREASED GENETIC EXCHANGE

Transfer of genetic information between species that do not interbreed is a form of mutation. Considerable success has already been achieved in this area via radiation-induced translocations, which were initiated by Sears (1956) in his transfer of disease resistance from *Aegilops umbellulata* to wheat. This work was followed by similar transfers of disease resistance genes utilizing radiation (Acosta, 1961; Knott, 1961; Driscoll and Jensen, 1963; Sharma and Knott, 1966; Wienhues, 1966). Riley et al. (1968) achieved a similar transfer of yellow-rust resistance from *Aegilops comosa* by genetically removing pairing-suppressing genes on chromosome 5B of wheat.

Selection of genes for pairing suppression is likely to have been a common occurrence during the evolution of polyploid species. Removal of such genes by mutagenic and chromosome-breaking agents has already been achieved in wheat (Wall et al., 1971; Sears, 1975) and should be possible in other polyploid species once suitable selection techniques are developed. Once pairing is achieved, crossing over can be enhanced either by the application of external radiation (Henderson, 1970) or more efficiently by the incorporation of [^{3}H]orotic acid (Singh et al., 1974) at the time of meiotic prophase.

REFERENCES

Abplanalp, H., Lowry, D. C., Lerner, I. M., and Dempster, E. R. (1964). *Genetics* **50**, 1083–1100.

Acosta, A. (1961). Ph.D. Thesis, University of Missouri, Columbia.
Allard, R. W. (1975). Genetics 79, 115–126.
Allard, R. W., Babbel, G. R., Clegg, M. T., and Kahler, A. L. (1972a). Proc. Natl. Acad. Sci. U.S.A. 69, 3043–3048.
Allard, R. W., Kahler, A. L., and Weir, B. S. (1972b). Genetics 72, 489–503.
Amano, E. (1968). Mutat. Res. 5, 41–46.
Anonymous (1976). "Improvement of Vegetatively Propagated Plants and Tree Crops," IAEA-194, IAEA, Vienna.
Auerbach, C. (1967). Science 158, 1141–1147.
Axtell, J. D. (1976). In "Evaluation of Seed Protein Alterations by Mutation Breeding," pp. 45–53. IAEA, Vienna.
Beard, B. H. (1970). Radiat. Bot. 10, 47–57.
Bogyo, T. P., Scarascia-Mugnozza, G. T., Sigurbjörnsson, B., and Bagnara, D. (1969). In "Induced Mutations in Plants," pp. 699–717. IAEA, Vienna.
Brock, R. D. (1965). Radiat. Bot. 5, Suppl., 451–464.
Brock, R. D. (1967). Radiat. Bot. 7, 193–203.
Brock, R. D. (1969). In "Induced Mutation in Plants," pp. 93–100. IAEA, Vienna.
Brock, R. D. (1971a). Mutat. Res. 11, 181–186.
Brock, R. D. (1971b). Radiat. Bot. 11, 181–196.
Brock, R. D. (1976). Environ. Exp. Bot. 16, 241–153.
Brock, R. D. (1979). In "Seed Protein Improvement in Cereals and Grain Legumes," Vol. I, pp. 43–55. IAEA, Vienna.
Brock, R. D., Friederich, E. A., and Langridge, J. (1973). In "Nuclear Techniques for Seed Protein Improvement," pp. 329–338. IAEA, Vienna.
Broertjes, C. and van Harten, A. M. (1978). "Application of Mutation Breeding Methods in the Improvement of Vegetatively Propagated Crops." Elsevier, Amsterdam.
Carlson, P. S. (1973). Science 180, 1366–1368.
Cerdá-Olmedo, E., Hanawalt, P. C., and Guerola, N. (1968). J. Mol. Biol. 33, 705–719.
Chaleff, R. S., and Carlson, P. S. (1975). In "Modification of the Information Content of Plant Cells" (R. Markham et al., eds.), pp. 197–214. North-Holland Publ., Amsterdam.
Clegg, M. T., Allard, R. W., and Kahler, A. L. (1972). Proc. Natl. Acad. Sci. U.S.A. 69, 2474–2478.
Dix, P. J., and Street, H. E. (1975). Plant Sci. Lett. 5, 231–237.
Dobzhansky, T. (1970). "Genetics of the Evolutionary Process." Columbia Univ. Press, New York.
Doll, H., Køie, B., and Eggum, B. O. (1974). Radiat. Bot. 14, 73–80.
Driscoll, C. J., and Jensen, N. F. (1963). Genetics 48, 459–468.
Favret, E. A., and Ryan, G. S. (1966). In "Mutations in Plant Breeding," pp. 49–61. IAEA, Vienna.
Frankel, O. H., and Bennett, E. (1970). In "Genetic Resources in Plants—Their Exploration and Conservation," IBP Handb. No. 11. Blackwell, Oxford.
Gardner, C. O. (1969). In "Induced Mutations in Plants," pp. 469–476. IAEA, Vienna.
Gathercole, R. W. E., and Street, H. E. (1976). New Phytol. 77, 29–41.
Gaul, H. (1965). Radiat. Bot. 5, Suppl., 407–426.
Gottschalk, W. (1968). In "Mutations in Plant Breeding II," pp. 97–109. IAEA, Vienna.
Gottschalk, W. (1976). In "Induced Mutations in Cross Breeding," pp. 71–78. IAEA, Vienna.
Gregory, W. C. (1968). Radiat. Bot. 8, 81–147.
Gupta, A. K., and Swaminathan, M. S. (1967). Radiat. Bot. 7, 521–527.
Gustafsson, Å. (1965). Radiat. Bot. 5, Suppl., 323–337.

Gustafsson, A. (1976). *Proc. Int. Congr. Radiat. Res., 5th, 1974,* pp. 81–95. Academic Press, New York.

Gustafsson, A., and Lundqvist, U. (1976). *In* "Induced Mutations in Cross Breeding," pp. 45–53. IAEA, Vienna.

Hagberg, A., and Karlsson, K.-E. (1969). *In* "New Approaches to Breeding for Improved Plant Protein," pp. 17–21. IAEA, Vienna.

Hagemann, R., and Scholz, F. (1962). *Zuechter* **32,** 50–59.

Harvey, P. H., Levins, C. S., and Wernsman, E. A. (1972). *Adv. Agron.* **24,** 1–27.

Heimer, Y. M., and Filner, P. (1970). *Biochim. Biophys. Acta* **215,** 152–165.

Henderson, S. A. (1970). *Annu. Rev. Genet.* **4,** 295–324.

James, T., and Jacobs, M. (1976). *Proc. Int. Symp. Arabidopsis Res., 2nd, 1976,* (A. R. Kranz, ed.), pp. 85–95. J. W. Goethe University, Frankfurt/Main.

Johnson, V. A., Mattern, P. J., Wilhelmi, K. D., and Kuhr, S. L. (1978). *In* "Seed Protein Improvement by Nuclear Techniques," pp. 23–32. IAEA, Vienna.

Kahler, A. L., and Allard, R. W. (1970). *Crop Sci.* **10,** 444–448.

Kawai, T. (1969). *In* "Induced Mutations in Plants," pp. 137–151. IAEA, Vienna.

Kihlman, B. A. (1966). "Action of Chemicals on Dividing Cells." Prentice-Hall, Englewood Cliffs, New Jersey.

Knott, D. R. (1961). *Can. J. Plant Sci.* **41,** 109–123.

Krull, C. F., and Borlaug, N. E. (1970). *In* "Genetic Resources in Plants—Their Exploration and Conservation" (O. H. Frankel and E. Bennett, eds.), Chapter 37. Blackwell, Oxford.

Levy, A., and Ashri, A. (1978). *Mutat. Res.* **51,** 347–360.

Lifschyts, E., and Falk, R. (1969). *Mutat. Res.* **8,** 147–155.

Lundqvist, U. (1975). *In* "Barley Genetics III" pp. 162–163. Verlag Karl Thiemig, München.

Lyons, M. F., Phillips, R. J. S., and Searle, A. G. (1964). *Genet. Res.* **5,** 448–467.

"Manual on Mutation Breeding" 2nd Ed. (1977). IAEA, Vienna.

Mertz, E. T., Bates, L. S., and Nelson, O. E. (1964). *Science* **145,** 279–280.

Mikaelsen, K., Ahnström, G., and Li, W. C. (1968). *Hereditas* **59,** 353–374.

Mottinger, J. P. (1970). *Genetics* **64,** 259–271.

Muller, H. J. (1927). *Science* **66,** 84–87.

Murray, M. J. (1969). *In* "Induced Mutations in Plants," pp. 345–370. IAEA, Vienna.

"Mutation Breeding Newsletters" Nos. 4–14 (1974–1979), IAEA, Vienna.

Nakayama, K., Tanaka, H., Hagino, H., and Kinoshita, S. (1966). *Agric. Biol. Chem.* **30,** 611–616.

Natarajan, A. T., and Shivasankar, G. (1965). *Z. Vererbungsl.* **96,** 13–21.

Nilan, R. A. (1972). *In* "Induced Mutations and Plant Improvement" pp. 141–151. IAEA, Vienna.

Palmer, J. E., and Widholm, J. (1975). *Plant Physiol.* **56,** 233–238.

Parodi, P. C., and Nebreda, I. M. (1979). *In* "Seed Protein Improvement in Cereals and Grain Legumes, II" pp. 201–208. IAEA, Vienna.

Persson, G., and Hagberg, A. (1969). *Hereditas* **61,** 115–178.

Rédei, G. P. (1974). *Z. Pflanzenzecht.* **73,** 87–96.

Rick, C. M. (1966). *Genetics* **53,** 85–96.

Rick, C. M., and Butler, L. (1956). *Adv. Genet.* **8,** 267–382.

Riley, R., Chapman, V., and Johnson, R. (1968). *Nature (London)* **217,** 383–384.

Röbbelen, G. (1969). *Arabidopsis Inf. Serv.* **6,** 17–18.

Savin, V. N., Swaminathan, M. S., and Sharma, B. (1968). *Mutat. Res.* **6,** 101–107.

Scarascia-Mugnozza, G. T., Bagnara, D., and Bozzini, A. (1972). *In* "Induced Mutations and Plant Improvement," pp. 183–197. IAEA, Vienna.

Scossiroli, R. E. (1977). In "Manual on Mutation Breeding," 2nd ed. pp. 117–123. IAEA, Vienna.

Sears, E. R. (1956). Brookhaven Symp. Biol. 9, 1–22.

Sears, E. R. (1975). Genetics 80, 74.

Sharma, D., and Knott, D. R. (1966). Can. J. Genet. Cytol. 8, 137–143.

Sigurbjörnsson, B., and Micke, A. (1974). In "Polyploidy and Induced Mutations in Plant Breeding," pp. 303–343. IAEA, Vienna.

Singh, C. B., Brock, R. D., and Oram, R. N. (1974). Radiat. Bot. 14, 139–145.

Stadler, L. J., and Roman, H. (1948). Genetics 33, 273–303.

Swaminathan, M. S. (1969). In "Induced Mutations in Plants," pp. 719–734. IAEA, Vienna.

Swaminathan, M. S., and Sarma, N. P. (1968). Curr. Sci. 37, 685–686.

Tuleen, N. A., Caldecott, R. S., and Snyder, L. A. (1968). In "Mutation in Plant Breeding II," pp. 73–76. IAEA, Vienna.

von Wettstein, D. (1961). Can. J. Bot. 39, 1537–1545.

Wall, A. M., Riley, R., and Chapman, V. (1971). Genet. Res. 18, 311–328.

Weir, B. S., Allard, R. W., and Kahler, A. L. (1972). Genetics 72, 505–523.

Weir, B. S., Allard, R. W., and Kahler, A. L. (1974). Genetics 78, 911–919.

Widholm, J. M. (1972a). Biochim. Biophys. Acta 261, 52–58.

Widholm, J. M. (1972b). Biochim. Biophys. Acta 279, 48–57.

Widholm, J. M. (1974). In "Tissue Culture and Plant Science" (H. E. Street, ed.), pp. 287–299. Academic Press, New York.

SECTION V

FUTURE PROSPECTS

Chapter 11

The Shape of Things to Come

Sylvan H. Wittwer

I. INTRODUCTION

Food is our most important renewable resource. Plants provide, directly or indirectly, up to 95% of the world's food supply. Botanists have identified approximately 350,000 species of plants. Of these, about 3000 have been tried as food sources. Less than 300 are currently

The Biology of Crop Productivity
Copyright © 1980 by Academic Press, Inc.
All rights of reproduction in any form reserved
ISBN 0-12-159850-0

used worldwide in organized agriculture. There are about 100 crops grown in the United States for food, feed, or fiber that have an annual economic value of $1 million or more. A mere eight plants—rice, wheat, corn, sugarcane, soybeans, millet, cassava, and potatoes— provide most of the food and income for people in developing countries. Other important crops include banana, coconut, yams, sweet potatoes, barley, oats, rye, pigeon peas, chick peas, mung beans, cowpeas, soybeans, peanuts, and a great variety of fruits and vegetables. Globally, 24 crops, essentially, stand between people and starvation. They are in the approximate order of importance: rice, wheat, corn, potatoes, barley, sweet potatoes, cassava, soybeans, oats, sorghum, millet, sugarcane, sugar beets, rye, peanuts, field beans, chick peas, pigeon peas, mung beans, cowpeas, broad beans, yams, bananas, and coconuts. Cereal grains constitute the most important food group on earth. They provide 60% of the calories and 50% of the protein consumed by the human race. Twenty percent of the protein comes from seed legumes. Fruits and vegetables are secondary staple food crops. Hundreds of millions of people depend primarily for food and income on what is produced in gardens and small holdings.

An extremely important food resource is found in the forages, pasture crops, and plants on the rangelands of the earth. These crops are indigestible for people, but can be converted to useful food and fiber products by ruminant livestock.

Projections for programming crop productivity for the future dictate that attention must be given to the biology of a relatively few crop species. Adequacy of our food supply mandates that attention be given to both stability or dependability, as well as enhancement of production.

II. BIOLOGICAL PROCESSES THAT LIMIT CROP PRODUCTIVITY

Control and regulation of the biological processes that relate to the productivity of economically important food crops will hold the key to future food adequacy. New technologies in this area should be nonpolluting, without noise, should be subject to few, if any, regulatory constraints, and would add to or preserve the resources of the earth. New technologies should also, if possible, address the global problems of climatic impacts, soil erosion, desertification, deforestation, shortage of firewood, adequacy and dependability of our food supply, uncertain-

TABLE I
Global Problems Relating to Crop Productivity

Poverty	Soil erosion
Inflation	Changing climate
Malnutrition	Shortage of firewood
Unemployment	Uncertainties of energy supplies
Deforestation	Toxic chemicals in the environment
Desertification	Adequacy and dependability of food supply
Population increase	

ties of our energy supply, unemployment, inflation, malnutrition, poverty, toxic chemicals in the environment, and population increase (Table I).

An international conference (Brown *et al.*, 1976) and several National Academy of Sciences' reports (1975a–e, 1977a–h) have addressed the control of these processes with a priority listing for research. They may be summarized as follows: (1) greater photosynthetic efficiency; (2) improved biological nitrogen fixation; (3) genetic improvement and new cell fusion technologies; (4) greater resistance to competing biological systems; (5) more efficiency in nutrient uptake and utilization; (6) reduction in nitrogen losses from nitrification and denitrification; (7) greater resistance to environmental stresses; and (8) identification of hormonal systems and mechanisms (Table II). Each of these will be reviewed below.

A. Photosynthetic Efficiency

Many conferences have been held in which the results of research on photosynthesis have been reported and published. The most recent was

TABLE II
Next Generation of Plant Science Research

Greater photosynthetic efficiency
Improved biological nitrogen fixation
Genetic improvement and new cell fusion technologies
Greater resistance to competing biological systems
More efficiency in nutrient uptake and utilization
Reduction in losses from nitrification and denitrification
Greater resistance to environmental stresses
Identification of hormonal systems and mechanisms

the Fourth International Congress on Photosynthesis held September 4–6, 1977, at Reading in the United Kingdom (Hall et al., 1978). Few studies, however, have focused on crop productivity. Research on photosynthesis continues to be listed as a high priority for increasing crop production. It must be recognized as the primary source of energy for plant growth, yield enhancement, and biological nitrogen fixation.

Photosynthesis is the most important biochemical process on earth. Its improved efficiency holds the key to the future adequacy of our food supplies. The greatest unexploited resource that strikes the earth is sunlight. Photosynthesis is the most extraordinary mechanism ever devised. Man has specialized in and depends on the culture of sun-loving plants. Green plants, as yet, are the primary harvesters of free solar energy. They are net producers of food and energy on a renewable basis. All farm practices directed toward increased crop productivity must ultimately relate to an increased appropriation of solar energy in the plant system. Agriculture is, basically, a solar energy processing machine. It is the only industry that utilizes today's incident solar radiation, and is man's largest current user of solar energy.

Harvesting the sun, however, requires the management of land, and often of irrigation water, fertilizer, and other proxies. The geometry of agriculture demands that crops be distributed over the land in a layer a few inches thick for maximization of the capture of sunlight. Livestock must also be dispersed for most effective utilization of grazing, pasture, savannah, and prairie lands. The sun strikes everywhere. It is, therefore, the intent in agriculture to collect and store solar energy as food, feed, and fiber in plant and animal products, and to do it with utmost efficiency. That efficiency, however, which averages less than 2% annually for the major food crops, is very low (Bassham, 1977; Hardy, 1978). For most crops, the efficiency of solar energy utilization does not exceed 1%. Many environmental pressures affect photosynthesis, and there is great diversity among plants (Black et al., 1978).

There are many researchable alternatives for the enhancement of photosynthesis (Brown et al., 1976; National Academy of Sciences, 1975a–e, 1977a–h). They include (1) identification and control of the mechanisms that regulate and could reduce the wasteful processes of both dark- and light-induced (photo) respiration; (2) mechanisms responsible for the redistribution of photosynthates which, in turn, regulate yield and maximize the "Harvest Index" (Jain, 1975); (3) resolution of the hormonal mechanisms and identification of growth regulators and heritable components that control flowering and leaf senescence (Abu-shakra et al., 1978); (4) improvements in plant architecture and anatomy, cropping systems, planting designs, and cultural practices for better light reception; and (5) carbon dioxide enrichment of crop atmospheres. Plant breeding research has not generally been aimed at improving the photosynthetic process. Furthermore, the relationship between photosynthesis and crop yield is complex. Photosynthetically positive mutants should be sought. Any physiological–genetic prolongation of the functionally active state of chloroplasts and/or delay in leaf senescence would be important for the enhancement of photosynthetic productivity (Nasyrov, 1978). The future of the world's food supply and much of its energy may well reside at the door of photosynthesis and the subsequent partitioning of the products of photosynthesis into the harvested parts. The simplicity of the approach belies its credibility among the many options for support of new solar energy-producing and conserving technologies. Even with the high fossil energy inputs consumed in the culture of major agronomic crops, the ratio of food energy produced to that consumed is greater than one, and ranges from two to five for major cereal grains (Hardy, 1978). The energy output exceeds the input by a factor of two to five.

Enhancement of crop productivity for increasing biological solar energy conversion in the future is a topic of much discussion. A plethora of reports have appeared (Calvin, 1976; Lipinsky, 1978; Pimentel et al., 1978; Hammond, 1977; Council on Environmental Quality, 1978). Next to hydropower, biomass is now the largest source of commercial solar energy in the United States and many other nations. The biomass resource could increase dramatically with more efficient photosynthetic conversion of solar energy. The sources of biomass now available for conversion to energy, however, represent only about 2% of the current fossil energy consumption (Pimentel et al., 1978). Expectations of large increases in energy from energy farming are not realistic, because of current and increasingly severe constraints of land and water resources. There are, however, signal opportunities available in greater solar energy conversion through agriculture and forestry.

B. Nitrogen Fixation

The largest single industrial input into agricultural food production is nitrogen fertilizer. It accounts for 30–40% of total crop productivity. It is, however, energy intensive and demanding of nonrenewable energy resources. Natural gas equivalent to 300×10^6 barrels of oil is consumed annually for the synthesis of anhydrous ammonia by the Haber–Bosche process of nitrogen fertilizer production. Nitrogen fertilizer now accounts for about one-third of all the energy going into agricultural production.

The alternative is biological nitrogen fixation. It constitutes approximately 70% of the total nitrogen fixed, worldwide. It is the second most important biochemical process on earth. Symbiotic nitrogen is the most efficient way of providing fixed nitrogen for plant growth. There is no loss from leaching or denitrification. It is the primary source of food protein. It is agriculturally important with legumes, some nonlegumes, and has potential for many crops. A major volume, dealing with the limitations and potential of biological fixation in the tropics, has appeared (Dobereiner et al., 1978).

The first initiative for a new technology in biological nitrogen fixation should be with nodulated legumes and nonlegumes (Evans and Barber, 1977), and with the Anabaena-Azolla combinations in rice paddies and other crops, such as taro.

Legumes, in particular, have a demonstratedly efficient system, with good chances for a quick payoff. Furthermore, legumes make important global contributions to yield improvement and continuing productive food systems in the tropics, substropics, and for temperate-zone agriculture (Moomaw et al., 1977). They provide seed pods for man, forages for livestock, a means for soil improvement, and ground cover for alleviation of soil erosion (Hinson and Hartwig, 1977). There are some legumes of great potential that have not yet been fully developed or utilized for food or feed (Sinha, 1977). One is the pods and seeds of the desert mesquite. Others are the winged bean and Leucaena, a forage tree crop of the tropics. All parts of the winged bean plant may be harvested for human food.

Legumes have rhizobial associations in root nodules, which provide a built-in nitrogen source. Nevertheless, legumes may still obtain up to 75% or more of their nitrogen from that already in the soil. Yet, that which is fixed in the nodule is rate limiting for growth. Production of all legumes could be substantially increased if nitrogen fixation in the nodules were improved. It has been dramatically demonstrated that photosynthates are a limiting factor in nitrogen fixation (Hardy, 1978). A major effort should be directed toward increasing the photosynthetic energy source in legumes. One of the most remarkable opportunities resides in the forage legumes (alfalfa, clovers). Their capacity for N_2 fixation generally exceeds that of the seed legumes (soybeans, beans, peas, lentils, peanuts) by a factor of two (Silver and Hardy, 1976). Clarification of the metabolic processes that provide this energy needs attention. A second approach should be the development of superstrains of rhizobia for each of the several species that infect the major food legumes, increase the rate of infectivity, optimize the efficiency with which nitrogen is fixed per unit of energy conserved, and prolong the capability for nitrogen fixation into the seed filling period. An alternative is to improve the host plant and its environment. We need to explore the effects of variety, age, pH, temperature, soil nutrient levels, and chemical growth regulants.

Rhizobial technology and soil microbiology are neglected sciences in the United States and other developed countries. Similarly neglected are farming systems, specifically related to cropping systems, that make use of legume green manure and winter cover crops and inter-cropping of legumes with nonlegumes. Lack of research in these areas has been prompted, at least until recent years, by cheap and abundant energy and fertilizer. Legume–rhizobial and Anabaena–Azolla com-binations constitute built-in, naturally slow release systems for provid-ing nitrogen to food crops. Environmental pollution and nutrient loss is minimized. These are technologies that can aid in assuring our future food supply. They relate to the biology of crop productivity. The number and diversity of reports (Newton and Nyman, 1976; Delwiche, 1978; Dobereiner et al., 1978; Gutschiek, 1978; Hollaender, 1977; Mac-Neil et al., 1978; Peters, 1978; Shanmugam et al., 1978; Torrey, 1978) appearing on the potentials in research for biological nitrogen fixation are exciting. Over 100 proposals for increased federal support of biolog-ical nitrogen fixation research were prepared for fiscal year 1977–1978. This was for a single competitive grant program administered by the U.S. Department of Agriculture. The interest and human resources exist for major breakthroughs in this field, if research support can be obtained.

Natural gas is currently the primary fuel (95%) used to produce anhydrous ammonia. It requires 30 ft^3 of natural gas to produce 1 lb of nitrogen. About 3% of the natural gas used in the United States now goes into the production of over 10 million metric tons of the world's 45 million tons of nitrogen fertilizer. If the current trend in fertilizer usage continues, and we assume an annual 3% increase in food produc-tion, the total natural gas requirement for nitrogen fertilizer production alone, by the year 2000, will increase from 3 to 10% of the nation's supply. This is with the assumption that our supplies will then be as adequate as now. For this, there is little hope. Moreover, 500 new large-scale ammonia plants, costing an estimated $50 billion, which would produce a product at an annual cost of $40–50 billion, will be required within less than 25 years. This projected natural gas depen-dency of chemically fixed nitrogen fertilizer remains as one of the most flagrant violations of good economics, use of a nonrenewable resource, and possible environmental disaster. It is inconceivable that we should go this route. The alternative is research, as outlined above, directed toward enhancing biological nitrogen fixation (Wittwer, 1977a).

Abiotic nitrogen fixation, utilizing renewable energy resources, must also remain an option. One possibility is the production of ammonia in solar cells utilizing nitrogen gas, water, and catalysts. Zero energy inputs into nitrogen fixation, with appropriate catalysts, is another. A nitrogen fixation generator for farm use, which will appropriate the renewable energy resources of wind, waterfalls, or sunlight is being designed (Treharne et al., 1978).

C. Genetic Improvement

The genetic resources of the earth for crop improvement are enormous. Preservation of genetic materials of the principal food crops is now proceeding on a systematic and worldwide basis. The process is relatively simple for cereal grains, the seed legumes, forages, and many vegetables. Those that are vegetatively propogated (potatoes, sweet potatoes, cassava, fruit trees), however, pose a special problem. There is now an effort to freeze meristems in liquid nitrogen in order to preserve genetic stocks of vegetatively propagated food crops. The challenge will then be to initiate regrowth, utilizing appropriate metabolites, growth regulants, and culture media.

A resume of accessions, assembled from the latest annual reports of the several International Agricultural Research Centers, shows 40,000 for rice; 26,000 for wheat; 12,000 for maize; over 14,000 for grain sorghum; and 5000 for pearl millet. There were over 12,000 accessions for potatoes in 1976, and over 2000 for cassava. Chick peas show a figure of near 11,000, plus 47 wild species. There are 5530 accessions for pigeon peas, and near 3000 each for peanuts and field beans. The ultimate goal, however, is not fulfilled in the collection and preservation of genetic resources, but in their utilization (Sprague and Finlay, 1977). These plant genetic resources now being assembled will truly shape the future of world crop productivity.

The standard techniques of selection—based on phenotypic expression, controlled hybridization, and more recently, selection for better nutritional qualities—have given us superstrains of rice, wheat, maize, .sorghum, millet, some legumes, and many new fruits and vegetables.

One of the most remarkable records of achievements relating to the biology of crop improvement and utilizing conventional methods of plant breeding is the legacy of hybrid corn development in the United States. The substitution of hybrid for open-pollinated corn has increased yields by 15 to 30% (Sprague et al., 1978), and released 30 million acres of land for the production of other crops—largely soybeans. Resistance to most diseases known to afflict the major food crops now resides in the existent species. Much yet lies ahead for genetic adaptation of the major food crops. No wheat varieties are yet suitable for the lowland tropics, and there are at least 100 million acres not suited for present rice varieties.

An equally exciting area for future research is to genetically alter crops to get higher yields from soils that are infertile or too acidic, toxic, or saline for varieties now in use. Vast land areas of the earth, including those in the United States are either not utilized, or are underutilized for economically important crop production (Wright and Ferrari, 1977). One classic example is the report of Epstein and Norlyn (1977). Marketable yields have been obtained in California with a salt-tolerant research line of barley irrigated with water from the Pacific Ocean. This genetic approach to saline crop production has been proven with barley, and is applicable to other crops. Barley grown with seawater was found satisfactory as a feed, and yields were appreciable. This development could be the shape of things to come in genetically opening a vast new, hertofore inaccessible, water resource for crop production. Few regulatory constraints would likely be leveled on this new technology. Genetically controlled plant nutrition will surely play a key role in the future of crop production.

Genetic resources will continue to be utilized for improvement of the nutritional (biological) value of food crops. Cereals still dominate the diets of most people. Progress in genetically raising the levels of protein and critically deficient amino acids in cereal grains has been singular (Burton, 1977; Milner et al., 1978). Rice, wheat, and barley selections have been identified with higher protein levels. There is no cheaper, better, or quicker way to solve the protein needs of people in most agriculturally developing nations than to improve the cereals that they eat. Both the biological value and the level of the protein of maize have been enhanced using the opaque-2 recessive gene, and, more recently, in maize of normal background. Triticale, a new synthetic species, with its improved nutritional contributions, great adatability, and high yields, is now receiving limited commercial acceptance (Hulse and Spurgeon, 1974).

Recent evidence indicates that the protein quality of cereals is inversely related to their prolamine content (Axtel, 1976). It varies from a low of 5 to 10% for rice and oats, to intermediate levels of 30–40% for wheat and barley, to a high of 50–60% for sorghum and maize. Maize and sorghum are high in prolamine. These photosynthetically efficient species (C_4 plants) under hot, dry conditions are designated as "coarse" grains; whereas rice and wheat, being less efficient (C_3 plants) in fixing solar energy and carbon dioxide, are known as the "nobel" grains. Combining the higher productivity of cereal crops with superior protein quality and "nobel" grain characteristics remains as one of the great plant research challenges. The solution can be approached both chemically and genetically.

Genetic engineering has emerged as a series of events to cover new techniques of cell culture, protoplast fusion, and plasmid modification and transfer. An entire volume has recently been devoted to "Genetic Engineering for Nitrogen Fixation" (Hollaender, 1977). Significant advances have occurred in defining techniques for isolating protoplasts (plant cells without walls), their fusion, and for providing culture media for rapid regeneration into new plants (Gamborg and Holl, 1977). With protoplast culture has come haploid production (Sink and Padmanabhan, 1977; Bajaj, 1975). New freeze-storage techniques and the establishment of gene banks of plant cells, as well as of meristems, will be a means of preserving rare and useful genetic materials (Bajaj and Reinert, 1976). These new cellular approaches to plant breeding, sometimes described as somatic cell genetics, could become a major avenue for broad crosses, new species building with greater yield, resistance to biological and environmental stresses and to toxins, and for improved nutritional quality (Parke and Carlson, this volume). Protoplast fusion offers hope of tapping genetic material not now available, because of sterility barriers between genera and species (Day, 1977). Results of studies show that transformations and regeneration of parasexual hybrids from fixed protoplasts could revolutionize agricultural crop productivity. However, the ability to produce material that can be readily introgressed into established plant breeding programs remains a major challenge (Holl, 1975). The approach has been emphasized in recent documents outlining high-priority, mission-oriented basic research related to the enhancement of food production (Office of Technology Assessment, 1977; National Research Council, 1977a). There is promise for crop improvement.

D. Efficiency in Nutrient Uptake

Fertilizer manufacture is the most important industrial input into agricultural productivity. Nitrogen fertilizer inputs exceed $1 billion annually in the United States for corn alone. Yet, only 50% of the nitrogen and less than 35% of the phosphorus and potassium applied as fertilizer in the United States are recovered by crops. The recovery of fertilizer nitrogen in the rice paddies of the tropics is only 25 to 35%.

The balance is lost to the environment. Denitrification loses nitrogen in the atmosphere. Nitrification encourages losses in the soil from leaching. Nitrification is also a prerequisite to losses from denitrification. Food production and crop productivity could be greatly improved if these enormous losses, particularly in the warm soils of the tropics, could be even partially reduced. The single, recently identified factor most responsible for no increase in rice yields on Asian farms is the low level of nitrogen fertilizer available (International Rice Research Institute, 1977).

A worldwide annual loss of 12 to 15 million tons of nitrogen fertilizer can be ascribed to denitrification alone (Tiedje, 1978). Losses from nitrification are equally as great. Nitrification inhibitors, both natural and synthetic, applied with ammonia or urea, are effective deterrents to leaching and atmospheric losses of nitrogen. Their use is just beginning on a global scale. Research in this area should be of the highest priority. Substantial progress could be made in 5 to 10 years. The result could be a significant reduction in fertilizer cost and usage. Nonrenewable resources would be perserved, crop productivity would be increased, and a potential environmental hazard reduced (Bremner and Blackmer, 1978). Denitrification occurs only under anaerobic soil conditions. This may be alleviated by reducing nitrification, soil compaction, improved drainage, use of soil improving crops, and careful attention to irrigation procedures. Research emphasis on reduction of losses of nitrogen fertilizer applied to crops (Huber et al., 1977) should hold priority equal to that for devising means of nitrogen fixation, utilizing renewable rather than nonrenewable resources.

The facilitation of nutrient uptake by microorganisms (fungi) in symbiotic associations with the roots of higher plants is emerging as one of the most exciting frontiers for the enhancement of crop production. The efficiency of plant roots in absorbing nutrients from the soil can be improved. Mycorrhizae, particularly the endomycorrhizae and the subgroup referred to as vesicular-arbuscular, may result in large increases in the uptake of phosphorus and other poorly mobile nutrients. Almost all food crops respond. Vesicular-arbuscular mycorrhizae can be viewed as fungal extensions of roots. They help roots absorb fertilizer and can stimulate growth and nitrogen fixation by legumes, especially in phosphorus-deficient soils. There are superior strains of mycorrhizae, and crops can be inoculated with them. Mycorrhizae fungi have been reported to increase significantly the yields of cereal grains and many vegetable crops. The profound effects of these fungi have only recently been appreciated (Sanders et al., 1975; Safri, Chapter 6, this volume; Tansey, 1977). They facilitate nutrient uptake by changing the amounts, concentrations, and properties of minerals available to plants, both in forestry and in agriculture. The potential is not only for a substantial increase in conventional crop production, but for the expansion of productivity of economic plants in areas that now have an unfavorable climate and nonproductive soils.

Research in soil ecology, relating to the role of living organisms in recycling raw materials for plant growth, is almost a vacuum in current agricultural science and technology. Equally fascinating is the microbiology of aerial plant surfaces and the role of phyllosphere microorganisms in plant mineral nutrition (Dickinson and Preece, 1976).

If the recent rates of progress that have occurred in research with mycorrhizae can be sustained, substantial impacts in crop productivity through inoculation of superior strains of mycorrhizae could be realized within 10–20 years. The results would be nonrenewable resource conservation, enhancement of crop productivity, an expansion of the land resource base, and the use of a technology not likely to be subject to regulatory constraints. This approach would be a prime example of optimizing the natural environment for improved crop production.

Foliar applications of fertilizer have long been declared the most efficient method of fertilizer placement (Wittwer and Bukovac, 1969). Technology of application, however, is still lacking. Future yield barriers may well be broken up, by utilizing the absorptive capacity of leaves and roots, for applying nutrients at crucial stages of development. Great hope was expressed for nutrient foliar sprays following results on soybeans in 1975 (Garcia and Hanway, 1976). The results of extensive experimental foliar spraying of nutrients in all the major soybean-producing areas in the United States during 1976 and 1977 for yield enhancement have not confirmed the outstanding results achieved in 1975. Nevertheless, the rising costs of fertilizer and its nonrenewable resource requirement should be a continuing stimulus for further developments of this technology.

There are still other ways of increasing crop productivity and of simultaneously reducing fertilizer loss. The gradient mulch system for growing tomatoes in Florida is one (Geraldson, 1975). It is a high-level, low-cost concept, utilizing and maintaining a nonvariable root environment, achieved by a plastic mulch, a constant water table, and precise fertilizer placement.

E. Resistance to Competing Biological Systems

Field losses from pests (insects, diseases, weeds, nematodes, rodents) for the world's major food crops are truly enormous, approximately

35% (National Academy of Sciences, 1977b). All major crops suffer losses before harvest that exceed 20%. Chemical pesticides have played a dominant role in the control of pests, and will continue to do so in the near future. Approximately 1.4 billion lb of synthetic organic pesticides were produced worldwide in 1976. The United States expended $1.8 billion for pesticides in 1975 (Office of Technology Assessment, 1978; National Academy of Sciences, 1975a). Chemical pesticides have accounted for 20% of the increase in farm output during the past 25–30 years, during which time production has doubled. Since World War II, there has been an ever-increasing dependence on pesticides. Historians will likely refer to the latter half of the 20th century as the "organic pesticide era." Meanwhile, reliance on this single line of defense has introduced problems of pesticide resistance, destruction of natural enemies, outbreaks of secondary pests, reductions in pollinators, potential environmental livestock and human health problems, rising economic costs, and increasing regulatory constraints (Kendrick, 1978). Regulatory constraints and costs relating to the use of pesticides have multiplied exponentially. Nevertheless, regulations relating to the use of pesticides have given us more information about their human health effects than we have about any other group of chemicals.

Future alternative strategies for integrated pest control, as now being developed by teams of scientists, if implemented, will likely result in the use of more pesticides in agriculturally developing nations, and less in the more developed (Glass and Thurston, 1978). For small farm peasant agriculture, it is not a future option, it is an immediate urgency. The intent of the projected, widely used systems approach in pest management will be to reduce cost of pest control, impose less of an environmental insult, create greater production dependability, and increase yields. This will come through the use of natural enemies and parasites, identification and creation of genetically resistant varieties, improved cultural practices, environmental monitoring, and more timely and efficient use of chemicals. Until now, agricultural crop protection technology has become obsolete at an alarming rate. It will continue to do so, but there will be progressively greater efficiency in the use of chemicals because of economic cost, their environmental impact, and their failing reliability, in view of acquired resistance of the pests to chemical control. The anticipated, more judicious use of chemicals in integrated pest management systems should result in gains for food safety and fewer regulatory constraints. Whereas the possibility may exist for some agriculturally developing nations to bypass the fossil age, they will not likely be able to bypass the chemical pesticide era (Glass and Thurston, 1978). It is, however, strikingly significant that most developing countries have not yet been caught in the treadmill of pesticides and pesticide resistance, and they have thus far largely escaped the pesticide syndrome. Meanwhile, significant progress with integrated pest management programs has, however, been achieved for some insects on cotton, alfalfa, soybeans, citrus, apples, and greenhouse-grown tomatoes (Way, 1977; Haskell, 1977; Huffaker and Croft, 1976; Croft, 19765; Riedl and Croft, 1978; Glasshouse Crops Research Institute, 1976). There are still many challenges ahead for these crops and for others, such as potatoes and onions. Success, now and in the future, will depend on interactions between scientists from many disciplines and a greatly expanded technically educated extension service. One of the big steps in the next 10–20 years will be real time management of agricultural systems, including pests. In an era of few stable resources, we must develop integrated pest control measures. But this will require a change in attitudes of scientists so engaged to look beyond their own narrow field of interest. There may be the opportunity to partially replace chemicals with information, and to put people with technical information back on the farm.

Considerable evidence has now accumulated to implicate secondary plant metabolites as defensive agents in plant to plant relationships. Studies of allelopathy in crop plants have revealed toxic compounds in asparagus and sorghum roots and shoots, and in the fruits and seeds of the cucumber. Residues of sorghum plants and Sudan grass have provided excellent control of annual grass weeds in both the greenhouse and field. Allelopathy is a widespread phenomenon among crop plants (Rice, 1974; Putnam and Duke, 1974). It may provide an interesting alternative to the use of chemical herbicides, which are now the most extensively used of all chemicals in agricultural production. No significant breakthrough in the field application of allelopathy has yet occurred with any of the major food crops. The rapid obsolescence of current crop protection technology, however, suggests that some possibilities should be explored.

There has been, till now, a constant battle between man, the scientist, and nature in achieving disease resistance in high-yielding plants. Resistance has an average half-life of only 5 years. One of the inevitable consequences of modern agriculture appears to be that the most widely adapted of the new improved crop varieties are highly vulnerable to new strains of plant diseases (National Academy of Sciences, 1972). The Southern corn leaf blight that destroyed a substantial part of the U.S. crop in 1970 is one example. Another was downy mildew, which afflicted hybrid pearl millet in the 1960's. Traditional plant breeding methods have resulted in new varieties in which disease resistance is specific and dependent upon a single gene. A possible alternative approach is the "multiline" concept, which is being pursued with new rust-resistant wheats. A multiline variety is created mechanically. Seeds of several lines that are similar in appearance and genetic makeup, but which have different genes for resistance to rust, are mixed together. This concept, if proven, could be the shape of things to come. Immunity would be lasting, and resistance would be permanent and achieved at low cost.

F. Resistance to Environmental Stresses

Environmental stresses, alone or in combination, constitute the primary limiting factor(s) for increasing and expanding the production of many, if not most, of the world's crops. Those that limit crop productivity include drought, cold, heat, salt, toxic ions, and air pollutants (Brown et al., 1976). Plants, unlike people, livestock, and other animals, are immobile. Environmental adaptability, thus, becomes preeminent. Any means of increasing the resistance of plants to high and low temperatures, drought and water stress, adverse soil conditions, and other environmental hazards, holds great promise for enhancement of the amount of food, as well as the dependability of the supply. Through the use of short-season, early-planted, single-cross maize hybrids, commercial production in the United States has moved 500 miles further north during the past 50 years. Winter wheat production has been extended northward by 200 miles. Hybrid sorghum and millets are moving into hot, dry areas not heretofore adapted for cereal grain production. The new synthetic species, triticale, has resistance to aluminum toxicity. Thus, millions of acres of heretofore nonproductive land can be opened for food cropping. Characteristic of the new seeds (rice and wheat) of the "Green revolution" are varieties that are day neutral and will produce grain at any latitude. There are also genetic strains of rice, wheat, and barley that have greater resistance to both cold and alkalinity. This, coupled with earlier maturity, has made possible a "two paddy system" in South Korea, where previously only one crop per year could be grown. Potato varieties have been identified with moderate frost resistance and cold hardiness (Mendoza and Estrada, 1979).

Plants can be made more "climate-proof" by genetic improvement and by appropriate soil, water, and pest management. The use of weather and climatic information in the selection of crop varieties for a particular climatic setting, the strategic planning of the size and operation of an irrigation system, or alternative strategies in pest management can reduce the adverse effects of climate and weather on crop productivity (National Academy of Sciences, 1976).

Controlled environment agriculture can greatly increase food crop productivity and the dependability of supplies. By far the most extensive means of modifying the environment is irrigation. Food production suffers from some degree of water dificiency over the entire globe. Currently, there are more than 100 million ha of the land surface of the earth under irrigation for crop production. Irrigated crop land constitutes about 15% of the total under cultivation. The higher productivity of irrigated land, however, results in 30% of the world's food. China, India, the Soviet Union, Pakistan, and the United States account for more than 70% of the world's total, in the order listed. The total irrigated land in the United States increased from 8 to 17 million ha from 1939 to 1969. China has more irrigated land than any other country in the world—one-third of the world's total. The area has doubled since 1952, where irrigated land has increased from 20 to 41% of the total. Egypt's agriculture is entirely dependent on irrigation. There are 6.5 million acres that support 40 million people. The Nile river is now a closed system.

Looking to the future, India, Sri Lanka, the Soviet Union, and Bangladesh expect to double the amount of irrigated land, and they have the renewable water resources to do it. This will not only increase the productivity of a given crop, but will enable year-round production. However, it will require vast capital inputs. Irrigation will also greatly increase food security, through greater dependability of supply and less vulnerability to climatic and weather variabilities. Largely through irrigation, new seeds, and fertilizer, China has doubled the yields of the major food grains in two decades, despite recurring droughts.

The most intensive food-producing systems on earth are those where crops are grown in greenhouses or under the protection of other structures. This offers the ultimate in stable production at high levels. The chief constraint of fully controlled-environment agriculture is that it demands a maximum in capital, management, and resource inputs. It is high technology and resource intensive. Nevertheless, the potential exists. Hydroponic culture facilitates control of both the top and root environments. The very latest developments in hydroponics have occurred in northern Europe with the Nutrient Film Technique (Cooper and Charlesworth, 1977; Rudd-Jones, 1977). This is the most sophisticated technology yet conceived for the improvement and control of crop production in greenhouses. It takes full advantage of maximizing the control of the total environment and optimizing the uptake of both water and nutrients by plant roots.

G. Hormonal Mechanisms and Plant Development

There are many chemicals, endogenous and exogenous, at hormonal levels that offer control of the biological processes that limit crop productivity. Previously, most efforts have been confined to fruits, vegetables, and ornamental crops (Wittwer, 1971). Some noteworthy and beneficial effects include (1) promotion of rooting and propagation; (2) initiation or termination of dormancy in seeds, buds, and tubers; (3) induction or retardation of aging (senescence); (4) promotion or delay of flowering; (5) enhancement or prevention of leaf and/or fruit drop; (6) control of fruit set and development; (7) control of plant or organ size; (8) modification of sex expression; (9) chemical pruning; (10) increased resistance to pests and to the environmental stresses of water, temperature, and air pollution; (11) prevention or delay of post-harvest spoilage; (12) regulation of plant and fruit composition; (13) influence on mineral uptake; (14) change of timing in crop development; and (15) enhanced coloration of fruit (Aung, 1977).

There are some exciting new developments. The use of diverse sugarcane ripeners for enhancement of sugar production in Hawaiian sugar plantations is now standard practice (Nickell, 1977b). Increases in sugar yield of over 10% are achieved. An almost equal increase is achieved with gibberellins (Moore, 1977; Nickell, 1977a). The oleoresin ("pitch") yield of conifers has been greatly increased in remote areas with such materials as paraquat (Parham, 1976). Ethylene-generating compounds ("Ethrel," "Ethad") have greatly improved the flow of latex in the commercial production of rubber trees (Dickenson, 1976). Gibberellins have induced important species of conifers to flower in 4 to 6 years, compared with the natural sequence of 10–20 years to flower, and another 20 years to produce significant quantities of seed (Pharis and Ross, 1976). The treatment of young guayule plants with 2-(3,4-dichlorophenoxy)-triethylene markedly stimulates the accumulation of natural rubber in the stems and roots. This could make the desert shrub of North America a viable domestic source of hydrocarbons, including rubber (Yokoyama, 1977).

Most of the irrigated rice, the number one food crop of the earth, is sown in nursery beds and then hand transplanted in the field. Transplanted rice is more productive than that sown broadcast. Millions of plants are grown in small areas. Greater ease of transplanting could likely be enhanced by treatment of seedlings with appropriate growth regulators that would produce stronger and more uniform plants (Hudson, 1976).

The pattern of crop canopies and plant architecture can be dramatically changed with growth regulators. This has been achieved with many fruit trees, soybeans, and cereal grains. Better light-receiving systems are formed, and with some cereal grains, lodging is prevented and yields are increased (Wunsche, 1977). Growth regulators have effects on food quality. Flavor, taste, juiciness, and eatability, in addition to shape, color, firmness, and freedom from blemishes, are becoming increasingly important with fruits and vegetables. It is likely that flavor could be greatly improved by growth regulator treatment. many are now used as "harvest-aid" chemicals.

Considerable progress has occurred in the identification of new active materials—both synthetic and natural. The number of gibberellins is near 60. Triacontanol (Ries *et al.*, 1977) has opened a new dimension for higher alcohols. Foliar sprays in milligram per hectare quantities have significantly increased the yields of field grown crops and stimulated the growth of rice plants grown in the dark (Ries and Wert, 1977). Nickell (1978) has pointed out that agricultural research, until now, has been primarily concerned with increasing crop yields through the use of fertilizers, perticides, irrigation, and better management, coupled with variety development and genetic improvements. Little attention has been given to the control of biological processes that limit productivity. The stage is now set to shape further crop productivity increases through the use of chemicals for the physical manipulation of the plant. It is likely that a useful role for growth regulants can be found for all crops and for all biological processes, for every developmental stage.

III. THE NEXT GENERATION OF PLANT SCIENCE RESEARCH

These have been detailed in the initiatives described above, and were listed in Table II. Each can be characterized as mission-oriented basic research. They all related to the control and regulation of the biological processes that limit crop productivity. They add to, rather than diminish, resources essential to crop productivity. They are nonpolluting and without noise. They are the areas identified in recent National Academy of Sciences/National Research Council reports and elsewhere as grossly underfunded; where no nation is making any substantial research investment; where industrialized, developed nations—including the United States with its vast human, financial, and natural resources—could make their greatest contributions to the agricultural development of Third World nations. They would directly enhance the productivity of forests, grasslands, and croplands—three of the four biological systems which, according to L. R. Brown (1978b), form the foundation of the global economic system; and they would indirectly improve the fourth, that of fisheries. Such technologies would be scale neutral and economically, socially, politically, and ecologically sound. They could ease the inevitable transition we must make from nonrenewable to renewable resources (Wittwer, 1978b).

IV. MANAGEMENT OF RESOURCES

A. Climate

Climate is a specific, scarce resource that needs to be allocated for specific crops in specific locations. Climate, as a resource, should be viewed not so much globally, but locally and regionally. "Climate fertility" should become established as equally important to that of "soil fertility." For example, in the midwestern United States, corn and soybeans are the leading crops. The climate resources can be allocated between soybeans and corn. Corn, in turn, can be allocated either as food for people or as feed for livestock. The climates of the Pacific Northwest, the west coast, western Michigan, and New York in the United States can be allocated to the production of alternative fruits and vegetables. Temperatures in each instance are moderated by large bodies of water. In west Texas, it may be a division between cotton and sorghum.

There is the future challenge of making climate a more useful and less hazardous resource. On a global scale, it is now exacting an enormous toll in reduced crop productivity and potential food production. Desertification, for example, is a worldwide menace affecting every inhabited continent, with the possible exception of Europe (San Pietro, 1978). It annually destroys 12 to 17 million acres. Otherwise, arable land is turned into stony wastes or heaps of drifting sand. Prolonged drought often accelerates the destruction. The National Research Council document, Climate and Food (National Academy of Sciences, 1976), addresses in detail the effects of changing climatic patterns on crop productivity.

The most obvious impact of climate and weather is on agriculture and crop and food production. This has been manifested most dramatically in recent years in the year by year fluctuations in grain production in the Soviet Union, the periodic failure of the monsoons in South Asia (India), the prolonged drought of the early 1970's in the African Sahel, that of the mid-1970's in western Europe, and the drought in the corn belt in the United States in 1974. The last event resulted in a 22% reduction in major food and feed grains, which was more devastating than the climate-induced corn blight of 1970. Climate and weather remain as the most determinant factors in crop productivity, and, in turn, on food supply.

The changing composition of the atmosphere is a part of the climate resource for either enhancing or detracting from crop productivity. Particulates and gases found therein—natural or of human origin—are absorbed by the aerial parts of plants (Wittwer and Bukovac, 1969), and if released through precipitation, may be taken up by roots. Acid rainfall is common over all of the United States east of the Mississippi River, and in localized industrial areas of the western Unites States (National Academy of Sciences, 1975b; U.S. Department of Agriculture and Ohio State University, 1975). Its full effects on agricultural crops, forests, and natural ecosystems have not been assessed. Air quality standards, thus far, have been associated with activities of people, with little attention given to renewable resource productivity (Williams, 1978). Crop losses from air pollution may be minimized by the selection and development of tolerant cultivars, modification of cultural practices, application of antioxidant chemicals, and modifying the nutrition of plants (Brown et al., 1976). The affects of the atmosphere on the biosphere, and what we do about it, will help shape the world of tomorrow.

The carbon dioxide (CO_2) in the atmosphere is a part of the climate resource base for crop porduction. Carbon dioxide concentrations ambient to plant foliage remain the single most important rate-determinant for further increases in photosynthesis. No exceptions to increased growth from CO_2 enrichment have yet been reported. It works for all the major food crops, and elevated levels will accelerate the growth of forest trees and their seedlings. It is no longer necessary to design and conduct experiments to establish the efficacy of CO_2 enrichment for increasing yields in commercially grown greenhouse crops, where the atmosphere can be contained. All respond with generally greater production and enhancement of quality, especially during early seedling stages. The magnitude of the response is light dependent, but beneficial effects are derived over a wide spectrum of light intensities—either daylight or artificial. Many experiments have now demonstrated that the optimum CO_2 concentration ranges between 1000 and 1500 ppm. This is three to five times greater than the current atmospheric level (Strain, 1977; Wittwer, 1977c).

A threefold increase (330 to 1000 ppm) in the levels of atmospheric carbon dioxide will greatly increase photosynthetic productivity and, at the same time, prevent losses from photorespiration (photorespiration is essentially eliminated). With legumes (soybeans), this also results in an almost six-fold increase in nitrogen fixed per hectare (Hardy and Halvelka, 1975). While these beneficial effects have been recorded, they have been difficult to apply, as yet, on a large scale, other than in commercial greenhouse crop production (National Science Foundation, 1978), although models have been suggested (Bassham, 1977). There is a continuing challenge here for plant biochemists, geneticists, and physiologists to find ways of increasing photosynthetic efficiency by reducing photorespiration, whether it be through CO_2 enrichment, chemicals, or breeding. Translation of increased photosynthates into increased nitrogen fixation in legumes and possibly other plants needs further exploration. The rewards would be a greatly enhanced supply of food and other renewable resources, with minimal regulatory infringement.

Somewhat converse to the well-documented beneficial effects of elevated levels of CO_2 on crop productivity are a series of recent reports (Baes et al., 1976; Woodwell, 1978; Siegenthaler and Oeschger, 1978; Stuiver, 1978) projecting that catastrophic consequences will result from heating of the atmosphere if CO_2 continues to increase at the current rate. It has even been suggested that the CO_2 gas released by the fossil fuel-burning industry should be heavily taxed.

Few of the conclusions that have been drawn, including the effects of CO_2 on the atmosphere, are clear. While the available records indicate that from 1949 until now the CO_2 concentration in the atmosphere has increased, there is little evidence of an increase in global temperature. The reverse, has, in fact, been true.

Contrary to the above uncertainties, we know that improved plant growth and crop production require more CO_2. Agricultural, forestry, and food production research should concentrate on, among other things, developing methods to enable plants to increase their CO_2 fixation. One thoroughly demonstrated approach is to increase the CO_2 content of the atmosphere. If there are substantial increases in the atmospheric CO_2, with resultant adverse environmental effects, serious efforts should be made to optimize this resource through enhancement of food and biomass production (Lipinsky, 1976; Bassham, 1977; Radmir and Kok, 1977). Other research efforts that would slow the increase in a presumably high atmospheric level of CO_2 would be reduction in soil losses from water and soil erosion (Brink et al., 1977), conservation or zero tillage, wider use of soil improvement crops to raise organic matter levels in soils, and reforestation of now barren landscapes. Such technologies would preserve, protect, and add to the earth's resources, and should not require additional regulations. If the presumably undesirable effects of rising levels of atmospheric carbon dioxide can be validated, we can expect firm technological advances to incorporate more carbon into the biosphere.

B. Land, Water, and Energy Interrelationships

We have no viable option for the immediate future, other than to create more energy-efficient land and water use conservation strategies. New soil and water conservation and management technologies can be developed to increase yields of both large and small holdings. To introduce the science of resource conservation into farms of all sizes would be to exploit one of the greatest opportunities for the enhancement of global food production, and it can be done without a negative impact on the regulatory environment.

The problems are massive. There are increasing constraints on the substitutability of energy, land, and water in agricultural production. First, prime agricultural land is disappearing on a global scale because of irreversible use. Second, that which is left is being seriously degraded by compaction, loss of organic matter, and by wind and water erosion. As the land resource base is driven harder, the options for enhancing crop productivity, in meeting regulatory constraints, and in the use of water for irrigation, energy, mechanization, and human labor become less.

Problems of soil erosion are global (see Tables I and II). For 40 years, the Soil Conservation Service of the U.S. Department of Agriculture has promoted sound conservation practices, supported by technical and financial assistance, education, persuasion, and appeals to good land stewardship. It has not been very effective. After more than 40 years, no more than 25% of our farmlands are under approved conservation practices. Meanwhile, we continue to lose enormous amounts (8.3 tons ha^{-1} year^{-1}, for a total of 2.8 billion tons) of topsoil from our best lands. This continues to pollute and sediment our lakes, streams, and estuaries, and invoke additional regulatory actions. This situation, coupled with massive deforestation, is even worse in many tropical developing countries (Brink et al., 1977; Eckholm, 1976; Pimentel et al., 1976).

1. Land

Crop land worldwide is about 1.5 billion ha, with about 200 million ha in the United States. Best estimates are that there is at least twice as much land physically available worldwide for crop production as is presently being used. Only about one-half of the suitable crop land is now being cultivated.

The United States has a climate and land resource base for crop production second to none. The corn belt constitutes the largest contiguous area devoted to crop production in the world, with the climate least frequented by drought. Of the regions of the world most productive, in an agricultural sense, the United States has a fertility of climate as well as of soil (McQuigg, 1978).

The land resource base can change with time and technology. Land productivity may be improved as well as depleted by cropping. The original crop plands of western Europe and Japan were vastly inferior to what they are today. This is currently reflected by wheat yields in western Europe and rice yields in Japan, which are double those of the United States. One of the most common sounds in China is the blasting of hills to open more land for cultiviation (Chou, 1977). The use of lime, chemical fertilizers, animal manure, green manure, irrigation, and better farming practices has transformed the sandy soils of the eastern seaboard of the United States into some of the most productive vegetable-growing soils in the world. Similarly, the nonproductive and acidic, organic-sand soils of the lake states have been made highly productive for a variety of fruits, vegetables, and root crops. Alaska's potential agricultural land for crop production exceeds the state of Iowa in area.

Reduced tillage is an example of an important land resource conservation technology (U.S. Department of Agriculture, 1977b). The moldboard plow, long a symbol of American agriculture, has created insolvable losses from wind and water erosion. The use of appropriate chemicals for weed control has now established the reality of improved crop productivity without plowing the land. The plow is gradually being retired. Over 3 million ha (corn, soybeans, wheat) in the United States were planted in 1977 without tillage, and on over 20 million ha tillage was reduced from the conventional level. Reduced tillage is the most significant technology yet developed for the control of soil erosion, maximization of cover on the land, and for the conservation of energy, labor, water, soil fertility, and organic matter for the main food-producing areas of the earth (Triplett and Van Doren, 1977). In addition, a higher proportion of sloping land in hilly areas can be brought into production or planted to more profitable crops.

Successful conservation tillage requires two important inputs—first, an appropriate herbicide; second, specially adapted seed drills for use on sod or nontilled soil. Use of herbicides mandates registration and clearance by regulatory bodies. The development and release of appropriate chemicals for the killing of sod and subsequent weed control will continue to have an impact on the development and speed with which zero tillage and reduced tillage can be used in both United States and world agriculture. There is the potential, however, of bringing into food production tens of millions of hectares of land heretofore unsuitable for agricultural purposes and of reducing soil erosion to essentially zero levels. Many crops on many soils should be adapted to this method of culture, on both mineral and organic soils that are eroding badly.

2. Water

Water is the key resource for future agricultural development in many parts of the world. Food production suffers from some degree of water deficiency over the entire globe. Currently, there are approximately 230 million ha of the land surface of the earth under irrigation for crop production (Jensen, 1977), with one-tenth of the total, or 23 million ha, in the United States. Irrigated cropland constitutes about 15% of the total now under cultivation. The high productivity of irrigated land, however, results in 30% of the world's food. Of the estimated 3419 million ha of potential agricultural land in the world, 470 million could be irrigated (Buringh, 1977).

World food production goals must face the water limitations and optimize the management of the water resources that now exist. The water resource base of the earth, however, is enormous. Seventy percent of the earth's surface is covered with water, most of which is saline. Only 1% is fresh water, and 99% of the fresh water is underground (Shoji, 1977). Most of the fresh water (80–85%) withdrawn in the United States is consumed in agricultural production, the greatest amount going to irrigation.

The number of kilograms of water needed to produce a kilogram of food is an important variable. Practically no research has been done in this area, although numerous symposia have been held on irrigation and the efficiency of water use (Hagen et al., 1967; McGinnies and Goldman, 1969; Pierre et al., 1967; U.S. Department of Agriculture, 1975). Large differences in transpiration losses exist among species, varying from a scale of 100 for pineapple, to 400–500 for cereals and seed legumes, to over 1000 for some fruits and vegetables. The water requirement of sugarcane per unit land area in Hawaii is five times that of pineapple. A report from Israel (Shalhevet et al., 1977) indicates that crops vary widely in their efficiency of water use. Sorghum will produce 1.72 kg of grain per millimeter of water applied, compared with

1.23 for wheat, 0.65 for peanuts, and only 0.24 for cotton. Water limitations can alter the harvest index and, thus, modify the relationship between crop yield and productivity (Fischer and Turner, 1978). There are unexploited adaptations to water limitations among annual plants under semiarid conditions. For example, very high rates of C_3 photosynthesis have been identifed in a herbaceous desert annual (Mooney et al., 1976).

Water management schemes adapted to the semiarid tropics have been given little attention. There is an ever widening gap between the productivity of irrigated and nonirrigated agriculture. This is being accompanied by increasing population pressures on the land and recurrent cycles of drought. There is a lack of technology for insuring dependable harvests and to meet increased food needs.

Equally important are new water management technologies for food crop production. Making more efficient use of available water supplies offers the greatest technological opportunities, least encumbered by regulatory constraints. The efficiency of using conventionally applied irrigation water varies from less than 30% globally, to 20–40% in the United States, to 80–85% in Israel.

Drip or trickle irrigation is sometimes referred to as the "Blue Revolution." It was first developed for large-scale crop production in Israel, and may reduce by 50% the water now used in conventional irrigation systems (flooding, sprinkling, furrow) for food crop production. Worldwide, there are now 162,000 ha of cropland equipped with drip irrigation systems. Three times this amount is projected for 1981. California has 15% of the total (Gustafson, 1978). There are many other concurrent advantages of drip irrigation for high-value crops: (1) it reduces operating costs; (2) soil erosion is reduced to a minimum; (3) no land is wasted to build irrigation ditches; and (4) there is no leaching, runoff, or drainage water pollution. Weed control and distribution of fertilizer can be optimized, and crop and soil management and harvest operations can be conducted without interference. Water of higher salinity than would be acceptable with other methods can be utilized (Shoji, 1977). The prospects for high-frequency irrigation, on some crops, hold even greater promise for efficient water use, with less capital investment, resource inputs, and management (Rawlins, 1977).

Water management schemes adapted to the semiarid tropics have been given little attention. There is an ever-widening gap between the productivity of irrigated and nonirrigated agriculture. This is being accompanied by increasing population pressures on the land and recurrent cycles of drought. There is a serious lack of technology for insuring dependable harvests, the magnitude of which approaches the enhancement of production itself in importance (National Academy of Sciences, 1975e).

One of the most promising methods for increasing our usable water resource is precipitation augmentation through cloud seeding. There is, however, no area of technology so vulnerable to regulatory (environmental, legal, social, political, and economic) constraints.

A predicted increase in winter snowpack from cloud seeding in the Colorado River Basin would provide an increase of 2 million acre-feet of water, with no new water resource management facilities. The annual benefits for the West would be approximately $13 million. A benefit of $30 million could be expected with the construction of new basin facilities. Additional water from snow augmentation in the western mountains would cost $1 to $1.50 per acre-foot. This can be compared with costs of $25–$50 for providing additional water by interbasin transfers. It would be considerably cheaper than other augmentation procedures, such as desalination of saltwater and condensation of geothermal steam.

Recent precipitation enhancement research in Florida based on new cloud seeding technologies suggests very positive results (Woodley et al., 1977). Dynamic seeding of cumuliform clouds increased aerial rainfall. A high degree of significance was obtained with a capability of enhancing summer rainfall by 25% over total target areas. A 50% increase was obtained with a single floating target. Many of the types of clouds found in Florida in the summer are similar to those in the midwestern corn belt. The potential for precipitation enhancement in the Midwest, the major food-producing area of the nation and the breadbasket of the world, has not been scientifically determined. Herein may reside the most significant contribution that research can make toward increasing the water resources in the United States during the next 10–15 years (Huff and Vogel, 1977). Any successful technologies for rainfall enhancement must also include an evaluation and assessment of weather modification related to socioeconomic, legal, and environmental impacts. It will be very difficult to assemble a viable approach to a major technological achievement that would have great potential for an enormous breakthrough, not only in increasing agricultural productivity, but in enhancing its dependability.

The freshwater resources of the earth are not being efficiently utilized in irrigation for agricultural production. China, India, the Soviet Union, Pakistan, and the United States account for more than 70% of the world's total irrigated land, in the order listed. The total irrigated land in the United States increased from 8 to 17 million ha from 1939 to 1969. There were 23 million ha in 1976. China has more irrigated land than any country in the world, with one-third of the total, and 41% of its cropped area is irrigated. India, Sri Lanka, the Soviet Union, and Bangladesh expect to double the amount of irrigated land they now have, and they have the water resources to do it. This will not only increase the productivity of a given crop, but will enable year-round production. Irrigation will also greatly increase food security through greater dependability of supply and with less vulnerability to climate and weather uncertainties. Largely through irrigation, new seeds, and fertilizer, China has doubled the yields of the major food grains in two decades, despite recurring droughts. The Planning Commissions of India, the Soviets, and the Prime Minister of Sri Lanka look to vast new irrigation schemes as the primary catalyst for renewed agricultural development and food security.

Expansion of irrigated agriculture will have an impact on the regulatory environment. Sprinkler irrigation systems require more operating energy, but may be less subject to regulatory constraints than surface systems (Jensen, 1977). They are also best for undulating land, highly permeable soils, and for supplemental applications. With expansion of irrigation must come total water management systems, including drainage. Disposal of waste waters must be regulated. While the land resource base can initially be made more productive, there are increased hazards of salinization, and new breeding grounds may be created for insects that serve as vectors for human disease. Legal, social, and environmental problems can multiply.

There are two serious problems relating to irrigated crop production in parts of the Great Plains of the United States (Sanghi and Johnson, 1978). One is the increasing prices and uncertainties of supplies of energy for operating irrigation pumps. The other is the depletion of ground water reserves.

There are vastly under utilized freshwater resources that could, with modern technology input, be used for agriculture. One example will suffice. The boundary waters of Minnesota and Canada abound with indigenous stands of wild rice. About 10,000 ha are harvested annually in Minnesota, with 8000 ha cultivated in artificial paddies. Wild rice is a unique food. The demand in recent years has forced the price to $8/lb or more for processed grain. Recent developments relating to the creation of shatterproof varieties and mechanical harvesting could open a vast new food resource from the lakes and streams of the North (Elliott and Oelke, 1977).

An even greater potential exists for saline and brackish waters. Reference has already been made to the recent genetic breakthrough in the adaptation of crops that will grow in seawater (Epstein and Norlyn, 1977). Further technological advances utiliaing the genetic approach to saline crop production can be expected. The potential is enormous. Progress has already been made with tomatoes (Rick, 1978), and work with other saline-tolerant crops (alfalfa, sugar beets) will undoubtedly follow.

3. Energy

The fossil energy resources of this nation are not known (Abelson, 1977). A measurement of the world's nonrenewable and recoverable energy reserves assigns 49% of the total to North America (Stout et al., 1977). The current "energy crisis" in the United States is not one of supply, but of an overdependence on fossil fuels, particularly petroleum, which is not uniformly distributed worldwide.

Much attention has been paid to the energy-intensive requirements of American agriculture. While the United States uses over one-fourth of the world's energy to serve one-fifteenth of the world's population, the U.S. farmer feeds over one-fourth of the world's population on 1% of the world's energy. Solar energy aside, agriculture requires only 3% of the total energy used in the United States. Agriculture is a solar energy-processing machine, and for the major food crops returns two to four units of energy for each unit it consumes. The total food system is more demanding and uses approximately 16.5% of the total U.S. energy budget.

Nevertheless, American agriculture is energy dependent (Boersma, 1977; Council for Agricultural Science and Technology, 1977; Heichel, 1976; National Academy of Sciences, 1975e, 1977c, p 196–240; Pimentel et al., 1975, 1976; Splinter, 1976; Stout et al., 1977; U.S. Department of Agriculture, 1977b). It is susceptible to reduced energy supplies and higher costs. The most vulnerable input is nitrogen fertilizer, which accounts for about 33% of the total fossil fuel energy now going into agricultural production. This is followed by irrigation, which for the entire United States accounts for 13% (Council for Agriculture Science and Technology, 1977). Jensen (1977) has given the figure as 20% of the total agricultural energy budget. Sixty percent of the energy used in irrigated agriculture is for irrigation. Pesticides require 5% of the total. Other energy-vulnerable operations include crop drying, food processing, dairying, transportation, storage (especially refrigeration), and greenhouse heating (Wittwer, 1977b).

Fossil energy conservation practices in food production require attention. Biological nitrogen fixation, as an alternative to chemical fixation, is an example of such a practice. This could become operational at the farm level through more extensive use of legume green manure and winter cover crops, and through intercropping legumes with non-legumes. The no-till or reduced tillage and drip irrigation systems of soil and water management, discussed earlier, can be adapted to many locations and will conserve not only energy, but soil, water, and organic matter as well, in addition to reducing compaction and increasing the efficiency of fertilizers and herbicides. New pest management systems and technologies for pesticide applications can reduce energy inputs. There are alternative energy input systems in food production; many options exist (Johnson, et al., 1977; Ward et al., 1977). Similarly, there are many alternatives for the production of biogas and the conversion of biomass to energy (National Academy of Sciences, 1977c). All biomass, however, is not readily available or collectible. Land should not be diverted from food production, or the biomass product from that which is necessary to prevent soil erosion and maintain soil organic matter.

Crop productivity research strategy of the past has been to grow two blades of grass or two ears of corn where one grew before—irrespective of resource input. Greater production efficiency measured by output was the goal. The result was plentiful food at low cost. Meanwhile, most existing agricultural technologies in the United States and other industrialized nations, heavily dependent on fossil fuels and chemicals, have evolved during an era characterized by low cost and abundant energy. Few agricultural scientists, even as of this writing, recognize the impending impact of resource constraints. The high fossil energy subsidy to agriculture cannot continue forever. The agricultural output of the United States has been closely tied to the availability of fossil fuel inputs. Direct spin-offs of an energy-intensive agriculture include increased specialization (monoculture), less resiliency, and large-scale operations, accompanied by a movement away from small- and medium-sized production units (Edens, 1977).

C. Appropriate Technology

This concept stems, in part, from the realization that many of the "hard-high" technologies relating to crop production as developed in western industrialized nations may be inappropriate for the developing world, and may not be appropriate for the future destiny of the developed world. It stems, in part, from "small is beautiful" (Schumacher, 1973), and "bigger may not be better." The focus is often on the needs of developing countries (National Academy of Sciences, 1977a). The appropriate technology concept attacks the large-scale, centralized, monoculture capital-energy–transport–skill intensive technology of modern agriculture as damaging to the environment and to human welfare, especially to the welfare of the nonaffluent and the international poor. Conversely, appropriate technology focuses on labor-intensive operations, small farms, polyculture, heterogenous germ plasm, farming systems, little or no fertilizer or chemicals, biological controls for insects and diseases, and conservation tillage. It emphasizes the nonpolluting, decentralized inputs derived from solar energy, and is defined by its benign environmental and equitable and humanistic impacts (National Science Foundation, 1977b).

Technologies, as developed by the industrialized western nations, are highly mechanized, labor saving, large scale, and are capital-, management-, and resource- (energy, water, fertilizer, pesticide) intensive. For 40 years, the United States has aimed at greater efficiency in production, irrespective of resource inputs which, until recently, have been cheap and plentiful. Among some of the global problems (see Table I) are poverty, malnutrition, underemployment, scarcity of resources, shortages of energy, soil erosion, toxic chemicals in the environment, and the adequacy and dependability of our food supply. Appropriate technology presumably is designed to alleviate these problems. For crop production, it means strategies for poor farmers that focus on technologies that are labor intensive and that result in stable production of conventional crops at high levels, and on research that is scale-neutral as to farm size and is nonpolitical. It implies small, less energy-intensive equipment (Wijewardene, 1977); smaller, highly productive units; and the use of renewable rather than nonrenewable resources. It relates to solar versus fossil energy, and emphasizes the construction of storages with local renewable materials for the preservation of indigenous production. It means optimization of the production of biologically fixed nitrogen versus that which is chemically fixed. Crop rotations, intercropping, and cropping systems are emphasized. It means pest management without pesticide chemicals. Organic gardening is a part of the movement.

The comparative productivity of such crop production systems with those of contemporary American agriculture has not been accurately assessed. Technologies can be labor intensive, small scale, and economically viable if they result in increments of production. This is true of hybrid cotton in India. Thousands of laborers are required to hand pollinate the flowers with a resulting doubling of yields (Sharma, 1975).

Much of the rhetoric of the "Green Revolution" centers on the resulting inequalities between large- and small-scale farmer. Most all international development programs now look to the small-scale farmer as the central figure. The small farm can be a viable economic unit. Technologies addressed to small-scale, labor-intensive, capital- and resource-sparing crop production systems would capture an unexploited fronteir. The incomes of 1 billion people depend on farms of 5 ha or less. Seventy-five percent of all farms in tropical Asia are smaller than 2 ha. In Japan, 92% are 2 ha or less. The average farm size in the Phillippines is 3 ha. Sixty-nine percent of all farms in Central America are less than 5 ha; and the average farm size of 20 African countries is only 5.4 ha. The output per hectare on these mini-holdings can significantly exceed that of the large U.S. farms. Small increments of fertilizer, water, or pesticies, or of other technologies or social or economic incentivies in Southeast Asia, Latin America, or Africa would have telling effects on crop production.

The issue of the small-scale or limited-resource farm is not foreign to the needs of the United States. According to 1976 data, 72% of all U.S. farms gross less than $20,000 and are classified as small farms. Yet, most all U.S. agricultural research efforts are still directed to large-scale commercial or modern agriculture.

V. EXPLORING THE LIMITS OF CROP PRODUCTIVITY

The biological limits of crop productivity have been neither achieved nor defined. Projected grain production for the 1977–1978 crop year will be an all-time record of 1300 million metric tons. The global increase in yields of the major cereal crops since World War II is without precedent in agricultural history (McQuigg, 1978). Particularly significant have been some of the records in Japan, western Europe, Mexico, Columbia, the United States, and the Punjab state in India. The most remarkable crop production record for all time has been in India's Punjab. A three-fold increase in food grain production was achieved in 10 years (1966 to 1976).

A. Analysis of Current Yield Plateaus

Within the very shadow of unprecedented progress in the enhancement of food crop productivity has come a plateauing of yields of the major food crops of the earth. Yields of wheat, maize, sorghum, soybeans, and potatoes in the United States have not increased since 1970 (Wittwer, 1978b). This is true of maize, potatoes, wheat, and cassava in

Latin America. The yields of rice in India, Bangladesh, Indonesia, Nepal, Pakistan, Philippines, Sri Lanka, and Thailand were the same in 1976 as in 1970, even with a substantial input of high-yielding varieties (International Rice Research Institute, 1977). Overall world grain yields have declined (L. R. Brown, 1978a). Increased production has been achieved largely by bringing more land under cultivation.

The phenomenon needs careful analysis. Possible causal factors are listed in Table III. There are fewer options in the use of water, land, energy, fertilizer, pesticides, and for mechanization. These resources are becoming more costly, subject to more constraints, and less available. Some are nonrenewable. Meanwhile, soil erosion continues unabated, nationally and globally. Topsoil continues to be lost at an enormous rate. Soil organic matter is still on the decline. There is greater soil compaction from excess and untimely tillage. Air pollution is progressively more severe. Additional land areas brought under cultivation may be less productive.

Some would credit the recent plateauing of crop yields to adverse and fluctuating climate and weather. Season-to-season variations, however, are far more significant than any identifiable long-term trends. There is no evidence that technology has reduced the sensitivity of grain yields to weather. On the other hand, technology may be working to insulate yields from unfavorable weather (Haigh and McQuigg, 1977). Many of the recent advances in technology which could enhance productivity are highly dependent on use of more energy resources. The rising costs of energy relative to crop prices may be limiting the adoption of new practices that could increase yields. If this is true, then the plateauing of yields may be expected to continue. L. R. Brown (1978a) has pointed out that the obstacles to increased crop productivity in many nations may be more political than technological.

Regulatory and financial constraints on the use of labor, chemicals,

TABLE III
Causes of Plateauing in Agricultural Productivity

Soil erosion—loss of topsoil
Loss of organic matter—soil compaction
Chemical soil residues—air pollution
More less productive land under cultivation
Increased pressures on productive land base
Fewer options for water, fertilizer, pesticide uses
Climate and weather fluctuations
Increased regulatory constraints
Decreased support for agricultural research

been developed, but can be expected to have a major impact on future animal agricultural development throughout the tropics.

Jojoba is a desert shrub with remarkable resistance to drought, high salinity, and temperatures that are lethal to most other plants. It is native to the Sonoran Desert, which covers parts of Mexico, Arizona, and California. Jojoba nuts contain an oily liquid (about 50% by weight) that makes a lubricant base superior to that derived from sperm oil, a fact that is strategically important (National Academy of Sciences, 1977f).

Guayule is a shrub that grows in the deserts of North America. It provides an alternative source of natural rubber almost identical with that of the rubber tree (National Academy of Sciences, 1977g).

E. Cropping Systems

Agricultural systems where two or more useful plants are grown simultaneously will receive increasing attention. Farmers with limited resources in the tropics and subtropics have long used this technology for increasing food production and cash income. Legume–cereal grain combinations are most common. Many terms have been employed to describe the systems of polyculture involved. They include multiple cropping, maximum cropping, mixed cropping, intercropping, relay planting, interplanting, and interculture (Kass, 1978). Results generally indicate that polyculture is beneficial to crop production, since total crop yields may be substantially increased. There are reports where each crop, in combination with another, produces more than if it were grown alone. The result is a very significant increase in total production when the values of each are added together (Rao and Willey, 1978; De, 1978). More nutrients are delivered into the biomass produced, and water use is more efficient. The potentials for polyculture cropping systems research, the combinations possible, the unknowns of root interactions, and special considerations of the semiarid tropics are outlined in several National Academy of Sciences' reports as supporting papers to the World Food and Nutrition Study (National Academy of Sciences, 1977b, pp. 66–73, 1977h). Definite limitations are imposed by polyculture in the harvest of the crop and essentially upon any farm operation that is to be mechanized.

Forages constitute a mixed cropping system, usually of grasses and legumes. Indirectly, they constitute an enormous food resource. They provide a feed supply for approximately 2.5 billion ruminant animals useful to man. The primary, and often exclusive, feed for livestock in developing countries is forages. Permanent pastures and rangelands in the United States cover more territory than does cultivated cropland. Forages not only serve as feed for ruminant animals, but they reduce soil erosion and enrich the soil. They are produced in many places where cultivated crops cannot be grown. Their production is an essential component of appropriate, long-term land use (Hodgson, 1976, 1978).

There are many opportunities to enhance the productivity of range and pasture resources. In the United States, it is technically and economically feasible to double the carrying capacity of rangelands. A coordinated international program of improved plant species (both legumes and grasses), vegetation modification, mechanical soil treatments, fertilization, water control, and livestock management would add a tremendous resource to the crop productivity potential of the world (National Academy of Sciences, 1975e). The land and water resources for forage production in the tropics are enormous. Here, there are almost 1.5 billion ha of potential land for forages that has little utility for cultivated cropping. Livestock grazing in many areas is possible throughout the year. Mixtures of legumes and grasses can regulate the balance between energy and protein. One of the driving forces in ruminant animal production is improved nutrition. Globally, this must come largely from improvements in the production and management of forages.

F. Future Determinants of Crop Productivity—Summary and Conclusions

Never was the time more opportune to seek for greater crop productivity. Ninety-five percent of the food resources of the earth come directly or indirectly from plants. They provide feed for livestock and wildlife, and are the primary sources of renewable and natural fibers. They provide the timber and lumber for construction, and are the source of firewood. Many products for industrial uses are derived from them. There are about 25 crops that literally stand between man and starvation. Projections of the World Food and Nutrition Study (National Academy of Sciences, 1977a) indicate that food production must be increased by about 3 to 4% per year to the end of the century to meet the needs of annual population increases and the demands of an increasingly affluent society. This poses the greatest challenge ever presented to those engaged in food production. The present plateauing of crop yields is a significant reversal. The ingredients of productivity—new technology, resource inputs, and economic incentives—must be reassessed. The current erosion of support for research on the en-

hancement of crop productivity must be corrected. There must be improved management, utilization, conservation, and protection of resources (climate, land, water, energy, fertilizer, pesticides) essential for
the productivity of crops for future generations. The potential contributions of research have been detailed and priorities listed (National
Academy of Sciences, 1975e, 1977a; Brown et al., 1976). Major changes
in policy relating to research allocations, organizational prerequisites,
and institutional structures are called for. There must be a reaffirmation
and recognition by U.S. and international academicians that agriculture is a respectable and modern science (Mayer and Mayer, 1974). A
move is on to have the sciences of food production and agricultural
systems represented within the International Council of Scientific
Unions (ICSU). A Committee on the Application of Science to Agriculture (CASA) has been proposed. Food exports from the United States
have risen percipitously during the past 5 years. The estimate for agricultural exports in 1978 is $25 billion. Yet, the role of agricultural
technology—specifically crop production technology—in maintaining
a balance of payments in international trade is not mentioned in the
report of the National Science Board (National Science Foundation,
1977a).

Specific research initiatives are called for. There is considerable hope
for the future (H. Brown, 1978). The biological processes that control
and limit crop productivity have first priority. They include the grossly
neglected areas of improved photosynethetic efficiency, biological nitrogen fixation, genetic improvement utilizing both traditional approaches and new cellular techniques, improved resistance to competing biological systems and environmental stresses, greater efficiency in
nutrient uptake and recovery, and regulation of plant development and
productivity through hormonal mechanisms. Research in these areas
would have the greatest payoff in crop productivity, the technologies
are nonpolluting, and they would add to rather than diminish the
earth's resources (Wittwer, 1978b).

Some specifics relative to future determinants of crop productivity
have been summarized by Evans (1975) and Seigler (1977). First is the
efficiency of energy use. This relates not only to photosynthetic harvesting of energy from the sun and crop respiration, but to an increasing degree from inputs of energy from fossil fuels derived from prehis-
toric photosynthesis. The canopy structure, harvest index, storage
capacities or sinks, and partitioning of assimilates can be powerful
determinants of yield and plant productivity. Each can be modified.
Crop productivity of the future will also be determined by less genetic
vulnerability to climate, chemicals, and pathogens. There will be pre-

dictive models for pest management, simulation models for the production of each major crop, and climate and programming of crop production in polyculture and for closed systems.

The greatest of all the natural resources, and the most unpredictable and least controllable, for crop production are the weather and climate. They are the most determinant factors, relating to the stability and adequacy of our food supply. Land, water, energy, and chemical resources for crop production will become increasingly costly. Greater efficiency in their use is mandated. Alternatives to resource inputs into crop production systems must be pursued, new crops must be identified, record yields must continue upward, and new models of productivity created. The options for improving crop productivity are many. The challenge is to be sufficiently selective so that the present needs of society can be met and our resources preserved for future generations.

The potential capacity for global crop production is enormous. There is an unprecedented opportunity to put reserve technology to work, create new technologies, manage our resources, and pursue modern means of communicating the results of research to producers. It took 40 years for hybrid corn to be universally adopted by U.S. farmers. For Iowa farmers, it was only 7 years (National Science Foundation, 1973). The time between discovery of new technology and its adoption must be shortened. There is a need to speed the flow of information from scientiests in research centers. New breeds of technologies and technologists are called for. Provision is needed for communication among scientists, constituting a blend extending from the applied field worker to the molecular biologist. Attention should be directed toward mission-oriented basic research with economically important crops. There should be special emphasis on the biological processes that control and limit productivity (Brown et al., 1976). Environmental monitoring and immediate translation of results to farmers for effective pest management is inevitable. This will be increasingly important as costs for new pesticide registrations continue to escalate, and the time from discovery to full registration continues to be prolonged. Rising demands for food, fiber, and renewable resources as industrial materials speak for a greater investment not only for research, but the diffusion of knowledge. The responsibility of a scientist no longer ends with a technical report to his professional colleagues in a refereed journal. The future viability of a scientific discipline will depend on how well the results of research relate to the solution of the common problems of society.

REFERENCES

Abelson, P. H. (1977). *Science* **198,** 451.

Abu-Shakra, S. S., Phillips, D. A., and Huffaker, R. C. (1978). *Science* **199,** 973–974.

Aung, L. H. (1977). *In* "Proceedings of the Fourth Annual Meeting Plant Growth Regulator Working Group," pp. 43–66. Hot Springs, Arkansas.

Axtel, J. D. (1976). *In* "Evaluation of Seed Protein Alterations by Mutation Breeding," pp. 45–53. IAEA, Vienna.

Baes, C. F., Jr., Goeller, H. E., Olson, J. S., and Rotty, R. M. (1976). Publication ORNL-5194. Oak Ridge Nat. Lab., Oak Ridge, Tennessee.

Bajaj, Y. P. S. (1975). *In* "Form, Structure and Function in Plants," pp. 107–115. Sarita Prakashan Press, Merrut, New Delhi, India.

Bajaj, Y. P. S., and Reinert, J. (1976). *In* "Applied and Fundamental Aspects of Plant Cell, Tissue, and Organ Culture" (J. Reinert and Y. P. S. Bajaj, eds.), pp. 757–789. Springer-Verlag, Berlin and New York.

Bassham, J. A. (1977). *Science* **197,** 630–638.

Bird, G. W. (1978). *In* "Symposium on the Development of Optimum Crop Production Systems for the Mid-South," p. 000. University of Arkansas, Fayetteville.

Black, C. C., Brown, M. E. and Moore, R. C. (1978). *In* "Limitations and Potentials for Biological Nitrogen Fixation in the Tropics," (J. Dobereiner, R. H. Burris, and A. Hollaender, eds.), pp. 95–110. Plenum, New York.

Boersma, L. (1977). *In* "Problems in Food Production and Nutrition," Pro. Symp., pp. 39–57. Nutr. Res. Inst., Oregon State University, Corvallis.

Bremner, J. M., and Blackmer, A. M. (1978). *Science* **199,** 295–296.

Brink, R. A., Densmore, W., and Hill, G. A. (1977). *Science* **197,** 625–630.

Brown, A. W. A., Byerly, T. C., Gibbs, M., and San Pietro, A., eds. (1976). "Crop Productivity—Research Imperatives." Mich. Agric. Exp. St.—Charles F. Kettering Found., East Lansing.

Brown, H. (1978). "The Human Future Revisited." Norton, New York.

Brown, L. R. (1978a). "The Twenty-Ninth Day." Norton, New York.

Brown, L. R. (1978b). "The Global Economic Prospect: New Sources of Economic Stress." Worldwatch, Paper 20. Washington, D.C.

Bull, T. A., and Glaszion, K. T. (1975). *In* "Crop Physiology" (L. T. Evans, ed.), pp. 51–72. Cambridge Univ. Press, London and New York.

Buringh, P. (1977). *World Dev.* **5,** 477–495.

Burton, G. W. (1977). *In* "Proceedings of the World Food Conference of 1976," pp. 71–86. Iowa State Univ. Press, Ames.

Calvin, M. (1976). "Photosynthesis as a Resource for Energy and Materials," Presented at 8th Int. Photochem. Congr. Edmonton, Alberta, Canada, August 11, 1975.

Chou, M. (1977). "China's Agricultural and U.S. Export Prospects," Res. Memo. No. 43. Hudson Institute, Croton-on-Hudson, New York.

Chou, M., Harmon, D. P., Jr., Kahn, H., and Wittwer, S. H. (1977). "World Food Prospects and Agricultural Potential." Praeger, New York.

Cooper, A. J., and Charlesworth, R. R. (1977). *Sci. Hortic.* **7,** 189–195.

Council of Agricultural Science and Technology (1977). "Energy Use in Agriculture: Now and in the Future." Rep. No. 68. Counc. Agric. Sci. Technol. Ames, Iowa.

Council on Environmental Quality (1978). "Solar Energy—Progress and Promise." Counc. Environ. Qual., Washington, D. C.

Croft, B. A. (1975). *Mich. State Univ. Ext. Bull.* **E-825.**

Day, P. R. (1977). *Science* **197**, 1334–1339.

De, R. (1978). "Legumes in Crop Rotations and Intercropping Systems." Indian Agric. Res. Inst., New Delhi.

Delwiche, C. C. (1978). *BioScience* **28**, 565–570.

De Wet, J. M. J. (1977). In "Crop Resources" (D. S. Seigler, ed.), pp. 111–118. Academic Press, New York.

Dickenson, P. B. (1976). *Outlook on Agric.* **9**, 88–94.

Dickinson, C. H., and Preece, T. F., eds. (1976). "Microbiology of Aerial Plant Surfaces." Academic Press, New York.

Dobereiner, J., Burris, R. L., and Hollaender, A., eds. (1978). "Limitations and Potentials for Biological Nitrogen Fixation in the Tropics." Plenum, New York.

Duncan, W. G. (1975). In "Crop Physiology" (L. T. Evans, ed.), pp. 23–50. Cambridge Univ. Press, London and New York.

Eckholm, E. P. (1976). "Losing Ground." Norton, New York.

Edens, T. C. (1977). "Agricultural Management in a New Era: The Role of Insect Survey and Detection," Entomol. Soc. Am. College Park, Maryland.

Elliott, W. A., and Oelke, E. A. (1977). *Crops Soils* **29** (8), 8–11.

Epstein, E., and Norlyn, J. D. (1977). *Science* **197**, 249–251.

Evans, H. J., and Barber, L. E. (1977). *Science* **197**, 332–339.

Evans, L. T., ed. (1975). "Crop Physiology." Cambridge Univ. Press, London and New York.

Fick, G. W., Loomis, R. S., and Williams, W. A. (1975). In "Crop Physiology" (L. T. Evans, ed.), pp. 259–295. Cambridge Univ. Press, London and New York.

Fischer, R. A., and Turner, N. C. (1978). *Annu. Rev. Plant Physio.* **29**, 277–317.

Gamborg, O. L., and Holl, F. B. (1977). In Genetic Engineering for Nitrogen Fixation" (A. Hollaender, ed.), pp. 299–316. Plenum, New York.

Garcia, R. L., and Hanway, J. J. (1976). *Agron. J.* **68**, 653–657.

Geraldson, C. M. (1975). *Proc. Fl. State Hortic. Soc.* **88**, 152–155.

Glass, E. H., and Thurston, H. D. (1978). *BioScience* **28**, 109–115.

Glasshouse Crops Reserach Institute (1976). The Biological Control of Tomato Pests Growers' Bulletin 3. Glasshouse Crops Res. Inst., Littlehampton, Sussex, England.

Gustafson, C. D. (1978). "107th Annual Report of the Secretary of the State Horticultural Society of Michigan for the year 1977," pp. 63–76. State Hortic. Soc., Grand Rapids, Michigan.

Gutschiek, V. P. (1978). *BioScience* **28**, 571–575.

Hageman, R. H. (1977). In "Proceedings of the Fourth Annual Meeting Plant Growth Regulating Working Group," pp. 14–42. Hot Springs, Arkansas.

Hagen, R. M., Haise, R. H., and Edminster, T. W. (1967). "Irrigation of Agricultural Lands," No. 11. Am. Soc. Agron., Madison, Wisconsin.

Haigh, P. A., and McQuigg, J. D. (1977). "Separating the Effects of Weather and Management on Crop Production." Columbia, Missouri.

Hall, D. O., and Combs, J., and Goodwin, T. W. eds. (1978). "Abstracts of the 4th International Congress on Photosynthesis." Biochemical Society, London.

Hammond, A. L. (1977). *Science* **197**, 745–746.

Hardy, R. W. F. (1978). "Report of the Public Meeting on Genetic Engineering for Nitrogen Fixation, " pp. 77–106. Nat. Sci. Found., Washington, D. C.

Hardy, R. W. F., and Halvelka, U. D. (1975). *Science* **188**, 633.

Haskell, P. T. (1977). *Outlook Agric.* **9**, 121–126.

Hauptli, H., and Jain S. (1978). *Cali. Agric.* **31**(9), 6–7.

Heichel, G. H. (1976). *Am. Sci.* **64**, 64–72.

Hinson, K., and Hartwig, E. E. (1977). "Soybean Production in the Tropics," FAO/UN, Rome.

Hodgson, H. J. (1976). Sci. Am. **234**, 61–75.

Hodgson, H. J. (1978). "Food from Plant Products—Forage," Presented at a Symposium on the Complementary Role of Plant and Animal Products in the U.S. Food System, Nov. 29–30, 1977. Nat. Acad. Sci., Washington, D. C.

Holl, F. B. (1975). Can. J. Genet. Cytol. **17**, 517–524.

Hollaender, A., ed. (1977). "Genetic Engineering for Nitrogen Fixation." Plenum, New York.

Huber, D. M., Warren, H. L., Nelson, D. W., and Tsai, C. Y. (1977). BioScience **27**, 523–529.

Hudson, J. P. (1976). Outlook Agric. **9**, 95–98.

Huff, F. A., and Vogel, J. L. (1977). "Assessment of Weather Modification in Alleviating Agricultural Water Shortages During Droughts," A report to the National Science Foundation from the Illinois State Water Survey of the University of Illinois, Urbana.

Huffaker, C. B., and Croft, B. A. (1976). Environ. Health Perspec. **14**, 167–183.

Hulse, J. H., and Spurgeon, D. (1974). Sci. Am. **231**, 72–80.

International Rice Research Institute (1977). "Constraints to High Yields on Asian Rice Farms: An Interim Report." Int. Rice Res. Inst., Los Banos, Philippines.

Jain, H. K. (1975). "Breeding for Yield and Other Atrributes in Grain Legumes." Indian Agric. Res. Inst., New Delhi.

Jensen, M. R. (1977). In "Proceedings of the Climate Technology Seminar," pp. 209–242. University of Missouri, Columbia.

Johnson, W. A., Stoltzfus, V., and Cranmer, P. (1977). Science **198**, 373–387.

Kass, D. C. L. (1978). "Polyculture Cropping Systems," Bull. 32. Cornell University, Ithaca, New York.

Kendrick, J. B., Jr. (1978). Calif. Agric. **32**, 3.

Knievel, D. P., Fritton, D. D., McKee, G. W., and Martsolf, J. D. (1977). Sci. Agric. **24**(3), 11.

Krenzer, E. G., Jr., Moss, D. N., and Crookston, R. K. (1975). Plant Physiol. **56**, 194–206.

Lipinsky, E. S. (1978). Science **199**, 644–651.

Loomis, R. S., and Williams, W. A. (1963). Crop Sci. **3**, 67–72.

McGinnis, W. G., and Goldman, B. J., eds. (1969). "Arid Lands in Perspective." Am. Assoc. Adv. Sci., Washington, D. C.

MacNeil, D., MacNeil, T., and Brill, W. J. (1978). BioScience **28**, 576–579.

McQuigg, J. D. (1978). "Agripower: Food, A Strategic Weapon?" Columbia, Missouri.

Mayer, A., and Mayer, J. (1974). J. Am. Acad. Arts Sci. (Daedalis) Summer, pp. 84–95.

Mendoza, H. A., and Estrada, R. N. (1979). In "Stress Physiology in Crop Plants" (H. Mussell and R. C. Staples, eds.) pp. 227–262. Wiley InterScience, N.Y.

Milner, M., Scrimshaw, N. S., and Wong, D. I. C. (1978). "Protein Resources and Technology: Status and Research Needs." Avi Publ., Westport, Connecticut.

Moomaw, J. C., Park, H. G., and Shanmugasundaram, S. (1977). "The Role of Legumes in South and Southeast Asia." Asian Vegetable Research and Development Center, Shanhua, Taiwan, Republic of China.

Mooney, H. A., Ehleringer, J., and Berry, J. A. (1976). Science **194**, 322–324.

Moorby, J., and Milthorpe, F. L. (1975). In "Crop Physiology" (L. T. Evans, ed.), pp. 225–257. Cambridge Univ. Press, London and New York.

Moore, P. H. (1977). In "Proceedings of the Fourth Annual Meeting Plant Growth Regulator Working Group," pp. 173–180. Hot Springs, Arkansas.

Nasyrov, Y. S. (1978). *Annu. Rev. Plant Physiol.* **29**, 215–237.

National Academy of Sciences (1972). "Genetic Vulnerability of Major Crops." Agric. Board, Natl. Acad. Sci., Washington, D. C.

National Academy of Sciences (1975a). "Contemporary Pest Control Practices and Prospects," Report of the Executive Committee, p. 1. Natl. Acad. Sci., Washington, D.C.

National Academy of Sciences (1975b). "Mineral Resources of the Environment," pp. 237–240. Natl. Acad. Sci., Washington, D.C.

National Academy of Sciences (1975c). "Unexploited Tropical Plants With Promising Economic Value." Natl. Acad. Sci., Washington, D.C.

National Academy of Sciences (1975d). "The Winged Bean, A High-Protein Crop for the Tropics." Natl. Acad. Sci., Washington, D.C.

National Academy of Sciences (1975e). "World Food and Nutrition Study. Enhancement of Food Production for the United States," Report of the Board on Agriculture and Renewable Resources. Nat. Res. Counc., Washington, D.C.

National Academy of Sciences (1976). "Climate and Food." Board on Agriculture and Renewable Resources, Natl. Acad. Sci., Washington, D.C.

National Academy of Sciences (1977a). "World Food and Nutrition Study. The Potential Contributions of Research." Nat. Res. Counc., Washington, D.C.

National Academy of Sciences (1977b). "World Food and Nutrition Study," Supporting Papers, Vol. I, p. 77. Natl. Acad. Sci., Washington, D. C.

National Academy of Sciences (1977c). "Methane Generation From Human, Animal, and Agricultural Wastes." Natl. Acad. Sci., Washington, D.C.

National Academy of Sciences (1977d). "Energy and Climate." Natl. Acad. Sci., Washington, D.C.

National Academy of Sciences (1977e). "Leucaena, Promising Forage and Tree Crop for the Tropics." Natl. Acad. Sci., Washington, D.C.

National Academy of Sciences (1977f). "Jojoba, Feasibility for Cultivation on Indian Reservations in the Sonoran Desert Region." Natl. Acad. Sci., Washington, D.C.

National Academy of Sciences (1977g). "Guayule: An Alternative Source of Natural Rubber." Natl. Acad. Sci., Washington, D.C.

National Academy of Sciences (1977h). "Supporting Papers: World Food and Nutrition Study," Vol. II, pp. 13–51 and 85–91. Natl. Acad. Sci., Washington, D.C.

National Dairy Development Board (1977). "Special Report of the Anand Milk Union Limited (AMUL)." Kaira District, Gujarat State, India.

National Science Foundation (1973). "Interactions of Science and Technology in the Innovative Process: Some Case Studies," Contract NSF-C 667. Battelle Columbus Laboratories, Columbus, Ohio.

National Science Foundation (1977a). "Science Indicators 1976," Report of the National Science Board, pp. 3–4 and 40. Natl. Sci. Found., Washington, D.C.

National Science Foundation (1977b). "Appropriate Technology and Agriculture in the United States." Natl. Sci. Found., Washington, D.C.

National Science Foundation (1978). "An Assessment of Controlled Environment Agriculture," A report submitted by the International Research and Technology Corporation. Natl. Sci. Found., Washington, D.C.

Newton, W. E., and Nyman, C. J., eds. (1976). "Nitrogen Fixation," Vols. I and II. Washington State Univ. Press, Pullman.

Nickell, L. G. (1977a). *In* "Ecophysiology of Tropical Crops" (P. de T. Alvim and T. T. Kozlowski, eds.), pp. 89–111. Academic Press, New York.

Nickell, L. G. (1977b). *Adv. Che. Ser.* **159**, 6–22.

Nickell, L. G. (1978). Plant Growth Regulators. C and EN Special Report Oct. 9, 1978, pp. 18–33.

Office of Technology Assessment (1977). "Organizing and Financing Basic Research to Increase Food Production." Off. Technol. Assess., Washington, D.C.

Office of Technology Assessment (1978). "Assessment of Alternative Pest Management Strategies in Food Production." Off. Technol. Assess., Washington, D.C.

Parham, M. R. (1976). *Outlook Agric.* **9,** 76–81.

Peters, G. A. (1978). *BioScience* **28,** 580–585.

Pharis, R. P., and Ross, S. D. (1976). *Outlook Agric.* **9,** 82–87.

Pierre, W. H., Kirkham, D., Pesek, J., and Shaw, R., eds. (1967). "Plant Environment and Efficient Water Use." Am. Soc. Agron. and Soil Sci. Soc. Am., Madison, Wisconsin.

Pimentel, D., Dritschilo, W., Krummel, J., and Kutzman, J. (1975). *Science* **190,** 765–761.

Pimentel, D., Terhune, E. C., Dyson-Hudson, R., Rochereau, S., Samis, R., Smith. E. A., Denman, D., Reifschneider, D., and Shepard, M. (1976). *Science* **194,** 149–155.

Pimentel, D., Nafus, D., Vergara, W., Papaj, D., Jaconetta, L., Wulfe, M., Olsirg, L., Frech, K., Loye, M., and Mendoza, E. (1978). *BioScience* **28,** 376–382.

Putnam, A. R., and Duke, W. B. (1974). *Science* **185,** 370–372.

Radmir, R., and Kok, B. (1977). *BioScience* **27,** 599–605.

Rao, M. R., and Willey, R. W. (1978). "Current Status of Intercropping Research and Some Suggested Experimental Procedures." Int. Crops Res. Inst. Semi-Arid Trop.

Rawlins. S. L. (1977). *Ann. N.Y. Acad. Sci.* **300,** 121–128.

Rice, E. L. (1974). "Allelopathy." Academic Press, New York.

Rick, C. M. (1978). *Cali. Agric.* **31**(9), 32–33.

Riedl, H., and Croft, B. A. (1978). *Mich., Agric. Exp. Stn., Res. Rep.* **337.**

Ries, S. K., and Wert, V. (1977). *Planta* **135,** 77–82.

Ries, S. K., Wert, V., Sweeley, C. C., and Leavitt, R. A. (1977). *Science* **195,** 1339–1341.

Ries, S. K., Richman, T. L., and Wert, V. F. (1978). *J. Am. Soc. Hortic. Sci.* **103,** 361–364.

Rodale Press, Inc. (1977). "Proceedings of the First Amaranth Seminar." Rodale Press, Emmaus, Pennsylvania.

Rojko, A., O'Brien, P., Regier, D., Coffing, A., and Bailey, L. (1978). "Alternative Futures for World Food in 1985," Foreign Agric. Econ. Rep. No. 149. Econ. Stat., and Coop. Serv., U.S. Dep. Agric., Washington, D.C.

Rudd-Jones, D. (1977). In "Proceedings of an International Symposium on Controlled Environment Agriculture," Compiled by Merle H. Jensen, pp. 216–224. Environ. Res. Lab., University of Arizona, Tucson.

Sanders, F. E., Mosse, B., and Tinker, P. B., eds. (1975). "Endomycorrhizas." Academic Press, New York.

Sanghi, A. K., and Johnson, D. (1978). "The Ground Water and Energy Supply Situation for Great Plains Irrigation," Rep. NSF/RA-78-0018. Center for Biology of Natural Systems, Washington University, St. Louis, Missouri.

San Pietro, A. (1978). "International Workshop Summary Report on BioSaline Research." Nat. Sci. Found., Washington, D.C.

Schumacher, E. F. (1973). "Small is Beautiful. Economics as if People Mattered." Harper, New York.

Seigler, D. S., ed. (1977). "Crop Resources." Academic Press, New York.

Shalhevet, J., Mantell, M., Bielorai, H., and Shimski, D. (1977). "Irrigation of Field and Orchard Crops Under Semi-Arid Conditions,IIIC Publ. No. 1. Int. Inf. Cent., Bet Dagan, Israel.

Shanmugam, K. T., O'Gara, F., Anderson, K., and Valentine, R. C. (1978). *Annu. Rev. Plant Physiol.* **29,** 263–276.

Sharma, S. C. (1975). "Impact of Cultivation of Hybrid Cotton on the Economy of Indian Farmers." Indian Agric. Res. Inst., New Delhi.

Shoji, K. (1977). *Sci. Am.* **237,** 62–68.

458 SYLVAN H. WITTWER

555555555555555
Siegenthaler, U., and Oeschger, H. (1978). *Science* **199**, 388–395.
Silver, W. S., and Hardy, R. W. F. (1976). "Biological Fixation in Forage Livestock Systems," Spec. Pub. No. 28, pp. 1–34. Am. Soc. Agron., Madison, Wisconsin.
Sinha, S. K. (1977). "Food Legumes: Distribution, Adaptability and Biology of Yield." FAO/UN, Rome.
Sink, K. C., and Padmanabhan, V. (1977). *HortScience* **12**, 143–148.
Splinter, W. E. (1976). *Sci. Am.* **234**, 90–99.
Sprague, E. W., and Finlay, K. W. (1977). In "Proceedings of the World Food Conference of 1976," pp. 367–374. Iowa State Univ. Press, Ames.
Sprague, G. F., Alexander, D. E., and Dudley, J. W. (1978). "Research Priorities in Plant Breeding," Spec. Rep. Department of Agronomy, University of Illinois, Urbana-Champaign.
Stout, B. A., Myers, C. A., Hurand, A., and Faidley, L. W. (1977). "Energy for Worldwide Agriculture." Michigan State University, East Lansing.
Strain, B. R., ed. (1977). "Preliminary Report Workshop on Anticipated Plant Response to Global Carbon Dioxide Enrichment." Duke University, Durham, North Carolina.
Stuiver, M. (1978). *Science* **199**, 644–651.
Tansey, M. R. (1977). In "Microorganisms and Minerals" (E. D. Weinburg, ed.), pp. 345–385. Dekker, New York.
Tiedje, J. M. (1978). In "Biological Transformations of Inorganic Nitrogen, p. 000. Paper presented in Am. Assoc. Adv. Sci., Washington, D.C.
Torrey, J. G. (1978). *BioScience* **28**, 586–592.
Trapp, J. N., and Thompson, S. R. (1977). *South. J. Agri. Econ.* July, pp. 197–205.
Treharne, B., Moles, M. R., and McKibben, C. K. (1978). "A Nitrogen Fertilizer Generator for Farm Use," Tech. Note 1. Charles F. Kettering Found., Dayton, Ohio.
Triplett, G. B., Jr., and Van Doren, D. M. (1977). *Sci. Am.* **237**, 62–68.
Tummala, R. L., and Haynes, D. L. (1977). *Environ. Entomol.* **6**, 339–349.
Tummala, R. L., Haynes, D. L., and Croft, B. A., eds. (1976). "Modeling for Pest Mangement—USA/USSR." Michigan State University, East Lansing.
U.S. Department of Agriculture (1975). "Proceedings of the Water Harvesting Symposium." U.S. Dep. Agric., Washington, D.C.
U.S. Department of Agriculture (1976). "Proceedings of the First International Symposium on Acid Precipitation and the Forest Ecosystem." U.S. For. Serv. Gen. Tech. Rep. NE-23. USDA, Washington, D.C.
U.S. Department of Agriculture (1977a). "Cultivation of Neglected Tropical Fruits with Promise." USDA, Washington, D.C.
U.S. Department of Agriculture (1977b). "Farm Index (September)," pp. 8–11 and 12–13. Econ. Res. Serv., USDA, Washington, D.C.
U.S. Department of Agriculture and Ohio State University (1975). "First International Symposium on Acid Precipitation and the Forest Ecosystem." Ohio State University, Columbus.
Ward, G. M., Knox, P. L., and Hobson, B. W. (1977). *Science* **198**, 265–271.
Way, M. J. (1977). *Outlook Agric.* **9**, 127–135.
Wijewardene, R. (1977). "Engineering for Appropriate Technology Farming Systems." Int. Inst. Trop. Agric., Ibadan, Nigeria.
Williams, W. T. (1978). "Effects on Plants of Sulfar Pollutants from Coal Combustion," Rep. 7866, Citizens for a Better Environment, San Francisco, California.
Wittwer, S. H. (1971). *Outlook Agric.* **6**, 206–217.
Wittwer, S. H. (1975). *Science* **188**, 579–584.
Wittwer, S. H. (1977a). In "Genetic Engineering for Nitrogen Fixation" (A. Hollaender, ed.), pp. 515–519. Plenum, New York.

Wittwer, S. H. (1977b). *In* "Proceedings of a Workshop Aug. 18–19, Ezra Taft Benson Agriculture and Food Institute," pp. 17–32. Brigham Young University, Provo, Utah.

Wittwer, S. H. (1977c). *In* "Crop Physiology" (U. S. Gupta, ed.), pp. 310–333. IBH Pub., Co., New Delhi, India.

Wittwer, S. H. (1978a). *Ceres* **11**(2), 17–22.

Wittwer, S. H. (1978b). *Science* **199**, 375.

Wittwer, S. H., and Bukovac, M. J. (1969). *In* "Handbuch der Pflanzenernährung und Düngung" (K. Scharrer and H. Linser, eds.), pp. 235–261. Springer-Verlag, Berlin and New York.

Woodley, L. W., Jordan, J. A., Simpson, J., Biondini, R., and Flueck, J. (1977). "NOAA's Florida Area Cumulus Rainfall Results, 1970–1976." Nat. Oceanic Atmos. Adm., Washington, D.C.

Woodwell, G. M. (1978). *Sci. Am.* **238**, 34–43.

Wright, M. J., and Ferrari, S. A. eds. (1977). "Proceedings of Workshop on Plant Adaptation to Mineral Stress in Problem Soils." Agric. Exp. Stn., Cornell University, Ithaca, New York.

Wunsche, A. (1977). *J. Agron. Crop Sci.* **145**, 238–253.

Yokoyama, H., Hayman, E. P., Hsu, W. J., and Poling, S. M. (1977). *Science* **197**, 1076–1078.

Subject Index

A

Abscisic acid, 20, 21, 32, 110, 135, 136, 326
Acaulospora, 234
Acetylene, reduction, 57, 58, 67
Acid rain, 432
Acyrthosiphon pisum, 171, 173
Adaptability, 88, 89, 122–124, 129
Adenosine triphosphate, 55, 56, 59, 62,
 260, 261, 271, 279, 286, 287
Aegilops comosa, 406
Aegilops umbellulata, 406
Agricultural by-product, as fuel source,
 49
Agricultural production, 45, 80–83, 414–
 428, 443–447, 450–452, *see also*
 Yield
 developing nations, 79, 82, 83, 427, 428,
 441–443
 energy requirements, 44–50, 79, 80, 82,
 83, 415–419, 440, 441, 451
 industrialized nations, 79–82, 414, 428,
 430, 435, 443–447
Agricultural research, 343–345, 430, 431,
 451, 452
 regulations, 445
Agriculture
 controlled-environment, 428
 energy intensive, 79–83, 417, 440, 441
Agrobacterium, 67
Air pollution, 432
Alfalfa, *see Medicago sativa*
Alfalfa mosaic virus, 167, 176
Alkalinity, resistance, 427
Alkylating agent, 390
Allele, 359, 364–366, 394, 404
Allelopathy, 426
Allergenicity, 346
Allium, 235

Amaranth, 448
Amaranthus, 31
Amaranthus graecizana, 16
Amaranthus hypochondriacus, 448
Amaranthus retroflexus, 16
Ambrosia artemisifolia, 16
Amino acid, 307, 390, *see also* specific
 acids
 synthesis, 138, 263–266, 270–272,
 279–286, 292
Ammonia, 54, 59
 assimilation, 259–265, 274–279
Anabaena, 54, 71, 418, 419
Anabaena cylindrica, 60, 64, 65
Aphid, 318, 319, 323, 331, 332, *see also*
 specific genus and species
 as vector, 161, 165, 170–173, 175
Apical dominance, 319–321, 326
Apomict, 396
Apple, 426
Arabidopsis, 388
Arabidopsis thaliana, 404
Arabis mosaic virus, 172, 245
Arachnid, as vector, 161
Araucaria cunninghamii, 241
Artemisia frigida, 16
Asparagine, 264, 265, 272, 279, 285
Asparagus, 426
Aspartate kinase, 280–283, 285
Assimilation, 125, 128, 129
 of ammonia, 259–265, 274–279
Atmospheric gas, 432
ATP, *see* Adenosine triphosphate
Auxin, transport, 316, 326
Avena byzantia, 226, 227
Avena sativa, 16, 414, 446
Awn, 120
 of wheat, 102, 104, 105
Azaserine, 262